Harry G. Lafuse

Dept. of Elec. Eng.
Univ. of Notre Dame

NETWORK SYNTHESIS

PRENTICE-HALL ELECTRICAL ENGINEERING SERIES

W. L. EVERITT, Ph.D., *Editor*

NETWORK SYNTHESIS

By

NORMAN BALABANIAN

Associate Professor of Electrical Engineering
Syracuse University

Englewood Cliffs, N.J.

PRENTICE-HALL, INC.

1958

Library of Congress Catalog Card No.: 58-11650

PRINTED IN THE UNITED STATES OF AMERICA

61104

DEDICATION

This book is dedicated to the principle that the problems which arise in human affairs, in all areas of activity, can best be solved by the mutual cooperation of human beings relying on their own intellectual and spiritual resources.

Preface

This book is designed as a graduate level textbook in that portion of linear electric network theory which is known as *synthesis*. It is assumed that the reader will be familiar with elementary Laplace transform theory, elementary properties of matrices, and functions of a complex variable at a level comparable with that of Churchill's *Complex Variables and Applications*, or LePage's *Complex Variables in Linear System Analysis*.

The book is intended for the serious student, one not merely interested in a parade of techniques for network design, but who desires to achieve a depth of understanding in the subject. Emphasis is placed on establishing realizability conditions for various classes of networks and network functions. Then, methods are developed for realizing one or more networks whenever a function of the given class is prescribed. Several of the topics treated have not previously appeared in book form. Among these are the realizability conditions and synthesis techniques of Fialkow and Gerst, and the Ozaki realization procedure.

The first chapter constitutes a survey of such topics in network analysis which will be important in the later development. The groundwork is laid for deriving the properties of the driving point impedance and admittance functions, as well as those of the open-circuit impedance and short-circuit admittance matrices, by expressing these in terms of the stored and dissipated energy functions.

One-port realizations are treated in Chapters 2 and 3. Networks with two kinds of elements are discussed in Chapter 2, while general RLC networks are reserved for Chapter 3. Discussion of Darlington's method is deferred until after the exposition of lossless two-port synthesis. Chapter 4 is devoted to establishing necessary realizability conditions on transfer functions of various classes of networks, the classification depending on the type of elements and the network structure.

The next four chapters, constituting approximately one-half of the entire book, are devoted to transfer function synthesis. Chapters 5 and 6 treat the case of lossless two-ports. These are followed by a discussion of

RC two-ports in Chapter 7 and, finally, general *RLC* two-ports in Chapter 8.

The final chapter considers the approximation problem in the frequency domain. This chapter, unlike the preceding ones, does not give a complete treatment of the topic specified in the chapter heading. There are several reasons for this, and they have been discussed in the introduction of the chapter. However, the relatively simple topics which are included in the chapter have not been given a cursory treatment. On the contrary, the same depth of understanding has been sought as for the preceding material.

It is impossible to give adequate credit to all the people who have contributed directly or indirectly to this book. The bibliography, which is far from exhaustive, partially serves this purpose. In addition, I would like to express my indebtedness to Dr. Wilbur R. LePage, my teacher and colleague, with whom over the years I have spent countless hours discussing the mysteries of network theory. Special thanks are due Dr. Jerome Blackman of the Department of Mathematics, Syracuse University and Mr. Makoto Sugisaki for their many valuable suggestions while reading the manuscript.

Syracuse, New York   *Norman Balabanian*

Contents

CONTENTS

Introduction

In this book we shall restrict ourselves to linear networks consisting of lumped, bilateral, and passive elements. The reasons for such a restriction are several. In the first place, many actual systems may be approximated by such an ideal one, so that study of such systems is useful in its own right. Secondly, concepts and techniques developed in such a study may be taken over directly, or easily adapted, in other systems where one or more of the idealizations are not valid. For example, when the "lumped" restriction is removed, leading to a microwave system, many of the concepts of lumped network synthesis still apply. Similar statements can be made when the "linear" or "passive" restriction is removed. Finally, the ideal system is the only one for whose solution general procedures exist.

The problem of finding the response of a given network to one or more excitation functions is solved by analyzing the network. The solution of this problem can always be uniquely determined. In contrast to this case, when both an excitation and a desired response are specified, and we are asked to find a network having the specified response to the given excitation, then we have a problem in network synthesis. One outstanding characteristic of this inverse problem is that a unique solution does not exist, *if one exists at all.* The types of external characteristics that are available for a given excitation from a linear, lumped, bilateral, and passive network are certainly limited. Thus, at the outset of a synthesis problem, we may be faced with the need for approximating a prescribed response with one that we know is obtainable from such networks. This constitutes the so-called *approximatior problem.*

The performance that is specified for the desired network may be either in the frequency domain or the time domain. Of course, the time response and the frequency response are related (through the Fourier and Laplace transforms) and so specification of the one implies specification of the other. However, recall that the first step in the synthesis process is to construct an approximating function. Approximation implies error. If the

1

approximation is performed in the time domain, the time domain error can be controlled, while if the approximation is performed in the frequency domain, the frequency domain error can be controlled. There exists no simple relationship between these two errors. Hence, if the time response is specified, with a tolerance on the permissible error, the approximation must be performed in the time domain.

After the approximation problem is solved and a realizable network function (driving point or transfer function) is at hand, there remains for us to find a suitable network having the given function as its driving point or transfer function. This is the *realization problem*. Consider what we are faced with in this problem. On the one hand, there are various classes of networks. These networks differ from each other by the number of terminals available for external connection (one-ports, two-ports), by the types of elements they contain (RC, LC, etc.), by their structure (ladder, bridge, etc.), and so forth. On the other hand, there are various classes of functions which are realizable as network functions. These functions differ in the permissible locations of their poles or their zeros, the signs of their residues or their real parts, and so forth.

Whenever it is discovered that a network class is paired off with a function class, so that if any member of the network class is analyzed it leads to a member of the function class, and any member of the function class can be realized by a network belonging to the network class, then a major breakthrough in network synthesis is achieved. Thus, the milestones in network synthesis are marked by the discovery of necessary and sufficient conditions for the realizability of a class of networks. A notable example of such a breakthrough was the discovery, by Otto Brune in 1931, that the driving point impedances of linear, passive, bilateral networks are rational positive real functions of a complex variable, and that any rational positive real function can be realized by such a network.

Proving sufficiency for the realizability of a function class by a network class involves finding at least one network of the network class which realizes any function in the function class. This network may not be desirable from a practical standpoint, because of its structure, or because it contains an excessive number of elements, or for other reasons. There may actually be many other networks differing from the first one in several respects—structure, type, size and number of elements, etc.—which realize the function class. These constitute *equivalent networks*, and their discovery is an important aspect of network synthesis. Availability of a great varity of network realizations of a given function permits us to select a suitable one for any given application.

Many of the realization techniques which we employ follow a well-defined pattern, a pattern which may be called the *classical model*. When the network function is given, say the driving point impedance of a one-port, we may first attempt to call upon past experience to identify a network having the given impedance. If this impedance is simple enough, we may succeed in the attempt and the synthesis will be complete. Thus, if the given impedance is ks, we recognize that this is the impedance of an inductance of value k. In all but the simplest cases this attempt at recognition will fail.

The next step is to systematically decompose the given function into components, each of which is simple enough to be recognizable. The realizations of the components are then interconnected in a way demanded by the process of decomposition. For example, if the given function is an admittance and it is decomposed into additive components, the entire function is realized by connecting the realizations of the components in parallel. In most cases it is not possible to decompose the original function in one step. Rather, a small realizable part of the function is separated from it, leaving a remainder function. This remainder function must be simultaneously realizable and also simpler than the original function, if progress toward a complete realization is to have been made. In the piece-meal decomposition process more than one step is usually involved, at the end of which the remainder function is in the same form as the original function (yet simpler). The partial network realizing the pieces that are removed from the original function constitutes a *cycle* in the realization procedure. The overall realization, then, consists of an interconnection of these cycles.

1

Fundamentals of Network Theory

The tourist who visits a foreign land and is unfamiliar with its language gains but a superficial knowledge of the customs and characteristics of its people. His understanding is immeasurably enhanced if he is able to converse with those around him in all walks of life. So it is with you who want to journey into the realm of network synthesis. In order to gain a thorough understanding of the subject in all its facets, it is necessary that you have an adequate background. Before embarking on the journey you should have a substantial grounding in network analysis, including a passing acquaintance with the use of matrices and a working knowledge of the theory of functions of a complex variable.

In this chapter we shall review some of the topics of network analysis which will be subsequently useful in synthesis. We shall lay the groundwork for an investigation into the properties of various network functions. The discussions will of necessity be brief, often resembling a mere outline.

1-1. Network analysis

Figure 1-1 shows an arbitrary linear bilateral network with lumped elements. Only two sources are shown explicitly but there may be other sources inside the network. Application of Kirchhoff's voltage law leads

Fig. 1-1. Arbitrary network.

5

to a set of simultaneous linear integrodifferential equations. Let us use the notation

$$a_{jk}i_k = L_{jk}\frac{di_k}{dt} + R_{jk}i_k + D_{jk}\int i_k dt \tag{1-1}$$

where $L_{jk} = \pm$ the inductance common between loops j and k. The plus sign is used when the reference directions of i_j and i_k in the common inductance coincide, while the minus sign is used when they are opposed. L_{kk} = sum of all inductances on the contour of loop k, R_{jk}, R_{kk}, same as above, with resistance substituted for inductance. D_{jk}, D_{kk}, same as above, with inverse capacitance substituted for inductance. Then this set of equations can be written,

$$a_{11}i_1 + a_{12}i_2 + \ldots + a_{1n}i_n = e_1$$
$$a_{21}i_1 + a_{22}i_2 + \ldots + a_{2n}i_n = e_2 \tag{1-2}$$
$$\cdots\cdots\cdots\cdots\cdots\cdots$$
$$a_{n1}i_1 + a_{n2}i_2 + \ldots + a_{nn}i_n = e_n$$

In these equations the i's are loop currents, while the e's are source voltages. Remember that these are not algebraic equations but a set of integro-differential equations. Their solution will depend on the type of forcing function the source voltages represent.†

The Laplace transform affords a method of solution for any (trans-formable) forcing function. Let us denote by capital letters the Laplace transforms of the corresponding functions which are denoted by a lower-case symbol. Assuming that the network is initially quiescent, the trans-form of Eqs. (1-2) can be written

$$b_{11}I_1(s) + b_{12}I_2(s) + \ldots + b_{1n}I_n(s) = E_1(s)$$
$$b_{21}I_1(s) + b_{22}I_2(s) + \ldots + b_{2n}I_n(s) = E_2(s) \tag{1-3}$$
$$\cdots\cdots\cdots\cdots\cdots\cdots\cdots$$
$$b_{n1}I_1(s) + b_{n2}I_2(s) + \ldots + b_{nn}I_n(s) = E_n(s)$$

where $s = \sigma + j\omega$ is a complex variable. These are now a set of algebraic equations in which

$$b_{jk} = sL_{jk} + R_{jk} + \frac{D_{jk}}{s} \tag{1-4}$$

† In the expressions for power and energy in the case of sinusoidal driving functions a troublesome factor of 2 will appear if peak values of the sinusoids are retained. For this reason we shall scale all functions of time by a factor $1/\sqrt{2}$.

The network functions with which we shall be dealing are ratios of transforms of certain voltages and currents. Hence such an amplitude scaling will have no effect on these functions.

It is now a simple matter to solve for the loop-current transforms. The solution is‡

$$I_k(s) = \sum_{j=1}^{n} \frac{\Delta_{jk}(s)}{\Delta(s)} E_j(s) \qquad (1\text{-}5)$$

where $\Delta(s)$ is the determinant of the system in Eqs. (1-3) and the Δ_{jk}'s are its cofactors. The elements of the determinant are b_{jk}. Thus, both Δ and its cofactors will be polynomials in s, divided by a power of s. The ratios of determinants in Eq. (1-5) will be rational functions of s with real coefficients. We shall refer to such functions as "real rational functions."

The inverse Laplace transform of Eq. (1-5) will give the solution to the original differential equations. Note that there are two sets of singular points of $I_k(s)$ in Eq. (1-5): the singularities of the driving-function transforms $E_j(s)$ and the zeros of $\Delta(s)$. The contributions of these singularities to the solution are identified as the *steady state* and the *transient*, respectively.

The transient solution for each loop current will consist of a sum of terms $A_i \epsilon^{s_i t}$, where the s_i's are the *natural frequencies*, or natural modes, of the network. They are the zeros of $\Delta(s)$. Since the loop currents of passive networks cannot increase indefinitely with time for finite driving functions, we conclude that the natural frequencies of a passive network cannot have positive real parts. That is, s_i must be restricted to the left-half s plane (or the $j\omega$ axis).

The steady-state solution will depend on the driving functions. There is considerable interest in the solution when the driving functions are sinusoidal. But sinusoids can be written as the sum of two exponentials; for example, $2 \cos \omega t = \epsilon^{j\omega t} + \epsilon^{-j\omega t}$. Hence, the steady-state solution for a sinusoid will be known when the solution for the exponential $\epsilon^{j\omega t}$ is known.

Suppose we consider a driving function ϵ^{st}, where $s = \sigma + j\omega$. Such a function has no physical interpretation for general values of s. However, the real or imaginary parts of ϵ^{st} are real functions of time; e.g., for $\sigma = 0$, the real part of ϵ^{st} is $\cos \omega t$. Figure 1-2 shows the behavior of the real part of ϵ^{st} for various values of σ and ω. These functions may represent physical source functions, at least for a finite length of time. The complex quantity s has been called many things, the most common name being *complex frequency*. Dimensionally it is reciprocal time. Its real part σ is measured in *nepers per second*, while its imaginary part is the *real angular frequency* and is measured in radians per second. It is quite confusing to call the

---

‡ The sign of Δ_{jk}, $j \neq k$, will depend on the reference direction of I_k. For a given reference direction Δ_{jk} will have one sign; for the opposite reference direction b_{ki} will change sign, and so will Δ_{jk}. Equation (1-5) will still give I_k.

imaginary part of a *complex* frequency the *real* frequency. Attempts have been made to coin a name for s. One possible name is *frequement*, combining the words "frequency" and "increment" or "decrement." In this book

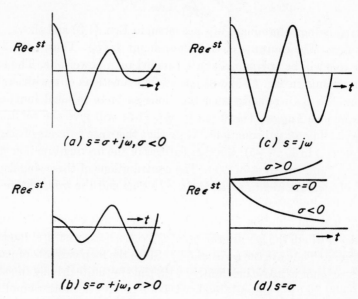

(a) $s = \sigma + j\omega, \sigma < 0$

(c) $s = j\omega$

(b) $s = \sigma + j\omega, \sigma > 0$

(d) $s = \sigma$

Fig. 1-2. $\mathrm{Re}\ (\epsilon^{st})\ \mathscr{E}\ \epsilon^{\sigma t} \cos \omega t$ for various values of σ and ω.

we shall use the name *complex frequency variable* or simply *frequency variable* for s. We shall avoid the use of the terms "real frequency" and "imaginary frequency." Instead we shall use phrases such as "for $s = j\omega$," "for imaginary values of s," "for real values of s," etc., whenever we want to restrict s to these values.

Let us now return to the network equations when the source functions are $e_j = E_{j0}\epsilon^{s_0 t}$, where s_0 is a particular value of s not equal to any of the zeros of $\Delta(s)$. The coefficient of this exponential is a complex number $E_{j0} = |E_{j0}|\epsilon^{j\theta}$. When $s_0 = j\omega_0$, the real part of $E_{j0}\epsilon^{s_0 t}$ will be $|E_{j0}| \cos (\omega_0 t + \theta)$. In this case the quantity E_{j0} is the phasor representing the trigonometric function. The Laplace transform of $e_j(t)$ will be $E_j(s) = E_{j0}/(s - s_0)$. In the partial fraction expansion of $I_k(s)$ in Eq. (1-5) the contributions of the poles of the driving functions (which lead to the steady-state solution) will be

$$I_k(s)\Big|_{\substack{\text{steady}\\\text{state}}} = \sum_{j=1}^{n} \frac{\Delta_{jk}(s_0)}{\Delta(s_0)} \frac{E_{j0}}{s - s_0} = \frac{1}{s - s_0} \sum_{j=1}^{n} \frac{\Delta_{jk}(s_0)}{\Delta(s_0)} E_{j0} \qquad (1\text{-}6)$$

By writing the right side of this expression as $I_{k0}/(s - s_0)$, which leads to the steady-state currents $i_k(t) = I_{k0}\epsilon^{s_0 t}$, we get

$$I_{k0} = \sum_{j=1}^{n} \frac{\Delta_{jk}(s_0)}{\Delta(s_0)} E_{j0} \qquad (1\text{-}7)$$

This equation bears a striking resemblance to Eq. (1-5)! the forms of the two equations are the same. In the present case the variables are the complex coefficients of the exponential functions, while the determinants are evaluated at $s = s_0$. Remember that s_0 is the frequency variable of the source and is some particular value of s, but *any* particular value. We may just as well drop the subscript. If we write

$$I_k = \sum_{j=1}^{n} \frac{\Delta_{jk}(s)}{\Delta(s)} E_j \qquad (1\text{-}8)$$

without any subscript on I_k or E_j and without the functional dependence on s explicitly indicated as in $I_k(s)$, we can interpret this equation to stand for either Eq. (1-5) or Eq. (1-7). That is to say, this equation can express the relationship between the Laplace transforms of the loop currents and driving functions for relaxed initial conditions, as well as the relationship between the phasors representing the steady-state solution for the loop currents and the driving functions when the latter are exponentials. In all the succeeding work we shall not distinguish between these two interpretations.

1-2. One-ports and two-ports

Networks are often classified according to the number of terminals, or terminal pairs, that are available for external connection. The simplest network from this point of view is the *one-terminal pair*, or *one-port*, shown in Fig. 1-3(a). Its performance is completely characterized by a single

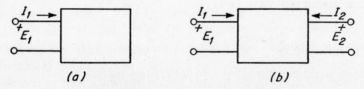

(a)   (b)

Fig. 1-3. A one-port and a two-port.

function, the *driving-point impedance* (or its reciprocal, the *driving-point admittance*). This is the ratio of E_1/I_1. An expression for this ratio can be obtained from Eq. (1-8) by removing all the source voltages except E_1. Thus

$$Z(s) = \frac{E_1}{I_1} = \frac{\Delta(s)}{\Delta_{11}(s)} \tag{1-9}$$

The impedance of a one-port is seen to be a rational function of s with real coefficients. The same is true of the admittance function. The zeros and poles of the impedance are the roots of $\Delta(s) = 0$ and $\Delta_{11}(s) = 0$, respectively. But these roots are the natural frequencies of the network with the input terminals short-circuited and with the terminals open, respectively. We conclude that the zeros and poles of $Z(s)$ cannot lie in the right half of the complex s plane (i.e., they will be either real and negative or complex with negative real part). The complex zeros and poles must come in conjugate pairs to ensure the realness of the coefficients.

Figure 1-3(b) shows a *two-terminal-pair* network, or *two-port*. The external behavior at the two pairs of terminals is described by writing relationships among the two voltages and two currents. One such relationship can be obtained from Eq. (1-8) by setting equal to zero all voltages except E_1 and E_2. The result will be

$$I_1 = y_{11}E_1 + y_{12}E_2 \tag{a}$$
$$I_2 = y_{21}E_1 + y_{22}E_2 \tag{b}$$

$$\tag{1-10}$$

where we have introduced the notation

$$y_{11}(s) = \frac{\Delta_{11}(s)}{\Delta(s)} \tag{a}$$

$$y_{12}(s) = y_{21}(s) = \frac{\Delta_{12}(s)}{\Delta(s)} \tag{b} \tag{1-11}$$

$$y_{22}(s) = \frac{\Delta_{22}(s)}{\Delta(s)} \tag{c}$$

These are the *short-circuit admittance parameters* of two-port. In matrix notation we can write Eq. (1-11) as

$$(I) = (y)(E) \qquad (y) = \begin{pmatrix} y_{11} & y_{12} \\ y_{21} & y_{22} \end{pmatrix} \tag{1-12}$$

We shall use simple parentheses to designate a matrix.

If we invert Eq. (1-10) or (1-12) to solve for the E's in terms of the I's, we shall get

$$(E) = (y)^{-1}(I) = (z)(I) \tag{1-13}$$

or

$$E_1 = z_{11}I_1 + z_{12}I_2 \qquad \text{(a)}$$

$$E_2 = z_{21}I_1 + z_{22}I_2 \qquad \text{(b)} \quad \text{(1-14)}$$

$$(z) = \begin{pmatrix} z_{11} & z_{12} \\ z_{21} & z_{22} \end{pmatrix} \qquad \text{(c)}$$

The inverse of the (y) matrix is labeled (z). The elements of (z) are the *open-circuit impedance parameters* of the two-port. From the definition of the inverse of a matrix we can write

$$z_{11} = \frac{y_{22}}{y_{11}y_{22} - y_{12}^2} = \frac{\Delta_{22}\Delta}{\Delta_{11}\Delta_{22} - \Delta_{12}^2} = \frac{\Delta_{22}}{\Delta_{1122}} \qquad \text{(a)}$$

$$z_{12} = \frac{-y_{12}}{y_{11}y_{22} - y_{12}^2} = \frac{-\Delta_{12}\Delta}{\Delta_{11}\Delta_{22} - \Delta_{12}^2} = -\frac{\Delta_{12}}{\Delta_{1122}} \qquad \text{(b)} \quad \text{(1-15)}$$

$$z_{22} = \frac{y_{11}}{y_{11}y_{22} - y_{12}^2} = \frac{\Delta_{11}\Delta}{\Delta_{11}\Delta_{22} - \Delta_{12}^2} = \frac{\Delta_{11}}{\Delta_{1122}} \qquad \text{(c)}$$

Here we used Eqs. (1-11) to relate the z parameters to Δ and its cofactors. The final equality was obtained by using the identity[†]

$$\Delta_{11}\Delta_{22} - \Delta_{12}^2 = \Delta\Delta_{1122} \qquad \text{(1-16)}$$

We have now obtained two relationships among the external currents and voltages. One other important set of parameters is the set of *chain parameters*. This set is obtained by expressing the current and voltage at one pair of terminals in terms of those at the other pair. Thus

$$E_1 = AE_2 - BI_2$$
$$I_1 = CE_2 - DI_2 \qquad \text{(1-17)}$$

Expressions for the *ABCD* parameters in terms of the y and z parameters can be obtained from Eq. (1-10) or Eq. (1-14). Obviously all these sets of parameters are related to each other.

Other relationships among the parameters are also possible. In Table 1-1 six sets of equations relating the external voltages and currents are given. The relationships between each parameter of one set and the parameters of the other sets are given in Table 1-2.[‡] Note that the signs in the equations apply for the reference conditions shown in the figure. Reversing the reference direction of I_2, for instance, will change some of the signs in the equations.

[†] See M. Bôcher, *Introduction to Higher Algebra*, Macmillan, New York, 1938.
[‡] See E. A. Guillemin, *Communication Networks*, vol. II, Wiley, New York, 1935.

The above discussion has served merely to introduce notation and collect the pertinent formulas. We have made no attempt as yet to determine the properties of the various parameters.

Table 1-1

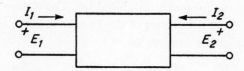

$\Delta(s)$ is the loop-impedance determinant of the network with both ends short-circuited.

$E_1 = z_{11}I_1 + z_{12}I_2$ $I_1 = y_{11}E_1 + y_{12}E_2$
$E_2 = z_{21}I_1 + z_{22}I_2$ $I_2 = y_{21}E_1 + y_{22}E_2$
$(E) = (z)(I)$ $(I) = (y)(E)$

. . . .

$E_1 = AE_2 - BI_2$ $E_2 = DE_1 - BI_1$
$I_1 = CE_2 - DI_2$ $I_2 = CE_1 - AI_1$

. . . .

$E_1 = h_{11}I_1 + h_{12}E_2$ $I_1 = g_{11}E_1 + g_{12}I_2$
$I_2 = h_{21}I_1 + h_{22}E_2$ $E_2 = g_{21}E_1 + g_{22}I_2$

. . . .

$|z| = z_{11}z_{22} - z_{12}^2$ $|h| = h_{11}h_{22} - h_{12}^2$
$|y| = y_{11}y_{22} - y_{12}^2$ $|g| = g_{11}g_{22} - g_{12}^2$
$|z| = \dfrac{1}{|y|}$ $AD - BC = 1$ $|h| = \dfrac{1}{|g|}$

All the discussion was based on the application of Kirchhoff's voltage law and the writing of loop-current equations. The determinants that appear are loop-impedance determinants. It is worthwhile to point out that a similar development can be carried out, starting with a set of node-voltage equations. Expressions for the two-port parameters in terms of node-admittance determinants can be obtained. You may carry this out as an exercise if you desire.

Two other sets of parameters are also in common use. These are the image parameters and the scattering parameters. Conventional filter theory makes use of the image parameters exclusively. The scattering-parameter formalism derives from a picture of waves incident on and reflected from the terminals of a network. They have found their greatest use in the study of microwave networks. We shall not use either of these sets of parameters in this book.

Table 1-2

z_{11}		$\dfrac{y_{22}}{\lvert y\rvert}$	$\dfrac{A}{C}$	$\dfrac{\lvert h\rvert}{h_{22}}$	$\dfrac{1}{g_{11}}$	$\dfrac{\Delta_{22}}{\Delta_{1122}}$
$z_{12}=z_{21}$		$-\dfrac{y_{12}}{\lvert y\rvert}$	$\dfrac{1}{C}$	$\dfrac{h_{12}}{h_{22}}$	$-\dfrac{g_{12}}{g_{11}}$	$-\dfrac{\Delta_{12}}{\Delta_{1122}}$
z_{22}		$\dfrac{y_{11}}{\lvert y\rvert}$	$\dfrac{D}{C}$	$\dfrac{1}{h_{22}}$	$\dfrac{\lvert g\rvert}{g_{11}}$	$\dfrac{\Delta_{11}}{\Delta_{1122}}$
y_{11}	$\dfrac{z_{22}}{\lvert z\rvert}$		$\dfrac{D}{B}$	$\dfrac{1}{h_{11}}$	$\dfrac{\lvert g\rvert}{g_{22}}$	$\dfrac{\Delta_{11}}{\Delta}$
$y_{12}=y_{21}$	$-\dfrac{z_{12}}{\lvert z\rvert}$		$-\dfrac{1}{B}$	$-\dfrac{h_{12}}{h_{11}}$	$\dfrac{g_{12}}{g_{22}}$	$\dfrac{\Delta_{12}}{\Delta}$
y_{22}	$\dfrac{z_{11}}{\lvert z\rvert}$		$\dfrac{A}{B}$	$\dfrac{\lvert h\rvert}{h_{11}}$	$\dfrac{1}{g_{22}}$	$\dfrac{\Delta_{22}}{\Delta}$
A	$\dfrac{z_{11}}{z_{12}}$	$-\dfrac{y_{22}}{y_{12}}$		$\dfrac{\lvert h\rvert}{h_{12}}$	$-\dfrac{1}{g_{12}}$	$-\dfrac{\Delta_{22}}{\Delta_{12}}$
B	$\dfrac{\lvert z\rvert}{z_{12}}$	$-\dfrac{1}{y_{12}}$		$\dfrac{h_{11}}{h_{12}}$	$-\dfrac{g_{22}}{g_{12}}$	$-\dfrac{\Delta}{\Delta_{12}}$
C	$\dfrac{1}{z_{12}}$	$-\dfrac{\lvert y\rvert}{y_{12}}$		$\dfrac{h_{22}}{h_{12}}$	$-\dfrac{g_{11}}{g_{12}}$	$-\dfrac{\Delta_{1122}}{\Delta_{12}}$
D	$\dfrac{z_{22}}{z_{12}}$	$-\dfrac{y_{11}}{y_{12}}$		$\dfrac{1}{h_{12}}$	$-\dfrac{\lvert g\rvert}{g_{12}}$	$-\dfrac{\Delta_{11}}{\Delta_{12}}$
h_{11}	$\dfrac{\lvert z\rvert}{z_{22}}$	$\dfrac{1}{y_{11}}$	$\dfrac{B}{D}$		$\dfrac{g_{22}}{\lvert g\rvert}$	$\dfrac{\Delta}{\Delta_{11}}$
$h_{12}=-h_{21}$	$\dfrac{z_{12}}{z_{22}}$	$-\dfrac{y_{12}}{y_{11}}$	$\dfrac{1}{D}$		$-\dfrac{g_{12}}{\lvert g\rvert}$	$-\dfrac{\Delta_{12}}{\Delta_{11}}$
h_{22}	$\dfrac{1}{z_{22}}$	$\dfrac{\lvert y\rvert}{y_{11}}$	$\dfrac{C}{D}$		$\dfrac{g_{11}}{\lvert g\rvert}$	$\dfrac{\Delta_{1122}}{\Delta_{11}}$
g_{11}	$\dfrac{1}{z_{11}}$	$\dfrac{\lvert y\rvert}{y_{22}}$	$\dfrac{C}{A}$	$\dfrac{h_{22}}{\lvert h\rvert}$		$\dfrac{\Delta_{1122}}{\Delta_{22}}$
$g_{12}=-g_{21}$	$-\dfrac{z_{12}}{z_{11}}$	$\dfrac{y_{12}}{y_{22}}$	$-\dfrac{1}{A}$	$-\dfrac{h_{12}}{\lvert h\rvert}$		$\dfrac{\Delta_{12}}{\Delta_{22}}$
g_{22}	$\dfrac{\lvert z\rvert}{z_{11}}$	$\dfrac{1}{y_{22}}$	$\dfrac{B}{A}$	$\dfrac{h_{11}}{h}$		$\dfrac{\Delta}{\Delta_{22}}$

1-3. Transfer functions of two-ports

A simple transmission system consists of a source, a load, and a coupling network as shown in Fig. 1-4. (In this book we shall not be concerned with the problem of transmission from more than one source to more than one load.) We refer to the source impedance Z_1 and the load impedance Z_2 as the input and output terminations, respectively. Let us call the ratio of either of the quantities E_2 or I_2 to either of the quantities E_0 or I_0 a *transfer function*. The coupling network serves the purpose of providing a desired

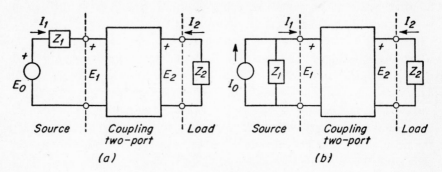

Fig. 1-4. Transmission system.

transfer function. More exactly, the magnitude or angle of the transfer function may be specified as a function of ω. The specifications will depend on the type of job (such as filtering or equalizing) which the coupling two-port is to perform. From these specifications it is necessary initially to determine a function of s which is realizable as a transfer function of the desired type of two-port (LC, RC, etc.). This constitutes the approximation problem. Near the end of the book we shall devote a chapter to a consideration of the approximation problem. However, for the most part we shall be interested in the realization problem. Thus our major problem is how to find the element values of a two-port when a realizable transfer function specifying its behavior is given and the conditions of loading at the input and output are specified.

At this point many of you will be dissatisfied. This is not the natural order of things, you will say. If you have the requirement for a filter, say, which must satisfy certain specifications, how can you postpone consideration of the approximation problem, you will ask. Where will the transfer function that you will realize come from? It is true that, in a particular synthesis task, both problems, approximation and realization, must be solved. However, as we shall see throughout the remainder of the book, all the characteristics of the networks we realize, their structure, the types and numbers of elements they contain, etc., depend on the locations of the poles and zeros of the transfer function. Given performance specifications can be satisfied equally well by transfer functions having widely differing pole and zero locations. For example, a given filtering task may be performed equally well by an RC filter or an LC filter. In other words, you can solve the approximation problem much more usefully if you know what the effects of placing poles and zeros in certain locations will be on the ease of realization. For this reason it is essential to become thoroughly familiar with the properties of transfer functions and with realization techniques before considering the approximation problem.

When the transfer function of a two-port is specified, the extent to which the behavior of the two-port is specified depends upon the prescribed input and output terminations. Thus, consider the network in Fig. 1-5(a). The source is a current source, and the output terminals are open. This can be described by saying that both terminations are open. The transfer function that is prescribed is E_2/I_1. But this is z_{21} (which is the same as z_{12}), the open-circuit transfer impedance. It appears that we have quite a bit of flexibility in meeting the specifications of this particular problem, since only one of the three parameters of the two-port is specified; the other two may be chosen arbitrarily within limits depending on the type of elements permitted in the two-port. Presumably we will choose them in such a way that the realization task is simplified.

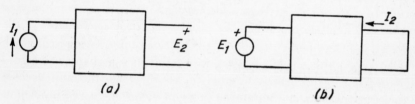

Fig. 1-5. Open- or short-circuit terminations at both ends.

Similarly, in the case of Fig. 1-5(b), the source is a voltage source, and the output is the short-circuit current. The prescribed function is $I_2/E_1 = y_{21}$ (which is the same as y_{12}), the short-circuit transfer admittance.

A very common situation is the one shown in Fig. 1-6. The output

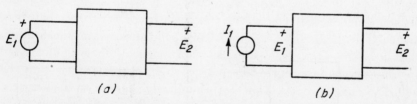

Fig. 1-6. Voltage source or current source with open-circuit output.

terminals are open-circuited. In part (a) the source is a voltage source, while in part (b) it is a current source. In either case the prescribed function is the voltage ratio E_2/E_1, which we shall designate $T_{12}(s)$. We can get expressions for this ratio from Eqs. (1-10) and (1-14). Thus

$$T_{12}(s) = \frac{E_2}{E_1} = \frac{-y_{12}}{y_{22}} = \frac{z_{12}}{z_{11}} \tag{1-18}$$

The minus sign with the y parameters is a result of the chosen reference direction for I_2 and has no other significance. In the present case two of the three parameters are involved, but only their ratio is prescribed. This is a slightly more complicated problem than the previous two, but still a certain amount of flexibility exists. When the transfer function $T_{12}(s)$ is given as a rational function of s, we shall need to find two functions z_{12} and z_{11} (or y_{12} and y_{22}) which satisfy realizability conditions for the type of network desired and whose ratio is the given function.

In all the cases considered so far the terminations were either open-circuited or short-circuited. Consider the case shown in Fig. 1-7, where one

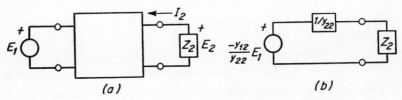

Fig. 1-7. One finite impedance termination with voltage source.

of the terminations is an impedance Z_2 and the source is a voltage source. Applying Thèvenin's theorem at the output terminals gives Fig. 1-7(b). From this circuit the transfer admittance, defined as the output current divided by the input voltage, can easily be found.

$$Y_{12}(s) = \frac{I_2}{E_1} = \frac{y_{12}Y_2}{Y_2 + y_{22}} \tag{1-19}$$

In this case again two of the three y parameters are involved, but in a more complicated manner than in Eq. (1-18).

Figure 1-8 shows the case of a finite load impedance Z_2 at one end with

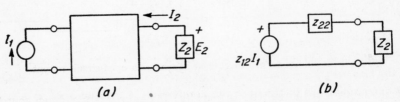

Fig. 1-8. One finite impedance termination with current source.

a current source at the other. Application of Thèvenin's theorem leads to part (b). From this the transfer impedance, defined as the output voltage divided by the input current, can be easily computed.

$$Z_{12}(s) = \frac{E_2}{I_1} = \frac{z_{12}Z_2}{Z_2 + z_{22}} \qquad (1\text{-}20)$$

This expression involves the terminating impedance and the z parameters in the same way that Y_{12} in Eq. (1-19) involves the terminating admittance and the y parameters. Again only two of the parameters are involved. Note that $Z_{12}(s)$ in Eq. (1-20) is not the reciprocal of $Y_{12}(s)$ in Eq. (1-19).

As a final case consider the general situation with finite terminations at both ends. In the most common situation the transmission network is inserted between a load which can be considered resistive and a physical source with a finite internal resistance as shown in Fig. 1-9. In this case

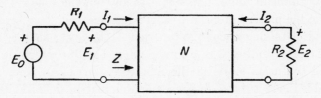

Fig. 1-9. Transmission network inserted between two finite resistances.

the response function of interest is the ratio of output voltage to source voltage, $T(s) = E_2/E_0$. In order to find an expression for this ratio in terms of the network parameters, we can write

$$I_1 = \frac{E_0}{R_1 + Z} \qquad (a)$$

$$\qquad\qquad\qquad\qquad\qquad (1\text{-}21)$$

$$\frac{E_2}{I_1} = \frac{R_2 z_{12}}{R_2 + z_{22}} \qquad (b)$$

The last expression is just Eq. (1-20) with R_2 used for Z_2. Substituting the first of these into the second gives

$$T(s) = \frac{E_2}{E_0} = \frac{R_2 z_{12}}{(R_1 + Z)(R_2 + z_{22})} \qquad (1\text{-}22)$$

This equation is not very useful in its present form because it contains the quantity Z. From Fig. 1-9 you can see that Z is the input impedance of the two-port when the opposite end is terminated. To get an expression for this impedance in terms of the parameters of the two-port, return to Eqs. (1-14) and solve for the ratio E_1/I_1 with the condition that

$E_2 = -R_2I_2$ (minus because of the reference conditions of E_2 and I_2). The result is

$$Z(s) = \frac{R_2z_{11} + |z|}{R_2 + z_{22}} \qquad (1\text{-}23)$$

where $|z| = z_{11}z_{22} - z_{12}^2$. This is a very important relationship in its own right, and we shall use it quite extensively in subsequent work. For the present, if we substitute it into Eq. (1-22), we shall get

$$T(s) = \frac{R_2z_{12}}{R_1R_2 + R_1z_{22} + R_2z_{11} + |z|} \qquad (1\text{-}24)$$

This is the relationship we were looking for. It contains all three of the z parameters. In a synthesis problem suppose that $T(s)$ is given to us as a rational function in s. Before we can realize the network, we shall have to recognize the set of three z parameters from the given function. This will be very difficult, if not impossible, in any but the simplest cases. For this reason the present problem is solved in stages.

Instead of talking about the function E_2/E_0, some authors use other functions related to this in very simple ways. For this reason considerable notational confusion exists in the literature. One of the difficulties encountered is the fact that a response function may be defined either as the ratio of an output to an input quantity or as its reciprocal. All the functions we have defined have been of the output/input variety. There is probably equal merit in either procedure. However, to avoid confusion, it is best to stick to one or the other. We shall consistently define network functions as output/input.

When the two-port in Fig. 1-9 is inserted between the source and the load, it is desired to know what effect the network has on the transmitted power. Let us define the *insertion power ratio* as the power delivered to the load with the network present divided by the power delivered to the load with the network removed. Since the load is the same in both cases, these two quantities are proportional to the squared magnitude of the cor-

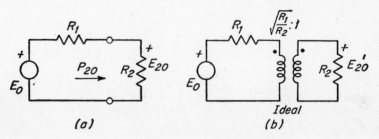

Fig. 1-10. Situation with network removed.

responding voltages. Let E_{20} and P_{20} denote the voltage and power at the load when the network is removed, as in Fig. 1-10(a), and let E_2 and P_2 denote these same quantities when the network is inserted. We define the *insertion voltage ratio* as

$$H(s) = \frac{E_2}{E_{20}} \tag{1-25}$$

The magnitude squared of this quantity for $s = j\omega$ is the insertion power ratio. We can easily find E_{20} in terms of E_0 from Fig. 1-10(a) so that Eq. (1-25) becomes

$$H(s) = \frac{E_2}{R_2 E_0/(R_1 + R_2)} = \frac{R_1 + R_2}{R_2} T(s) \tag{1-26}$$

The previous paragraph has focused attention on the load end of the network. Let us now consider conditions at the source end. Let P be the power transmitted into the two-port of Fig. 1-9. This power will have its maximum value $P_m = |E_0|^2/4R_1$ when $Z(j\omega) = R_1$.† When this happens, the voltage $E_1 = E_0/2$. The amount by which E_1 deviates from $E_0/2$ is an indication of the amount by which the power delivered to the network deviates from the maximum. Let us define the input-end *reflection coefficient* as

$$\rho(j\omega) = \frac{E_0/2 - E_1}{E_0/2} = \frac{I_1(R_1 + Z) - 2I_1 Z}{I_1(R_1 + Z)} = \frac{R_1 - Z(j\omega)}{R_1 + Z(j\omega)} \tag{1-27}$$

The power delivered to the network is equal to the real part of the input impedance times the magnitude squared of the input current. This is

$$P = U \left| \frac{E_0}{R_1 + Z(j\omega)} \right|^2 \tag{1-28}$$

where $Z(j\omega) = U(\omega) + jX(\omega)$. We can now write an expression for the difference between the maximum power and the actual power into the network,

$$P_m - P = \frac{|E_0|^2}{4R_1} - \frac{U|E_0|^2}{(U + R_1)^2 + X^2} = \frac{|E_0|^2}{4R_1} \left| \frac{(R_1 - U)^2 + X^2}{(R_1 + U)^2 + X^2} \right| = P_m |\rho(j\omega)|^2 \tag{1-29}$$

This can be rewritten as

$$|\rho(j\omega)|^2 = 1 - \frac{P}{P_m} \tag{1-30}$$

Let us now return to the load end of the network. From the definition of the insertion power ratio and Eq. (1-25) we can write

† Recall that all time functions, and hence their transforms, have been scaled by the factor $1/\sqrt{2}$.

$$|H(j\omega)|^2 = \left|\frac{E_2}{E_{20}}\right|^2 = \frac{P_2}{P_{20}} \tag{1-31}$$

From Fig. 10(a) we can readily calculate P_{20} in terms of R_1, R_2, and E_0. If we also remember that the maximum power that can be delivered to the network is $P_m = |E_0|^2/4R_1$, we can write

$$P_{20} = \frac{R_2|E_0|^2}{(R_1 + R_2)^2} = \frac{4R_1R_2}{(R_1 + R_2)^2} P_m \tag{1-32}$$

We now substitute this into Eq. (1-31). Finally, if we multiply numerator and denominator of the result by P, we get

$$|H(j\omega)|^2 = \frac{(R_1 + R_2)^2}{4R_1R_2} \frac{P_2}{P_m} = \frac{(R_1 + R_2)^2}{4R_1R_2} \frac{P_2}{P} \frac{P}{P_m} \tag{1-33}$$

Noting that the power into the network can never be larger than P_m and that the power delivered to the load can never be larger than the power into the network, we can deduce a necessary condition on the insertion power ratio for passive networks, viz.,

$$|H(j\omega)|^2 \leq \frac{(R_1 + R_2)^2}{4R_1R_2} \tag{1-34}$$

Using Eq. (1-26), we can write this condition in terms of $T(j\omega)$. Thus,

$$|T(j\omega)|^2 = \frac{R_2^2}{(R_1 + R_2)^2} |H(j\omega)|^2 \leq \frac{R_2}{4R_1} \tag{1-35}$$

Let us now eliminate the ratio P/P_m between Eqs. (1-33) and (1-30). We shall get

$$|\rho(j\omega)|^2 + \frac{4R_1R_2}{(R_1 + R_2)^2} \frac{P}{P_2} |H(j\omega)|^2 = 1 \tag{1-36}$$

This is a very valuable relationship. Equation (1-30) involves only source-end quantities. However, Eq. (1-36) ties load-end quantities to source-end quantities. The only blemish in this equation is the ratio P/P_2, which is the ratio of the power into the network to the power delivered to the load. This ratio will depend on the amount of power dissipation in the network. In the important case of a lossless two-port this ratio will be unity so that Eq. (1-36) becomes

$$|\rho(j\omega)|^2 + \frac{4R_1R_2}{(R_1 + R_2)^2} |H(j\omega)|^2 = 1 \tag{1-37}$$

Using Eq. (1-26), this can be written

$$|\rho(j\omega)|^2 + \frac{4R_1}{R_2} |T(j\omega)|^2 = 1 \tag{1-38}$$

In an effort to eliminate the constants involving R_1 and R_2 from the previous two equations, some authors define another function. Suppose that when the two-port is removed, it is replaced by an ideal transformer with a turns ratio $\sqrt{R_1/R_2}/1$ as shown in Fig. 1-10(b). From the primary side the load appears as a resistance R_1 so that the source resistance is matched. Hence the power delivered by the source to the load will equal its maximum value $P_m = |E_0|^2/4R_1$. Let the load voltage under these circumstances be called E'_{20} and the power delivered to the load be called P'_{20}. We can easily find E'_{20} in terms of E_0 from Fig. 1-10(b). If we now combine this with the expression for E_{20} from Fig. 1-10(a), we shall get

$$E'_{20} = \frac{R_1 + R_2}{\sqrt{4R_1R_2}} E_{20} \tag{1-39}$$

Now let us define another function $H'(s) = E_2/E'_{20}$, which we shall call the *transmission function* (it has also been called the *transmission coefficient*).† Using Eq. (1-39) and also Eq. (1-26), we get

$$H'(s) = \frac{E_2}{E'_{20}} = \frac{\sqrt{4R_1R_2}}{R_1 + R_2} H(s) = \sqrt{\frac{4R_1}{R_2}} T(s) \tag{1-40}$$

This expression shows that all three of the functions $T(s)$, $H(s)$, and $H'(s)$ have the same properties; they differ from each other simply by a multiplicative constant. In terms of H' Eqs. (1-37) or (1-38) can be written as

$$|\rho(j\omega)|^2 + |H'(j\omega)|^2 = 1 \tag{1-41}$$

The origin of the name transmission coefficient for H' is now apparent.

Let us now return to the synthesis problem of Fig. 1-9. Suppose that the prescribed function is $|T(j\omega)|^2$. This is related to the reflection coefficient through Eq. (1-38). The reflection coefficient is in turn related to the input impedance of the two-port through Eq. (1-27) and, finally, Z is related to the z parameters of the two-port through Eq. (1-23). At the present time we shall not go into the details of the procedure for going from a prescribed insertion ratio to the network parameters. We shall leave this until we discuss the actual realization in Chap. 6.

1-4. Magnitude and frequency normalizations

The order of magnitude of the element values that we meet in electric networks ranges all the way from 10^{-12} (for capacitances) to 10^6 or 10^7 (for resistances). Similarly, the frequency range of interest goes from a few cycles per second to millions of cycles per second. Thus the numbers we

---

† In the German literature the quantity $\log (1/|H'(j\omega)|)$ is called the *effective loss* (*Betriebsdämpfung*).

are likely to have in the network functions, for practical network elements, are not likely to be convenient numbers. On the other hand, the properties of these functions and the synthesis procedures which we shall develop do not depend on the absolute size of the coefficients in the network functions. It would therefore be wise to divorce the inconvenient size of coefficients from a discussion of properties of functions and synthesis techniques. This is accomplished by normalization.

Suppose that each R, L, and D in a network is multiplied by a constant K. Then each element in the network determinant will be multiplied by K, as seen in Eq. (1-4). The determinant itself, being of order n, will be multiplied by K^n. Each $(n-1)$-rowed cofactor of Δ will be multiplied by K^{n-1}, and each $(n-2)$-rowed cofactor will be multiplied by K^{n-2}. Now look at the two-port parameters given in Table 1-2. Those which are dimensionally impedance or admittance are the ratio of two determinants whose orders differ by 1. Those which are voltage or current ratios, like A and h_{12}, are the ratios of two determinants of the same order. Hence multiplying each R, L, and D in the network by a constant K will have the effect of multiplying each impedance function by the same constant and dividing each admittance by the constant. Any voltage or current ratios will be unaffected by this multiplication. The inverse is also true: if we multiply an impedance function by a constant K, then each R, L, and D in the network will be multiplied by K. This process is called *changing the impedance level*.

As an illustration, consider the network of Fig. 1-9. The impedance at the input terminals of the two-port is given in Eq. (1-23). This may be rewritten as

$$\frac{Z(s)}{R_2} = \frac{z_{11}/R_2 + |z|/R_2^2}{1 + z_{22}/R_2} \tag{1-42}$$

If we now define $Z'(s) = Z(s)/R_2$ and similarly for the other quantities in the equation, we can rewrite the equation in terms of the primed quantities. To simplify the notation, we shall drop the primes and get

$$Z(s) = \frac{z_{11} + |z|}{1 + z_{22}} \tag{1-43}$$

Formally this looks as if we set $R_2 = 1$ in Eq. (1-23). After we have gone through a realization procedure and have obtained a network, we can multiply each R, L, and D by the constant R_2. This will multiply the impedance by R_2, thus restoring the impedance level.

Another procedure that simplifies computation is that of frequency normalization. A new frequency variable is defined as the old variable divided by a constant, ω_0. Then the value $s = j\omega_0$ in the old variable becomes $j1$ in the new variable. The impedances of single network elements are R, sL, and D/s. If a network function is to be unaffected by the frequency scaling, then these single-element impedances should be unaffected. R is certainly not affected. The others will also be unaffected if we multiply L's by ω_0 and divide D's by ω_0.

In the previous paragraph we assumed the network was available when we made the frequency normalization. However, when we are undertaking a synthesis problem, we have a network function, not a network. We make the desired frequency normalization on the function. When we subsequently realize a network, the element values we get will be normalized values. In order to obtain actual values, we shall need to do the inverse of what we did in the previous paragraph.

To summarize, suppose a network realization is obtained on a normalized impedance and frequency basis, the normalizing factors being R_0 and ω_0. Let R_n, L_n, and D_n be the element values so obtained. Then the actual element values when the impedance level and the frequency are restored will be

$$R = R_n R_0$$

$$L = L_n \frac{R_0}{\omega_0} \tag{1-44}$$

$$D = D_n R_0 \omega_0 \quad \text{or} \quad C = \frac{C_n}{R_0 \omega_0}$$

It is clearly evident from these expressions that the normalized element values are dimensionless. In all the discussions that follow we shall be dealing with normalized functions so that, whenever a realization is obtained, the element values will be normalized values. The element values that will be shown on network diagrams will always be those of R_n, L_n, and C_n, unless explicitly stated otherwise. Since the functions are normalized, we will not be able to check dimensions.

1-5. Interconnections of two-ports

We mentioned briefly in the introduction that the classical model of synthesis consists in breaking the network functions down into simpler functions which are easily realizable. The over-all network realization then is obtained as an interconnection of these simple networks. Two-ports can be interconnected in several ways; which one is used in a particular problem depends on which network function is to be realized and how the breakdown into simpler functions is made. We shall now discuss some of these interconnections.

Figure 1-11 shows two two-ports connected in cascade. The over-all

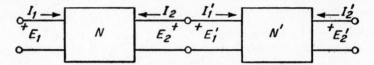

Fig. 1-11. Cascade connection of two-ports.

external voltages and currents are E_1, I_1, E_2', and I_2'. At the junction between the two we have $E_2 = E_1'$ and $-I_2 = I_1'$. In matrix notation this reads

$$\begin{pmatrix} E_2 \\ -I_2 \end{pmatrix} = \begin{pmatrix} E_1' \\ I_1' \end{pmatrix} \tag{1-45}$$

If we describe each network by its chain parameters, we can write

$$\begin{pmatrix} E_1 \\ I_1 \end{pmatrix} = \begin{pmatrix} A & B \\ C & D \end{pmatrix} \begin{pmatrix} E_2 \\ -I_2 \end{pmatrix} \qquad \text{(a)}$$

$$\tag{1-46}$$

$$\begin{pmatrix} E_1' \\ I_1' \end{pmatrix} = \begin{pmatrix} A' & B' \\ C' & D' \end{pmatrix} \begin{pmatrix} E_2' \\ -I_2' \end{pmatrix} \qquad \text{(b)}$$

The common voltage and current at the junction can be eliminated from these equations by using Eq. (1-45). Thus we can write

$$\begin{pmatrix} E_1 \\ I_1 \end{pmatrix} = \begin{pmatrix} A & B \\ C & D \end{pmatrix} \begin{pmatrix} A' & B' \\ C' & D' \end{pmatrix} \begin{pmatrix} E_2' \\ -I_2' \end{pmatrix} \tag{1-47}$$

This equation says that the over-all chain matrix of a cascade of two two-ports is equal to the product of the individual chain matrices. There is no restriction on the structure of the individual two-ports in this interconnection. The extension to more than two two-ports is clear.

Another interconnection of interest is the parallel connection shown in

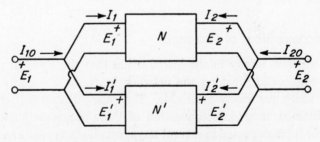

Fig. 1-12. Parallel connection of two-ports.

Fig. 1-12. The over-all terminal current at each end of the network is the sum of the terminal currents of the component networks. Thus

$$\begin{pmatrix} I_{01} \\ I_{02} \end{pmatrix} = \begin{pmatrix} I_1 \\ I_2 \end{pmatrix} + \begin{pmatrix} I_1' \\ I_2' \end{pmatrix} \tag{1-48}$$

If we describe each network by its y parameters, we can write

$$\begin{pmatrix} I_1 \\ I_2 \end{pmatrix} = \begin{pmatrix} y_{11} & y_{12} \\ y_{21} & y_{22} \end{pmatrix} \begin{pmatrix} E_1 \\ E_2 \end{pmatrix} \tag{a}$$

$$\begin{pmatrix} I_1' \\ I_2' \end{pmatrix} = \begin{pmatrix} y_{11}' & y_{12}' \\ y_{21}' & y_{22}' \end{pmatrix} \begin{pmatrix} E_1' \\ E_2' \end{pmatrix} \tag{b}$$

$$(1\text{-}49)$$

The terminal voltages of the two networks are the same. Hence, if we add the last two equations and use Eq. (1-48), we get

$$\begin{pmatrix} I_{01} \\ I_{02} \end{pmatrix} = \left[\begin{pmatrix} y_{11} & y_{12} \\ y_{21} & y_{22} \end{pmatrix} + \begin{pmatrix} y_{11}' & y_{12}' \\ y_{21}' & y_{22}' \end{pmatrix} \right] \begin{pmatrix} E_1 \\ E_2 \end{pmatrix} \tag{1-50}$$

This equation says that the y matrix of the parallel connection of two two-ports is equal to the sum of the y matrices of the individual two-ports. The extension to more than two two-ports is evident.

The description of the behavior of two-ports in parallel by means of Eq. (1-50) is not always possible. Each network, when alone, is described by one of Eqs. (1-49). For Eq. (1-50) to hold, we must ensure that we do not invalidate the previous relationships when we make the parallel connection. For example, the two networks shown in Fig. 1-13 cannot be

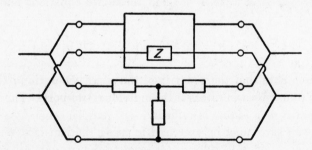

Fig. 1-13. Parallel connection for which Eq. (1-50) is not valid.

paralleled directly [and described by Eq. (1-50)] because the element labeled Z in the top network will be shorted by the bottom network. Thus the y matrix of the top network, when alone and when in parallel with the bottom network, will be different.†

† For a more complete discussion of the required conditions for parallel connection, see Guillemin (55).

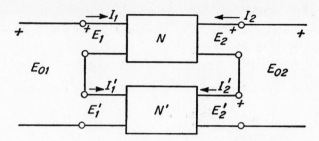

Fig. 1-14. Series connection of two-ports

The third type of two-port connection we shall discuss is the series connection shown in Fig. 1-14. The over-all voltage at each end is equal to the sum of the voltages of the individual two-ports. Thus

$$\begin{pmatrix} E_{01} \\ E_{02} \end{pmatrix} = \begin{pmatrix} E_1 \\ E_2 \end{pmatrix} + \begin{pmatrix} E_1' \\ E_2' \end{pmatrix} \tag{1-51}$$

If we describe each network by its z parameters, we can write

$$\begin{pmatrix} E_1 \\ E_2 \end{pmatrix} = \begin{pmatrix} z_{11} & z_{12} \\ z_{21} & z_{22} \end{pmatrix} \begin{pmatrix} I_1 \\ I_2 \end{pmatrix} \tag{a}$$

$$\tag{1-52}$$

$$\begin{pmatrix} E_1' \\ E_2' \end{pmatrix} = \begin{pmatrix} z_{11}' & z_{12}' \\ z_{21}' & z_{22}' \end{pmatrix} \begin{pmatrix} I_1' \\ I_2' \end{pmatrix} \tag{b}$$

The input currents and the output currents of the two networks are the same, respectively, so that, if we add these two equations and use Eq. (1-51), we get

$$\begin{pmatrix} E_{01} \\ E_{02} \end{pmatrix} = \left[\begin{pmatrix} z_{11} & z_{12} \\ z_{21} & z_{22} \end{pmatrix} + \begin{pmatrix} z_{11}' & z_{12}' \\ z_{21}' & z_{22}' \end{pmatrix} \right] \begin{pmatrix} I_1 \\ I_2 \end{pmatrix} \tag{1-53}$$

This equation says that the z matrix of the series connection of two two-ports is the sum of the z matrices of the individual two-ports. The extension to more than two two-ports is evident.

Here again care must be exercised in using the matrix description of the series connection of two-ports. Connecting the two-ports in series may change the z parameters of one or the other from what they were before the series connection. In such a case Eq. (1-53) will not be valid.†

Two other possible interconnections of two-ports are series-parallel and parallel-series. We shall not discuss these connections here, but you can easily show that the over-all h matrix for the series-parallel connection

† A more complete discussion is given in Guillemin (55).

is the sum of the h matrices of the individual two-ports. Similarly the overall g matrix of the parallel-series connection is the sum of the g matrices of the individual two-ports.

These statements are, again, valid only when the individual matrices are not modified by the interconnection.

1-6. Energy functions

In the previous sections of this chapter we used the passive nature of the networks under consideration twice. We used it first to establish locations of the poles of network functions. In Sec. 1-4 we used it again when we were able to state that the power delivered to the load through a passive transmission network cannot be greater than the power supplied at the input of the network. The passive nature of the networks can also be put into evidence by noting that the energy stored or dissipated in a passive network can never be negative. This fact will certainly have some effect on the performance of a passive network. Since network performance is described in terms of network functions (driving point and transfer), it should be possible to relate the network functions to the energy stored and dissipated in the network.

Let us return to Eqs. (1-3), which are the Laplace transforms of the loop equations of the network of Fig. 1-1 under quiescent initial conditions. The solution of these equations is given in Eq. (1-8). We showed that this expression can also represent the steady-state solution for sinusoidal driving functions if I_k and E_j are considered to be phasors and $s = j\omega$. In the latter case we can interpret Eqs. (1-3) as relationships among phasors if we replace s by $j\omega$ in b_{jk}. Let us now assume that there are no sources in Fig. 1-1 except at the input and output of the two-port and rewrite Eqs. 1-3, this time in matrix notation. The result is

$$(E) = s(L)(I) + (R)(I) + \frac{1}{s}(D)(I) \qquad (1\text{-}54)$$

where the voltage and current matrices are

$$(E) = \begin{pmatrix} E_1 \\ E_2 \\ 0 \\ \vdots \\ 0 \end{pmatrix} \qquad (I) = \begin{pmatrix} I_1 \\ I_2 \\ \vdots \\ I_n \end{pmatrix} \qquad (1\text{-}55)$$

and the loop-parameter matrices are

$$(L) = \begin{bmatrix} L_{11} & L_{12} & \cdots & L_{1n} \\ L_{21} & L_{22} & \cdots & L_{2n} \\ \cdots & \cdots & \cdots & \cdots \\ L_{n1} & L_{n2} & \cdots & L_{nn} \end{bmatrix} \quad (a)$$

$$(R) = \begin{bmatrix} R_{11} & R_{12} & \cdots & R_{1n} \\ R_{21} & R_{22} & \cdots & R_{2n} \\ \cdots & \cdots & \cdots & \cdots \\ R_{n1} & R_{n2} & \cdots & R_{nn} \end{bmatrix} \quad (b) \quad (1\text{-}56)$$

$$(D) = \begin{bmatrix} D_{11} & D_{12} & \cdots & D_{1n} \\ D_{21} & D_{22} & \cdots & D_{2n} \\ \cdots & \cdots & \cdots & \cdots \\ D_{n1} & D_{n2} & \cdots & D_{nn} \end{bmatrix} \quad (c)$$

Remember that the voltages and currents in Eqs. (1-55) can be either Laplace transforms in the general case or phasors in the case of sinusoidal driving functions. In the latter case s will take on the value $j\omega$ in Eq. (1-54).

Let us temporarily restrict ourselves to sinusoidal source functions so that the E's and I's are phasors. The complex power supplied by the source at the input will be $E_1 I_1^*$ (where * indicates the complex conjugate), while that supplied by the source at the output will be $E_2 I_2^*$. The total complex power delivered to the network can be obtained by multiplying the voltage matrix in Eqs. (1-55) by the transpose of the current matrix after each element is replaced by its conjugate. Thus

$$(I^*)^t(E) = (I_1^* I_2^* \ldots I_n^*) \begin{bmatrix} E_1 \\ E_2 \\ 0 \\ \vdots \\ 0 \end{bmatrix} = E_1 I_1^* + E_2 I_2^* \quad (1\text{-}57)$$

where $(I^*)^t$ denotes the matrix which is obtained from (I) by replacing each element in the matrix by its conjugate and then transposing rows and columns. Now look at Eq. (1-54). If we multiply both sides of this equation by $(I^*)^t$, we shall get (letting $s = j\omega$)

$$(I^*)^t(E) = (I^*)^t(R)(I) + j\omega[(I^*)^t(L)(I) - \frac{1}{\omega^2}(I^*)^t(D)(I)] \quad (1\text{-}58)$$

The left side of this equation is the total complex-power input to the network. Let us seek an interpretation for the right side. To this end define the functions

$$F = \tfrac{1}{2}(I^*)^t(R)(I) = \tfrac{1}{2} \sum_{j,k=1}^{n} R_{jk}I_jI_k^* \qquad (a)$$

$$T = \tfrac{1}{2}(I^*)^t(L)(I) = \tfrac{1}{2} \sum_{j,k=1}^{n} L_{jk}I_jI_k^* \qquad (b) \quad (1\text{-}59)$$

$$V = \frac{1}{2\omega^2}(I^*)^t(D)(I) = \frac{1}{2\omega^2}\sum_{j,k=1}^{n} D_{jk}I_jI_k^* \qquad (c)$$

The right sides of these are obtained by actually performing the indicated operations in the matrix products on the left. These quantities are quadratic functions of the variables. In order to get an interpretation for them, let us consider the simple network shown in Fig. 1-15. We can readily

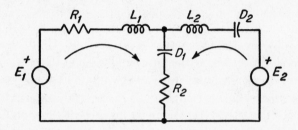

Fig. 1-15. Simple network for evaluating energy functions.

evaluate the functions in the preceding equation for this network. Thus

$$F = \tfrac{1}{2}(I_1^* I_2^*)\begin{pmatrix} R_1 + R_2 & R_2 \\ R_2 & R_2 \end{pmatrix}\begin{pmatrix} I_1 \\ I_2 \end{pmatrix} = \frac{R_1}{2}|I_1|^2 + \frac{R_2}{2}|I_1 + I_2|^2 \qquad (a)$$

$$T = \tfrac{1}{2}(I_1^* I_2^*)\begin{pmatrix} L_1 & 0 \\ 0 & L_2 \end{pmatrix}\begin{pmatrix} I_1 \\ I_2 \end{pmatrix} = \frac{L_1}{2}|I_1|^2 + \frac{L_2}{2}|I_2|^2 \qquad (b) \quad (1\text{-}60)$$

$$V = \frac{1}{2\omega^2}(I_1^* I_2^*)\begin{pmatrix} D_1 & D_1 \\ D_1 & D_1 + D_2 \end{pmatrix}\begin{pmatrix} I_1 \\ I_2 \end{pmatrix} = \frac{D_1}{2\omega^2}|I_1 + I_2|^2 + \frac{D_2}{2\omega^2}|I_2|^2 \quad (c)$$

From elementary considerations we know that the right side of the first of these equations is half the average power dissipated in the resistances of the network. Similarly the right side of the second equation is the average energy stored in the inductances, while the right side of the third is the average energy stored in the capacitances. It is not difficult to appreciate that these interpretations are generally true for a network of arbitrary complexity. We shall refer to the F, T, and V functions as *energy functions* (even though F has the dimensions of power). Since we know that the average value of the energy stored and the power dissipated in a passive network can never be negative, we form the important conclusion that *the* *energy functions can never be negative.* You may worry about the fact that the energy functions contain complex quantities, yet from their physical interpretation they ought to be real. To satisfy yourself that they are indeed real, take the complex conjugate of F, say. You will find that $F^* = F$, which is possible only if F is real.

Glance back at the energy functions defined in Eqs. (1-59). They are quadratic functions of the currents. Functions such as these are called *quadratic forms*. We have seen that the particular quadratic forms with which we are dealing are always real and never negative no matter what values, real or complex, the variables may take on. Quadratic forms which are always positive are called *positive definite*. If zero is also a possible value of the quadratic form, it is called *positive semidefinite*. The quadratic forms under consideration here are of the latter variety.

The positive definite character of a quadratic form, being independent of the values of the variables, must depend on the matrix of the quadratic form. If a quadratic form is definite or semidefinite, its matrix is also called definite or semidefinite, respectively. Hence we conclude that *the loop-parameter matrices (L), (R), and (D) are positive semidefinite.*

In terms of the energy functions we can rewrite Eq. (1-58) and get

$$(I^{*t}E) = 2F + j2\omega[T - V] \tag{1-61}$$

It is now clear that this equation expresses the power balance between the complex-power input to the network on the one hand and the real power dissipated and the reactive power stored in the network on the other.

Let us now remove the temporary restriction to sinusoidal source functions and return to the loop equations of Eq. (1-54). The E's and I's are now considered to be Laplace transforms. Although it will no longer have the physical significance of computing the total power input to the network, let us again multiply this equation by $(I^*)^t$. The result will be

$$(I^*)^t(E) = (I^*)^t(R)(I) + s(I^*)^t(L)(I) + \frac{1}{s}(I^*)^t(D)(I)$$

$$= F_0 + sT_0 + \frac{V_0}{s} \tag{1-62}$$

where
$$F_0 = (I^*)^t(R)(I) \qquad \text{(a)}$$
$$T_0 = (I^*)^t(L)(I) \qquad \text{(b)} \quad \text{(1-63)}$$
$$V_0 = (I^*)^t(D)(I) \qquad \text{(c)}$$

A comparison of these functions with the corresponding energy functions in Eqs. (1-59) shows that corresponding ones differ merely by a multiplicative positive constant. We shall call these new functions energy functions also, although they no longer have the physical interpretation of energy. Clearly, they also are positive semidefinite, since they each have the same matrix as the corresponding average energy functions.

1-7. Properties of network functions

Now that we have defined the energy functions, we shall turn our attention to the formulation of the network functions in terms of them. The positive semidefinite nature of the energy functions will be strongly reflected in the properties of the various network functions.

First of all consider the case of a network with one pair of external terminals, a one-port. With $E_2 = 0$ Eq. (1-62) becomes

$$E_1 I_1^* = F_0 + sT_0 + \frac{V_0}{s} \tag{1-64}$$

The driving-point impedance $Z(s)$ and the admittance $Y(s)$ can be obtained from this equation as follows: The impedance is obtained by dividing both sides by $I_1 I_1^* = |I_1|^2$, while the admittance is obtained by first taking the conjugate of the equation and then dividing by $E_1 E_1^* = |E_1|^2$. The results will be

$$Z(s) = \frac{1}{|I_1|^2}\left(F_0 + sT_0 + \frac{V_0}{s}\right) \tag{a}$$

$$\tag{1-65}$$

$$Y(s) = \frac{1}{|E_1|^2}\left(F_0 + s^*T_0 + \frac{V_0}{s^*}\right) \tag{b}$$

These equations are of great importance. They express the relationship between the driving-point impedance and admittance and the energy functions. Note that these are not explicit expressions in terms of s. The energy functions are themselves functions of s through the fact that the currents I_j are functions of s.

At this point we should note that a completely analogous development can be carried out, starting with the current equilibrium equations, with the node voltages as variables. The stored energy and the power dissipated can be expressed in terms of capacitance, inverse inductance, and conductance. Thus the energy functions will involve the capacitance, inverse-inductance, and conductance matrices. Relationships just like Eqs. (1-65) will be obtained for the impedance and admittance in terms of these energy functions.

Let us examine the expression for the driving-point impedance a little more closely. The functions F_0, T_0, and V_0 are real and nonnegative for all values of s. The magnitude squared of I_1 is certainly positive. Now, if

s is real, certainly $Z(s)$ will also be real. On the other hand, if s is complex but its real part is not negative, $Z(s)$ will be complex and its real part will not be negative. Functions having these two properties, namely

1. real when s is real;
2. real part nonnegative when real part of s is nonnegative

are called *positive real functions*. (Brune named these functions in 1930.) The same investigation of the right side of Eq. (1-65b) will show that $Y(s)$ also satisfies these properties. We conclude that *the driving-point impedance or admittance functions of a passive bilateral network are positive real*. We shall have much more to say about these functions in the next two chapters.

Now let us consider the case of a network with two pairs of terminals, a two-port. In Eq. (1-62) replace the voltage matrix by its equivalent in terms of the z parameters from Eqs. (1-14). The result will be

$$(I^*)^t(z)(I) = z_{11}I_1I_1^* + 2z_{12} \operatorname{Re}(I_1I_2^*) + z_{22}I_2I_2^*$$

$$= F_0 + sT_0 + \frac{V_0}{s} \tag{1-66}$$

Since the right-hand side of this expression is a positive real function, the quadratic form on the left side must also be positive real. Just as we say the matrix of a positive definite quadratic form is also positive definite, in the same way we say the matrix of a positive real quadratic form is positive real. Thus we conclude that *the z matrix of a passive bilateral two-port is positive real*. The detailed properties of the z parameters follow from this fact.

We can derive a similar property of the y matrix by first taking the complex conjugate of Eq. (1-62). The right side becomes

$$[(I^*)^t(E)]^* = (I_1^*E_1 + I_2^*E_2)^* = E_1^*I_1 + E_2^*I_2$$

$$= (E^*)^t(I) \tag{1-67}$$

Hence the complete expression is

$$(E^*)^t(I) = F_0 + s^*T_0 + \frac{V_0}{s^*} \tag{1-68}$$

We can now replace the current matrix by its equivalent in terms of the y parameters from Eqs. (1-12). The result will be

$$(E^*)^t(y)(E) = F_0 + s^*T_0 + \frac{V_0}{s^*} \tag{1-69}$$

The right side of this expression is a positive real function. Hence we conclude that *the y matrix of a passive bilateral two-port is positive real*. All the detailed properties of the y parameters follow from this fact. We shall devote considerable time in Chap. 4 to exploiting the positive real nature of the z and y matrices to establish many important and useful properties of two-port functions.

Before terminating this section we can establish a few more interesting results. We have already seen that the zeros of the driving-point impedance of a network are the natural frequencies of that network. From considerations of stability we have already concluded that the natural frequencies of passive networks cannot lie in the right-half s plane. The same result follows by computing the zeros of the impedance in Eqs. (1-65). The result is

$$s = -\frac{F_0}{2T_0} \pm \sqrt{\left(\frac{F_0}{2T_0}\right)^2 - \frac{V_0}{T_0}} \qquad (1\text{-}70)$$

This equation does not give an explicit value for s because the energy functions are themselves functions of s. However, since these functions are real and nonnegative, we can see that the natural frequencies cannot lie in the right half plane.

In the special case of LC (lossless) networks $F_0 = 0$. The last equation reduces to $s = \pm j\sqrt{V_0/T_0}$. Thus the natural frequencies of lossless networks lie on the $j\omega$ axis. Similarly, in the case of RC networks, $T_0 = 0$, while for RL networks $V_0 = 0$. In these cases the natural frequencies will be given, respectively, by

$$s = -\frac{V_0}{F_0} \qquad (a)$$

$$\qquad\qquad\qquad\qquad (1\text{-}71)$$

$$s = -\frac{F_0}{T_0} \qquad (b)$$

In view of the positiveness of the energy functions we conclude that the natural frequencies of RC and RL networks lie on the negative real axis.

PROBLEMS

1-1. Find the chain matrix of the networks shown in Fig. P 1-1.

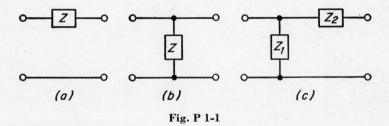

(a)   (b)   (c)

Fig. P 1-1

1-2. Show that the open-circuit transfer impedance z_{12} of the circuit shown in Fig. P 1-2 is

$$z_{12} = \frac{Z_1 z'_{12}}{Z_1 + Z_2 + z'_{11}}$$

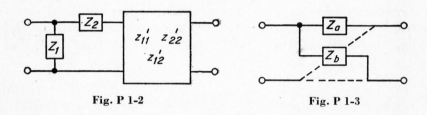

Fig. P 1-2   Fig. P 1-3

1-3. For the symmetrical lattice network of Fig. P 1-3 show that

$$z_{11} = \tfrac{1}{2}(Z_b + Z_a)$$
$$z_{12} = \tfrac{1}{2}(Z_b - Z_a)$$
$$y_{11} = \tfrac{1}{2}(Y_b + Y_a)$$
$$y_{12} = \tfrac{1}{2}(Y_b - Y_a)$$

1-4. Show that the symmetrical tee and symmetrical pi shown in Fig. P 1-4 will be equivalent to the lattice in Fig. P 1-3 if

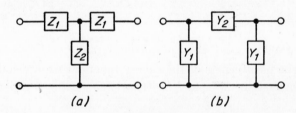

(a)   *(b)*

Fig. P 1-4

$$\left.\begin{aligned} Z_1 &= Z_a \\ Z_2 &= \tfrac{1}{2}(Z_b - Z_a) \end{aligned}\right\} \quad \text{for the tee}$$

$$\left.\begin{aligned} Y_1 &= Y_b \\ Y_2 &= \tfrac{1}{2}(Y_a - Y_b) \end{aligned}\right\} \quad \text{for the pi}$$

1-5. Show that the bridged-tee networks given in Fig. P 1-5 are equivalent to the symmetrical lattice under the listed conditions, by examining their z-system or y-system equations.

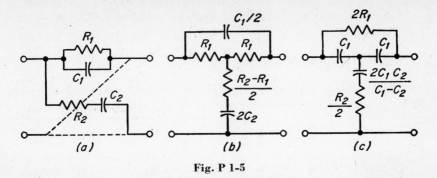

Fig. P 1-5

1-6. In the symmetrical lattice of Fig. P 1-6 the branch impedances are inverse with respect to R_0^2, that is, $Z_a Z_b = R_0^2$. Show that the input

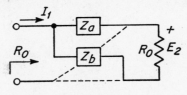

Fig. P 1-6

impedance is R_0 when the lattice is terminated in R_0. Such a lattice is called a "constant-resistance lattice." Show also that the transfer impedance is

$$Z_{12} = \frac{E_2}{I_1} = \frac{R_0(R_0 - Z_a)}{R_0 + Z_a}$$

1-7. Prove that necessary and sufficient conditions that a symmetrical two-port be constant-resistance $(R = 1)$ are $z_{11} = y_{11}$ and $z_{12} = -y_{12}$. A constant-resistance network is a network whose input impedance is equal to R when the network is terminated in a resistance R.

1-8. Prove that a necessary and sufficient condition that the resistance-terminated transfer impedance $Z_{12} = E_2/I_1$ of a lossless symmetrical two-port be an all-pass function is that the two-port be constant-resistance. An all-pass function is defined as a function having a constant magnitude.

1-9. The network in Fig. P 1-9 is lossless. Show that $|\rho_1(j\omega)|^2 = |\rho_2(j\omega)|^2$ where ρ_1 and ρ_2 are the reflection coefficients.

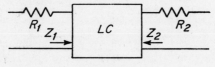

Fig. P 1-9

$$\rho_1(s) = \frac{R_1 - Z_1}{R_1 + Z_1}$$

$$\rho_2(s) = \frac{R_2 - Z_2}{R_2 + Z_2}$$

1-10. Figure P 1-10 shows a two-port which is the cascade connection of two simpler two-ports N_a and N_b. Show that the short-circuit transfer

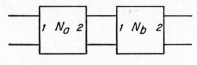

Fig. P 1-10

admittance and the open-circuit transfer impedance of the two-port will be given by

(a) $y_{12} = \dfrac{-y_{12a}y_{12b}}{y_{22a} + y_{11b}}$

(b) $z_{12} = \dfrac{z_{12a}z_{12b}}{z_{22a} + z_{11b}}$

The a and b subscripts refer to the component two-ports. These results are referred to as the "partitioning theorem."

1-11. (a) The transfer impedance of the network shown in Fig. P 1-11(a) is

$$Z_{12} = \frac{E_2}{I_1} = \frac{z_{12}}{1 + z_{22}}$$

Show that this function is also the voltage transfer function E_1/E_2 of the network in Fig. P 1-11(b). The two-port N is the same in both cases.

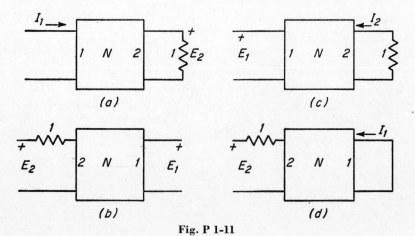

Fig. P 1-11

(b) The transfer admittance of the network shown in Fig. P 1-11(c) is

$$Y_{12} = \frac{I_2}{E_1} = \frac{y_{12}}{1 + y_{22}}$$

Show that this function is also the short-circuit admittance I_1/E_2 of the network in Fig. P 1-11(d). The two-port N is the same in both cases. This problem indicates that the situation in which the load is either a short or an open circuit while the source impedance is finite can be handled by the methods that apply when the load is finite and the source is either a current source or a voltage source.

2

Synthesis of One-Ports with Two Kinds of Elements

In the classification of networks according to the number of external terminals the two-terminal network, or *one-port*, is the simplest. We shall now embark on the task of the synthesis of one-ports. At this point it is possible to proceed along one of two paths. We could treat the general case of RLC networks immediately. The results for networks containing only two kinds of elements would then follow as special cases. However, it is easier to treat the special cases first. Furthermore, patterns of thought that are useful in the general case can be developed for the special case rather naturally. Hence in this chapter we shall restrict ourselves to one-ports containing only two kinds of elements. Historically the LC case was treated first. Modern network synthesis was born when Foster first stated his theorem in 1924. Foster's work was extended by Cauer shortly thereafter to the case of RC and RL networks.

2-1. Lossless one-ports

Networks in which resistance is absent—and hence $F = 0$—are called *lossless* networks. They are also sometimes called "reactance" networks.

The driving-point impedance of a lossless one-port can be obtained by using the expression in Eq. (1-9), in which the elements of the determinant are

$$b_{jk} = sL_{jk} + \frac{D_{jk}}{s} \tag{2-1}$$

Recall that Δ is the determinant of the network with the input terminals short-circuited, while Δ_{11} is a principal cofactor. But Δ_{11} is also the determinant of the network with the input terminals open. The zeros of Δ are

38

the natural frequencies of the network with short-circuited terminals, while the zeros of Δ_{11} are the natural frequencies with the terminals open. Since the natural frequencies of a lossless network lie on the $j\omega$ axis, as shown in Chap. 1, both the poles and zeros of $Z(s)$ lie on the $j\omega$ axis.

Now consider Eq. (1-65) for the driving-point impedance function, and assume that I_1 is real and equal to unity. This amounts to making a particular choice for the zero reference of angles and a magnitude normalization of the impedance. Since for a lossless network $F_0 = 0$, and since $s = \sigma + j\omega$, we get

$$Z(s) = sT_0 + \frac{V_0}{s} = \sigma T_0 + \frac{\sigma V_0}{\sigma^2 + \omega^2} + j\left(\omega T_0 - \frac{\omega V_0}{\sigma^2 + \omega^2}\right)$$

$$= U(\sigma,\omega) + jX(\sigma,\omega) \tag{2-2}$$

where U and X are the real and imaginary parts of Z. Of course, when $\sigma = 0$, the real part is zero. Parenthetically, note that $U > 0$ when $\sigma > 0$ and $U < 0$ when $\sigma < 0$, as well. We are particularly interested in the behavior of this function for $s = j\omega$, for which values $Z(s) = Z(j\omega) = jX(0,\omega)$. We can obtain some knowledge of this function if we determine the slope $dX/d\omega$. To this end, note that $Z(s)$ is an analytic function of s so that the Cauchy-Riemann equations involving its real and imaginary parts will apply. Using one of these, we get

$$\frac{\partial U}{\partial \sigma} = \frac{\partial X}{\partial \omega} \tag{2-3}$$

In taking the derivative of U we must remember that the energy functions are themselves functions of s (and hence of σ and ω). Thus

$$\frac{\partial U}{\partial \sigma} = T_0 + \frac{\sigma}{\partial \sigma}\frac{\partial T_0}{} + \frac{V_0(\omega^2 - \sigma^2)}{(\sigma^2 + \omega^2)^2} + \frac{\sigma}{\sigma^2 + \omega^2}\frac{\partial V_0}{\partial \sigma} \tag{2-4}$$

Combining Eqs. (2-3) and (2-4) and setting $\sigma = 0$, we get

$$\left.\frac{\partial X}{\partial \omega}\right|_{\sigma=0} = \frac{dX}{d\omega} = T_0 + \frac{V_0}{\omega^2} > 0 \tag{2-5}$$

Let us now observe that T_0 and V_0 are positive semidefinite quadratic forms. However, their sum must be positive definite, except in trivial cases which correspond to short circuits in the network. This is most easily understood by noting that $T_0 + V_0/\omega^2$, for $s = j\omega$, is just twice the sum of the average energy stored in the inductances and capacitances of the network. This sum is strictly positive for all values of ω. Equation (2-5) states the important result that *the slope of a reactance function is strictly positive at all frequencies.* An alternate way of expressing this is found by writing

$$\frac{dX}{d\omega} = \frac{d(jX)}{d(j\omega)} = \frac{dZ(s)}{ds}\bigg|_{s=j\omega} \tag{2-6}$$

It is now a simple matter to show that the positive-slope property is also valid for the admittance as well as the impedance. Thus

$$\frac{dY(s)}{ds} = \frac{d}{ds}\left(\frac{1}{Z}\right) = -\frac{1}{Z^2}\frac{dZ(s)}{ds} \tag{2-7}$$

When $s = j\omega$, $Z(j\omega) = jX$ and so $Z^2(j\omega)$ will be negative. This establishes the result that $dY/ds > 0$ when $s = j\omega$.

Using this property of reactance functions, it is possible to derive many other properties very simply. We already know that the poles and zeros lie on the $j\omega$ axis. Invoking the positiveness of slope, we can now state that *the poles and zeros of $Z(s)$ must be simple*. To show this, let $s_0 = j\omega_0$ be a zero of $Z(s)$. Then $Z(s)$ can be expanded in a Taylor series about $j\omega_0$. Since $Z(j\omega_0) = 0$, the first term will be absent. Thus

$$Z(s) = \frac{dZ(j\omega_0)}{ds}(s - j\omega_0) + \frac{1}{2!}\frac{d^2Z(j\omega_0)}{ds^2}(s - j\omega_0)^2 + \cdots \tag{2-8}$$

If $s = j\omega_0$ is a zero of multiplicity greater than 1, then the first derivative will also be zero at $j\omega_0$. This contradicts the positiveness of slope property. Therefore the zero must be simple. The simplicity of the poles of $Z(s)$ may be established by considering the zeros of $Y(s) = 1/Z(s)$ and using the same argument. Hence the factors of the numerator and denominator of $Z(s)$ must be of the form $s^2 + \omega_i^2$.

Another property we can derive simply is the *alternation* property of zeros and poles. A little thought will show that, if $Z(s)$ has two successive zeros, with no intervening poles, the slope of the curve of $X(\omega)$ versus ω will of necessity become negative somewhere between the two zeros. The same result will be true if there are two successive poles. Hence between every two zeros of $Z(s)$ there must be a pole, and vice versa.

We have now established that the numerator and denominator of $Z(s)$ are polynomials with simple zeros on the $j\omega$ axis. Each factor in the numerator and denominator due to a pair of conjugate zeros or poles is of the form $s^2 + \omega_i^2$. The value of each such factor is real when $s = j\omega$. But since $Z(j\omega)$ must be imaginary, we conclude that either the numerator or the denominator must have a factor s. That is to say, $Z(s)$ will have either a pole or a zero at $s = 0$. Considering the other extremity of the frequency range, we know that any pole or zero of $Z(s)$ at infinity must be simple. This means that the highest power in the numerator cannot differ from that of the denominator by more than 1. The two highest powers certainly cannot be the same, because this would require $Z(j\omega)$ to be real.

Hence the two highest powers must differ by exactly unity. This means that $Z(s)$ has either a pole or a zero at infinity. Thus both extremities of the frequency range are critical points (pole or zero) of $Z(s)$.

With the knowledge of $Z(s)$ which we have now acquired we can write

$$Z(s) = K \frac{a_0 + a_2 s^2 + \ldots + s^{2k}}{b_1 s + b_3 s^2 + \ldots + s^{2k-1}}$$

$$= K \frac{(s^2 + \omega_1^2)(s^2 + \omega_3^2) \ldots (s^2 + \omega_k)^2}{s(s^2 + \omega_2^2) \ldots (s^2 + \omega_{k-1}^2)} \qquad (2\text{-}9)$$

In this expression $Z(s)$ has a pole both at the origin and at infinity. In other cases these two points may both be zeros of $Z(s)$, or one may be a pole and the other a zero. In other words, $Z(s)$ is an odd rational function (the ratio of two polynomials, one of which is odd and the other even).

We have shown that the zeros and poles of $Z(s)$ are simple and alternate on the $j\omega$ axis. Furthermore, $Z(s)$ will have a zero or pole at both zero and infinity. The slope of $X(\omega)$ with respect to frequency will always be positive. A typical plot of $X(\omega)$ is shown in Fig. 2-1. In this plot both the

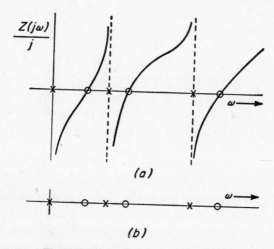

Fig. 2-1. Typical reactance function.

origin and infinity are singular points, but either may be zero for other reactance functions. When the actual values of the reactance are not needed but only the pole-zero distribution is of importance, the plot shown in part (b) of the figure can be used. This gives the *frequency pattern* of the given function. For completeness the critical points on the negative half of the axis should be included, but this information is redundant.

Additional useful properties of reactance functions can be derived based on the positive-slope property. One such property involves the residues of $Z(s)$ at its poles. Let $Z(s)$ have a pole at $s = j\omega_0$ with residue k_0. Suppose we expand $Z(s)$ in a Laurent series and differentiate. The result will be

$$Z(s) = \frac{k_0}{s - j\omega_0} + a_0 + a_1(s - j\omega_0) + a_2(s - j\omega_0)^2 + \ldots \quad (2\text{-}10)$$

$$\frac{dZ}{ds} = -\frac{k_0}{(s - j\omega_0)^2} + a_1 + 2a_2(s - j\omega_0) + \ldots \quad (2\text{-}11)$$

Now let us restrict s to the $j\omega$ axis. In the vicinity of the pole the first term will dominate. Thus the last equation becomes

$$\frac{dZ(s)}{ds}\bigg|_{s=j\omega} \doteq -\frac{k_0}{(j\omega - j\omega_0)^2} = \frac{k_0}{(\omega - \omega_0)^2} > 0 \quad (2\text{-}12)$$

The approximation gets better, of course, as s approaches $j\omega_0$. From the positiveness of the slope of the reactance function it follows that the residue must be real and positive. The residue at $s = -j\omega_0$ is also equal to k_0 since the residues at conjugate poles are conjugates (see Prob. 2-14).

So far we have dealt almost exclusively with the impedance function $Z(s)$. Since the positive-slope property applies to $Y(s)$ as well, everything we have proved about poles and zeros and residues applies to $Y(s)$ also.

Another interesting property of reactance functions can be easily established. If we take the ratio of $dX/d\omega$ as given in Eq. (2-5) and $|X/\omega|$ as given in Eq. (1-65) (with $I_1 = 1$ and $F_0 = 0$), we get

$$\frac{dX/d\omega}{|X/\omega|} = \frac{T_0 + V_0/\omega^2}{|T_0 - V_0/\omega^2|} \geq 1 \quad (2\text{-}13)$$

or

$$\frac{dX}{d\omega} \geq \left|\frac{X}{\omega}\right| \quad (2\text{-}14)$$

This condition is even stronger than the positiveness of slope. It says that the slope at any point on a reactance curve will be no less than the magnitude of the slope of a straight line drawn from the origin to that point. A similar conclusion follows from a consideration of the susceptance slope. Thus

$$\frac{dB}{d\omega} \geq \left|\frac{B}{\omega}\right| \quad (2\text{-}15)$$

where $Y(j\omega) = jB(\omega)$.

We have now established the necessary conditions that $Z(s)$ be the driving-point impedance of an LC network. The proof of these conditions was based on the positive definite character of the energy functions. The first condition that was proved, using this property of the energy functions, was the positiveness of the slope of the reactance. Since the susceptance was also shown to have a positive slope, the same properties can be established for an admittance. As a matter of fact, the impedance and the admittance of lossless networks satisfy identical conditions. A given rational function satisfying these conditions may be the impedance of one network while it is simultaneously the admittance of a second network. Thus we shall use the term *reactance function* to mean either the impedance or the admittance of an LC network.

When a rational function is given and we wish to determine whether or not it is a reactance function, it is not necessary to check it against all the necessary conditions we have established. In fact, since all the other conditions came from the positiveness of slope, we can apply only this latter criterion. However, this would require us to calculate the slope for all values of ω. Furthermore, even if we find that the rational function satisfies this necessary condition, we do not know how to use this condition alone to synthesize a network from the given function, thus proving the sufficiency of the condition. In the next section we shall show that the following set of *necessary* conditions is also *sufficient*:

Necessary and sufficient conditions that F(s) be the driving-point impedance or admittance of a lossless network are

1. *F(s) has simple poles restricted to the jω axis.*
2. *The residues at the poles are real and positive.*

2-2. Synthesis of lossless one-ports

In the previous section we derived the properties of the impedance and admittance functions of LC one-ports. We found necessary conditions that such a function must satisfy. This constitutes network analysis.

We now have the problem of determining *sufficient* conditions for a function to be the immittance† of a lossless network. This is part of network synthesis. Proving the sufficiency of a set of conditions involves finding a network whenever a function satisfying the set of conditions is given. However, a distinguishing feature of synthesis, contrasted with analysis, is the fact that a network realization of a given function (assuming one exists) is not unique. That is, there are a large number of equivalent networks realizing a given (realizable) function. Not all these networks

† This term combines the words *im*pedance and ad*mittance.* Since both of these functions have identical properties, it is convenient to use a single word in referring to them, whenever it is unimportant whether we mean E/I or I/E.

will be desirable, from the point of view of structure, number of elements, etc.

The job we have before us, then, is the determination of the sufficient conditions for realizability of a reactance function and the realization of one or more networks. The fundamental process of network synthesis was outlined in the introduction. This involves piecemeal decomposition of the given function such that each simple function can be realized as a simple component network. In the present case the process is even simpler because a complete breakdown of the function can be performed at the outset, and each term in the breakdown can be recognized as a simple network. In this way the realization is accomplished in one step.

We begin by writing

$$Z(s) = \frac{K(s^2 + \omega_1^2)(s^2 + \omega_3^2)(s^2 + \omega_5^2)}{s(s^2 + \omega_2^2)(s^2 + \omega_4^2)} \qquad (2\text{-}16)$$

This function can represent the general reactance function, since a more complicated function differs from this only in having more zeros and poles. We have already shown it to be necessary that the poles and zeros be simple and that the residues at these poles be positive. Now suppose that $Z(s)$ in Eq. (2-16) satisfies these conditions. The first step requires expanding $Z(s)$ in partial fractions.

$$Z(s) = \frac{k_0}{s} + \frac{2k_2 s}{s^2 + \omega_2^2} + \frac{2k_4 s}{s^2 + \omega_4^2} + k_\infty s \qquad (2\text{-}17)$$

Here the k's are residues at the corresponding poles, and the two terms involving a pair of conjugate poles have been grouped together into a single term. The residue at infinity is obtained formally by taking

$$\left. \frac{Z(s)}{s} \right|_{s \to \infty} = k_\infty \qquad (2\text{-}18)$$

The residues of rational functions at simple poles are usually found by evaluating the expression

$$k_i = (s - s_i)Z(s)|_{s = s_i} \qquad (2\text{-}19)$$

However, in the case of reactance functions a simpler expression can be found. Thus let us multiply both sides of Eq. (2-17) by $(s^2 + \omega_i^2)/2s$ and evaluate at $s^2 = -\omega_i^2$. The result will be

$$k_i = \left. \frac{(s^2 + \omega_i^2)Z(s)}{2s} \right|_{s^2 = -\omega_i^2} \qquad (2\text{-}20)$$

In evaluating the residue by this formula only real numbers will be involved. It is now clear that the partial-fraction expansion of an arbitrary reactance function will have the form

$$Z(s) = k_\infty s + \frac{k_0}{s} + \sum_{i=1}^{n} \frac{2k_i s}{s^2 + \omega_i^2} \qquad (2\text{-}21)$$

Equation (2-21) tells us that $Z(s)$ is the sum of several component impedances. The first and second terms are immediately recognized as the impedances of an inductance and a capacitance, respectively. Each

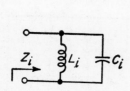

Fig. 2-2. Antiresonant circuit.

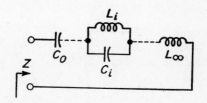

Fig. 2-3. First Foster form of lossless one-port.

of the remaining terms will be recognized as the impedance of a parallel resonant circuit as shown in Fig. 2-2. For this circuit we can write

$$Z_i(s) = \frac{sL_i}{s^2 L_i C_i + 1} = \frac{(1/C_i)s}{s^2 + (1/L_i C_i)} \qquad (2\text{-}22)$$

By comparing this expression for Z_i with the terms in Eq. (2-21) we find

$$C_i = \frac{1}{2k_i} \qquad \qquad \text{(a)}$$

$$\qquad\qquad\qquad\qquad\qquad\qquad\qquad (2\text{-}23)$$

$$L_i = \frac{1}{C_i \omega_i^2} = \frac{2k_i}{\omega_i^2} \qquad \text{(b)}$$

Hence the complete network realization of the given impedance will take the form shown in Fig. 2-3. The only way in which other reactance one-ports can differ from this one is in the addition of more parallel-tuned circuits, representing additional impedance poles, or in the absence of either C_0 or L_∞, or both, if the corresponding poles at zero or infinity are also absent.

This concludes the demonstration that the conditions already expressed as necessary are also sufficient for the realization of a reactance function. However, we have still the problem of determining other (equivalent) network realizations.

An alternate synthesis procedure starts with a consideration of the admittance function. Corresponding to the impedance of Eq. (2-16), we shall have

$$Y(s) = \frac{s(s^2 + \omega_2^2)(s^2 + \omega_4^2)}{K(s^2 + \omega_1^2)(s^2 + \omega_3^2)(s^2 + \omega_5^2)}$$

$$= \frac{2k_1 s}{s^2 + \omega_1^2} + \frac{2k_3 s}{s^2 + \omega_3^2} + \frac{2k_5 s}{s^2 + \omega_5^2} \qquad (2\text{-}24)$$

The partial-fraction expansion is shown in the last line. This equation tells us that the over-all admittance is made up of the sum of a number of component admittances. We readily recognize each term in Eq. (2-24) to

Fig. 2-4. Resonant circuit.

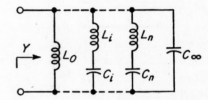

Fig. 2-5. Second Foster form of lossless one-port.

be the admittance of the series-tuned circuit shown in Fig. 2-4. The admittance of this circuit is

$$Y_i = \frac{sC_i}{s^2 L_i C_i + 1} = \frac{(1/L_i)s}{s^2 + 1/L_i C_i} \qquad (2\text{-}25)$$

Comparing this expression with one of the terms in the preceding partial fraction expansion, we find

$$L_i = \frac{1}{2k_i} \qquad \text{(a)}$$

$$C_i = \frac{1}{L_i \omega_i^2} = \frac{2k_i}{\omega_i^2} \qquad \text{(b)} \qquad (2\text{-}26)$$

The admittance of Eq. (2-24) has a zero at both zero and infinity. Other admittance functions can differ from this by having a pole at zero or at infinity. Thus the partial fraction expansion of the general admittance function will have the form

$$Y(s) = k_\infty s + \frac{k_0}{s} + \sum_{i=1}^{n} \frac{2k_i s}{s^2 + \omega_i^2} \qquad (2\text{-}27)$$

The pole at infinity can be realized as a shunt capacitance, while the pole at the origin can be realized as a shunt inductance. The complete realization is shown in Fig. 2-5.

We have now found two network realizations of a given reactance function. These were first introduced by Foster and carry his name. It is interesting to notice that both realizations have the same number of elements and that this number is the same as the number of pieces of information needed to specify the function completely. In Eq. (2-16) the six quantities ω_1, ω_3, ω_5 (the zeros), ω_2, ω_4 (the poles), and K (the *impedance-level* factor) completely determine $Z(s)$. In Eq. (2-17) the two pole locations and the four residues serve the same purpose. The network should have at least as many variable parameters (the network elements) as the function representing it has. It is apparent that the Foster realizations have the minimum number of elements that will realize the given function. In this sense they are called *canonic* forms.

Other equivalent realizations of a reactance function may be found by proceeding alternately first on an impedance, then on an admittance basis. One or more impedance poles may be realized in the first Foster form. Then the remainder function may be inverted and one or more admittance poles realized in the second Foster form. This procedure may be carried out until there is no remainder. At each step the remainder function will indeed be a reactance function.

Two network realizations which are also canonic can be obtained by proceeding in a special way according to the method just described. These were first presented by Cauer and are called *Cauer forms*. In the first Cauer form we deal exclusively with the pole at infinity. Either the impedance or the admittance must have a pole at infinity. In the former case the pole is removed and realized as a series inductance. The remaining impedance will have a zero at infinity so that its reciprocal will have a pole there. This pole is removed and realized as a shunt capacitance leaving an admittance with a zero at infinity. The impedance will then have a pole at infinity. The procedure of removing the pole at infinity alternately from the impedance and then the admittance can be continued until the function is exhausted. The resulting network will be a ladder with the appearance of Fig. 2-6.

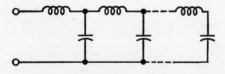

Fig. 2-6. First Cauer form.

If the original impedance has no pole at infinity, the first series inductance will be absent and the network will start with a shunt capacitance. Observe that the network of Fig. 2-6 has an impedance pole at zero frequency. Hence, if the original impedance has a zero at $s = 0$, the final shunt capacitance must be absent in the realization.

The second Cauer form is the dual of the first. We deal exclusively with the pole at $s = 0$; either $Z(s)$ or $Y(s)$ must have a pole there. Suppose $Z(s)$ has a pole at $s = 0$. This is removed and realized as a series capacitance. The remainder has an admittance pole at zero, which is realized as a shunt inductance. The process is repeated until there is no remainder. The realization is a ladder network of the form shown in Fig. 2-7. The

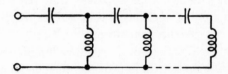

Fig. 2-7. Second Cauer form.

initial capacitance will be absent if the original impedance has no pole at zero. Observe that the impedance of Fig. 2-7 has a pole at infinite frequency. Hence, if the original impedance has no pole at infinity, the final shunt inductance must be absent in the realization.

The formal procedure in the alternate removal of an impedance and admittance pole at infinity or zero is carried out by noting that the impedance function of a ladder structure can be expressed as a continued frac-

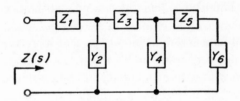

Fig. 2-8. Ladder network.

tion. In the network of Fig. 2-8 the series branches are labeled Z and the shunt branches Y. The impedance of the network can be written

$$Z = Z_1 + \cfrac{1}{Y_2 + \cfrac{1}{Z_3 + \cfrac{1}{Y_4 + \cfrac{1}{Z_5 + \cfrac{1}{Y_6}}}}} \qquad (2\text{-}28)$$

Such a continued fraction expansion of a given impedance function may be obtained as follows: (1) Divide the denominator into the numerator, starting with the highest powers, as in long division, stopping after the first term. The degree of the numerator of the remainder will be two lower than it was and one lower than that of the denominator (assuming that the impedance initially had a pole at infinity). (2) Invert the remainder function, and divide again, stopping after the first term. (3) Carry out the successive divisions and inversions until the process terminates. The process will surely terminate, since after each division the degree of the remaining numerator will be two less than it was before division. Of course, if the original function has no pole at infinity, then we first invert before carrying out the division. This procedure will give the first Cauer form.

Alternatively the division may be carried out by starting with the lowest powers. This will lead to the second Cauer form. Of course, if the original function has no pole at zero, then we invert first before dividing.

In the Cauer division process an element of the network is obtained every time a division is performed. A little thought will show that the number of divisions that must be performed before the process terminates is equal to the order of the rational function. By the order of a rational function we shall mean the order of the numerator or denominator, whichever is higher. Thus, if $Z(s)$ is

$$Z(s) = K \frac{s^n + a_{n-2}s^{n-2} + \ldots + a_2 s^2 + a_0}{s(s^n + b_{n-2}s^{n-2} + \ldots + b_2 s^2 + b_0)} \tag{2-29}$$

its order is $n + 1$. Furthermore, there are $n/2$ coefficients in the numerator and the same number of b coefficients in the denominator. The total number of quantities which characterize the impedance, including the impedance-level factor K, is thus $n + 1$, the same as the order. Hence the number of elements in the Cauer realizations is the same as that in the Foster realizations, this being the minimum number needed to realize the given impedance. Thus the Cauer forms are also *canonic*.

Other equivalent realizations may be obtained by alternately employing either Foster or either Cauer development. If you will observe that, at each step, it is not necessary to remove all of an impedance or admittance pole but only part of one, then you will see that an infinite number of realizations is possible. These, of course, will contain redundant elements and so will not be canonic. Such realizations may be useful in practice if they lead to more convenient or available element values.

As an example of these synthesis procedures, consider the impedance function

$$Z(s) = \frac{(s^2 + 1)(s^2 + 9)}{s(s^2 + 4)} = \frac{s^4 + 10s^2 + 9}{s^3 + 4s}$$

$$= \frac{9/4}{s} + \frac{15s/4}{s^2 + 4} + s \tag{2-30}$$

This impedance satisfies the necessary and sufficient conditions for realizability. The partial fraction expansion of $Z(s)$ leads to the first Foster form shown in Fig. 2-9(a).

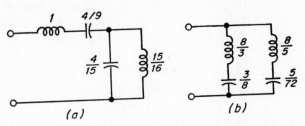

Fig. 2-9. Foster networks for numerical example.

Alternatively we can expand the admittance in partial fractions, to obtain

$$Y(s) = \frac{s(s^2 + 4)}{(s^2 + 1)(s^2 + 9)} = \frac{3s/8}{s^2 + 1} + \frac{5s/8}{s^2 + 9}$$

The second Foster form is shown in Fig. 2-9(b).

Since the given $Z(s)$ in Eq. (2-27) has a pole both at zero and at infinity, we can obtain both Cauer forms by starting the division with the given function before inverting. Starting with the highest powers, the division process is carried out as follows:

$$
\begin{array}{r}
s^4 + 10s^2 + 9 \enclose{verticalstrip}{} \quad s^3 + 4s \\
\underline{s^4 + 4s^2} \qquad s \leftarrow
\end{array}
$$

$$
\begin{array}{r}
s^3 + 4s \enclose{verticalstrip}{} \quad 6s^2 + 9 \\
\underline{s^3 + \tfrac{3}{2}s} \qquad \tfrac{1}{6}s \leftarrow
\end{array}
$$

$$
\begin{array}{r}
6s^2 + 9 \enclose{verticalstrip}{} \quad \tfrac{5}{2}s \\
\underline{6s^2} \qquad \tfrac{12}{5}s \leftarrow
\end{array}
$$

$$
\begin{array}{r}
\tfrac{5}{2}s \enclose{verticalstrip}{} \quad 9 \\
\tfrac{5}{18}s \leftarrow
\end{array}
$$

This leads to the continued-fraction expansion

$$Z(s) = s + \cfrac{1}{\dfrac{s}{6} + \cfrac{1}{\dfrac{12s}{5} + \cfrac{1}{\dfrac{5s}{18}}}}$$

The corresponding network is shown in Fig. 2-10(a).

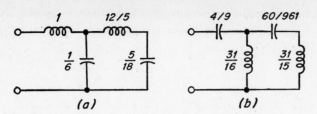

Fig. 2-10. Cauer networks for numerical example.

The second Cauer form is obtained by starting the division with the lowest powers.

$$
\begin{array}{r|l}
9 + 10s^2 + s^4 & \underline{4s + s^3} \\
& \dfrac{9}{4s} \leftarrow \\[2pt]
9 + \dfrac{9}{4}s^2 & \\
\hline
\end{array}
$$

$$
\begin{array}{r|l}
4s + s^3 & \underline{\frac{31}{4}s^2 + s^4} \\
4s + \dfrac{16}{31}s^3 & \dfrac{16}{31s} \leftarrow \\[2pt]
\hline
\end{array}
$$

$$
\begin{array}{r|l}
\frac{31}{4}s^2 + s^4 & \underline{\frac{15}{31}s^3} \\
\frac{31}{4}s^2 & \dfrac{961}{60s} \leftarrow \\[2pt]
\hline
\end{array}
$$

$$
\begin{array}{r|l}
\frac{15}{31}s^3 & \underline{s^4} \\
& \dfrac{15}{31s} \leftarrow \\
\end{array}
$$

This leads to the continued-fraction expansion

$$
Z(s) = \frac{9}{4s} + \cfrac{1}{\dfrac{16}{31s} + \cfrac{1}{\dfrac{961}{60s} + \cfrac{1}{\dfrac{15}{31s}}}}
$$

The corresponding network is shown in Fig. 2-10(b). Observe that all the realizations have the same number of elements.

Besides these canonic realizations any number of other realizations can be obtained by partial removal of a pole at any step in the Foster or Cauer procedures. Thus, suppose after subtracting the pole of $Z(s)$ at infinity as in the first Cauer form, we invert the remaining function and expand in partial fractions. The result will be

$$
Z_1(s) = Z(s) - s = \frac{6(s^2 + 3/2)}{s(s^2 + 4)}
$$

$$
Y_1(s) = \frac{1}{Z_1(s)} = \frac{s(s^2 + 4)}{6(s^2 + 3/2)} = \frac{s}{6} + \frac{5s/12}{s^2 + 3/2}
$$

Instead of removing the entire pole of Y_1 at infinity, suppose we remove half of it. This will lead to a shunt capacitance of value $1/12$ instead of $1/6$. If we take the reciprocal of the remaining admittance, we will get

$$Z_2 = \frac{1}{Y_1 - s/12} = \frac{36}{13s} + \frac{120s/13}{s^2 + 13/2}$$

This may now be realized in a Foster network. The complete realization is shown in Fig. 2-11. Of course, at this stage we could again only partially

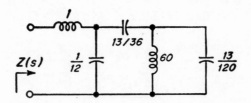

Fig. 2-11. Non-canonic realization of numerical example.

subtract one of the terms in Z_2 and carry on. This will lead to a more extensive network.

2-3. RC one-ports

There are two alternate methods of procedure in establishing the properties of RC (and also RL) driving-point immittances. It is possible to return to Eq. (1-65), which is valid for any driving-point impedance, and parallel the development for LC networks in terms of the energy functions. This is a completely satisfactory procedure. However, it means that we will need to repeat some of the things we have already done. If we can find a transformation that will transform the impedance of an RC network into that of an LC network, we can use the results already established for such networks in obtaining the properties of RC networks. We shall follow this latter procedure in order to bring variety into our experience.

The driving-point impedance of a network is given as a ratio of determinants in Eq. (1-9). For an RC network the elements of the determinant will be $b_{jk} = R_{jk} + D_{jk}/s$. Let us make the transformation $s = p^2$. Then

$$b_{jk} = R_{jk} + \frac{D_{jk}}{p^2} = \frac{1}{p}\left(pR_{jk} + \frac{D_{jk}}{p}\right) = \frac{1}{p}b'_{jk} \qquad (2\text{-}31)$$

where

$$b'_{jk} = pR_{jk} + \frac{D_{jk}}{p} \qquad (2\text{-}32)$$

Since $1/p$ is a common factor of each element in Δ and in Δ_{11}, it may be factored out of each row of both determinants. Let n be the number of rows in Δ. Then

$$\Delta(s) = \Delta(p^2) = \frac{1}{p^n}\,\Delta'(p) \qquad \text{(a)}$$

$$\Delta_{11}(s) = \Delta_{11}(p^2) = \frac{1}{p^{n-1}}\,\Delta'_{11}(p) \qquad \text{(b)}$$

$$(2\text{-}33)$$

where $\Delta'(p)$ is the determinant whose elements are b'_{jk}. Note that b'_{jk} is identical in form with the elements of the determinant of an LC network with the complex-frequency variable labeled p and R_{jk} replacing L_{jk}. The impedance function becomes

$$Z_{RC}(s) = Z_{RC}(p^2) = \frac{\Delta(p^2)}{\Delta_{11}(p^2)} = \frac{1}{p}\frac{\Delta'(p)}{\Delta'_{11}(p)} = \frac{1}{p}Z_{LC}(p) \qquad (2\text{-}34)$$

This expression gives us the desired relationship. It tells us that, if we have the impedance function of an LC network with p as the complex-frequency variable and we divide this function by p (which ensures only even powers in the result) and then replace p^2 by s, we will have the impedance function of an RC network. Since we know the properties of reactance functions, we can now determine those of RC impedance functions.

We have already established in Chap. 1 that the natural frequencies of an RC network lie on the negative real axis. Since the impedance zeros are the natural frequencies of the short-circuited network and the poles are those of the open-circuited network, both will be negative real. We can arrive at the same conclusion by considering a reactance function and its partial-fraction expansion, as given in Eq. (2-17) for example. We should change the complex-frequency variable to p, in order to comply with the notation in this section. If we now divide this expression by p and replace p^2 by s, we shall get, according to Eq. (2-34),

$$Z_{RC}(s) = K\,\frac{(s + \omega_1^2)(s + \omega_3^2)(s + \omega_5^2)}{s(s + \omega_2^2)(s + \omega_4^2)}$$

$$= k_\infty + \frac{k_0}{s} + \frac{2k_2}{s + \omega_2^2} + \frac{2k_4}{s + \omega_4^2} \qquad (2\text{-}35)$$

This is representative of the most general RC impedance function, since others differ from this only by the inclusion of additional terms like the last two or the deletion of one or both of the first two terms. We note that all the poles are simple and lie on the negative real axis. There may be a pole at $s = 0$ but this pole will be absent if $k_0 = 0$. In this case the impedance will have a finite positive value at $s = 0$. Furthermore, there can be no impedance pole at infinity; the value at infinity will be finite and will become zero if k_∞ is zero. The k's are the residues of the reactance function from which Eq. (2-35) was obtained, and so they are real and positive.

The properties of RC admittances can be considered by taking the reciprocal of Eq. (2-34). Thus

$$Y_{RC}(s) = pY_{LC}(p) \qquad (2\text{-}36)$$

This expression indicates that to obtain an RC admittance we multiply by p, a reactance function in which the complex-frequency variable is p; then we let $p^2 = s$. Since LC impedance and admittance functions have identical properties, we can again use Eq. (2-17). Multiplying by p and letting $p^2 = s$, we get

$$Y_{RC} = s\left(k_\infty + \frac{k_0}{s} + \frac{2k_2}{s + \omega_2^2} + \frac{2k_4}{s + \omega_4^2}\right) \qquad (2\text{-}37)$$

The admittance poles of an RC network are thus shown to be simple and to lie on the negative real axis. The admittance may have a pole at infinity, or it may have a finite value there (if k_∞ is zero). At the origin the admittance is finite; it will be zero if $k_0 = 0$. The k's in Eq. (2-37) are the residues, not of Y_{RC}, but of Y_{RC}/s. Thus we conclude that the residues of Y_{RC}/s are positive. Note that Y_{RC}/s will be finite at infinity, its value there being k_∞.

The partial-fraction expansions we have written for RC impedance and admittance function have used the notation of the corresponding reactance function. For future reference we should write these in a more natural notation. Thus

$$Z_{RC}(s) = k_\infty + \frac{k_0}{s} + \sum_{i=1}^{n} \frac{k_i}{s + \sigma_i} \qquad (2\text{-}38)$$

$$Y_{RC}(s) = k_\infty s + k_0 + \sum_{i=1}^{n} \frac{k_i s}{s + \sigma_i} \qquad (2\text{-}39)$$

These are general expressions. Although we have used the same notation for the poles and residues of both Z and Y, these are of course different. Note that the second equation is obtained by expanding, not Y, but Y/s, in partial fractions and then multiplying the result by s. Thus the k's are residues of Y/s.

Using the partial-fraction expansions in the previous equations, we can very simply establish a property analogous to the positiveness of slope of reactance functions for $s = j\omega$. If we take the derivatives of these two equations for real values of s, we will get

$$\frac{dZ_{RC}(\sigma)}{d\sigma} = -\left[\frac{k_0}{\sigma^2} + \sum_{i=1}^{n} \frac{k_i}{(\sigma + \sigma_i)^2}\right] \qquad \text{(a)}$$

(2-40)

$$\frac{dY_{RC}(\sigma)}{d\sigma} = k_\infty + \sum_{i=1}^{n} \frac{k_i \sigma_i}{(\sigma + \sigma_i)^2} \qquad \text{(b)}$$

Since the k_i's and σ_i's are all positive, it immediately follows that

$$\frac{dZ_{RC}(\sigma)}{d\sigma} < 0 \qquad \longleftarrow \qquad \text{(a)}$$

(2-41)

$$\frac{dY_{RC}(\sigma)}{d\sigma} > 0 \qquad \longleftarrow \qquad \text{(b)}$$

In words, this result says that the slope of an RC impedance function is strictly negative, while the slope of an RC admittance function is strictly positive, when these functions are plotted against real values of s.

This result shows a basic distinction between LC and RC functions. Whereas LC impedances and admittances are members of the same class of functions, RC impedances and admittances fall in two distinct classes.

We have already seen that the zeros and poles of an RC impedance or admittance are simple and lie on the negative real axis. From the fact that these functions are monotonic when s is real, it is easy to see that the zeros and poles must alternate.

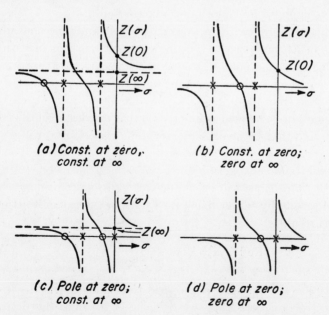

(a) Const. at zero, const. at ∞

(b) Const. at zero; zero at ∞

(c) Pole at zero; const. at ∞

(d) Pole at zero; zero at ∞

Fig. 2-12. Typical RC impedance or RL admittance functions.

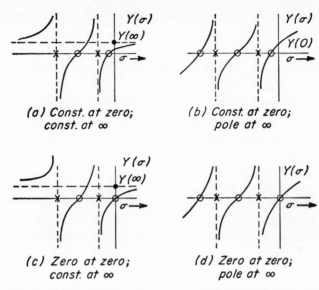

(a) Const. at zero; const. at ∞

(b) Const. at zero; pole at ∞

(c) Zero at zero; const. at ∞

(d) Zero at zero; pole at ∞

Fig. 2-13. Typical RC admittance or RL impedance functions.

Typical plots of RC impedance and admittance functions are shown in Figs. 2-12 and 2-13. Four cases of each are shown, indicating possible behavior at the origin and at infinity. It will later be shown that these same plots apply to RL immittance functions also.

We can now summarize the properties of the impedance and admittance functions of RC one-ports. These are rational functions in s with simple alternating zeros and poles restricted to the negative real axis.

In the case of an impedance function the first critical point (zero or pole) starting from the origin is a pole. The origin may or may not be a pole. There can be no pole at infinity, so that the degree of the numerator cannot exceed that of the denominator. The slope of $Z(s)$ will be negative for all real values of s. The residues of $Z(s)$ at all its poles will be positive. The partial-fraction expansion takes the form given in Eq. (2-38). When $s = j\omega$, the impedance will be complex. Its real and imaginary parts can be found readily by rationalizing each term in the partial-fraction expansion. The result is

$$\text{Re}\,[Z(j\omega)] = k_\infty + \sum_{i=1}^{n} \frac{k_i \sigma_i}{\sigma_i^2 + \omega^2} \qquad \text{(a)}$$

$$(2\text{-}42)$$

$$\text{Im}\,[Z(j\omega)] = -\left(\frac{k_0}{\omega} + \sum_{i=1}^{n} \frac{k_i \omega}{\sigma_i^2 + \omega^2} \right) \qquad \text{(b)}$$

From these expressions two conclusions can be drawn immediately:

1. The imaginary part of an RC impedance is negative along the positive imaginary axis.

2. The real part of an RC impedance is a monotonically decreasing function of frequency. This means that the slope of the real part is always negative along the $j\omega$ axis. This property can be established by differentiating Eq. (2-42a). But it follows quite readily by noting that each term of the summation in that equation decreases with ω. Thus the real part of the impedance has a higher value at zero frequency than it has at infinite frequency. This property of the real part should not be confused with the negativeness of the slope of $Z(\sigma)$.

In the case of an RC admittance function the first critical point starting from the origin is a zero. There can be no pole at the origin. The point at infinity may or may not be a pole, so that the degree of the denominator cannot exceed that of the numerator. The slope of the admittance function will be positive for all real values of s. The residues of the function $Y(s)/s$ will be positive at all its poles. Thus, given an RC admittance function, we form the partial fraction expansion of $Y(s)/s$. After multiplying through by s this takes the form of Eq. (2-39). The real and imaginary parts of the admittance for imaginary values of s can be found from the partial-fraction expansion. The result is

$$\operatorname{Re}\left[Y(j\omega)\right] = k_0 + \sum_{i=1}^{n} \frac{k_i}{1 + \sigma_i^2/\omega^2} \qquad \text{(a)}$$

$$\operatorname{Im}\left[Y(j\omega)\right] = \omega\left(k_\infty + \sum_{i=1}^{n} \frac{k_i\sigma_i}{\sigma_i^2 + \omega^2}\right) \qquad \text{(b)}$$

(2-43)

It follows that:

1. The imaginary part of an RC admittance is positive along the positive imaginary axis.

2. The real part of an RC admittance is a monotonically increasing function of ω. This means that the slope of the real part, when plotted against ω, is always positive.

Having established the necessary conditions satisfied by RC impedance and admittance functions, we shall now show that these are also sufficient by constructing at least one network when a function satisfying the necessary conditions is given. The basic pattern has already been established for LC networks.

According to the partial-fraction expansion in Eq. (2-38), an RC impedance is the sum of several component impedances. The first term, being a constant, corresponds to a resistance, while the second term is realized as a capacitance. Consider the circuit shown in Fig. 2-14(a). Its impedance is

$$Z_i = \frac{R_i}{sR_iC_i + 1} = \frac{1/C_i}{s + 1/R_iC_i} \tag{2-44}$$

By comparing this expression for Z_i with the other terms in the partial-fraction expansion in Eq. (2-38), we can write

$$C_i = \frac{1}{k_i}$$

$$R_i = \frac{1}{C_i\sigma_i} = \frac{k_i}{\sigma_i}$$

$$R_\infty = k_\infty$$

First Foster form (2-45)

Thus the complete realization of the function takes the form of Fig. 2-14(b). This is similar to the first Foster form for LC networks, but instead of inductance we have resistance. It was first developed by Cauer (24).

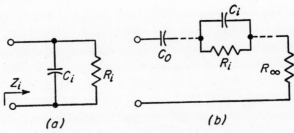

Fig. 2-14. First Foster form of RC one-port.

Alternatively, the second Foster form can be obtained by a consideration of the partial-fraction expansion of the Y/s function as in Eq. (2-39).

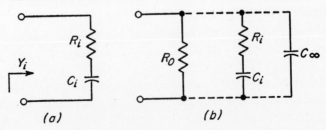

Fig. 2-15. Second Foster form of RC one-port.

The first two terms in the expansion are readily recognized as a shunt capacitance and a shunt resistance. The admittance of the circuit of Fig. 2-15(a) is

$$Y_i = \frac{sC_i}{1 + sC_iR_i} = \frac{(1/R_i)s}{s + 1/C_iR_i} \tag{2-46}$$

By comparing the expression for Y_i with the terms in Eq. (2-39) we can identify the parameters as

$$C_\infty = k_\infty$$

$$R_i = \frac{1}{k_i} \qquad \text{Second Foster form} \tag{2-47}$$

$$C_i = \frac{1}{\sigma_iR_i} = \frac{k_i}{\sigma_i}$$

Note that both Foster forms will contain the same number of elements as there are parameters in the partial-fraction expansion specifying the impedance or admittance. Hence these realizations contain the minimum possible number of elements, and in this sense they are canonic.

We could have obtained these realizations alternatively by a consideration of the transformation used in going from the LC to the RC network. Thus Eq. (2-32) shows that replacing inductance by resistance leads from the LC realization to the RC realization. Figure 2-14(b) follows from Fig. 2-3 by substituting resistance for inductance. This is also apparent by comparing the formulas for the element values in Eqs. (2-23) and (2-45). The transformation $s = p^2$ shows that $\omega_j^2 = \sigma_j$. There appears to be a difference of a factor of 2, but this is due only to a difference of notation. The k_i appearing in Eqs. (2-45) is the coefficient of a term in the partial-fraction expansion of Eq. (2-38). The coefficient of the corresponding term in the expansion of the reactance function of Eq. (2-21) is $2k_i$. Thus one way of obtaining the Foster realizations of a given RC impedance is to replace s by p^2, then multiply by p, obtaining a reactance function, according to Eq. (2-34). In the Foster realization of this reactance function replace L's by R's, and the job is complete.

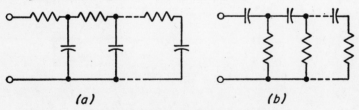

(a)   **(b)**

Fig. 2-16. Cauer forms of RC one-port.

The two Cauer forms shown in Fig. 2-16 can be obtained by using the same line of reasoning. However, in actually realizing a given RC impedance function, it is not necessary to transform first to an LC function.

The Cauer division can be performed directly on the given RC function. In performing the Cauer division more caution must be exercised than in the case of lossless networks. The reason for this is that RC impedances and admittances behave differently at zero and infinite frequency.

We have seen that the minimum value of the real part of an RC impedance on the $j\omega$ axis occurs at infinity. Suppose that an RC impedance function is given, regular at the origin and having a nonzero value at infinity. That is,

$$Z(s) = \frac{a_n s^n + a_{n-1} s^{n-1} + \ldots + a_1 s + a_0}{b_n s^n + b_{n-1} s^{n-1} + \ldots + b_1 s + b_0} \tag{2-48}$$

If we start the Cauer division from the highest powers, we shall get a_n/b_n as the first term, while starting from the lowest powers will give a_0/b_0 as the first term. These are the infinite-frequency and zero-frequency values of $Z(s)$, respectively; so we know that $a_n/b_n < a_0/b_0$. Hence, if we start the division from the lowest powers, we shall be subtracting from $Z(s)$ a constant larger than the infinite frequency value of $Z(s)$, thus leaving an impedance which has a negative value at infinity. Clearly, this makes no sense. There is no choice of the end from which the Cauer division is started.

Thus the first Cauer form is obtained by dealing with the infinite-frequency behavior, alternately of the impedance and the admittance remaining after each step. Similarly, the second Cauer form is obtained by dealing with the zero-frequency behavior of these two functions.

2-4. RL one-ports

The properties of RL impedance and admittance functions can be established in the same manner as the properties of RC functions. The elements in the determinant of an RL network are $b_{jk} = sL_{jk} + R_{jk}$. Let us again make the transformation $s = p^2$. Then

$$b_{jk} = p^2 L_{jk} + R_{jk} = p\left(pL_{jk} + \frac{R_{jk}}{p}\right) = pb'_{jk} \tag{2-49}$$

where

$$b'_{jk} = pL_{jk} + \frac{R_{jk}}{p} \tag{2-50}$$

The last expression has the same form as the elements in the determinant of an LC network except that inverse capacitance is replaced by resistance. The factor p is common in each element of Δ and Δ_{11}. Equations similar to Eqs. (2-33) can be written, but with p^n and p^{n-1} in the numerator instead of the denominator. Hence, when we take the ratio of Δ and Δ_{11}, an extra p is left after cancellation so that we get

$$Z_{RL}(s) = pZ_{LC}(p) \qquad (2\text{-}51)$$

with the transformation $s = p^2$. If we take the reciprocal, we see that

$$Y_{RL}(s) = \frac{1}{p}\, Y_{LC}(p) \qquad (2\text{-}52)$$

If we compare these last two expressions with Eqs. (2-36) and (2-34), respectively, remembering that lossless impedance and admittance functions have identical properties, we see that *an RL impedance function is identical with an RC admittance function* and that *an RL admittance is identical with an RC impedance function.* Hence we do not need to make any separate study of the properties of RL immittances. Figures 2-12 and 2-13 were labeled in terms of RL functions as well as RC functions in anticipation of the result just established. The partial-fraction expansion in Eq. (2-38) can be labeled Y_{RL} as well as Z_{RC}, while the expansion in Eq. (2-39) can be labeled Z_{RL} as well as Y_{RC}.

The Foster-form realizations of an RL driving-point function are obtained from the partial-fraction expansions of the impedance and the admittance in the same manner as for an RC function, with obvious changes in the type of element. Because of the interchange of admittances and impedance the two Foster forms will be the duals of the two RC

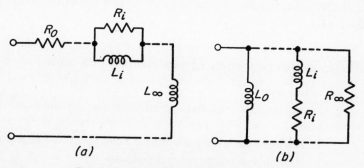

Fig. 2-17. Foster forms of RL one-ports.

Foster forms. The network realizations are shown in Fig. 2-17. The element values are obtained by duality considerations from the corresponding elements of RC networks. Thus for the first Foster form we have

$$L_i = \frac{1}{k_i}$$

$$R_i = \frac{\sigma_i}{k_i} \qquad (2\text{-}53)$$

$$R_\infty = \frac{1}{k_\infty}$$

Similarly the element values of the second Foster form are

$$R_i = k_i$$

$$L_i = \frac{k_i}{\sigma_i} \qquad (2\text{-}54)$$

$$L_\infty = k_\infty$$

Since $Y_{RL} = Z_{RC}$, the continued fraction expansion of an RC impedance can be considered to be the expansion of an RL admittance. Thus

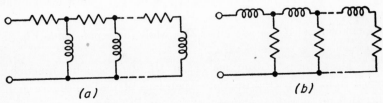

Fig. 2-18. Cauer forms of RL one-ports.

the Cauer realizations of an RL driving-point function will also be the
duals of the corresponding RC network. The two Cauer forms are shown
in Fig. 2-18.

2-5. Summary of properties of two element one-ports

    I. *LC* networks

       A. Necessary and sufficient conditions for driving-point immit-
tances

          1. Rational function with simple poles restricted to $j\omega$ axis

          2. Residues at poles real and positive

       B. Other properties of driving-point immittances

          1. Simple zeros restricted to $j\omega$ axis

          2. Zeros and poles alternate

          3. Ratio of odd-even or even-odd polynomials

          4. Slope of reactance or susceptance vs. frequency curve
strictly positive

   5. Slope of reactance or susceptance at any point on curve greater than the magnitude of the slope of a straight line drawn from the origin to the point
   6. Real part of impedance or admittance positive, zero, or negative when real part of s is positive, zero, or negative, respectively

II. *RC* and *RL* networks

   A. Necessary and sufficient conditions for Z_{RC} or Y_{RL}
      1. Rational function with simple poles restricted to negative σ axis
      2. Residues of Z_{RC} or Y_{RL} at all poles positive
      3. No pole at infinity
   B. Other properties of Z_{RC} or Y_{RL}
      1. Simple zeros restricted to negative σ axis
      2. Zeros and poles alternate
      3. First critical point on σ axis is a pole
      4. Slope of $Z_{RC}(\sigma)$ or $Y_{RL}(\sigma)$ strictly negative
      5. The imaginary part of $Z_{RC}(j\omega)$ or $Y_{RL}(j\omega)$ negative
      6. The real part of $Z_{RC}(j\omega)$ or $Y_{RL}(j\omega)$, a monotonically decreasing function
      7. Minimum value of real part for $s = j\omega$ occurs at infinity.
   C. Necessary and sufficient conditions for Y_{RC} or Z_{RL}
      1. Rational function with simple poles restricted to negative σ axis
      2. Residues of Y_{RC}/s or Z_{RL}/s positive
      3. No pole at $s = 0$
   D. Other properties of Y_{RC} or Z_{RL}
      1. Simple zeros restricted to negative σ axis
      2. Zeros and poles alternate
      3. First critical point on σ axis is a zero
      4. Slope of $Y_{RC}(\sigma)$ or $Z_{RL}(\sigma)$ strictly positive
      5. Imaginary part of $Y_{RC}(j\omega)$ or $Z_{RL}(j\omega)$ positive
      6. Real part of $Y_{RC}(j\omega)$ or $Z_{RL}(j\omega)$ a monotonically increasing function
      7. Minimum value of real part for $s = j\omega$ occurs at zero

PROBLEMS

2-1. Find the Foster and Cauer canonic forms for the following reactance functions: (a) $Z(s)$ has poles at $s = 0$, $\pm j3/2$ and $\pm j4$. It has zeros at $s = \pm j1$, $\pm j3$, and $\pm j5$. The residue in the pole at the origin is 2.

(b) $Z(s) = \dfrac{K(s^2 + \omega_1^2)(s^2 + \omega_3^2)}{s(s^2 + \omega_2^2)}$

$$\omega_1 = 1$$

$$\omega_2 = 2$$

$$\left.\frac{dZ}{ds}\right|_{s=j1} = 2$$

$$\left.\frac{dY}{ds}\right|_{s=j2} = 1$$

2-2. The impedance of a certain transmission line is given by $Z(s) = \coth \pi s$. Find a lumped-parameter lossless network whose impedance $Z_0(s)$ approximates the given one at low frequencies. (a) Choose two pairs of internal poles and two pairs of internal zeros of $Z_0(s)$ to coincide with those of $\coth \pi s$.

(b) Choose two pairs of internal poles of $Z_0(s)$ and their residues to coincide with those of $\coth \pi s$.

(c) Choose two pairs of internal poles of $Y_0(s) = 1/Z_0(s)$ and their residues to coincide with those of $1/\coth \pi s$.

Compare the approximation obtained in the three cases. By internal poles or zeros is meant finite nonzero poles or zeros.

2-3. An impedance function has zeros at $s = -1$, -2, and -3; and it has poles at $s = -1.5$ and -2.5. The function behaves like $s/10$ for very large values of s. (a) Write the analytic expression for $Z(s)$.

(b) Determine the value of the real part of $Z(s)$ at zero and infinity. (Is it RL or RC?)

(c) Find the four canonic forms

2-4. The admittance of an RC network has zeros at $s = 0$, -2, and -5. The slope of $Y(\sigma)$ at each of these points is unity. For large values of s the admittance approaches the value 2. Realize one Foster and one Cauer form for $Y(s)$.

2-5. Prove that the residues of an RC admittance or an RL impedance at all internal poles are negative.

2-6. Two impedances Z_1 and Z_2 are said to be complementary if their sum is a constant for all values of s. Complementary admittances are similarly defined. (a) Let $Z_1(s)$ be the impedance of an RC network having no pole at the origin and no zero at ∞. It is desired to find two other impedances $Z_2(s)$ and $Z_3(s)$ such that $Z_1(s) + Z_2(s) = K$ and also $Y_1(s) + Y_3(s) = K$. Find the condition on K in terms of certain coefficients of $Z_1(s)$ such that both these conditions are simultaneously satisfied.

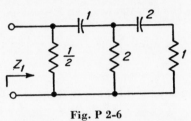

Fig. P 2-6

(b) The network of Fig. P 2-6 whose impedance is $Z_1(s)$ is to be connected in series or in parallel with another network with impedance $Z_2(s)$ such that

$$Z_1(s) + Z_2(s) = 1 \qquad \text{or} \qquad \frac{1}{Z_1(s)} + \frac{1}{Z_2(s)} = 1$$

Determine a Cauer form of network for $Z_2(s)$. Is it possible for both these relationships to be satisfied simultaneously? (of course, with different Z_2 functions)

2-7.† Let $P(s)$ be a polynomial with negative real zeros only. Prove that $P'(s)/P(s)$ and P/sP' are RC impedance functions. The prime denotes derivative.

Note: This will prove that $P'(s)$ has negative real zeros only.

2-8.† Let $P(s)$ be a poynomial with zeros on the $j\omega$ axis only. Prove that $P'(s)/P(s)$ is an LC impedance or admittance.

2-9.† Let $P(s)$ be a polynomial with negative real roots only. Prove that $KP(s) + sP'(s)$ has negative real roots only, where K is a real positive constant.

2-10.† Let $F(s) = P(s)/Q(s)$ be an RC admittance or an RC impedance function. Prove that $\dfrac{d^nP(s)/ds^n}{d^nQ(s)/ds^n}$ will also be an RC admittance or an RC impedance, respectively.

2-11.† Let $Z(s) = P(s)/Q(s)$ be a reactance function. Prove that $\dfrac{d^nP/ds^n}{d^nQ/ds^n}$ is a reactance function.

2-12. Let $Y(s)$ be the admittance of an RC one-port. Then

$$Y(s) = k_\infty s + k_0 + \sum_{i=1}^{n} y_i \qquad y_i = \frac{k_i s}{s + \sigma_i}$$

(a) Show that $\text{Im } y_i = \omega|y_i'|$, where $y_i' = dy_i/ds$.

† The proofs of these results were first given by Reza (100a).

(b) Show that $\operatorname{Im} Y(s) > 0$ for $s = \sigma + j\omega$, $\omega > 0$.

(c) Show that $\operatorname{Im} Y(s) \geq \omega|Y'(s)|$ for $s = \sigma + j\omega$, $\omega > 0$.

2-13. Let $Z(s)$ be the impedance of an RC one-port; then

$$Z(s) = k_\infty + \sum_{i=0}^{n} z_i \qquad z_i = \frac{k_i}{s + \sigma_i}$$

(a) Show that $|\operatorname{Im} z_i| = \omega|z_i'|$.

(b) Show that $\operatorname{Im} Z(s) < 0$ for $s = \sigma + j\omega$, $\omega > 0$.

(c) Show that $|\operatorname{Im} Z(s)| \geq \omega|Z'(s)|$ for $s = \sigma + j\omega$, $\omega > 0$.

2-14. Let $F(s)$ be a rational function with real coefficients. Let s_0 and s_0^* be a pair of complex conjugate poles of $F(s)$. Show that the residue at $s = s_0^*$ is the conjugate of the residue at $s = s_0$.

2-15. From Eq. (2-2) it is apparent that, if $Z(s)$ is the impedance of a lossless one-port, then

$$\operatorname{Re} Z > 0 \qquad \text{if} \qquad \operatorname{Re} s > 0$$

$$\operatorname{Re} Z < 0 \qquad \text{if} \qquad \operatorname{Re} s < 0$$

$$\operatorname{Re} Z = 0 \qquad \text{if} \qquad \operatorname{Re} s = 0$$

Show that these conditions are sufficient as well as necessary for an odd rational function with real coefficients to be a reactance function.

3

Synthesis of General Passive One-Ports

We are now ready to launch ourselves into a study of one-ports containing all three elements, resistance, capacitance, and inductance (including mutual inductance). In the last chapter we discussed the necessary and sufficient conditions for a function to be the impedance or admittance function of a one-port containing two kinds of elements only. Our objective now is to do the same for the more general network. We have already established that the impedance or admittance function of such a network is a positive real function of s. A study of positive real functions will therefore reveal the detailed properties of impedance functions. Having acquired this familiarity with positive real functions, we shall be in a position to establish the sufficient conditions for realizability of a one-port. The final task will be to obtain several alternative equivalent realizations of a one-port, starting from a function satisfying the sufficient conditions.

3-1. Properties of positive real functions

In Chap. 1 we found expressions for the impedance and admittance functions of a one-port in terms of the energy functions T_0, V_0, and F_0. From the form of these expressions we were able to conclude that the impedance and admittance are positive real functions of s. We define a positive real function as follows:

A function $F(s)$ of a complex variable s is called positive real if

1. $F(s)$ is real when s is real.

2. $\mathrm{Re}\, F(s) \geq 0$ when $\mathrm{Re}\,(s) \geq 0.$ (3-1)

Condition 1 implies that all other parameters in $F(s)$ other than s (such as coefficients, exponents, etc.) are real. In condition 2 the two equality signs do not hold simultaneously unless they hold identically. For instance, from Prob. 2-15 we find that the equality sign holds identically for a reactance function.

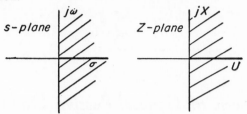

Fig. 3-1. Mapping of a positive real function.

Figure 3-1 shows sketches of the s and Z complex planes. The positive real property means that the right-half s plane maps into the right-half Z plane, while the real s axis maps onto the real Z axis. (The positive real s axis goes into the positive real Z axis, but nothing is said about the negative real s axis.) It can go anywhere on the real Z axis.

From the results of Prob. 2-15 we see that a reactance function is a positive real function of s, but of a special type. Not only does the right-half s plane go into the right-half Z plane, but the left-half s plane goes into the left-half Z plane as well. This fact makes the reactance function simpler than the general positive real function.

We established in Eqs. (1-65) that the immittance functions of a passive bilateral one-port are positive real functions (pr for short). However, the immittance functions of *lumped* networks are further restricted—they are rational functions of s (ratios of two polynomials). In fact, not only is the positive real and rational property necessary, but it is also sufficient for realizability of a one-port. Demonstration of this fact will constitute a large part of this chapter. In doing this we shall have to make extensive use of the theory of functions of a complex variable, and we shall assume familiarity with the fundamental concepts of this theory.

Our first objective will be to establish the major properties of pr functions. In the first place we shall show that if $Z(s)$ is a pr function it must be regular in the right-half s plane. To demonstrate this, we invoke a theorem which states that the real part of a function of a complex variable changes sign $2n$ times in the neighborhood of a pole of multiplicity n. To prove the theorem, let $Z(s)$ have an nth-order pole at $s = s_0$ and expand $Z(s)$ in a Laurent expansion about s_0.

$$Z(s) = \frac{a_{-n}}{(s - s_0)^n} + \frac{a_{-n+1}}{(s - s_0)^{n-1}} + \cdots + \frac{a_{-1}}{s - s_0} + a_0 + a_1(s - s_0) + \cdots$$

$$(3\text{-}2)$$

As s approaches the pole, the first term dominates. Hence, very near the pole we may write

$$Z(s) \doteq \frac{a_{-n}}{(s - s_0)^n} \tag{3-3}$$

Now let us take a circular path around the pole at s_0, as shown in Fig. 3-2(a). The radius r of the circle is assumed small, in line with the approxi-

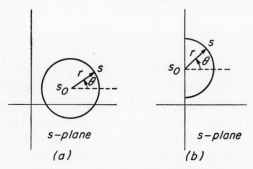

Fig. 3-2. Contour in right-half plane.

mation in the last equation. Assuming a_{-n} is also complex, we can write

$$s - s_0 = r\epsilon^{j\theta} \tag{a}$$

$$a_{-n} = K\epsilon^{j\phi} \tag{b}$$

$$\tag{3-4}$$

so that Eq. (3-3) and its real part become

$$Z(s) = \frac{K}{r^n} \epsilon^{j(\phi - n\theta)} \tag{a}$$

$$\mathrm{Re}\,[Z(s)] = \frac{K}{r^n} \cos{(n\theta - \phi)} \tag{b}$$

$$\tag{3-5}$$

As the variable point s goes around the circular contour once, θ goes from zero to 2π. The sign of the cosine changes $2n$ times, thus proving the theorem.

By the definition of a positive real function the real part of $Z(s)$ is never negative for any value of s in the right half plane. This means that the real part cannot change sign at all, which, in turn, requires $n = 0$. It follows that $Z(s)$ can have no poles in the right-half s plane.

We should also consider the possibility of a pole on the axis as shown in Fig. 3-2(b). In this case s is in the right half plane when θ is in the range $-\pi/2 \le \theta \le \pi/2$. We also know that the cosine function is positive when its argument is in the range $-\pi/2$ to $\pi/2$. Hence, looking at Eq. (3-5), we deduce that $\mathrm{Re}\,[Z(s)]$ will be positive if $n\theta - \phi$ lies in the range $-\pi/2$ to $\pi/2$. Since θ also lies in this range, this condition can be satisfied only if $n = 1$ and $\phi = 0$. $n = 1$ means that the pole is simple. In this case $a_{-n} = a_{-1}$ is the residue at the pole, and the condition we just established ($\phi = 0$) means that the residue must be real and positive. We conclude that it is possible for a pr function to have a pole on the $j\omega$ axis provided that the pole is simple and has a real positive residue.

Another useful property of pr functions is the following: The reciprocal of a pr function is also pr. Thus, if $Z(s)$ is a pr function, its reciprocal is

$$Y(s) = \frac{1}{Z(s)} = \frac{1}{U + jX} = \frac{U}{U^2 + X^2} - j\frac{X}{U^2 + X^2} \qquad (3\text{-}6)$$

where U and X are the real and imaginary parts of Z. It follows that the real part of Y will be positive whenever U is positive. Since, in addition, $Y(s)$ is real when $Z(s)$ is real, then $Y(s)$ is pr. By the preceding property Y must have no poles in the right half plane. Since the poles of Y are the zeros of Z, we can now state that, *if $Z(s)$ is a pr function, it can have neither zeros nor poles in the right half plane. Any zeros or poles on the $j\omega$ axis must be simple. The residues at such poles must be positive.*

This property tells us something of the relative degrees of the numerator and denominator of a pr function. Since the point at infinity may be considered to lie on the $j\omega$ axis, any pole or zero at infinity must be simple. This means that the highest powers of s in numerator and denominator cannot differ by more than 1. Considering a possible pole or zero at $s = 0$ leads to the conclusion that the lowest powers of numerator and denominator cannot differ by more than 1 either. In contrast to a reactance function, however, an arbitrary pr function need not have a pole or a zero at zero or infinity; the highest and lowest powers of numerator and denominator may be the same.

In order to test whether or not a given function is positive real, we have no recourse now but to apply the definition. This is not a very convenient test since it involves examining the real part of a given function for all values of s in the right half-plane, as required by the definition. We need to find some conditions which are sufficient for a function to be positive real and which, at the same time, are easy to apply as a test.

Let us digress slightly to discuss some theorems from the theory of functions of a complex variable, which we will need both in our present search for properties of pr functions and in subsequent work. Let $F(s)$ be a function of a complex variable, regular within a given region of the s plane and on its boundary C. Let the largest value of the magnitude of $F(s)$ for every point on C be M. That is $|F(s)| \leq M$ for all s on C. Then, it is true that the magnitude of $F(s)$ for all values of s inside C will be no greater than M, its maximum value on the boundary. This theorem is called the *maximum modulus theorem*. To prove the theorem, consider the circular region with center s_0 and radius r, shown in Fig. 3-3, and apply

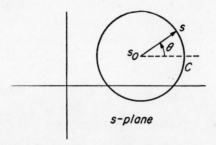

Fig. 3-3. Proof of the maximum modulus theorem.

Cauchy's integral formula. Letting s denote any point on the circumference this formula is

$$F(s_0) = \frac{1}{2\pi j} \oint_C \frac{F(s)}{s - s_0}\, ds \qquad (3\text{-}7)$$

We are assuming that $F(s)$ is regular inside the circular region and on the boundary. In polar coordinates we can write

$$s - s_0 = r\epsilon^{j\theta}$$
$$ds = jr\epsilon^{j\theta}\, d\theta \qquad (3\text{-}8)$$

When we substitute these into Eq. (3-7), we get

$$F(s_0) = \frac{1}{2\pi} \int_0^{2\pi} F(s)\, d\theta \qquad (3\text{-}9)$$

We are really interested in the magnitude of $F(s_0)$; so let us take the absolute value of both sides of Eq. (3-9). Then

$$|F(s_0)| = \frac{1}{2\pi}\left|\int_0^{2\pi} F(s)\, d\theta\right| \le \frac{1}{2\pi} \int_0^{2\pi} |F(s)|\, d\theta \qquad (3\text{-}10)$$

The last step follows from the fact that the absolute value of a sum (or integral) of complex numbers is not greater than the sum (or integral) of the absolute values of the numbers. Furthermore, by hypothesis $|F(s)| \le M$ at all points on the boundary. If we replace $|F(s)|$ in the integrand by the constant M, the inequality in Eq. (3-10) will be strengthened. Finally integration will yield

$$|F(s_0)| \le M \qquad (3\text{-}11)$$

The result states that the magnitude of $F(s)$ at the center of a circle is no greater than the largest value taken on by the magnitude of $F(s)$ at any point on the circumference of the circle. Furthermore, by tracing the steps of the development, you can see that the equality sign in the last equation can apply only if $F(s)$ is equal to M everywhere inside the circle.

The fact that the largest value of the magnitude of $F(s)$ occurs on the boundary of a region of regularity was proved only for a circular region. However, the result is general. You can prove this by assuming that the maximum occurs at an interior point of an arbitrary region and then showing that this contradicts the special result we just proved by taking a circle about the interior point.

Let us now apply the maximum modulus theorem to the function $F(s) = \epsilon^{-Z(s)}$. Let $Z(s) = U + jX$ be regular in a region. Then $F(s)$ will be regular there also. The magnitude of $F(s)$ is

$$|F(s)| = |\epsilon^{-(U+jX)}| = \epsilon^{-U} \tag{3-12}$$

The maximum value of the magnitude of $F(s)$ will occur on the boundary of the region of regularity. But the maximum of ϵ^{-U} will occur where U is a minimum. We conclude that the minimum value of the real part of $Z(s)$ will occur on the boundary of the region of regularity.

We are now ready to use this theorem to derive an important property of pr functions. We have already seen that a positive real function is regular in the right-half s plane. It may have poles on the $j\omega$ axis, but these must be simple. If there are poles on the $j\omega$ axis, let us imagine that we expand the given $Z(s)$ into partial fractions and group all the terms containing the j-axis poles. Call this $Z_1(s)$ and call the rest of the function, which now contains no j-axis poles, $Z_2(s)$. All the poles of $Z_1(s)$ are on the $j\omega$ axis, and the residues are all positive; so $Z_1(s)$ qualifies as a reactance function. We can write

$$Z(s) = Z_1(s) + Z_2(s) \tag{a}$$
$$\mathrm{Re}\,[Z(j\omega)] = \mathrm{Re}\,[Z_1(j\omega)] + \mathrm{Re}\,[Z_2(j\omega)] = \mathrm{Re}\,[Z_2(j\omega)] \tag{b}$$

$$(3\text{-}13)$$

since $\mathrm{Re}\,[Z_1(j\omega)]$ is zero.

The theorem discussed above may now be applied to $Z_2(s)$, which is regular in the entire right-half s plane and on the boundary. Then, according to the theorem, the minimum value of the real part of $Z_2(s)$ occurs on the $j\omega$ axis, which is the boundary of the region of regularity. If the real part is positive on the $j\omega$ axis, then it surely will be positive at any point in the right half plane. Adding the reactance function $Z_1(s)$ to $Z_2(s)$ can do nothing but increase the real part at any point inside the right half plane according to the result established in Prob. 2-15.

The above considerations lead us to state the following necessary and sufficient conditions for the positive realness of a function. Of course, the function should be rational (for a lumped network) with real coefficients.

In addition, *a function of the complex variable s will be positive real if and only if:*

1. *The function is regular in the right-half s plane;*
2. *Any poles on the jω axis are simple with real positive residues;*
3. *The real part of the function is nonnegative on the jω axis.*

Thus, instead of examining the real part of the function for all values of s in the right half plane, we break the job into three parts, each of which is considerably simpler to apply.

In the preceding discussion of positive real functions we have formulated our ideas in terms of rectangular coordinates, starting from the very definition of pr functions. Additional useful information can be gathered by a reformulation in terms of polar coordinates. The result we wish to establish involves a relationship between the angle of $Z(s)$ and that of s in the right half plane. We already know that, when s is real and positive (that is, $\arg s = 0$), Z is also real and positive ($\arg Z = 0$). To obtain a further relationship, let us transform both the frequency variable and the pr function in the following way:

$$p = \frac{s - k}{s + k} = \frac{s/k - 1}{s/k + 1} \qquad (3\text{-}14)$$

$$W = \frac{Z(s) - Z(k)}{Z(s) + Z(k)} = \frac{Z(s)/Z(k) - 1}{Z(s)/Z(k) + 1} \qquad (3\text{-}15)$$

A word of explanation is needed about the notation in the last equation. As the equation stands, if we keep Z as a variable, the right-hand side defines a function of Z. However, if we replace Z by its value in terms of s, the right-hand side will define a new function (of s), say, $W'(s)$. Finally we can replace s by its value in terms of p by taking the inverse of Eq. (3-14). This will then lead to a new function (of p), say, $W''(p)$. Of course, $W(Z) = W'(s) = W''(p)$. For convenience, we shall use the same symbol, W, to stand for each of these functions. The quantities k and $Z(k)$ are positive constants. It is convenient to normalize both s and $Z(s)$ by writing $k = 1$ and $Z(k) = Z(1) = 1$. An alternative viewpoint is to introduce new variables $s' = s/k$ and $Z'(s) = Z(s)/Z(k)$ and write the transformations in terms of these new variables. The primes are then dropped for purposes of simpler notation. In either case the transformations become

$$p = \frac{s - 1}{s + 1} \qquad (3\text{-}16)$$

$$W = \frac{Z - 1}{Z + 1} \qquad (3\text{-}17)$$

We should not lose sight of the fact that s and Z are normalized quantities.

Aside from the fact that different symbols are used, these last two equations are identical. In the language of function theory these are bilinear transformations. In order to accomplish our purpose, we must study the mapping properties of this transformation. However, we shall consider only those properties useful to us at present.

Let us treat Eq. (3-16) explicitly. With $s = \sigma + j\omega$, we can write

$$p = \frac{s-1}{s+1} = \frac{(\sigma-1)+j\omega}{(\sigma+1)+j\omega} = \sqrt{\frac{(\sigma-1)^2+\omega^2}{(\sigma+1)^2+\omega^2}}\, \epsilon^{j\gamma} \qquad \text{(a)}$$

$$\text{(3-18)}$$

where $\quad \gamma = \tan^{-1}\dfrac{\omega}{\sigma-1} - \tan^{-1}\dfrac{\omega}{\sigma+1} = \tan^{-1}\dfrac{2\omega}{\sigma^2+\omega^2-1}$ (b)

In the first equation p is written in polar form. We observe that the $j\omega$ axis of the s plane ($\sigma = 0$) maps onto the circumference of the unit circle in the p plane. When σ is positive—corresponding to the right-half s plane —p falls inside the unit circle.

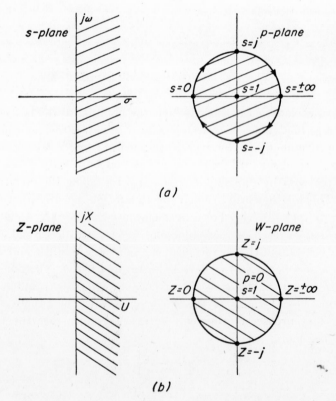

(a)

(b)

Fig. 3-4. Mapping properties of the bilinear transformation.

Thus Eq. (3-16) maps the right-half s plane onto the interior of the unit circle in the p plane, the map of the $j\omega$ axis being the unit circle itself. Similar statements apply to the mapping of Eq. (3-17). The right-half Z plane maps onto the interior of the W-plane unit circle. These transformations are illustrated in Fig. 3-4. The familiar Smith Chart is precisely this type of transformation. Since $Z(s)$ is pr, the right-half s plane maps into the right-half Z plane, which in turn maps onto the interior of the W-plane unit circle. Furthermore, the right-half s plane maps inside the p-plane unit circle also, through Eq. (3-16). Thus the positive real character of $Z(s)$ relates the interiors of the two unit circles. Because of the normalizations which we made, Z is equal to 1 when $s = 1$. These points correspond, respectively, to $W = 0$ and $p = 0$; so the origin of the p plane maps onto the origin of the W plane.

The positive σ axis goes onto the real p axis from -1 to $+1$. Similarly the positive real Z axis goes onto the real W axis from -1 to 1. We conclude that the angle of s is zero at all points on the real p axis from -1 to $+1$. Likewise, the angle of Z is zero at all points on the real W axis from -1 to $+1$.

The $j\omega$ axis of the s plane corresponds to $|p| = 1$. Since $Z(s)$ is pr, the complex values that Z takes on when $s = j\omega$ will lie in the right-half Z plane (or on the jX axis). This corresponds to points inside (or on the boundary of) the W-plane unit circle. So we can write

$$|W| \le 1 \qquad \text{for} \qquad |p| = 1 \tag{3-19}$$

At this point we need a fact from the theory of functions of a complex variable. This is called *Schwarz's lemma* (57). Let $W(p)$ be regular on and within a circle of radius R, *its value at $p = 0$ being zero*. Let the maximum value of $|W|$ on the circle be M. Then, at any point p *inside* the circle, *except at $p = 0$*,

$$|W(p)| < |p| \frac{M}{R} \tag{3-20}$$

At $p = 0$, $W = 0$ so that an equality sign will hold. Similarly the inequality will become an equality if $W(p) = p$. This theorem is easily proved by use of the maximum-modulus theorem.

In our case $W(p)$ satisfies the conditions of Schwarz's lemma. The radius of the circle (in the p plane) is unity, and according to Eq. (3-19) the maximum value M on the circle is also unity. Hence we can write

$$
\begin{aligned}
|W| < |p| \qquad &\text{for} \qquad 0 < |p| < 1 \qquad &\text{(a)}\\
|W| = |p| \qquad &\text{for} \qquad p = 0 \qquad &\text{(b)}
\end{aligned}
\tag{3-21}
$$

It is now a simple matter to substitute for W and p from Eqs. (3-16) and (3-17). In these expressions let us write

$$Z = U + jX = |Z|\epsilon^{j\theta} \tag{3-22}$$

$$s = \sigma + j\omega = \epsilon^{j\alpha} \tag{3-23}$$

The fact that we have set the magnitude of s equal to unity should not bother you. Remember that this is a normalized variable; a normalized value of unity means an "unnormalized" value of k—and k is any positive number.

Making these substitutions in Eq. (3-21), we get

$$\left|\frac{Z-1}{Z+1}\right|^2 < \left|\frac{s-1}{s+1}\right|^2$$

or

$$\frac{(U-1)^2 + X^2}{(U+1)^2 + X^2} < \frac{(\sigma-1)^2 + \omega^2}{(\sigma+1)^2 + \omega^2} \tag{3-24}$$

When this expression is simplified and the polar form is used, we get

$$\frac{\cos\theta}{\cos\alpha} > \tfrac{1}{2}\left(|Z| + \frac{1}{|Z|}\right) \tag{3-25}$$

A plot of the function in parentheses is shown in Fig. 3-5. It has a minimum value of 2, which occurs when $|Z| = 1$. Thus the right-hand side of

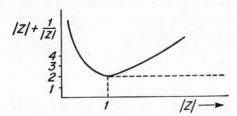

Fig. 3-5. Plot of $|Z| + 1/|Z|$ against $|Z|$.

the equation is strictly greater than unity except at $|Z| = 1$ which corresponds to the origin in the p plane. It follows that $\cos\theta$ will be strictly greater than $\cos\alpha$ and so $|\theta|$ *will be strictly less than* $|\alpha|$.

This conclusion was derived starting from Eq. (3-21a). Hence it results from a consideration of all points in the interior of the unit circles except the origins. The origins of the p and W planes correspond to $s = 1$ and $Z = 1$, respectively. At these points the angles are equal. To complete the story, we should also consider the boundaries. The boundary of the p-plane unit circle corresponds to the $j\omega$ axis, on which the angle of s is $\pm\pi/2$. Either the function $Z(j\omega)$ will be purely imaginary (and so its angle will be $\pm\pi/2$), or it will be complex with a positive real part (so that its angle will lie between $-\pi/2$ and $+\pi/2$). In this case, $|\theta|$ will be less than or equal to $|\alpha|$.

To summarize, we can write the facts we have established as follows: *If $Z(s)$ is a positive real function, then it necessarily follows that*

$$|\arg Z(s)| < |\arg s| \quad \text{for} \quad 0 < |\arg s| < \pi/2$$

$$|\arg Z(s)| = |\arg s| \quad \text{for} \quad |\arg s| = 0 \qquad (3\text{-}26)$$

$$|\arg Z(s)| \leq |\arg s| \quad \text{for} \quad |\arg s| = \pi/2$$

Actually these conditions are sufficient as well as necessary that $Z(s)$ be positive real (see Prob. 3-7).

3-2. Testing for positive realness

In the preceding section we formulated the necessary and sufficient conditions for a function to be positive real. The purpose of the present section is to establish tests to determine whether or not a given function satisfies these conditions.

Let us assume that the functions presented to us will be rational and will have real coefficients. There remains to determine whether the function is regular in the right half plane, whether j-axis poles are simple with positive residues, and whether the real part is nonnegative on the $j\omega$ axis.

We define a *Hurwitz* polynomial to be a polynomial with all its zeros in the left half plane. Zeros on the $j\omega$ axis are also permitted as a special case. To distinguish between these, we shall refer to the former type of polynomial as *strictly* Hurwitz. Our first purpose, then, is to check whether or not the denominator of the given function is a Hurwitz polynomial. Let this polynomial be $P(s)$, with even and odd parts $m(s)$ and $n(s)$, and write

$$P(s) = a_0 + a_1 s + a_2 s^2 + \ldots + a_q s^q$$
$$= (s + \sigma_1) \ldots (s + \sigma_k)(s^2 + 2\sigma_{k+1}s + \sigma_{k+1}^2 + \omega_{k+1}^2) \ldots$$
$$(s^2 + 2\sigma_m s + \sigma_m^2 + \omega_m^2)$$
$$= m(s) + n(s) \qquad (a)$$
$$m(s) = a_0 + a_2 s^2 + \ldots + a_q s^q \qquad (b) \quad (3\text{-}27)$$
$$n(s) = a_1 s + a_3 s^3 + \ldots + a_{q-1} s^{q-1} \qquad (c)$$

There is no loss in generality in assuming q to be even, as we have done. There are certain properties of Hurwitz polynomials that we can check merely by inspection. For example, if $P(s)$ is Hurwitz, it is necessary that none of its coefficients be negative or zero. (In the case of a polynomial all of whose zeros are on the $j\omega$ axis, which is the extreme limit of a Hurwitz polynomial, every other coefficient will be zero.) This is easy to see by considering Fig. 3-6, which shows the possible locations of the zeros of a Hurwitz polynomial. The factors in the polynomial due to these zeros will have one of the following forms: $s + \sigma_0$ for a real zero, $(s + \sigma_0)^2 + \omega_0^2$ for a complex pair, and $s^2 + \omega_0^2$ for an imaginary pair, where σ_0 is a positive number. Products of such factors cannot lead to negative coefficients, nor to zero coefficients, by cancellations among terms.

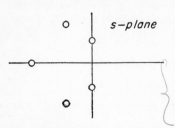

Fig. 3-6. Locations of zeros of Hurwitz polynomial.

Let us now discuss a more refined check on the Hurwitz character of a given polynomial. Let $P(s) = m + n$ be a Hurwitz polynomial. Consider the ratio of the even part to the odd part. This can be written

$$F(s) = \frac{m(s)}{n(s)} = \frac{(m + n) + (m - n)}{(m + n) - (m - n)}$$

$$= \frac{P(s) + P(-s)}{P(s) - P(-s)} = \frac{P(s)/P(-s) + 1}{P(s)/P(-s) - 1}$$

With the definition

$$G(s) = \frac{P(s)}{P(-s)} \qquad (3\text{-}28)$$

we can express $F(s)$ in terms of $G(s)$, and vice versa, as follows:

$$F = \frac{G + 1}{G - 1} \qquad (a)$$

$$\qquad\qquad\qquad (3\text{-}29)$$

$$G = \frac{F + 1}{F - 1} \qquad (b)$$

The function $F(s) = m/n$ is the ratio of the even part to the odd part of a Hurwitz polynomial. In the previous chapter we found that reactance functions are ratios of even and odd polynomials. Our purpose now is to find a relationship between reactance functions and the even and odd parts of Hurwitz polynomials.

To this end consider the relationship between G and F expressed in Eq. (3-29b). This is a bilinear transformation similar to those in Eq. (3-16) or (3-17), but with one difference; it is the *left* half of the F plane which is mapped into the interior of the unit circle of the G plane, rather than the right half. The j axis of the F plane becomes the unit circle in the G plane. This is illustrated in Fig. 3-7.

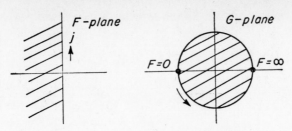

Fig. 3-7. The mapping $G = \dfrac{F+1}{F-1}$.

We can express the important mapping property of the two planes analytically as follows:

$$|G| \gtreqless 1 \qquad \text{imply} \qquad \operatorname{Re} F \gtreqless 0, \qquad \text{respectively} \qquad (3\text{-}30)$$

This condition involves the magnitude of G, which, from the definition in Eq. (3-28), involves the magnitudes of $P(s)$ and $P(-s)$. Remember that $P(s)$ is a polynomial with real coefficients, so that its zeros are either real or complex conjugates. Consider a polynomial with a real zero at $s = \sigma_0$ and a pair of complex conjugate zeros at $s = \sigma_1 \pm j\omega_1$. This polynomial and its magnitude can be written

$$P(s) = (s - s_0)(s - s_1)(s - s_1^*)$$

$$|P(s)|$$
$$= \sqrt{[(\sigma - \sigma_0)^2 + \omega^2][(\sigma - \sigma_1)^2 + (\omega - \omega_1)^2][(\sigma - \sigma_1)^2 + (\omega + \omega_1)^2]}$$
$$= \sqrt{[(\sigma - \sigma_0)^2 + \omega^2][(\sigma - \sigma_1)^4 + 2(\sigma - \sigma_1)^2(\omega^2 + \omega_1^2) + (\omega^2 - \omega_1^2)^2]}$$
$$\text{(a)}$$
$$(3\text{-}31)$$

$$|P(-s)|$$
$$= \sqrt{[(\sigma + \sigma_0)^2 + \omega^2][(\sigma + \sigma_1)^4 + 2(\sigma + \sigma_1)^2(\omega^2 + \omega_1^2) + (\omega^2 - \omega_1^2)^2]}$$
$$\text{(b)}$$

The magnitude of the polynomial $P(-s)$ is obtained by reversing the sign of σ, since the sign of ω will have no effect on the magnitude.

Let us now assume that all the zeros of $P(s)$ are in the left half plane, which means that σ_0 and σ_1 are negative. This is illustrated in Fig. 3-8. Let us consider the following three cases in turn: (1) The variable point s is in the right half plane, which means that σ is positive. The point $-s$ will then lie in the left half plane. Comparison of Eqs. (3-31a) and (3-31b) for this case will show that $|P(s)| > |P(-s)|$. (2) The variable point s is in the left half plane, which means that σ is negative. For this case we

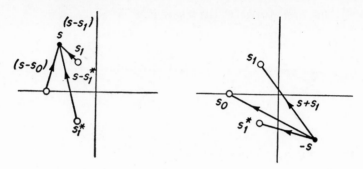

Fig. 3-8

find $|P(s)| < |P(-s)|$. (3) Finally the variable point is on the $j\omega$ axis, which means $\sigma = 0$. In this case we find $|P(s)| = |P(-s)|$.

The conclusions in the preceding paragraph are unaltered if there are additional left-half-plane factors in the polynomial $P(s)$. We can summarize these results for a Hurwitz polynomial in the following way:

$$\text{Re } s \gtreqless 0 \qquad \text{imply} \qquad |G| \gtreqless 1, \quad \text{respectively} \qquad (3\text{-}32)$$

Combining this expression with the one in Eq. (3-30), and remembering that $F = m/n$, we get

$$\text{Re}\left(\frac{m}{n}\right) \gtreqless 0 \qquad \text{for} \qquad \text{Re } s \gtreqless 0, \quad \text{respectively} \qquad (3\text{-}33)$$

Now refer back to Prob. 2-15. There you are asked to establish the result that the conditions just listed are sufficient to guarantee that the function m/n is a reactance function. Taking this theorem as proved, we have now shown that the ratio of the even to the odd part (or vice versa) of a Hurwitz polynomial is necessarily a reactance function.

However, this is not exactly what we want. We want to take a polynomial and determine whether or not it is Hurwitz. We really need the converse of what we have established. Unfortunately the converse is not completely valid.† This is easily appreciated by considering the ratio $|P(s)/P(-s)|$ when $P(s)$ has a zero in the right half plane, say, at $s = s_2$. Then, by forming the magnitudes as in Eqs. (3-31), we shall find that Eq. (3-32) cannot be satisfied, except in the event that $s = -s_2$ is also a zero of $P(s)$. In such a case $P(s)$ and $P(-s)$ will have a common factor which will cancel, thus permitting Eq. (3-32) to be satisfied. The ratio of the even to the odd part of this non-Hurwitz polynomial will thus be a reactance function.

† This was pointed out by Prof. J. Blackman of Syracuse University.

As an illustration, consider the polynomial

$$P(s) = s^5 + 2s^4 + 3s^3 + 6s^2 + 4s + 8$$
$$= (s + 2)(s^2 + s + 2)(s^2 - s + 2)$$

This is not a Hurwitz polynomial. Nevertheless the ratio of its even and odd parts is

$$\frac{2s^4 + 6s^2 + 8}{s(s^4 + 3s^2 + 4)} = \frac{2}{s}$$

which is certainly a reactance function.

The condition that $P(s)$ and $P(-s)$ have a common factor can also be satisfied if $P(s)$ has a pair of conjugate zeros on the $j\omega$ axis. In such a case $P(s)$ will have a factor $s^2 + \omega_i^2$. It is clear that $P(-s)$ will also have this factor so that a cancellation takes place in the ratio $P(s)/P(-s)$.

Based on this discussion, we can now state the following theorem:

If the ratio of the even and odd parts of an arbitrary polynomial $P(s)$ is a reactance function, then either $P(s)$ is a Hurwitz polynomial or it is a Hurwitz polynomial times an even polynomial. The zeros of this even polynomial can fall in one of three categories: (1) conjugate pairs on the $j\omega$ axis; (2) pairs of real zeros, one being the negative of the other; (3) groups of four complex zeros symmetrically arranged about both the real and the imaginary axes as in the numerical example given above. In any case this even polynomial will be a factor of both the even part and the odd part of $P(s)$ and, hence, will have no effect on their ratio.

In the case of a pair of real zeros, one in the right and the other in the left half plane, the polynomial $P(s)$ will have some negative coefficients. Hence we can rule it out of further consideration.

We now have a powerful test to determine whether or not a given polynomial is Hurwitz (short of actually computing the roots). We take the ratio of the even to the odd part of the given polynomial and determine whether or not it satisfies the conditions of a reactance function. Here we can proceed in two alternate ways, corresponding to the Foster or Cauer methods of synthesis of reactance functions. In the first method we can imagine expanding m/n or its reciprocal in partial fractions. For this we shall need to find the poles and the residues of one of these functions. If the original polynomial is less than the seventh degree, this will involve factoring no more than a quadratic.

The alternate procedure involves carrying out a continued fraction expansion. If the coefficients are all positive, a realizable LC network can be found, indicating that m/n is a reactance function. If any negative coefficients appear, the original polynomial is proved to have zeros in the right half plane.

If the first alternative is used in checking the Hurwitz property of a polynomial $P(s)$, the procedure involves finding the poles of m/n and then finding the residues at these poles. To find the poles, we factor $n(s)$. Any j-axis zeros of $P(s)$, and any right-half-plane zeros accompanied by their images in the left half plane will make their appearance at this point. If there are any zeros of the latter variety, the testing will be over, since $P(s)$ is then shown to be non-Hurwitz. The j-axis zeros of $P(s)$, if any, cannot be poles of m/n. Hence, when we calculate the residues of m/n at these points, we shall get zero. A zero residue at one of the zeros of $n(s)$ will tell us that this point is also a zero of $P(s)$.

If we use the second alternative and carry out the Cauer-division process, eventually nothing will be left in numerator and denominator except identical even polynomials due to the common factors of m and n. These will then cancel, terminating the division process prematurely. The denominator that is left just before the procedure terminates will contain the common factors of m and n. Factoring this denominator will expose the j-axis zeros of $P(s)$ and any right-half-plane zeros which, together with their left-half-plane images, form an even polynomial with positive co-efficients.

As an example, consider the following polynomial:

$$P(s) = s^6 + 4s^5 + 6s^4 + 12s^3 + 11s^2 + 8s + 6 \tag{3-34}$$

$$m = s^6 + 6s^4 + 11s^2 + 6$$

$$n = 4s^5 + 12s^3 + 8s$$

$$\frac{m}{n} = \frac{s^6 + 6s^4 + 11s^2 + 6}{4s^5 + 12s^3 + 8s} = \frac{1}{4}s + \frac{3}{4s} + \frac{0}{s^2 + 1} + \frac{0}{s^2 + 2} \tag{3-35}$$

The roots of the denominator of m/n are easily found and two of the residues are found to be zero. Furthermore the rest of the poles are simple with positive residues. Hence $P(s)$ is Hurwitz, with two pairs of j-axis zeros at $s = \pm j1$ and $s = \pm j\sqrt{2}$. In this case we can find the rest of the zeros by recombining the partial-fraction expansion in Eq. (3-35) to get

$$\frac{m}{n} = \frac{s^2 + 3}{4s}$$

Thus the polynomial remaining after the j-axis zeros of $P(s)$ are removed, say $P_1(s)$, is

$$P_1 = s^2 + 3 + 4s = (s + 3)(s + 1) \tag{3-36}$$

By this process not only did we find out whether or not $P(s)$ was Hurwitz, but we also determined its zeros.

If we carry out the alternate procedure, we get

$$
\begin{array}{r|l}
s^6 + 6s^4 + 11s^2 + 6 & \underline{4s^5 + 12s^3 + 8s} \\
\underline{s^6 + 3s^4 + 2s^2} & \quad s \\
4s^5 + 12s^3 + 8s \mid \overline{3s^4 + 9s^2 + 6} & \quad \dfrac{}{4} \\
\underline{4s^5 + 12s^3 + 8s} \mid \quad \dfrac{4}{3}s & \\
0 &
\end{array}
$$

We see that the process terminates before the degrees of the numerator and denominator are reduced to zero. Hence $P(s)$ must have j-axis or right half plane zeros. These are the zeros of the divisor just before the process terminates, which is

$$(3s^4 + 9s^2 + 6) = 3(s^2 + 1)(s^2 + 2) \tag{3-37}$$

When this is divided into $P(s)$ we have left

$$\frac{P(s)}{(s^2 + 1)(s^2 + 2)} = (s^2 + 4s + 3) = (s + 1)(s + 3) \tag{3-38}$$

The answers given by the two methods agree, as they should.

Remember that our purpose is to see whether or not a given rational function is positive real. So far, we have discussed a method of determining whether the function is regular in the right-half s plane. Furthermore we have located the j-axis poles, if any, and can certainly tell whether or not they are simple. The residues at such poles can be computed by standard methods to determine whether or not they are positive. It remains for us to check on the real part of the given function for all values of ω.

Let the given function be $Z(s)$, and write

$$Z(s) = \frac{m_1(s) + n_1(s)}{m_2(s) + n_2(s)} \tag{3-39}$$

The m's and n's represent the even and odd parts, respectively, of the numerator and denominator. When $s = j\omega$ and only in this case (except possibly at isolated points in the s plane), the m's will be real, while the n's will be imaginary. Let us separate $Z(s)$ into its even and odd parts. This is done by multiplying numerator and denominator by $m_2 - n_2$. The result is

$$Z(s) = \frac{m_1 m_2 - n_1 n_2}{m_2^2 - n_2^2} + \frac{m_2 n_1 - m_1 n_2}{m_2^2 - n_2^2} \tag{3-40}$$

The first term is even, while the second term is odd. For arbitrary values of s each of these terms will be complex. However, when $s = j\omega$, they will reduce to the real and imaginary parts of Z, respectively. Hence we can write

$$\text{Re } Z(j\omega) = U(\omega^2) = \frac{N(\omega^2)}{D(\omega^2)} = \frac{m_1 m_2 - n_1 n_2}{m_2^2 - n_2^2}\Bigg|_{s=j\omega} \tag{3-41}$$

N and D stand for numerator and denominator, respectively.

This is an even function of ω, and so we have labeled it $U(\omega^2)$. Suppose we do not set $s = j\omega$ on the right-hand side. This will be equivalent to replacing ω^2 by $-s^2$. Hence we shall label the resulting function $U(-s^2)$.

Our objective is to examine the right side of the last equation for all values of ω to see whether or not it ever becomes negative. Note that, for $s = j\omega$, the denominator is the sum of squares of the real and imaginary parts of a complex quantity, and this is always positive. So we need to consider the numerator only. For positive realness we must require

$$N(\omega^2) = (m_1 m_2 - n_1 n_2)|_{s=j\omega} \geq 0 \tag{3-42}$$

We have already mentioned that this is an even function of ω. Hence we can write

$$N(\omega^2) = (m_1 m_2 - n_1 n_2)|_{s=j\omega}$$
$$= K(\omega^2 + s_1^2)(\omega^2 + s_2^2) \ldots (\omega^2 + s_n^2) \tag{3-43}$$

In terms of s, since $s^2 = -\omega^2$ when $s = j\omega$, this becomes

$$N(-s^2) = K(s_1^2 - s^2)(s_2^2 - s^2) \ldots (s_n^2 - s^2) \tag{3-44}$$

This is the numerator of the even part of $Z(s)$. It is the analytic continuation of $N(\omega^2)$ and is a *bona fide* function of s, even when s takes on complex values. However, it becomes the numerator of the real part of Z only when $s = j\omega$. We shall now investigate the permissible locations of the zeros of the polynomials in the last two equations if the condition in Eq. (3-42) is to be satisfied.

At this point it is convenient to introduce a change of variable. Since only the square of ω appears in Eq. (3-43), let $\omega^2 = x$. All real values of ω fall in the range $0 \leq x \leq \infty$. Equivalently we can set $x = -s^2$ in Eq. (3-44). In either case we shall get

$$N(x) = K(x - x_1)(x - x_2) \ldots (x - x_n) \tag{3-45}$$

The zeros of this polynomial may be complex, negative real, or positive real. Consider two factors involving a pair of conjugate zeros $x_1 = a_1 + jb_1$ and $x_1^* = a_1 - jb_1$.

$$(x - x_1)(x - x_1^*) = [(x - a_1) + jb_1][(x - a_1) - jb_1] \tag{3-46}$$

The second factor on the right is the conjugate of the first factor, so that the product can never be negative for any real positive value of x. In the case of a negative real root $x = -a$, the corresponding factor is $x + a$, which also can never become negative for real positive values of x.

For a real positive zero $x = +a$, the corresponding factor $x - a$ will change sign as x passes through $+a$. This means that $N(x)$ will surely become negative, unless a is a double (or even-order) zero of $N(x)$. In this case $N(x)$ will have a factor $(x - a)^2$ and will not change sign.

We conclude that $N(x)$ will be positive for all positive values of x (which correspond to all real values of ω) provided that any positive zeros of $N(x)$ are of even order (including zero order, meaning no positive roots). Stated in a different way, we can say that a real rational function $Z(s)$ will have a nonnegative real part on the entire $j\omega$ axis provided that the numerator of its even part has no odd-order zeros on the $j\omega$ axis.

For a given rational function $Z(s)$ as in Eq. (3-39), we can form the polynomial $N(x)$ according to Eq. (3-42) and the change of variable $\omega^2 = x$. If the coefficients of $N(x)$ are all of the same sign, Descartes's rule of sign will tell us there are no positive roots. However, this is not a conclusive method when there are changes of sign among the coefficients. There is a method of testing a polynomial to determine whether or not it has any zeros in a given interval of the real axis, and the order of such zeros. This is Sturm's theorem.[†] We shall state the theorem and give an example of its use but shall make no attempt to prove it here.

The theorem makes use of a set of *Sturm functions*, which are obtained as follows: Let the given polynomial and its first derivative be

$$P_0(x) = a_0 + a_1x + a_2x^2 + \ldots + a_nx^n \qquad \text{(a)}$$
$$P_1(x) = P_0'(x) = a_1 + 2a_2x + \ldots + na_nx^{n-1} \qquad \text{(b)}$$

$$(3\text{-}47)$$

(The prime indicates differention.)

These are the first two Sturm functions. We form the next one by dividing P_0 by P_1 and stopping when the remaining dividend is one degree lower than P_1. This will usually take a two-term quotient but sometimes will occur after the first term. This remaining dividend is labeled $-P_2(x)$. The succeeding Sturm function is formed by dividing P_1 by P_2 and again stopping when the remaining dividend is one degree lower than the divisor. This is $-P_3$. This process is similar to the Cauer division except that the quotient usually consists of two terms. We can write the process concisely as

$$P_0 = q_1P_1 - P_2$$
$$P_1 = q_2P_2 - P_3$$

$$(3\text{-}48)$$

$$\cdots\cdots\cdots$$

$$P_{k-2} = q_{k-1}P_{k-1} - P_k$$

[†] See L. E. Dickson, *New First Course in the Theory of Equations*, John Wiley & Sons, Inc., New York, 1935.

Observe that, if P_k is zero, then P_{k-1} is a factor of P_{k-2}. Working back through the Sturm functions, we shall find that P_{k-1} is a factor of both P_1 and P_0. Thus P_{k-1} contains all the multiple roots of P_0 with a multiplicity one less than that occurring in P_0. This follows from the fact that a root of P_0 of multiplicity m will be a root of its derivative with a multiplicity $m - 1$. In this fashion all the multiple roots of P_0 are found, together with their multiplicity. Of course, if the polynomial P_{k-1} is of high order, finding its roots may be a job in itself. In this case the Sturm procedure can be applied to P_{k-1}.

Suppose now that the Sturm functions are formed as in Eqs. (3-48) until the last one, P_k, is a constant. This will happen if P_0 has no multiple zeros. (If the original polynomial has multiple zeros, these are found by the Sturm procedure. After these are factored out, call the remaining polynomial P_0.) Let a and b ($a < b$) be real numbers which are not zeros of $P_0(x)$. Sturm's theorem says that *the number of real zeros of $P_0(x)$ between the two numbers a and b is the excess in the number of variations in sign of the Sturm functions for $x = a$ over the number of variations in sign for $x = b$.* Table 3-1 will serve as an aid in understanding this. It represents a particular case where $k = 5$. The theorem states that in this case the number of zeros of $P_0(x)$ between a and b is one.

Table 3-1

	P_0	P_1	P_2	P_3	P_4	P_5	Number of variations in sign
$x = a$	$+$	$-$	$-$	$+$	$-$	$+$	4
$x = b$	$-$	$+$	$+$	$-$	$-$	$+$	3

For our present purpose the range of x in which we are interested includes all nonnegative values. Thus the values zero and infinity correspond to a and b. The signs of the Sturm functions at these extreme values are the signs of the constant terms and the signs of the highest-power terms, respectively, and so are determined simply by inspection.

Let us now illustrate the methods of testing for positive realness which we have discussed. Consider the function

$$Z(s) = \frac{2s^4 + 7s^3 + 11s^2 + 12s + 4}{s^4 + 5s^3 + 9s^2 + 11s + 6} = \frac{m_1 + n_1}{m_2 + n_2} \qquad (3\text{-}49)$$

This is a rational function with real coefficients, all of which are positive and nonzero. We first perform a Hurwitz test on the denominator.

$$\frac{m_2}{n_2} = \frac{s^4 + 9s^2 + 6}{5s^3 + 11s} = \frac{s}{5} + \frac{6}{11s} + \frac{\frac{224}{275}s}{s^2 + \frac{11}{5}} \tag{3-50}$$

Since the poles of m_2/n_2 are on the $j\omega$ axis and are simple with real residues, $m_2 + n_2$ is a Hurwitz polynomial [the process also shows that $Z(s)$ has no j-axis poles].

The next job is to investigate the real part. To this end we construct $N(-s^2) = m_1 m_2 - n_1 n_2$

$$= (2s^4 + 11s^2 + 4)(s^4 + 9s^2 + 6) - (7s^3 + 12s)(5s^3 + 11s)$$
$$= 2(s^8 - 3s^6 - 11s^4 - 15s^2 + 12) \tag{3-51}$$

Setting $-s^2 = x$, we get

$$N(x) = 2(x^4 + 3x^3 - 11x^2 + 15x + 12) \tag{3-52}$$

Descartes's rule of sign does not give us any conclusive information about the number of positive roots in this case, and so we resort to Sturm's theorem. Observe from Eqs. (3-48) that we can multiply any Sturm function by a positive constant without altering the result of the theorem. We shall take advantage of this fact to avoid inconvenient numbers. The Sturm functions are formed as follows:

$N_0 = 2(x^4 + 3x^3 - 11x^2 + 15x + 12)$

$N_1 = 2[4x^3 + 9x^2 - 22x + 15]$

$\frac{N_0}{N_1} = \frac{x^4 + 3x^3 - 11x^2 + 15x + 12}{4x^3 + 9x^2 - 22x + 15} = \frac{1}{4}\left(x + \frac{3}{4}\right) - \frac{1}{16}\frac{115x^2 - 246x - 147}{N_1}$

$N_2 = 115x^2 - 246x - 147$

$\frac{N_1}{N_2} = \frac{4x^3 + 9x^2 - 22x + 15}{115x^2 - 246x - 147} = \frac{1}{115}(4x + 17.55) - 20.65\frac{-x - 1.81}{N_2}$

$N_3 = -x - 1.81$

$\frac{N_2}{N_3} = \frac{115x^2 - 246x - 147}{-x - 1.81} = -115x + 454 - \frac{-674}{N_3}$

$N_4 = -674$

Table 3-2

	N_0	N_1	N_2	N_3	N_4	Number of variations in sign
$x = 0$	+	+	−	−	−	1
$x = \infty$	+	+	+	−	−	1

Since the last Sturm function is a constant, there are no repeated roots. The number of variations in sign of the Sturm functions is the same at both extremities, indicating that there are no real positive roots. The given function is thus shown to be positive real.

3-3. Realization of positive real functions—preliminary

Let us pause briefly and review what we have accomplished. We have shown that the driving-point impedance or admittance of a passive, bilateral, lumped network is a positive real function of s. We have further established necessary and sufficient conditions for a rational function to be positive real, and we know how to test a given function to determine whether or not it fulfills these conditions. It remains for us now to demonstrate that, given an arbitrary positive real rational function, we can find a passive, bilateral, lumped network whose driving-point impedance or admittance is equal to the given pr function. This will establish the sufficiency of the pr condition for driving-point immittances.

In our attempt to find a network realization for a given pr function we may be tempted to proceed as in the synthesis of two-element one-ports by expanding the given function in partial fractions. If we can recognize each term as the impedance or admittance of a component network, then the series or parallel connection of these components will yield the complete synthesis, as in the Foster realization of reactance functions. This idea appears to have merit, and we shall pursue it further.

In the first place, if a given impedance function has j-axis poles, we can write

$$Z(s) = k_\infty s + \frac{k_0}{s} + \sum_{j=1}^{n} \frac{2k_j s}{s^2 + \omega_j^2} + Z_1(s) \qquad (3\text{-}53)$$

in which the j-axis poles are shown explicitly and $Z_1(s)$ is regular on the $j\omega$ axis but has all the other poles of $Z(s)$. The real part of $Z_1(j\omega)$ is equal to the real part of the given function on the $j\omega$ axis. Hence $Z_1(s)$ is positive real. The terms in the partial-fraction expansion on the right side can be realized in a series connection of lossless networks as in the first Foster form. The resulting network will have the form shown in Fig. 3-9(a).

Now suppose that $Z_1(s)$ has j-axis zeros. We can invert it and write

$$Y_1(s) = \frac{1}{Z_1(s)} = k_{\infty 1} s + \frac{k_{01}}{s} + \sum_{i=1}^{m} \frac{2k_i s}{s^2 + \omega_i^2} + \frac{1}{Z_2(s)} \qquad (3\text{-}54)$$

Following the same reasoning as before, we find $Z_2(s)$ to be a positive real function. The partial realization of $Z_1(s)$ will take the form shown in Fig. 3-9(b).

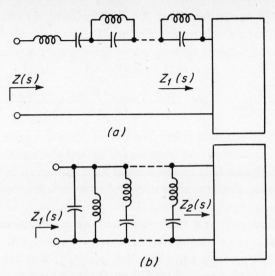

$Z(s)$

$Z_1(s)$

(a)

$Z_1(s)$

$Z_2(s)$

(b)

Fig. 3-9. Realization of j-axis poles and zeros.

We may now find that Z_2 has poles on the $j\omega$ axis, in which case these can be realized in the form of Fig. 3-9(a). Continuing this process, we will eventually end up with a remainder impedance which has neither zeros nor poles on the $j\omega$ axis. In this case the numerator and denominator must be of the same degree.

We use the expressions *reactance reduction* and *susceptance reduction* to describe the process of removing poles on the $j\omega$ axis from the impedance function and the admittance function, respectively. We can think of the reactance reduction as a modification of the imaginary part of an impedance without affecting the real part. When all the j-axis poles are removed from an impedance function, the reactive part of the function can no longer be altered without at the same time modifying the real part. This leads to the idea of a *minimum-reactance* pr function, by which we mean an impedance that has no poles on the $j\omega$ axis. In a similar manner we define a *minimum-susceptance* pr function as an admittance that has no poles on the $j\omega$ axis (or an impedance that has no zeros on the $j\omega$ axis). Bode (15) was the first to define these functions.

In this terminology the first step in our contemplated realization procedure is to apply reactance and susceptance reduction alternately, until a minimum-reactance minimum-susceptance function is obtained. The degree of the numerator of such a function will be the same as the degree of the denominator. All the poles of this function will lie in the interior of the left-half s plane. Following our major theme, we can expand this function in partial fractions. We shall immediately encounter something new. Whereas, in treating LC or RC functions, we found all the poles to be simple, this is no longer true for arbitrary pr functions. Thus in our partial-fraction expansion we may meet terms like

$$\frac{1}{(s+a)^k} \quad \text{or} \quad \frac{a_k s^k + a_{k-1} s^{k-1} + \ldots + a_1 s + a_0}{(s^2 + b_1 s + b_0)^k} \qquad (3\text{-}55)$$

which are due to multiple poles. We cannot recognize such terms as the driving-point immittance of simple component networks. Hence this realization technique fails in the general case. However, in special cases with simple poles, this procedure may lead to a realization (see Prob. 3-12 for restrictions).

Let us return now to a minimum-reactance minimum-susceptance pr function which is to be the impedance function of a one-port. The real part of the function is nonnegative along the $j\omega$ axis. If it is not already zero at some value of ω, we can subtract from the function a real number that does not exceed the smallest value that the real part takes on for any value of ω. The remaining function will have the same poles as the original one, and its real part on the $j\omega$ axis will be not less than zero; so it will be pr. Its reactive part will be unaltered. This process is termed *resistance reduction.* The largest constant we can subtract and still have a pr remainder is the smallest value of the real part on the $j\omega$ axis. The remaining function will then have a zero real part somewhere on the $j\omega$ axis. We will call such a function a *minimum-resistance* function. This situation is not quite the same as the minimum-reactance (or minimum-susceptance) case. A function may be minimum-reactance without being minimum-susceptance, and vice versa. However, a minimum-resistance function is at the same time minimum-conductance. That is, if the real part of a function is zero at some value of ω, the real part of its reciprocal will also be zero there. It would be completely appropriate, then, to call such functions *minimum–real-part* functions. No committment is made as to whether the positive real function is an impedance or an admittance. We should point out, however, that these last statements are true only for a minimum-reactance minimum-susceptance function. For example, the function $s/(s+a)$ has a zero real part at $s = 0$. But its reciprocal is $1 + a/s$, which has a unity real part for all values of $s = j\omega$.

Let us return to the realization problem. After we have obtained a minimum-reactance minimum-susceptance function, we can subtract from this function or its reciprocal the smallest value that the real part assumes on the $j\omega$ axis, thus obtaining a minimum–real-part function. Functions which are minimum-reactance, minimum-susceptance, and minimum–real-part will be called *minimum functions.* This removed constant is realized as a series resistance or a shunt resistance depending on whether the function is an impedance or an admittance. It may be that the remaining function now has a j-axis pole or zero, which may be removed, in turn, as a reactance structure. If the minimum real part occurs at $\omega = 0$ or infinity and this value is removed, the remaining function will surely have a zero at the corresponding value of s. This is true since the imaginary part of the pr function is already zero at these extreme frequencies; removing the real part will result in a zero of the function.

In some cases the complete realization may be obtained by the alternate application of what we may term *imaginary-part reduction* and *real-part reduction.* As an example, consider the impedance function

$$Z(s) = \frac{2s^3 + 3s^2 + 7s + 4}{s^3 + 3s^2 + 2s + 6} = \frac{2s^3 + 3s^2 + 7s + 4}{(s + 3)(s^2 + 2)} \qquad (3\text{-}56)$$

This has a pair of conjugate poles on the $j\omega$ axis. We can remove these poles from the function, obtaining a shunt-tuned circuit as a series branch. The remaining function becomes

$$Z_1(s) = Z(s) - \frac{s}{s^2 + 2} = \frac{2(s + 1)}{s + 3} \qquad (3\text{-}57)$$

This is a minimum-reactance minimum-susceptance function. We can proceed either with Z_1 or with its reciprocal. If we proceed with Z_1, we find that it has a minimum real part of $\frac{2}{3}$, which occurs at $s = 0$. If we remove this, we shall create a zero at $s = 0$. This, in turn, can be removed as a shunt inductance. Thus

$$Z_2(s) = Z_1(s) - \frac{2}{3} = \frac{4s}{3(s + 3)} \qquad (a)$$

$$Y_2(s) = \frac{1}{Z_2} = \frac{9}{4s} + \frac{3}{4} \qquad (b)$$

$$(3\text{-}58)$$

When the shunt inductance of $\frac{4}{9}$ is removed, we are left with a constant,

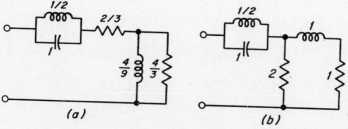

(a)   *(b)*

Fig. 3-10. Realization of a simple positive real function.

which of course is realized as a resistance. The complete realization is shown in Fig. 3-10(a).

Alternatively we can deal with Y_1, the reciprocal of Z_1, after the reactance reduction. We find that the minimum value of the real part of Y_1 is $\frac{1}{2}$, and it occurs at infinity. If we subtract this from Y_1 in the form of a shunt resistance, we shall create a zero at infinity. The reciprocal function will, of course, have a pole at infinity, which we can realize as a series inductance. Thus

$$Y_2 = Y_1 - \frac{1}{2} = \frac{1}{s+1} \tag{3-59}$$

$$Z_2 = \frac{1}{Y_2} = s + 1 \tag{3-60}$$

After removal of the series inductance we are left with a constant which is realized as a resistance. This alternate realization is also shown in Fig. 3-10.

We went through this simple example in rather unnecessary detail only to show the fundamental procedure that we would follow in a more complicated example.

3-4. Brune realization

Up to this point we have taken some relatively simple steps in our attempt to realize a given positive real function. First we remove poles and zeros of the function on the $j\omega$ axis and realize these as reactive series and shunt branches. Having achieved a minimum-reactance minimum-susceptance function, we then subtract the minimum value of the real part in the form of a series or shunt resistance. If this step creates a zero on the $j\omega$ axis, we can perform some further imaginary-part reduction. As we showed in the last section, alternate application of these two steps alone may lead to a complete realization in some cases.

Suppose that the real-part reduction does not create a zero of the remaining function on the $j\omega$ axis. This will pose a completely new problem. To carry on the discussion, let us consider a biquadratic minimum-reactance minimum-susceptance function.

$$Z_0(s) = \frac{s^2 + a_1's + a_0'}{s^2 + b_1s + b_0} \tag{a}$$

$$U(\omega^2) = \operatorname{Re} Z_0(j\omega) = \frac{\omega^4 + (a_1'b_1 - a_0' - b_0)\omega^2 + a_0'b_0}{(b_0 - \omega^2)^2 + b_1^2\omega^2} \tag{b}$$

$$\tag{3-61}$$

To guarantee that $Z_0(s)$ is positive real, its coefficients must be positive. In addition, the zeros of $U(\omega^2)$ in terms of ω^2 should not be real and positive unless they are equal. This condition is ensured if the discriminant of the numerator of $U(\omega^2)$ is not positive. Simplifying the expression for the discriminant leads to the condition

$$(\sqrt{a_0'} - \sqrt{b_0})^2 \le a_1' b_1 \qquad (3\text{-}62)$$

If the equality sign applies, then the real part of $Z(j\omega)$ will have a double zero on the $j\omega$ axis.

Our problem now is to determine the smallest value of $U(\omega^2)$ and the frequency at which it occurs. This may be at zero, infinity or a finite non-zero value. Let us make the change of variable $\omega^2 = x$ as we did before and plot the function $U(x)$. Figure 3-11 shows possible $U(x)$ functions.

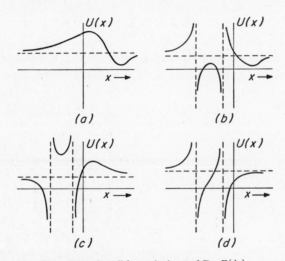

Fig. 3-11. Possible variations of Re $Z(j\omega)$.

The region of interest is the positive x axis; the negative x axis corresponds to the real axis of the s plane. If the minimum real part occurs at zero or infinity, as in Fig. 3-11(c) and (d), removal of this value will create a zero of the remaining impedance at the corresponding value of s. The admittance will have a pole there, and this can be removed as a shunt inductance or capacitance, respectively.

When the minimum value of the real part occurs at a finite nonzero frequency ω_0, we meet an essentially different situation. In this case removal of the minimum real part leaves a function which has a purely imaginary value at ω_0. The remaining impedance, which we have called a *minimum* function, is still a biquadratic, though; it has the same denominator, but the coefficients in the numerator are different. Thus, if $Z(s)$ is the remaining impedance function, let us write

$$Z(s) = \frac{s^2 + a_1 s + a_0}{s^2 + b_1 s + b_0} \tag{3-63}$$

This impedance is a minimum function, its real part being zero at $s = j\omega_0$. Hence we can write

$$Z(j\omega_0) = jX \tag{3-64}$$

The reactance X may be positive or negative. Assume temporarily that X is positive. We know that the impedance of an inductance has a positive imaginary value at positive frequencies; so let us consider removing an inductance L_1 which at $s = j\omega_0$ has a reactance X. That is,

$$L_1 = \frac{X}{\omega_0} \tag{3-65}$$

Removing this inductance creates a zero of the remaining impedance at $s = j\omega_0$, which can be realized as a series-resonant branch in shunt

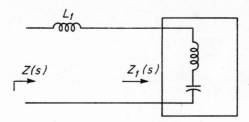

Fig. 3-12. Initial steps in Brune cycle.

across the rest of the network. This configuration is shown in Fig. 3-12. Let us carry out analytically the steps which we have just described.

After removing L_1 we shall have

$$Z_1 = Z - sL_1 = \frac{s^2 + a_1 s + a_0}{s^2 + b_1 s + b_0} - sL_1$$

$$= \frac{-L_1 s^3 + (1 - b_1 L_1)s^2 + (a_1 - b_0 L_1)s + a_0}{s^2 + b_1 s + b_0} \tag{3-66}$$

This remaining impedance is seen to have a pole at infinity which was not there before. Furthermore the residue at the pole is negative. Hence *this function is not even pr.* Nevertheless it has a zero at $j\omega_0$ so that we can write its reciprocal as

$$Y_1 = \frac{1}{Z_1} = \frac{s/L_2}{s^2 + \omega_0^2} + \frac{1}{Z_2(s)}$$

$$= \frac{sZ_2/L_2 + s^2 + \omega_0^2}{(s^2 + \omega_0^2)Z_2}$$

$$= \frac{sP_1/L_2 + (s^2 + \omega_0^2)P_2}{(s^2 + \omega_0^2)P_1} \tag{3-67}$$

where we have set

$$Z_2 = \frac{P_1(s)}{P_2(s)}$$

By comparing the last line of this equation with the reciprocal of Z_1 in Eq. (3-66), we see that $P_1(s)$ must be a linear function of s. Writing $P_1 = A_1 s + A_0$, we can determine the coefficients A_0 and A_1 by comparing coefficients in the two equations. Similarly we see that $P_2(s)$ must be a constant and that we can determine its value by comparing coefficients. Carrying out this process, we find

$$Z_2(s) = -\frac{L_1\omega_0^2}{b_0} s + \frac{a_0}{b_0} \tag{3-68}$$

The first term in Eq. (3-67) represents a series-resonant branch. Having found Z_2, we can now solve for the elements of the series-resonant branch from Eq. (3-67). The result is

$$L_2 = \frac{L_1\omega_0^2}{b_0 - \omega_0^2} \tag{a}$$

$$C_2 = \frac{1}{L_2\omega_0^2} = \frac{b_0 - \omega_0^2}{\omega_0^4 L_1} \tag{b}$$

$$\tag{3-69}$$

We now have the realization shown in Fig. 3-12, including the element values. We see from Eq. (3-68) that Z_2 has a pole at infinity, but with a negative residue. This can be removed as a negative inductance $L_3 = -L_1\omega_0^2/b_0$. The remainder is a resistance of value $a_0/b_0 = Z_1(0)$. The complete realization is shown in Fig. 3-13.

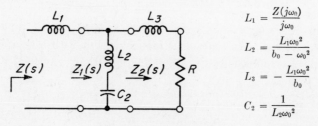

$$L_1 = \frac{Z(j\omega_0)}{j\omega_0}$$

$$L_2 = \frac{L_1\omega_0^2}{b_0 - \omega_0^2}$$

$$L_3 = -\frac{L_1\omega_0^2}{b_0}$$

$$C_2 = \frac{1}{L_2\omega_0^2}$$

Fig. 3-13. A Brune cycle.

There are several points to clear up in this discussion. In the first place the values for L_2 and C_2 as given by Eqs. (3-69) involve the difference $b_0 - \omega_0^2$. We do not yet know whether or not this quantity is positive. To establish this, we need to return to Eq. (3-63) for the impedance. We get one expression involving ω_0 and the coefficients by setting Re $[Z(j\omega_0)] = 0$. Next we substitute this relationship into the expression we get by assuming that the imaginary part of $Z(j\omega_0)$ is positive. This leads to the result

$$(b_0 - \omega_0^2)\left(1 + \frac{b_1 \omega_0^2}{b_0 a_1}\right) > 0 \qquad (3\text{-}70)$$

(The details are left for you as an exercise.) This requires $b_0 - \omega_0^2$ to be positive, which in turn ensures that L_2 and C_2 are positive.

Second, the value of the inductance L_3 is negative. In its present form, then, the realization of Fig. 3-13 is not physical. To overcome this difficulty, recall that the transformer and the tee circuit of inductances shown

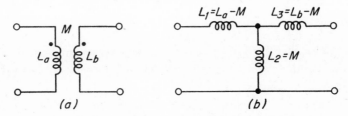

Fig. 3-14. Transformer and its equivalent circuit.

in Fig. 3-14 are equivalent. The square of the coefficient of coupling of the transformer is

$$\frac{M^2}{L_a L_b} = \frac{L_2^2}{(L_1 + L_2)(L_2 + L_3)} = 1 - \frac{L_1 L_2 + L_2 L_3 + L_1 L_3}{(L_1 + L_2)(L_2 + L_3)} \qquad (3\text{-}71)$$

We now replace the tee circuit of inductances in the Brune realization of Fig. 3-13 by an equivalent transformer. Using the values of the inductances given in the figure, we find that

$$L_1 L_2 + L_2 L_3 + L_1 L_3 = 0 \qquad (3\text{-}72)$$

This means that the transformer is realizable, but with a coupling coefficient of unity as shown by the preceding equation. The final realization takes the form of Fig. 3-15.

A third point that should be mentioned is the following: In actually going through a Brune realization for a specific problem it is not necessary to retrace all the steps following Eq. (3-65). We went through the development merely to establish the existence of the realization for the case of the biquadratic minimum function. The element values given in Figs. 3-13 and 3-15 are the end result.

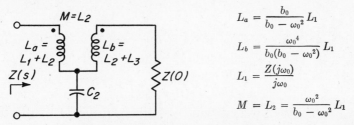

$$L_a = \frac{b_0}{b_0 - \omega_0^2} L_1$$

$$L_b = \frac{\omega_0^4}{b_0(b_0 - \omega_0^2)} L_1$$

$$L_1 = \frac{Z(j\omega_0)}{j\omega_0}$$

$$M = L_2 = \frac{\omega_0^2}{b_0 - \omega_0^2} L_1$$

Fig. 3-15. Brune cycle with transformer.

This completes the discussion when the value of the reactance in Eq. (3-64) is positive. If the value of this reactance is negative, a completely similar procedure can be followed. The inductance L_1 in Eq. (3-65) will now be negative, but the impedance Z_1 in the following equation will be pr. Hence the inductances L_2 and L_3 will be positive, but you will find that the condition of unity coupling is again satisfied. You are urged to go through the details of the development for this case.

We have now completely demonstrated the Brune realization of a biquadratic minimum positive real function. We shall next consider a minimum pr function of arbitrary complexity. Let us define the *rank* of a rational function as the sum of the degrees of the numerator and denominator polynomials. For the type of function considered these degrees will be the same, say, n. The rank will then be $2n$. Let the given function be

$$Z(s) = \frac{s^n + a_{n-1}s^{n-1} + \ldots + a_1s + a_0}{s^n + b_{n-1}s^{n-1} + \ldots + b_1s + b_0} \tag{3-73}$$

Since $Z(s)$ is a minimum function, its real part is zero at some point on the $j\omega$ axis. We know how to proceed if this minimum occurs at zero or infinity; so let us assume that it occurs at some finite frequency $s_0 = j\omega_0$. We can then write

$$Z(j\omega_0) = jX = j\omega_0 L_1 \tag{3-74}$$

just as before. At $s = j\omega_0$, Z is purely reactive and either positive or negative. In either case remove an inductance L_1, whose value is given in the last equation. This will be either positive or negative. The remaining function will be

$$Z_1(s) = Z(s) - L_1s \tag{3-75}$$

It will have a pole at infinity and a zero at $j\omega_0$, and it will be pr only if X is negative. Let us temporarily assume that X is negative. The inductance

L_1 will then be negative. The zero of $Z_1(s)$ at $s = j\omega_0$ can be realized by considering the reciprocal of Z_1 (which will be pr).

$$Y_1 = \frac{1}{Z_1} = \frac{s/L_2}{s^2 + \omega_0^2} + Y_2(s) \tag{3-76}$$

where $1/L_2 = 2$ times residue of Y at $s = j\omega_0$ and $Y_2 = 1/Z_2$ is the remaining function. The left-hand side has a zero at infinity (since Z_1 has a pole there); so the right-hand side must also. It follows that Y_2 will have a zero at infinity, which means that $Z_2(s)$ must have a pole at infinity. The residue at this pole can be found by putting Eq. (3-75) into (3-76) and noting the behavior of Z_2 as s goes to infinity.

$$\lim_{s \to \infty} \frac{Z_2}{s} = \lim_{s \to \infty} \frac{1/s}{Y_1 - \dfrac{s/L_2}{s^2 + \omega_0^2}}$$

$$= \lim_{s \to \infty} \frac{1}{\dfrac{1}{Z(s)/s - L_1} - \dfrac{s^2/L_2}{s^2 + \omega_0^2}} = -\frac{L_1 L_2}{L_1 + L_2} \tag{3-77}$$

Hence the residue of Z_2 at infinity is

$$L_3 = -\frac{L_1 L_2}{L_1 + L_2} \tag{3-78}$$

The pole at infinity can now be removed as a series inductance, leaving a remainder

$$Z_3(s) = Z_2(s) - L_3 s \tag{3-79}$$

If the procedure we have been following is to be worthwhile, this remaining function should be of lower rank than the original impedance. To find the rank of $Z_3(s)$, we retrace our steps and see what effect the various operations we have performed have had. Writing only the degrees of each function, we see that

$$
\begin{array}{cc}
Z \to \dfrac{n}{n} & Y_2 \to \dfrac{n-2}{n-1} \\[2mm]
Z_1 \to \dfrac{n+1}{n} & Z_2 \to \dfrac{n-1}{n-2} \\[2mm]
Y_1 \to \dfrac{n}{n+1} & Z_3 \to \dfrac{n-2}{n-2}
\end{array} \tag{3-80}
$$

Thus $Z_3(s)$ is a positive real function with a rank of $2(n-2)$, four less than the rank of $Z(s)$. The realization is shown in Fig. 3-16(a). It differs from Fig. 3-13 by the fact that a more general pr function $Z_3(s)$, rather than a resistance, appears at the end of the cycle.

The inductances in the realization are related by Eq. (3-78). If we rewrite this equation, we find that it reduces to Eq. (3-72), which expresses the fact that the transformer equivalent of the inductance tee is perfectly coupled. This equivalent is shown in Fig. 3-16(b).

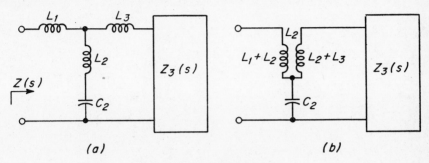

Fig. 3-16. A Brune cycle.

Let us return to Eq. (3-74) and assume that X is now positive. Then L_1 will be positive, and Z_1 in Eq. (3-75) will no longer be positive real. Let us see how it differs from a pr function. In fact, the result we shall establish is a general one, and so we shall use a general notation.

Let $Z(s)$ be a pr function regular at infinity and with $Z(0) \neq 0$. Consider the function

$$Z_1(s) = Z(s) - Ks \qquad (3\text{-}81)$$

where K is a positive constant. We shall show that $Z_1(s)$ *has exactly one zero in the right half plane and that this zero is simple and lies on the σ axis.* For the proof we shall need the condition on the angle of a pr function as given in Eqs. (3-26). If $Z_1(s)$ is to be zero at $s = s_0$, then $Z(s_0)$ should equal Ks_0. In particular the angle of $Z(s_0)$ should equal the angle of s_0 (since the angle of Ks_0 is the same as that of s_0). According to Eqs. (3-26) the only place at which the angle of $Z(s)$ and that of s are equal in the right half plane is the σ axis. Thus any zeros of $Z(s) - Ks$ in the right half plane must occur on the σ axis.

Suppose there are two values of s, namely, $s = \sigma_1$ and $s = \sigma_2$, at which $Z_1(s)$ is zero. That is,

$$Z(\sigma_1) = K\sigma_1 \qquad (a)$$
$$Z(\sigma_2) = K\sigma_2 \qquad (b) \qquad (3\text{-}82)$$

Return to the bilinear transformation in Eq. (3-15), and choose the normalizing factor k so that $W = 0$ when $s = \sigma_1$. That is,

$$W(\sigma_1) = \frac{Z(\sigma_1) - Z(k)}{Z(\sigma_1) + Z(k)} = 0 \qquad (3\text{-}83)$$

or $$k = \sigma_1 \qquad (3\text{-}84)$$

Now let us evaluate W when $s = \sigma_2$. We get

$$W(\sigma_2) = \frac{Z(\sigma_2) - Z(k)}{Z(\sigma_2) + Z(k)} = \frac{Z(\sigma_2) - Z(\sigma_1)}{Z(\sigma_2) + Z(\sigma_1)} \qquad (3\text{-}85)$$

But the values of $Z(\sigma_2)$ and $Z(\sigma_1)$ are given by Eqs. (3-82). When these are substituted in the last equation, we get

$$W(\sigma_2) = \frac{\sigma_2 - \sigma_1}{\sigma_2 + \sigma_1} = \frac{\sigma_2 - k}{\sigma_2 + k} = p(\sigma_2) \qquad (3\text{-}86)$$

The last equality follows from the transformation in Eq. (3-14). This equation states that W and p are equal when $s = \sigma_2$. But, according to Eqs. (3-21), $|W| = |p|$ only when $p = 0$ (if W is not identically equal to p). With $p(\sigma_2) = 0$, it follows that $\sigma_2 = k = \sigma_1$. This proves that $Z_1(s) = Z(s) - Ks$ has at most a single zero in the right half plane.

We can show that $Z_1(s)$ must have at least one zero on the positive real axis by noting that $Z_1(0) = Z(0) > 0$ by hypothesis. Furthermore, since $Z(s)$ is regular at infinity, $Z_1(\sigma) \to -K\sigma$ as $\sigma \to +\infty$. Thus $Z_1(\sigma)$ changes sign as σ goes from 0 to infinity, which means the plot of $Z_1(\sigma)$ versus σ must cross the σ axis at least once. Since there is *at most* a single zero, but there must be *at least* one, we conclude that there is *exactly* a single zero in the right half plane.

We have now shown that $Z_1(s) = Z(s) - Ks$ has exactly one zero in the right half plane (on the real axis) when the pr function $Z(s)$ is regular at infinity and has a finite nonzero value at the origin. However, we have not established the multiplicity of this zero. We can easily show that the zero is not of second order by noting that a second-order zero will lead to a plot of $Z(\sigma)$ versus σ similar to Fig. 3-17. This is not possible since

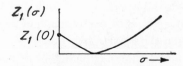

Fig. 3-17. Plot of $Z_1(\sigma)$.

we know that $Z_1(\sigma) \to -\infty$ as $\sigma \to \infty$. In fact, the same reasoning will show that any even-order zero is not possible. The only remaining possibility is an odd-order zero of multiplicity greater than 1. In a later section we shall prove that this is also impossible (see Probs. 3-15 and 3-14).

Now we can return to the realization problem. If the value of X in Eq. (3-74) is positive, $Z_1(s)$ in Eq. (3-75) will not be pr. However, we have just shown that it will have exactly a single zero on the positive real axis.

Suppose we formally go through the same realization procedure that we did for the case $X < 0$, even though Z_1 is not pr. Its reciprocal Y_1 will have one pole in the right half plane, but since Re $[Z_1(j\omega)]$ = Re $[Z(j\omega)]$ ≥ 0, then Re $[Y_1(j\omega)] \geq 0$.

The admittance $Y_1(s)$ has a pair of j-axis poles at $s = \pm j\omega_0$. In order to write Y_1 in the form of Eq. (3-76), we must ensure that the residue of Y_1 at $s = j\omega_0$ is real and positive. This residue is

$$k = \lim_{s \to j\omega_0} (s - j\omega_0)Y_1(s) = \lim_{s \to j\omega_0} \frac{s - j\omega_0}{Z(s) - X(\omega_0)s/\omega_0}$$

If we write $Z(j\omega) = U(\omega) + jX(\omega)$ and evaluate the limit by the use of l'Hospital's rule, we find for the residue

$$k = \frac{1}{dZ(j\omega_0)/j\,d\omega - X(\omega_0)/\omega_0} = \frac{1}{dX(\omega_0)/d\omega - X(\omega_0)/\omega_0}$$

The right side follows from the fact that the real part of $Z(j\omega)$ has a double zero at $s = j\omega_0$ so that $dU/d\omega = 0$ there. We conclude that the residue of Y_1 at $s = j\omega_0$ is real. It remains to show that the residue is positive. For this purpose return to Eq. (2-14) where we showed that, for a reactance function,

$$\frac{dX}{d\omega} \geq \frac{X}{\omega}$$

(since X is positive and we are talking about a positive ω, the magnitude bars can be omitted). If you review the argument on which this result was based, you will see that the result is also valid for any pr function at a frequency for which the energy function F_0 (and hence the real part of the pr function) is zero.

As a consequence of this discussion we can conclude that the value of L_2 obtained in Eq. (3-76) will be real and positive. After subtracting the j-axis poles from $Y_1(s)$ we see that the remaining admittance $Y_2(s)$ will have the same pole in the right half plane that $Y_1(s)$ has and again Re $[Y_2(j\omega)] \geq 0$. Its reciprocal, $Z_2(s)$, will have a single zero in the right half plane but Re $Z_2(j\omega) \geq 0$. It will also have a pole at infinity with a negative residue. When this pole is realized as a negative inductance L_3, the remaining impedance $Z_3(s)$ will satisfy all conditions of positive real-ness, except possibly for that lone zero in the right half plane. We shall now show that this zero disappears when we remove L_3 so that $Z_3(s)$ is positive real.

What we have obtained formally is the realization of Fig. 3-16 but with different values of the L's from before. We can compute $Z(s)$ from the figure.

$$Z(s) - L_1 s = \frac{[L_3 s + Z_3(s)](C_2 L_2 s^2 + 1)}{C_2(L_2 + L_3)s^2 + 1 + C_2 s Z_3(s)} \qquad (3-87)$$

The left-hand side of this equation has a single zero in the right half plane, say, at $s = k$; the right-hand side must be zero there also. Since $C_2 L_2 k^2 + 1$ cannot be zero for a positive k, we must have

$$Z_3(k) + k L_3 = 0 \qquad (3-88)$$

Our purpose is to show that $Z_3(s)$ does not have the zero in the right half plane that $Z_1(s)$ has. This we have now done, since the last equation says that $Z_3(s)$ has the value $-k L_3$, and not zero, at the right-half-plane zero of $Z_1(s)$. Furthermore, since L_3 is negative, $Z_3(k)$ is a positive number.

This completes the demonstration that positive realness is a sufficient, as well as necessary, condition for the realization of a driving-point immittance function. The steps in the process are as follows: First remove all poles and zeros on the $j\omega$ axis, in any order, until a minimum-reactance minimum-susceptance function is obtained. Now find the minimum value of the real part of this function on the $j\omega$ axis, and remove it (as a series or shunt resistance). If the minimum occurs at zero or infinity, further reactance or susceptance reduction is possible. If the minimum occurs at a finite nonzero frequency, ω_0, a Brune cycle will result. One of the inductances L_1 or L_3 will be negative, depending on whether the remaining reactance, after subtraction of the minimum real part, is negative or positive. In either case the element values are found from the same formulas. A physical realization requires the use of *perfect* transformers (unit coupling).

The Brune cycle reduces the rank of the function by 4. The same sequence of steps is repeated (where applicable) and the rank reduced still further until the function is exhausted.

We should point out that the Brune realization will not always require a perfect transformer. If the original positive real function is an impedance and has a pole at infinity, this is normally realized as a series inductance, say, L_0. This inductance can then be combined with the inductance L_1 of the Brune section and, depending on the relative sizes of L_0 and L_1, may lead to a tee network of inductances all of which are positive or, at worst, will lead to a transformer with less than unity coupling. An example of this is provided in Prob. 3-6.

We shall now illustrate the Brune-realization procedure with a numerical example. It is desired to obtain a realization for the following impedance function:

$$Z(s) = \frac{s^3 + 2s^2 + s + 1}{s^3 + s^2 + 2s + 1} \tag{3-89}$$

$$N(-s^2) = (2s^2 + 1)(s^2 + 1) - (s^3 + s)(s^3 + 2s)$$
$$= (1 - s^2)(1 + s^2)^2 \tag{3-90}$$

The Hurwitz test shows that there are no poles or zeros in the right half plane or on the $j\omega$ axis. The last equation shows that $N(-s^2)$ has a pair of zeros on the $j\omega$ axis, but these are double zeros. Hence the given function is a minimum pr function. Its real part is zero at $\omega_0 = 1$. For the value of $Z(s)$ at $s = j1$ we find

$$Z(j1) = j1 = j\omega_0 L_1 \tag{3-91}$$

Hence $L_1 = 1$

We next remove an impedance $sL_1 = s$ from $Z(s)$ and get

$$Z_1(s) = Z - s = \frac{(1 - s^2)(1 + s^2)}{s^3 + s^2 + 2s + 1} \tag{3-92}$$

We have thus created a zero on the $j\omega$ axis. This zero is removed by taking the reciprocal of Z_1 and computing the residue at the pole. Thus

$$\frac{1}{L_2} = \frac{s^2 + 1}{s} Y_1(s)\big|_{s=j} = \frac{s^3 + s^2 + 2s + 1}{s(1 - s^2)}\bigg|_{s=j} = \frac{1}{2}$$

With $\omega_0 = 1$ we now have the shunt-branch parameters,

$$L_2 = 2 \tag{3-93}$$

$$C_2 = \frac{1}{L_2\omega_0^2} = \frac{1}{2}$$

Next we subtract the admittance of the shunt branch from $Y_1(s)$ and get

$$Y_2(s) = Y_1 - \frac{s/2}{s^2 + 1} = \frac{1 + 3s/2}{1 - s^2}$$

The reciprocal of this function has a pole at infinity with a residue $-\frac{2}{3}$. When this is removed, we get

$$Z_3 = Z_2 - L_3 s = \frac{1 - s^2}{1 + 3s/2} - \left(-\frac{2s}{3}\right) = \frac{2}{3}\frac{3 + 2s}{2 + 3s} \tag{3-94}$$

This completes the Brune cycle, leaving a very simple function as a remainder. We observe that this is an RC impedance function, its minimum real part occurring at infinity. We get

$$Z_3(s) = \frac{4}{9} + \frac{1}{27s/10 + 9/5} \tag{3-95}$$

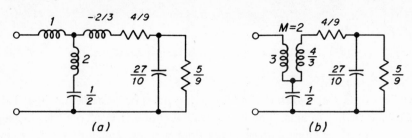

Fig. 3-18. Brune realization of positive real function.

The complete realization, together with the transformer equivalent, is shown in Fig. 3-18.

3-5. Bott-Duffin realization

When first announced, the Brune-realization technique had great significance because it established sufficient conditions for realizability of a driving-point immittance function. From the practical point of view, however, the realization leaves much to be desired. The reason for the appearance of the negative inductances, necessitating a perfectly coupled transformer, is the insistance on a ladder form of realization. We know that other structures exist. Perhaps, if we relax our requirement of a ladder structure, we can find other realizations that do not embody the perfect transformers required by Brune. We should expect to pay for this in some other manner, possibly by the appearance of additional elements.

The first attempt in this direction was made by Bott and Duffin (18), utilizing a theorem due to Richards (102a). Since the Bott-Duffin realization technique is intimately tied up with this theorem, we shall first discuss the theorem.

Let $Z(s)$ be a pr function, and let us again use the bilinear transformations given in Eqs. (3-14) and (3-15). By simple algebra we can write

$$\frac{W}{p} = \frac{Z(s) - Z(k)}{Z(s) + Z(k)} \frac{s + k}{s - k} = \frac{1 - F(s)}{1 + F(s)} \tag{3-96}$$

where

$$F(s) = \frac{kZ(s) - sZ(k)}{kZ(k) - sZ(s)} \tag{3-97}$$

Equation (3-96) is again a bilinear transformation, the two variables being F and W/p. (It differs from the previous ones we considered by a minus sign, which affects only the angle of W/p and not its magnitude. Since we need only the magnitude of W/p for our purposes, this sign will have no significance.) Thus the right-half F plane is mapped onto the interior of the unit circle in the W/p plane, the j axis falling on the circumference of the circle. The inside of the unit circle in the W/p plane is described by writing

$$\left|\frac{W}{p}\right| < 1 \qquad \text{or} \qquad |W| < |p| \tag{3-98}$$

But, according to Eqs. (3-21), this corresponds to the interior of the p-plane unit circle. Thus the interior of the p-plane unit circle maps into the interior of the W/p-plane unit circle. But, by the transformation of Eq. (3-14), the former is the map of the right-half s plane. Thus, finally, we have the result that the right-half s plane maps into the right-half F plane. By giving proper attention to the boundaries of the right half plane as well, we can write Re $F \geq 0$ when Re $s \geq 0$. In addition, since $Z(s)$ is pr, $F(s)$ is real when s is real. Hence we can state Richards's theorem as follows: *If $Z(s)$ is pr, $F(s)$, given by Eq. (3-97), is also pr.* The various transformations involved are illustrated in Fig. 3-19.

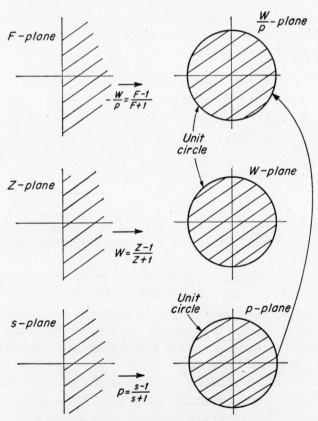

Fig. 3-19. Transformations of Richards' theorem.

Let us now check on the rank of $F(s)$. Suppose that $Z(s)$ is a minimum function of rank $2n$ [numerator and denominator of $Z(s)$ both of degree n]. Superficially, it looks as if the degree of the numerator of $F(s)$, as well as that of the denominator, will be $n + 1$, giving $2(n + 1)$ for the rank of F. However, the form of the numerator of $F(s)$ is the same as that of the right-hand side of Eq. (3-81), and hence the numerator has a zero in the right half plane. (We see by inspection that it occurs at $s = k$.) But we just showed that $F(s)$ is pr and cannot have any zeros in the right half plane. We conclude that the denominator of $F(s)$ must also have a zero at $s = k$ in order to cancel the zero of the numerator. This reduces the rank of $F(s)$ by at least 2, making the degree of the numerator, as well as that of the denominator, at most equal to n.

As a matter of fact, consideration of the rank of $F(s)$ and that of $Z(s)$ will permit us to complete the proof that the multiplicity of the right-half-plane zero of $Z(s) - Ks$ is exactly unity, for a $Z(s)$ which is regular at infinity and nonzero at $s = 0$. Let us invert Eq. (3-97) and solve for $Z(s)$. If we write $F(s)$ as the ratio of two polynomials with no common factors, $F(s) = P(s)/Q(s)$, we shall get

$$\frac{Z(s)}{Z(k)} = \frac{kF(s) + s}{k + sF(s)} = \frac{kP(s) + sQ(s)}{kQ(s) + sP(s)} \tag{3-99}$$

We have already established that the right-half-plane zero of the numerator of $F(s)$ cannot be double. Suppose it is triple. Then, since $F(s)$ is pr, this must be canceled by a triple zero of the denominator. Looking at Eq. (3-97), this means that $P(s)$ and $Q(s)$ will each be of degree $n - 2$. Consequently, according to the preceding equation, the numerator and denominator of $Z(s)$ will each be of degree $n - 1$, contrary to the assumption that they are each of degree n. This proves that a triple zero in the right half plane is impossible. Of course, a higher-order zero will be ruled out even more strongly by the same reasoning.

It may be well to point out that the rank of $F(s)$ need not be the same as that of $Z(s)$. From Eq. (3-99) we can see that the degree of $P(s)$ and $Q(s)$ can each be $n - 1$ and still give $Z(s)$ a rank of $2n$ as assumed. This is possible if, in addition to the simple positive real zero common to the numerator and denominator of Eq. (3-97), there is a common negative real zero as well. (See Prob. 3-24)

The Bott-Duffin realization technique, which we shall now discuss, starts in the same manner as the Brune realization. A given impedance function is first reduced to a minimum function by imaginary-part and real-part reduction, so that the real part is zero at a finite nonzero frequency ω_0. At this frequency the imaginary part is either positive or negative. To start with, consider the case $X > 0$, and write

$$Z(j\omega_0) = jX = j\omega_0 L_1, \qquad L_1 = X/\omega_0 \qquad (3\text{-}100)$$

At this point the procedure diverges from the Brune procedure. We turn to the pr function $F(s)$ in Eq. (3-97). If we invert it and solve for $Z(s)$:

$$Z(s) = \cfrac{1}{\cfrac{k}{Z(k)s} + \cfrac{F(s)}{Z(k)}} + \cfrac{1}{\cfrac{s}{kZ(k)} + \cfrac{1}{Z(k)F(s)}} \qquad (3\text{-}101)$$

As yet k is an arbitrary positive number. Let us choose k such that

$$Z(k) = kL_1 \qquad (3\text{-}102)$$

where L_1 is given in Eq. (3-100). This is possible, since we know that the function $Z(s) - L_1 s$ has a real positive zero, which we shall denote by k. With this substitution, Eq. (3-101) becomes

$$Z(s) = \frac{1}{1/L_1 s + 1/Z_1(s)} + \frac{1}{C_1 s + 1/Z_2(s)} \qquad (3\text{-}103)$$

where

$$Z_1(s) = \frac{kL_1}{F(s)}$$

$$Z_2(s) = kL_1 F(s) \qquad (3\text{-}104)$$

$$C_1 = \frac{1}{k^2 L_1}$$

The impedances Z_1 and Z_2 are seen to be inverse with respect to $k^2 L_1^2$. Returning to Eq. (3-97) and using Eq. (3-102), we see that, when $s = j\omega_0$, $F(s) = 0$. Hence $Z_1(s)$ will have a pole at $s = j\omega_0$, and $Z_2(s)$ will have a zero there, so that we can write

$$Z_1(s) = \frac{s/C_2}{s^2 + \omega_0^2} + Z_1'(s) \qquad (a)$$

$$\qquad\qquad\qquad\qquad\qquad\qquad (3\text{-}105)$$

$$Z_2(s) = \frac{1}{\dfrac{s/L_3}{s^2 + \omega_0^2} + \dfrac{1}{Z_2'(s)}} \qquad (b)$$

The realization of Eq. (3-103) now takes the form of Fig. 3-20. Note that $L_2 C_2 = L_3 C_3 = 1/\omega_0^2$.

Since $F(s)$ is of rank no higher than that of $Z(s)$, the functions Z_1 and Z_2 have this property also. The primed impedances then have a rank 4 less than that of the unprimed impedances. This completes one cycle of the Bott-Duffin procedure. The next step in the realization is to take each of the impedances Z_1' and Z_2' and repeat the synthesis procedure.

In the simple case of a biquadratic the Bott-Duffin realization will yield Fig. 3-20 with Z_1' and Z_2' replaced by resistances $R_1 = Z_1(\infty)$ and $R_2 = Z_1(0)$, respectively. You can see this by noting the behavior of the reactive elements at the two extreme frequencies.

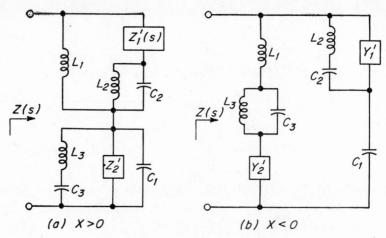

Fig. 3-20. Bott-Duffin realizations.

Let us now return to the case where the remaining reactance is negative, after the minimum resistance is removed. The susceptance will then be positive; so we can write

$$Y(j\omega_0) = -j\frac{1}{X} = j\omega_0 C_1$$

$$C_1 = -\frac{1}{\omega_0 X} > 0 \tag{3-106}$$

A completely analogous development is now carried out. Instead of Eq. (3-97) we write

$$F(s) = \frac{kY(s) - sY(k)}{kY(k) - sY(s)} \tag{3-107}$$

which is pr if $Y(s)$ is pr. The considerations of the rank of $F(s)$ are the same as before. Setting $Y(k) = kC_1$ and inverting the last equation, we get

$$Y(s) = \frac{1}{1/sC_1 + 1/Y_1(s)} + \frac{1}{sL + 1/Y_2(s)} \tag{3-108}$$

where
$$Y_1(s) = \frac{kC_1}{F(s)}$$

$$Y_2(s) = kC_1 F(s) \tag{3-109}$$

$$L_1 = \frac{1}{k^2 C_1}$$

The notation here might become a little confusing; note that there is no relationship between Y_1 and Y_2 in this development and Z_1 and Z_2 in the previous development.

We see that Y_1 and Y_2 are inverse with respect to $k^2 C_1^2$. Since $F(s)$ is zero at $s = j\omega_0$ according to Eq. (3-107), Y_1 will have a pole while Y_2 will have a zero there. Thus we can write

$$Y_1(s) = \frac{s/L_2}{s^2 + \omega_0^2} + Y_1'(s)$$

$$Y_2(s) = \cfrac{1}{\cfrac{s/C_2}{s^2 + \omega_0^2} + \cfrac{1}{Y_2'(s)}}$$

(3-110)

The realization of Eq. (3-108) takes the form of Fig. 3-20(b). The functions Y_1' and Y_2' are 4 less in rank than Y. The cycle is now repeated on these functions. In the case of the biquadratic function these two admittances reduce to $Y(\infty)$ and $Y(0)$ respectively. Again note that $L_2 C_2 = L_3 C_3 = 1/\omega_0^2$.

We have now established a significant fact. *Any positive real function can be realized as a driving-point immittance function without transformers.* In some cases this will take a ladder structure; in other, more complicated cases as described in this section, a nonladder structure will be required. It is apparent that this result is achieved at the expense of a large number of elements.

To acquire some insight on the structure of the Bott-Duffin realization, consider the network in Fig. 3-21. This is a bridge network with Z_0 con-

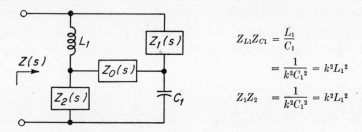

Fig. 3-21. Generalized Bott-Duffin realization.

stituting the detector arm. The conditions listed in the figure indicate that the bridge is balanced so that the voltage across Z_0 is zero. Hence the driving-point impedance $Z(s)$ will not be affected by Z_0. A glance at Eqs. (3-104) and (3-109) shows that the bridge balance conditions are satisfied by both Bott-Duffin realizations.[†] Figure 3-20(a) is obtained when Z_0 is short-circuited, while Fig. 3-20(b) is obtained when Z_0 is an open circuit. Any other intermediate value of Z_0 will also yield a realization for the given

† This was first pointed out by F. M. Reza (99).

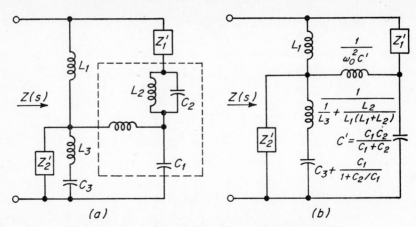

Fig. 3-22. Conversion of Bott-Duffin realization for $X > 0$.

driving-point impedance. Obviously we would not put additional elements in the detector arm if they did not serve a useful purpose.

We can use the flexibility discussed in the previous paragraph actually to reduce the number of elements in the Bott-Duffin realization as pointed out by Storer (125). To see how we can accomplish this, consider Fig. 3-22(a), which is a redrawing of Fig. 3-20(a), but with the short circuit in the detector arm replaced by an inductance L. The circuit inside the dotted lines can be replaced by a pi equivalent. This transformation will be physically realizable if the value of L is chosen so that the resonant frequency of L and C_1 is equal to the resonant frequency of L_2 and C_2 (2). The tee and its pi equivalent are shown in Fig. 3-23. We see that L_3' and

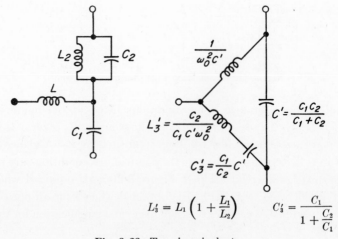

$$L_3' = L_1 \left(1 + \frac{L_1}{L_2} \right) \qquad C_3' = \frac{C_1}{1 + \dfrac{C_2}{C_1}}$$

Fig. 3-23. Tee-pi equivalents.

C_3' have a resonant frequency of ω_0. Because of this fact, when the tee is replaced by its equivalent pi in Fig. 3-22(a), the branches composed of L_3C_3 and $L_3'C_3'$ can be combined in parallel into a single branch with capacitance equal to the sum of C_3 and C_3' and inductance whose reciprocal is the sum of the reciprocals of L_3 and L_3'. The final network is shown in Fig. 3-22(b).

What we did was to add one element to the Bott-Duffin realization. Then we performed a tee-pi transformation which permitted us to combine four elements into two. The net result is a reduction of one element in the Bott-Duffin realization of Fig. 3-20(a).

A similar procedure can be followed in the case of the second Bott-Duffin realization shown in Fig. 3-24(a) (see Prob. 3-10). This leads to the realization of Fig. 3-24(b). These modifications of the Bott-Duffin realizations lead to an unbalanced bridge structure.

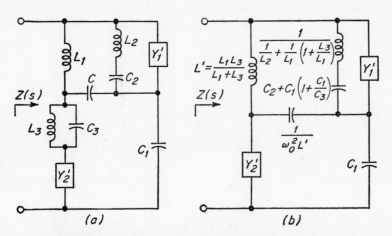

Fig. 3-24. Conversion of Bott-Duffin realization for $X < 0$.

To illustrate this procedure, let us obtain a Bott-Duffin realization for the following impedance function, which we have already realized by the Brune procedure in the last section:

$$Z(s) = \frac{s^3 + 2s^2 + s + 1}{s^3 + s^2 + 2s + 1} \qquad (3\text{-}111)$$

We found that this is a minimum function, the real part being zero at $\omega = 1$. We found the imaginary part to be $X = 1$ at this frequency, and hence $L_1 = 1$.

The first step in the Bott-Duffin procedure is to find the value of k by solving the equation $Z(k) = kL_1$. We get

$$\frac{k^3 + 2k^2 + k + 1}{k^3 + k^2 + 2k + 1} - k = \frac{1 - k^4}{k^3 + k^2 + 2k + 1} = 0$$

Hence
$$k = 1 \tag{3-112}$$

$$Z(k) = Z(1) = 1$$

Next we form the positive real function $F(s)$, using Eq. (3-97). Thus

$$F(s) = \frac{Z(s) - s}{1 - sZ(s)} = \frac{s^4 - 1}{s^4 + s^3 - s - 1} = \frac{(s^2 + 1)(s^2 - 1)}{(s^2 + s + 1)(s^2 - 1)}$$

$$= \frac{s^2 + 1}{s^2 + s + 1} \tag{3-113}$$

We find that the rank of $F(s)$ is less than that of the original function, owing to the cancellation of a left-half-plane zero as well as one in the right half plane.

The next step is to compute $Z_1(s)$ and $Z_2(s)$ from Eq. (3-104). We get

$$Z_1(s) = \frac{1}{F(s)} = \frac{s}{s^2 + 1} + 1 \tag{a}$$

$$\tag{3-114}$$

$$Z_2(s) = F(s) = \frac{1}{s/(s^2 + 1) + 1} \tag{b}$$

From these we compute the element values to be

$$C_2 = 1 \qquad\qquad L_3 = 1$$

$$L_2 = \frac{1}{C_2\omega_0^2} = 1 \qquad C_3 = \frac{1}{L_3\omega_0^2} = 1 \tag{3-115}$$

$$Z_1 = 1 \qquad\qquad Z_2 = 1$$

The complete realization is shown in Fig. 3-25(a). The modified realization

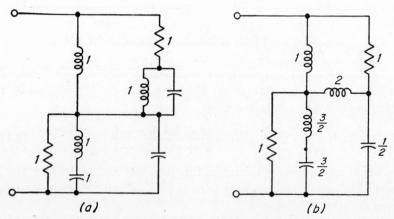

(a) (b)

Fig. 3-25. Bott-Duffin realization and storer modification of numerical example.

shown in part (b) of the figure is obtained by replacing the short circuit in the detector arm of the bridge by an inductance which resonates with C_1. A subsequent tee to pi transformation leads to the realization shown. The details are left for you.

Note that the modified Bott-Duffin realization has seven elements—the same number as the Brune realization. Although the Bott-Duffin synthesis leads to redundant elements in the synthesis of most impedance functions, it is not so wasteful in some cases, as in the present example.

3-6. Determination of a positive real function from its even part

We have now discussed two different realization techniques whereby an arbitrary positive real rational function can be realized as the driving-point function of a passive, bilateral, lumped network. Each of these procedures suffers from a disadvantage. In the Brune process perfectly coupled transformers are often required, while the Bott-Duffin realization requires a large number of elements. There is room for other realization techniques which do not require perfect transformers, yet involve fewer elements than the Bott-Duffin realization.

A contribution to this problem was made by Darlington, who showed that an arbitrary positive real function can be realized as a lossless two-port terminated in a resistance. However, this does not constitute a solution to the problem of realization of pr functions so much as it constitutes a reformulation of the problem in different terms. Thus the Darlington technique transforms the problem from the realization of a single pr function to the realization of a set of two-port open-circuit impedance parameters or short-circuit admittance parameters. We shall defer the discussion of the Darlington procedure to a later chapter after we have discussed synthesis of two-ports for prescribed z or y parameters.

Besides these general techniques, which apply to the synthesis of any positive real function, other procedures exist which will yield a realization for special classes of pr functions. The Foster and Cauer techniques fall into this catagory. Since the definition of a pr function is tied up so intimately with the real part, we should expect the properties of the real part of a pr function to affect in an essential way the realization of the function.

Given a pr function $Z(s)$, we can, of course, compute the real part according to Eq. (3-41). The question arises, Given a function which is to be the real part of a positive real function, is the pr function uniquely determined? To this we shall have to answer "no," because we know that to any pr function we can add a reactance function without affecting the real part. On the other hand, a pr function is an analytic function of s. As such, its real and imaginary parts are related uniquely through a pair of Hilbert transforms (57) or, in more popular terminology, through Bode's formulas (16), provided it has no poles on the $j\omega$ axis. Thus a given impedance real part will determine an imaginary part, and the two together will define a unique minimum reactance function. The trouble is that this is an extremely complicated procedure even if we can evaluate the required integrals.

Fortunately there are other (algebraic) methods for determining a pr function from its real part. More exactly, the pr function is determined from its *even part*, which is the analytic continuation of the real part evaluated at $s = j\omega$. One of these methods is due to Gewertz (51). Using the previously defined notation, we can write

$$Z(s) = \frac{m_1 + n_1}{m_2 + n_2} = \frac{a_0 + a_1 s + \ldots + a_n s^n}{b_0 + b_1 s + \ldots + b_n s^n} \qquad (3\text{-}116)$$

$$\text{Re } [Z(j\omega)] = U(\omega^2) = \frac{N(\omega^2)}{D(\omega^2)}$$

$$U(-s^2) = \frac{N(-s^2)}{D(-s^2)} = \frac{m_1 m_2 - n_1 n_2}{m_2^2 - n_2^2}$$

$$= \frac{A_0 + A_1 s^2 + \ldots + A_m s^{2m}}{B_0 + B_1 s^2 + \ldots + B_n s^{2n}} \qquad (3\text{-}117)$$

The function that is given is the ratio of the two polynomials in the last line. The degree of the numerator is at most equal to that of the denominator so that $m \leq n$.

Let us first examine the denominator polynomial,

$$D(-s^2) = (m_2 + n_2)(m_2 - n_2) \qquad (3\text{-}118)$$

Our job is to find the Hurwitz polynomial $m_2 + n_2$ from the given even polynomial $D(-s^2)$. Suppose s_0 is a zero of $m_2 + n_2$; that is, $m_2(s_0) + n_2(s_0) = 0$. Let us look at the polynomial $m_2 - n_2$ and evaluate it at $s = -s_0$. We shall find that

$$m_2(-s_0) - n_2(-s_0) = m_2(s_0) + n_2(s_0) = 0 \qquad (3\text{-}119)$$

because m_2 is an even polynomial, while n_2 is odd. The conclusion is that the zeros of $m_2 - n_2$ are the negatives of the zeros of $m_2 + n_2$.

The denominator polynomial $D(-s^2)$ is an even polynomial in s. In terms of s^2 the zeros of an even polynomial may be real and positive, real and negative, or complex. Typical zeros are shown in Fig. 3-26. A real positive s^2 zero will lead to two zeros in the s plane, one being positive, the other negative, both with the same magnitude. A real negative s^2

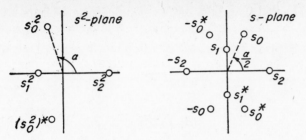

Fig. 3-26. Typical locations of zeros of an even polynomial.

zero will lead to a pair of conjugate imaginary zeros in the s plane. Finally a pair of complex conjugate s^2 zeros will lead to four zeros in the s plane symmetrically placed with respect to both the real axis and the imaginary axis. This type of configuration we shall refer to as *quadrantal symmetry* (82). With this terminology we can state that the zeros of an even polynomial occur in quadrantal symmetry.

In our present case, given $U(-s^2)$, we factor the denominator polynomial $D(-s^2)$. This will have no zeros on the $j\omega$ axis, and the other zeros will come in quadruplets of complex zeros or pairs of real zeros as in Fig. 3-26. Since $m_2 + n_2$ must be a Hurwitz polynomial, all its zeros must lie in the left half plane. Furthermore we showed that the zeros of $m_2 - n_2$ must lie in the right half plane. Hence all the zeros of $D(-s^2)$ which lie in the left half plane belong to $m_2 + n_2$. In this way half the problem of determining the impedance function in Eq. (3-116) is solved. It remains to find the a coefficients in that equation.

To do this, let us substitute the expressions for m_1, m_2, n_1, and n_2 in terms of the a and b coefficients into the expression $N(-s^2) = m_1m_2 - n_1n_2$. Comparing coefficients of this result with the given $N(-s^2)$ permits us to solve for the unknown coefficients. Thus

$$m_1m_2 - n_1n_2 = (a_0 + a_2s^2 + \ldots + a_ns^n)(b_0 + b_2s^2 + \ldots + b_ns^n)$$
$$- (a_1s + a_3s^3 + \ldots)(b_1s + b_3s^3 + \ldots)$$
$$= A_0 + A_1s^2 + \ldots + A_ns^{2n} \qquad (3\text{-}120)$$

$$A_0 = a_0b_0$$

$$A_1 = a_0b_2 + b_0a_2 - a_1b_1$$

$$A_2 = a_0b_4 + a_2b_2 + a_4b_0 - a_1b_3 - a_3b_1$$

. . . .

$$A_k = \sum_{j=-k}^{k} (-1)^{k+j} a_{k+j} b_{k-j} \qquad (3\text{-}121)$$

Equations (3-121) form a set of simultaneous linear equations in the a coefficients. They look formidable but are actually simple to solve. The a and b coefficients are zero for $k > n$. Thus, when $n = 3$, the equations reduce to

$$A_0 = a_0 b_0$$
$$A_1 = a_0 b_2 + b_0 a_2 - a_1 b_1$$
$$A_2 = a_2 b_2 - a_1 b_3 - a_3 b_1 \qquad (3\text{-}122)$$
$$A_3 = -a_3 b_3$$

The first and last give the solutions for a_0 and a_3 immediately. When these are substituted in the center two equations, only two unknowns are left. Similar simplification is achieved for higher-order functions as well.

Note that the impedance obtained by this procedure will be a minimum-reactance function. Any other function differing from this one by a sum of terms of the form $ks/(s^2 + \omega_i^2)$ will still have the same real part.

Bode has described an alternate method for determining $Z(s)$ from a given $\text{Re}\,[Z(j\omega)]$. This follows from the recognition that

$$\text{Re}\,[Z(j\omega)] = \tfrac{1}{2}\,[Z(s) + Z(-s)]_{s=j\omega}$$

so that
$$2U(-s^2) = Z(s) + Z(-s) \qquad (3\text{-}123)$$

Let us assume that $Z(s)$ is minimum-reactive since only such a function can be determined uniquely from the given $U(-s^2)$. The poles of $Z(s)$ are in the left half plane, while those of $Z(-s)$ are in the right. The function $U(-s^2)$ has both these sets of poles. Suppose we find the residues of both sides of Eq. (3-123) at the left-half-plane poles of $U(-s^2)$. The contribution to the residues of the right-hand side by $Z(-s)$ will be zero since it has no poles in the left half plane. Hence the residues of $Z(s)$ at its poles are twice the residues of $U(-s^2)$ at its left-half-plane poles. Furthermore, since $Z(s)$ is minimum-reactive, both $Z(s)$ and $Z(-s)$ approach a constant R_∞ as $s \to \infty$ (this may be zero). Thus the partial-fraction expansion of $Z(s)$ is completely determined.

In both the Gewertz and the Bode methods it is necessary to find the poles of $U(-s^2)$ so that neither method has a computational advantage in this respect. Bode's method involves computation of residues, and these will ordinarily be complex, whereas the solution of Eq. (3-121) involves real numbers only.

Although we have used the impedance $Z(s)$ in this development, the same thing holds true for an admittance function. We merely have to interchange the symbols Z and Y and use the term minimum-susceptance instead of minimum-reactance.

We have now demonstrated that starting with an even rational function of s with no poles on the $j\omega$ axis, including infinity, we can determine a unique minimum-imaginary-part positive real function whose even part is equal to the given rational function.

3-7. Miyata realization of a positive real function

Let us now consider positive real functions whose real parts have special properties. We shall exclude poles on the $j\omega$ axis for reasons discussed earlier. In particular we should like to obtain realizations for functions whose even parts have zeros at infinity or zero, or both. Let us consider an impedance function $Z(s)$ and write

$$Z(s) = \frac{m_1 + n_1}{m_2 + n_2}$$

$$= \frac{a_n s^n + a_{n-1}s^{n-1} + a_{n-2}s^{n-2} + \ldots + a_1s + a_0}{s^n + b_{n-1}s^{n-1} + \ldots + b_1s + b_0} \qquad (3\text{-}124)$$

with the stipulation that $b_0 \neq 0$ in order to avoid a pole at the origin. On the other hand, either a_n or a_0, or both, may be zero, leading to a zero at infinity or at the origin, or both, respectively. For the even part of $Z(s)$ we can write

$$U(-s^2) = \frac{N(-s^2)}{D(-s^2)} = \frac{A_n s^{2n} + A_{n-1}s^{2(n-1)} + \ldots A_1s^2 + A_0}{m_2^2 - n_2^2} \qquad (3\text{-}125)$$

where

$$A_n = a_n$$

$$A_{n-1} = a_{n-2} + a_n b_{n-2} - a_{n-1}b_{n-1}$$

$$\cdot \; \cdot \; \cdot \; \cdot \; \cdot \; \cdot \; \cdot \; \cdot \; \cdot \; \cdot \; \cdot \; \cdot \; \cdot \; \cdot \; \cdot \; \cdot \qquad (3\text{-}126)$$

$$A_1 = a_2 b_0 + b_2 a_0 - a_1 b_1$$

$$A_0 = a_0 b_0$$

We have assumed that n is even; if it is odd, the sign of $N(-s^2)$ will be reversed. The denominator of $U(-s^2)$ is of the $2n$th degree. If neither a_0 nor a_n is zero, $U(-s^2)$ will have no zero at zero or infinity.

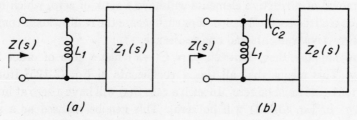

(a)   *(b)*

Fig. 3-27. Partial realization for real part zeros at the origin.

Suppose $N(-s^2)$ has a zero of order $2k$ at $s = 0$. This will require all the A coefficients from A_0 up to A_{k-1} to vanish, and $N(-s^2)$ will have a factor $(-s^2)^k$. Hence a_0 also will vanish, and $Z(s)$ will have a zero at $s = 0$. Its reciprocal will have a pole there, which can be realized as a shunt inductance $L_1 = b_0/a_1$, as shown in Fig. 3-27(a). The remaining admittance function will not have a pole at $s = 0$. We can write

$$Y_1(s) = \frac{m_2 + n_2}{m_1 + n_1} - \frac{1}{sL_1} = \frac{\frac{1}{s}\left(n_2 - \frac{m_1}{sL_1}\right) + \frac{1}{s}\left(m_2 - \frac{n_1}{sL_1}\right)}{(1/s)(n_1 + m_1)} \tag{3-127}$$

Since $Y_1(s)$ should have no pole at $s = 0$, we have divided numerator and denominator of the right side by s in order to cancel out the factor s which is contained in $m_1 + n_1$. This gives the last form of Eq. (3-127). The even part of $Y_1(s)$ can now be calculated as

$$U_1(-s^2) = \frac{\frac{n_1}{s^2}\left(n_2 - \frac{m_1}{sL_1}\right) - \frac{m_1}{s^2}\left(m_2 - \frac{n_1}{sL_1}\right)}{(1/s^2)(n_1^2 - m_1^2)} = \frac{\frac{N(-s^2)}{-s^2}}{(m_1^2 - n_1^2)/(-s^2)}$$

or

$$N_1(-s^2) = \frac{N(-s^2)}{-s^2} \tag{3-128}$$

We see that the even part of the remaining admittance function has lost a factor $(-s^2)$ by the removal of the shunt inductance L_1, and the rank of $Y_1(s)$ (which is the same as that of Z_1) is two less than that of $Z(s)$. $N_1(-s^2)$ now has a factor $(-s^2)^{k-1}$ so that $Y_1(s)$ also has a zero at $s = 0$. Its reciprocal has a pole there, and this can be realized as a series capacitance as shown in Fig. 3-27(b). By repeating the previous steps we shall see that the remaining impedance $Z_2(s)$ will have a rank two less than $Z_1(s)$, and its even part will have a factor $(-s^2)^{k-2}$. Thus we can continue in this fashion, alternately removing shunt inductance and series capacitance until, after removing k reactive elements, we arrive at a remainder $Z_k(s)$ whose even part does not have a zero at $s = 0$ and whose rank is $2(n - k)$. If $k = n$, that is to say, if $N(-s^2) = s^{2n}$, so that all zeros of the real part of the original impedance are at $s = 0$, then the remaining function after the removal of n reactive elements will have a rank of zero, which means it can be realized as a resistance. For such a case the realization is complete with n reactive elements and one resistance.

Now suppose that the even part $U(-s^2)$ has a zero of order $2k$ at infinity. This means that all the A coefficients in Eq. (3-125) from A_n down to A_{n-k+1} must be zero. In such a case $Z(s)$ will have a zero at infinity [since a_n in Eq. (3-124) will be zero]. This can be realized as a shunt capacitance. We can actually carry out steps similar to Eqs. (3-127) and

(3-128) to show that the even part of the remaining admittance will have a zero at infinity of multiplicity two less than that of $U(-s^2)$. Alternatively we can use the transformation $p = 1/s$, which transforms infinity into the origin, and thus reduce the present problem to the previous case. By either procedure we can alternately remove shunt capacitance and series inductance until we have removed k reactive elements. The details of the procedure are left for you as an exercise.

Note that, when $Z(s)$ in Eq. (3-124) has a zero at infinity, its rank will be odd. If, after reduction, we are to have a remainder function with no zero or pole at infinity, its rank must be even. Thus, when the last reactive element is removed, the rank of the remaining function must be reduced by only unity from that of the immediately preceding function. Thus, starting with $Z(s)$ of rank $2n - 1$, we shall terminate with Z_k of rank of $2(n - k)$. In particular, for $k = n$, that is, when all the zeros of $U(-s^2)$ are at infinity, the rank of Z_n will be zero, corresponding to a resistance. Again the complete realization will consist of n reactive elements and a single resistance.

Finally the even part may have a combination of these properties; i.e., it may have a zero of order $2k$ at $s = 0$ and a zero of order $2j$ at infinity. If $k + j = n$, which means that the even part has no other zeros, then again the complete realization will consist of n reactive elements and a single resistance. However, now k of these elements will consist of shunt inductance and series capacitance, while the rest will be shunt capacitance and series inductance.

We shall now discuss a realization procedure due to Miyata which utilizes the properties discussed above. The realization procedure is not general, in that it applies only to a restricted class of positive real functions. We shall be able to see what the restrictions are after we discuss the procedure.

Consider the impedance function $Z(s)$ given in Eq. (3-117) with the even part given in Eq. (3-118). Let us rewrite this last equation as follows:

$$U(-s^2) = \frac{A_n s^{2n}}{D(-s^2)} + \frac{A_{n-1} s^{2(n-1)}}{D(-s^2)} + \cdots + \frac{A_1 s^2}{D(-s^2)} + \frac{A_0}{D(-s^2)}$$

$$= U_n(-s^2) + U_{n-1}(-s^2) + \cdots + U_1(-s^2) + U_0(-s^2) \qquad (3\text{-}129)$$

The even parts $U_k(-s^2)$ have the property that all their zeros are at zero or infinity. If the coefficients A_k have the correct sign, then each of the quantities U_k will be positive for all values of $s = j\omega$. Consequently each of the even parts will correspond to an impedance which can be realized as a network containing n reactive elements plus a resistance, according to the previous discussion. The series connection of these networks will give a realization for the original $Z(s)$. For $U_k(\omega^2)$ to be nonnegative for all values of ω, we require

$$A_k s^{2k}\big|_{s=j\omega} = (-1)^k A_k \omega^{2k}$$

to be nonnegative. This means that all the A coefficients with odd subscript must be negative and those with even subscript positive. More concisely $(-1)^k A_k \geq 0$. This, then, is the essential restriction on the realization procedure. We shall refer to pr functions which satisfy the condition as belonging to the *Miyata class*. At the end of this section we shall discuss an interpretation of this restriction in terms of the permissible locations of the roots of $N(-s^2)$.

Let us now return to the realization technique. We already know how to find the impedance functions $Z_k(s)$ from the even parts $U_k(-s^2)$; we can do this by either the Gewertz or the Bode procedure. However, the work of carrying out this process for each of the component impedances will prove tedious. We notice that the denominators of all the component even parts are the same. Miyata developed a scheme which will permit using the Gewertz procedure, say, only once in finding all the component impedances. We proceed as follows:

The starting point is a minimum-reactance minimum-susceptance positive real function. (If there are originally any poles or zeros on the $j\omega$ axis, these can be realized by reactive structures.) We now form the even part as in Eq. (3-129). We next consider the even function

$$U_a(-s^2) = \frac{1}{D(-s^2)} = \frac{1}{m_2^2 - n_2^2} \tag{3-130}$$

where $m_2 + n_2$ is the denominator of the given function $Z(s)$, and, using the Gewertz or Bode procedure, form from this the positive real function

$$Z_a = \frac{m_1' + n_1'}{m_2 + n_2} \tag{3-131}$$

which has the previous function as its even part. This has the same denominator as the original function but a different numerator. Now we form the functions

$$F_k(s) = \frac{N_k(-s^2)(m_1' + n_1')}{m_2 + n_2} \tag{3-132}$$

where $N_k(-s^2)$ is the numerator of the kth term in Eq. (3-129). These functions will not be positive real (except for $k = 0$ since N_0 is just a constant) because the numerators will exceed the denominators in degree by more than unity. However, the even part of $F_k(s)$ is $U_k(-s^2)$, as you can easily verify. Let us now divide the denominator into the numerator by long division, stopping when the numerator no longer exceeds the denominator in degree. The result will be a polynomial $Q_k(s)$ plus a rational function. Thus

$$F_k(s) = Q_k(s) + Z_k(s) \tag{3-133}$$

$$U_k(-s^2) = \text{even part of } Q_k + \text{even part of } Z_k(s) \tag{3-134}$$

The even part of the polynomial $Q_k(s)$ will consist of the sum of all the even powers of s. If there are even powers of s in Q_k, then the right side of the last equation will become infinite as $s \to \infty$, whereas the left side we know does not. We conclude that $Q_k(s)$ contains no even powers of s, and hence has no even part. Therefore

$$\text{Even part of } Z_k(s) = U_k(-s^2) \tag{3-135}$$

Furthermore the poles of $Z_k(s)$ are the same as the poles of the given pr function and so are in the left half plane. Hence $Z_k(s)$ is a positive real function.

The job is now complete. We have been able to obtain a positive real function for each of the component even parts in Eq. (3-129), using the Gewertz or Bode procedure only once.

Let us illustrate the procedure with an example. We require a Miyata realization for the impedance function

$$Z(s) = \frac{s^2 + 7s/3 + 2}{s^2 + 3s + 3} \tag{a}$$

$$U(-s^2) = \frac{s^4 - 2s^2 + 6}{s^4 - 3s^2 + 9} \tag{b}$$

$$\tag{3-136}$$

We first have to check the coefficients in the numerator of $U(-s^2)$. We find that they satisfy the required condition. Next we construct the pr function $Z_a(s)$, which has as its even part

$$U_a(-s^2) = \frac{1}{s^4 - 3s^2 + 9} \tag{3-137}$$

Using the Gewertz procedure, we find

$$Z_a(s) = \frac{1}{9} \frac{s + 3}{s^2 + 3s + 3} \tag{3-138}$$

Finally, using this expression in Eq. (3-132), we get

$$F_0(s) = \frac{6 \cdot \frac{1}{9}(s+3)}{s^2 + 3s + 3} = \frac{\frac{2}{3}s + 2}{s^2 + 3s + 3} \tag{a}$$

$$F_1(s) = \frac{-2s^2 \cdot \frac{1}{9}(s+3)}{s^2 + 3s + 3} = -\frac{2}{9}s + \frac{\frac{2}{3}s}{s^2 + 3s + 3} \tag{b} \quad (3\text{-}139)$$

$$F_2(s) = \frac{s^4 \cdot \frac{1}{9}(s+3)}{s^2 + 3s + 3} = \frac{1}{9}s^3 - \frac{1}{3}s + \frac{s^2 + s}{s^2 + 3s + 3} \tag{c}$$

so that the three component impedances are

$$Z_0(s) = \frac{\frac{2}{3}s + 2}{s^2 + 3s + 3} \tag{a}$$

$$Z_1(s) = \frac{\frac{2}{3}s}{s^2 + 3s + 3} \tag{b} \quad (3\text{-}140)$$

$$Z_2(s) = \frac{s^2 + s}{s^2 + 3s + 3} \tag{c}$$

These can now be realized by carrying out a continued-fraction expansion. The complete realization of $Z(s)$ as the series connection of the three component networks is shown in Fig. 3-28(a).

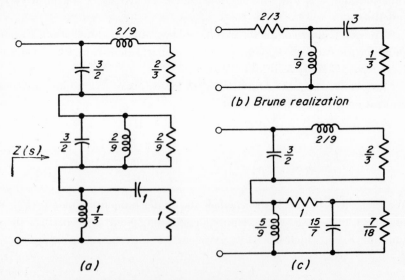

(b) Brune realization

(a)   (c)

Fig. 3-28. Miyata realization compared with Brune realization.

The impedance used in this particular example could have been realized more simply, as shown in Fig. 3-28(b), so that the Miyata method was not really necessary. However, the example points up a feature of the Miyata realization, viz., the excessive number of elements required. This is due to the number of components into which the given even part is decomposed.

If we could decompose the even part into a smaller number of components, while maintaining the pr character of each part, this would help reduce the number of elements required. The question is one of decomposing an even polynomial in ω whose coefficients are all positive into a small number of even polynomials whose coefficients are also all positive, but which are of reduced degree or contain powers of ω^2 as factors, or both. Many types of such decompositions are possible, a number of which have been discussed by Kuh (73). We shall illustrate one possible breakdown with the numerical example just used. Instead of decomposing the numerator of Eq. (3-136, b) into three terms, let us break it into two terms, keeping the constant term as N_0 and combining the other two terms into N_1. Thus

$$U(-s^2) = \frac{s^4 - 2s^2 + 6}{s^4 - 3s^2 + 9} = \frac{s^2(s^2 - 2)}{s^4 - 3s^2 + 9} + \frac{6}{s^4 - 3s^2 + 9} \quad \text{(a)}$$

$$U_0 = \frac{6}{s^4 - 3s^2 + 9} \quad \text{(b)} \quad \text{(3-141)}$$

$$U_1 = \frac{-s^2(2 - s^2)}{s^4 - 3s^2 + 9} \quad \text{(c)}$$

The same procedure is followed as before for computing the impedances of which these are the even parts. Of course, Z_0 is the same as before. To compute Z_1, we write

$$F_1(s) = (s^4 - 2s^2)Z_a(s) = \frac{s^4 - 2s^2}{9} \frac{s + 3}{s^2 + 3s + 3}$$

$$= \frac{s^3}{9} - \frac{5s}{9} + \frac{s^2 + 5s/3}{s^2 + 3s + 3} \quad \text{(3-142)}$$

Hence
$$Z_1(s) = \frac{s^2 + 5s/3}{s^2 + 3s + 3} = \frac{1}{\dfrac{9}{5s} + \dfrac{s + \frac{6}{5}}{s + \frac{5}{3}}} \quad \text{(3-143)}$$

Since $U_1(-s^2)$ has a factor $-s^2$, we can remove a shunt inductance. According to Eq. (3-128), the numerator of the even part of the remaining function will be the same as the numerator of U_1, but with the factor $-s^2$ missing. This is easily verified in the present simple example. In fact $Z_1(s)$ is readily expanded in a continued-fraction expansion to give

$$Z_1(s) = \frac{s^2 + 5s/3}{s^2 + 3s + 3} = \frac{1}{\dfrac{9}{5s} + \dfrac{1}{1 + \dfrac{1}{\dfrac{15s}{7} + \dfrac{18}{7}}}} \quad \text{(3-144)}$$

The complete realization is shown in Fig. 3-28(c). This realization saves two reactive elements when compared with the first Miyata realization.

This example illustrates a general procedure for pr functions of the Miyata class. Instead of decomposing the even part of a given positive real function into a number of terms equal to the number of terms in the numerator, as in Eq. (3-129), we decompose it into two terms as follows:

$$U(-s^2) = \frac{A_0 + A_1 s^2 + \ldots + A_k s^{2k}}{D(-s^2)} + \frac{A_{k+1} s^{2(k+1)} + \ldots + A_n s^{2n}}{D(-s^2)} \quad (3\text{-}145)$$

Let us assume that $A_0 \neq 0$ and $A_n \neq 0$. Then the first term in this equation will have a $2(n - k)$th-order zero at infinity, while the second term will have a $2(k + 1)$th-order zero at $s = 0$. Hence, according to the discussion at the beginning of this section, a realization of the form shown in Fig. 3-29 will be obtained. The first ladder will have $n - k$ reactive ele-

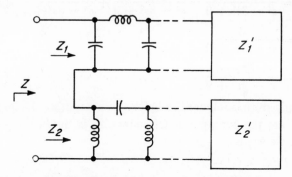

Fig. 3-29. Modified Miyata realization.

ments and a remaining function whose rank is $2k$ (recall that the rank of the original function is $2n$). Furthermore the numerator of the even part of the remaining function will not be changed. Similarly the second ladder will have $k + 1$ reactive elements. The remaining function will have a rank $2n - 2(k + 1)$, and the numerator of its even part will be the same as that of the second term in Eq. (3-145) except for the factor $s^{2(k+1)}$.

At this stage the remaining functions may be simple enough so that they can be easily realized. This was true in the numerical example. If the remaining functions are still of high order, we can repeat the same procedure. You can appreciate that the resulting structure will have the form of a tree.

In special cases other decomposition schemes may lead to alternative realizations. Some of these are suggested as problems at the end of the chapter.

Let us now turn to a consideration of the restriction on the signs of the coefficients of $N(-s^2)$. For simplicity of statement we can say that the signs of all the coefficients of $N(\omega^2)$ must be positive. It is clear that the co-efficients of a polynomial are dependent on the locations of the zeros of the polynomial. We know, for example, that the coefficients of a Hurwitz polynomial are all positive. Thus left-half-plane zeros are a sufficient condition for a polynomial to have positive coefficients. But this is not a necessary condition; polynomials may have zeros in the right half plane and still have positive coefficients.

The following theorem gives a necessary and sufficient condition (78). *If a polynomial $P(z)$ of degree n has no negative coefficients, it will have no zeros in the sector bounded by rays emanating from the origin and making*

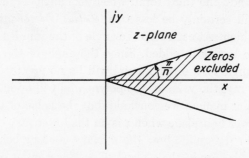

Fig. 3-30. Forbidden region for zeros of a polynomial with positive coefficients.

angles $\pm\pi/n$ with the positive real axis. Figure 3-30 shows the excluded region. The proof of the theorem is relatively easy. Let us write

$$P(z) = a_0 + a_1 z + a_2 z^2 + \ldots + a_n z^n \qquad (3\text{-}146)$$

Consider the closed contour in the z plane formed by the two rays and a circular arc at an arbitrary radius r as shown in Fig. 3-31. Suppose we

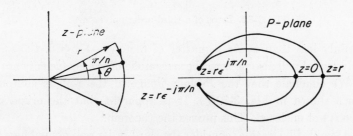

Fig. 3-31. Polynomial mapping of a z plane contour onto a P plane.

traverse the contour in a clockwise direction, starting at the origin. According to the Principle of the Argument the number of times the P-plane image of this contour encircles the origin is equal to the number of zeros of the polynomial enclosed by the contour (since there are no poles). At all points on the ray in the first quadrant the angle of z is constant at π/n. Each term in the polynomial will thus have an angle less than π (except the last term, which will have an angle of exactly π). Hence the angle of the sum of all the terms will never exceed π. This is most easily shown in the following way: At a fixed value of z suppose we add the first two terms of the polynomial. The first term has an angle zero, while the second one has an angle π/n. The sum will have an angle somewhere between zero and π/n depending on the magnitude of z and the relative size of the coefficients. To this sum we add the third term, which has angle $2\pi/n$. The angle of the resultant will certainly be less than $2\pi/n$. We continue adding the terms in this fashion. At each step the angle of the sum is no greater than the angle of the last term added. Since the angle of the highest power term is π, the angle of the polynomial will be no greater than π. Thus, along the upper ray, the value of the polynomial will lie in the upper half plane. In a similar manner we conclude that the value of the polynomial will lie in the lower half plane when z is on the lower ray.

We must now determine how the P-plane contour behaves when we traverse the circular arc in the z plane. Consider a point on the arc with polar coordinates $re^{j\theta}$ with $0 \le \theta < \pi/n$. By the same reasoning we employed before the angle of the polynomial will be no greater than $n\theta$, which

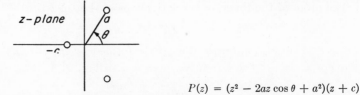

$$P(z) = (z^2 - 2az \cos \theta + a^2)(z + c)$$

Fig. 3-32. Zeros of a third-order polynomial.

is certainly less than π. As a matter of fact, when $\theta = 0$, the angle of the polynomial will also be zero (because none of the coefficients are negative). We conclude that the P-plane image of the z-plane contour has the form shown in Fig. 3-30(b). It is apparent that the origin of the P plane is not enclosed. This proves the theorem.

As a simple illustration, consider the third-order polynomial having the zeros shown in Fig. 3-32. It is

$$\begin{aligned} P(z) &= (z^2 - 2az \cos \theta + a^2)(z + c) \\ &= z^3 + (c - 2a \cos \theta)z^2 + (a^2 - 2ac \cos \theta)z + ca^2 \end{aligned} \quad (3\text{-}147)$$

To ensure that none of the coefficients will be negative, we must satisfy the condition

$$2a \cos \theta \leq c \leq \frac{a}{2 \cos \theta} \qquad (3\text{-}148)$$

Thus c must fall within the range indicated. For this range to exist, the right-hand extreme must certainly be no less than the left-hand extreme. Or

$$\frac{a}{2 \cos \theta} \geq 2a \cos \theta$$

$$\cos \theta \leq \tfrac{1}{2}$$

$$\theta \geq \frac{\pi}{3} \qquad (3\text{-}149)$$

which is in agreement with the theorem.

Let us now return to the problem of determining the implications of requiring positive coefficients for $N(\omega^2)$. Let us make the transformation $s^2 = -z$, where $z = x + jy$. This reduces to $\omega^2 = x$ when $s = j\omega$. The two planes are shown in Fig. 3-33. The left-half z plane maps into the shaded

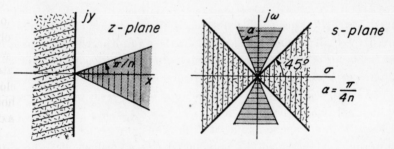

Fig. 3-33. The transformation $s^2 = -z$.

wedges between the two 45° lines in the s plane. If all the zeros of $N(-s^2)$ fall in this region, when we make the transformation $-s^2 = z$, all the zeros of $N(z)$ will fall in the left-half z plane. Hence all the coefficients of $N(z)$ will be positive, which, in turn, means that all the coefficients of $N(\omega^2)$ will be positive. Thus, location of the zeros of $N(-s^2)$ in the region described is a sufficient condition for positive coefficients of $N(\omega^2)$, but it is not necessary.

The region in the z plane from which zeros of $N(z)$ are excluded if the coefficients are to be positive maps into the wedge-shaped region in the s plane centered on the $j\omega$ axis and bounded by lines making an angle $\alpha = \pi/2n$ with the $j\omega$ axis. Thus, if $N(\omega^2)$ is of degree $2n$ in ω and all the coefficients are positive, then the zeros of $N(-s^2)$ cannot lie in this wedge of total angle $2\alpha = \pi/n$. It follows that it is possible for $N(-s^2)$ to have some zeros in the unshaded part of the plane while all the coefficients of $N(\omega^2)$ are still positive.

This discussion points up the fact that the applicability of the Miyata synthesis procedure is dependent on the locations in the s plane of the zeros of the even part of the positive real function.

Now suppose that initially not all the coefficients of $N(\omega^2)$ are positive. We should like to perform some operation which makes all the coefficients positive, while at the same time it does not affect the real part. As a matter of fact we have already seen an example of how this can be done. Glance back at Eq. (3-147) and Fig. 3-32. Suppose we consider the quadratic factor to be the polynomial under consideration. It has a negative coefficient. If the right-half-plane zeros are suitably located, we can find a factor $z + c$ by which the given polynomial can be multiplied such that the resulting polynomial has only positive coefficients. This is an example of a more general theorem, which can be stated as follows:

Let $N(z)$ be a polynomial with real coefficients which has no zeros on the positive real axis. Then there exists a polynomial $P(z)$ all of whose zeros lie on the negative real axis and are distinct, such that the polynomial $N(z) \cdot P(z)$ has coefficients that are all positive. This theorem was proved by Fialkow and Gerst (45). In their proof it was demonstrated that the order of the necessary polynomial $P(z)$ will depend on how close the zeros of $N(z)$ are to the positive real axis; the order increases without limit as a zero of $N(z)$ approaches closer and closer to the positive real axis. We shall not repeat the proof here.

This theorem can be applied to the even polynomial $N(-s^2)$ by the transformation $-s^2 = z$. The polynomial $P(-s^2)$, which corresponds to $P(z)$, will have factors of the form $a_j^2 - s^2$, which becomes $a_j^2 + \omega^2$ for $s = j\omega$.

Let us now apply this theorem to our problem. We shall assume that the given function $Z(s)$ is not a minimum function so that the real part has no zeros on the finite $j\omega$ axis. Suppose some of the coefficients in the numerator of the real part are negative. That is, $N(\omega^2)$ has some negative coefficients. We multiply numerator and denominator of $U(\omega^2)$ by factors $\omega^2 + a_j^2$, with suitably chosen values of a_j, until the numerator no longer has any negative coefficients. The Miyata procedure can now be applied. To be practically useful, of course, the number of factors needed should be small; otherwise the complexity of the resulting network will be intolerable.

In terms of s the multiplying factors are $a_j^2 - s^2 = (a_j - s)(a_j + s)$. Let us see what effect these factors have on the impedance function. To be specific, let us consider a single factor $a_0^2 - s^2$.

$$U(-s^2) = \frac{N(-s^2)}{m_2^2 - n_2^2} \frac{a_0^2 - s^2}{a_0^2 - s^2}$$

$$= \frac{N(-s^2)(a_0^2 - s^2)}{[(m_2 + n_2)(a_0 + s)][(m_2 - n_2)(a_0 - s)]} \qquad (3\text{-}150)$$

From the last form it is apparent that $m_2 + n_2$, the denominator of $Z(s)$, is multiplied by the factor $s + a_0$. The numerator of $Z(s)$ must be multiplied by this factor, as well, in order to maintain the same $Z(s)$. Factors such as this are called *surplus factors*. They have no effect on the impedance function but provide additional realization techniques which would not otherwise be possible.

To generalize this result, let us multiply the numerator and denominator of $Z(s)$ by the surplus Hurwitz polynomial $m_0 + n_0$.

$$Z(s) = \frac{m_1 + n_1}{m_2 + n_2} \frac{m_0 + n_0}{m_0 + n_0} = \frac{(m_1 m_0 + n_1 n_0) + (n_1 m_0 + n_0 m_1)}{(m_2 m_0 + n_2 n_0) + (n_2 m_0 + n_0 m_2)} \qquad (3\text{-}151)$$

When we compute the even part, we get

$$U(-s^2) = \frac{(m_1 m_2 - n_1 n_2)(m_0^2 - n_0^2)}{(m_2^2 - n_2^2)(m_0^2 - n_0^2)} \qquad (3\text{-}152)$$

Thus the numerator and denominator of the even part are multiplied by $m_0^2 - n_0^2$.

Now we consider the reverse procedure. In order to convert a given pr function into a function of the Miyata class, we multiply the numerator and denominator of the even part by surplus factors of the form $a_j^2 - s^2$. All these factors taken together constitute a surplus polynomial which we can label $m_0^2 - n_0^2$. The surplus polynomial by which the pr function itself must be multiplied, in order that its even part be multiplied by $m_0^2 - n_0^2$, is the polynomial $m_0 + n_0$, which is formed from all the left-half-plane zeros of $m_0^2 - n_0^2$.

As an example of the use of surplus factors, consider the impedance function

$$Z(s) = \frac{2s^2 + 3s + 3}{s^2 + 3s + 4} \qquad (a)$$

$$N(\omega^2) = 2\omega^4 - 2\omega^2 + 12 \qquad (b) \qquad (3\text{-}153)$$

We see that one of the coefficients of $N(\omega^2)$ is negative so that the Miyata procedure cannot be applied directly. Hence we multiply $Z(s)$ by surplus factors. The polynomial $N(z)$ (with $z = -s^2$) is a quadratic whose roots make an angle of 78.2° with the positive real axis. This is quite far from the axis, and we would anticipate the need of very few surplus factors. Suppose we try a single factor. Let us multiply $N(\omega^2)$ by $\omega^2 + a^2$. Then

$$N_1(\omega^2) = (\omega^2 + a^2)N(\omega^2)$$

$$= 2\omega^6 + 2(a^2 - 1)\omega^4 + 2(6 - a^2)\omega^2 + 12a^2 \quad (3\text{-}154)$$

For all the coefficients to be positive we must have

$$1 \leq a^2 \leq 6 \quad (3\text{-}155)$$

Choosing either one of the extreme values of a^2 will make one of the coefficients vanish, thus requiring fewer component impedances in the Miyata realization. Thus, with $a^2 = 1$, we shall have

$$N_1(\omega^2) = 2\omega^6 + 10\omega^2 + 12 \quad (3\text{-}156)$$

The numerator and denominator of $Z(s)$ must be multiplied by the factor $(s + \sqrt{1})$ so that $Z(s)$ becomes

$$Z(s) = \frac{2s^3 + 5s^2 + 6s + 3}{s^3 + 4s^2 + 7s + 4} \quad (3\text{-}157)$$

The Miyata procedure can now be carried out and will lead to three ladder networks connected in series. This is left for you as an exercise.

PROBLEMS

3-1. Let $Z_1(s)$ and $Z_2(s)$ be positive real functions.
(a) Prove that $Z_1[Z_2(s)]$ is pr.
(b) Based on part (a), prove that $1/Z(s)$ is pr if $Z(s)$ is pr.
(c) Based on part (a), prove that $Z(1/s)$ is pr if $Z(s)$ is pr.

3-2. Test the following functions for positive realness:

(a) $Z(s) = \dfrac{s^2 + s + 1}{s^2 + s + 4}$

(b) $Z(s) = \dfrac{s^2 + s + 1}{s^2 + s + 2}$

(c) $Z(s) = \dfrac{22s^2 + 46s + 45}{44s^2 + 48s + 54}$

(d) $Z(s) = \dfrac{s^2 + s + 1}{s^3 + s^2 + 2s + 1}$

(e) $Z(s) = \dfrac{4s^3 + 8s^2 + 19s + 16}{16s^3 + 28s^2 + 32s + 12}$

(f) $Z(s) = \dfrac{s^4 + s^3 + 3s^2 + 2s + 1}{s^3 + s^2 + 2s + 1}$

(g) $Z(s) = \dfrac{s^4 + 3s^3 + 4s^2 + 3s + 1}{s^4 + 7s^3 + 6s^2 + 4s + 1}$

(h) $Z(s) = \dfrac{s^4 + 2s^3 + 3s^2 + s + 1}{s^4 + s^3 + 3s^2 + 2s + 1}$

(i) $Z(s) = \dfrac{2s^4 + 5s^3 + 6s^2 + 3s + 1}{2s^4 + 4s^3 + 7s^2 + 7s + 3}$

3-3. The following are "minimum" functions. Obtain a Brune and a Bott-Duffin realization:

(a) $Z(s) = \dfrac{2s^2 + s + 1}{2s^2 + 2s + 4}$

(b) $Z(s) = \dfrac{s^2 + s + 2}{2s^2 + s + 1}$

(c) $Z(s) = \dfrac{4s^2 + s + 1}{s^2 + s + 1}$

3-4. Synthesize the positive real functions in Prob. 3-2 by the Brune method.

3-5. Synthesize the positive real functions of Prob. 3-2 by the Bott-Duffin method. Reduce the number of elements by means of the Storer transformation.

3-6. Synthesize the following driving-point impedance function by Brune's method. Start the Brune cycle on the function as it stands without removing the pole at infinity. Find the coefficient of coupling of the transformer in the realization. Comment on the generality of this result.

$$Z(s) = \frac{s^3 + 5s^2 + 2s + 1}{s^2 + s + 1}$$

3-7. Prove that the conditions given in Eqs. (3-26) are sufficient for $Z(s)$ to be positive real.

3-8. Let $Z(s) = (m_1 + n_1)/(m_2 + n_2)$ be a positive real function. Prove that

$$P(s) = m_1 + K_1 n_1 + K_2 m_2 + K_3 n_2$$

is a Hurwitz polynomial, where the K's are positive constants.

3-9. After the removal of the minimum real part in the Brune process, suppose the remaining reactance is positive. Proceed on an admittance basis, and obtain the realization shown in Fig. P 3-9. From a consideration of the z-system parameters of the reactive network inside the dotted lines, show that this is equivalent to the Brune network of Fig. 3-16.

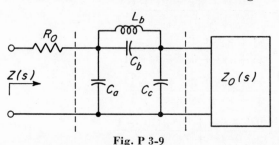

Fig. P 3-9

3-10. Show that the realization given in Fig. 3-24(b) can be obtained from that of Fig. 3-24(a) by going through a development similar to that following Fig. 3-22.

3-11. Prove that the derivative of a Hurwitz polynomial is Hurwitz. *Hint:* Show that $P'(s)/P(s)$ is a positive real function.

3-12. Consider the function

$$F(s) = \frac{k}{s - s_1} + \frac{k^*}{s - s_1^*} = \frac{2as + 2(a\sigma_1 - b\omega_1)}{(s + \sigma_1)^2 + \omega_1^2}$$

where

$$k = a + jb = |k|\epsilon^{j\alpha}$$

$$s_1 = -\sigma_1 + j\omega_1 = |s_1|\epsilon^{j(\phi + \pi/2)}$$

Figure P 3-12 shows the location of the pole and its residue in the complex plane.

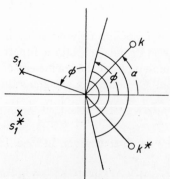

Fig. P 3-12

(a) Show that $F(s)$ will be positive real if and only if

    (1) $\text{Re}(k) = a > 0$

    (2) $\phi \geq \alpha$ or equivalently $\dfrac{\sigma_1}{\omega_1} \geq \dfrac{|b|}{a}$

(b) Show that $F(s)$ can be realized by one of the structures in Fig. P 3-12(a) as an impedance and by one of those in Fig. P 3-12(b) as an admittance.

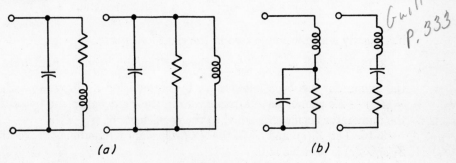

(a)   *(b)*

Fig. P 3-12a, b

(c) Let $G(s)$ be a pr function having only simple complex poles. Show that a Foster-like realization of $G(s)$ (a series or parallel connection of component networks like those in the previous two figures) can be obtained if and only if conditions (1) and (2) above are satisfied at all the poles.

(d) Now let $G(s)$ have simple real poles as well. Show that positiveness of the residues at all the real poles is sufficient for a Foster-like realization. Discuss the possibility of compensating for negative residues by borrowing from the constant term in the partial-fraction expansion of $G(s)$, if this term exists.

3-13. In the previous problem a synthesis procedure is developed for pr functions with simple poles. This requires certain conditions on the residues. Suppose these conditions are not satisfied for a pair of complex poles, and consider adding a constant k to the term representing such a pair of complex poles. That is, let

$$F(s) = \frac{a_1 s + a_0}{s^2 + b_1 s + b_0} = \frac{m_1 + n_1}{m_2 + n_2}$$

(a) Determine conditions on the numerator coefficients of $F(s)$ and on the value of k such that $F(s) + k$ can be written as a sum of two pr functions, one of which has the form $k m_2 / (m_2 + n_2)$. In case the conditions in the previous problem are not satisfied at all the poles, but the conditions just discovered are satisfied, then a Foster-like realization of a given pr function will still be possible, provided the constant term in the partial-fraction expansion is large enough to supply all the required constants.

(b) Obtain a realization of the following pr functions in the form suggested in part (a).

$$Z(s) = \frac{2s^2 + 3s + 5}{s^2 + 2s + 2}, \qquad Y(s) = \frac{s^2 + s + 2}{s^2 + s + 1}$$

3-14. Let $Z(s)$ be a pr function regular at the origin and having a finite, nonzero value at infinity. Prove that

$$Z_1(s) = Z(s) - \frac{1}{Cs} \qquad C \text{ a positive constant}$$

has exactly a single simple zero in the right half plane.

3-15. Let $Z(s) = \dfrac{s^2 + a_1 s + 1}{s^2 + b_1 s + b_0}$ be a pr function (the constant term in the numerator has been made unity by normalizing s.) Prove that $Z_1(s) = Z(s) - Ks$ cannot have a triple zero in the right half plane by setting the numerator coefficients equal to the coefficients of $(s - k)^3$.

3-16. Let $Z_1(s)$ and $Z_2(s)$ be RC impedance functions. Prove that $Z_1(s)/Z_2(s)$ is positive real.

3-17. (a) Obtain a Miyata realization of the function given in Eq. (3-157).

(b) Choose $a^2 = 6$ in Eq. (3-154), and obtain a Miyata realization of the resulting impedance. Compare with part (a).

3-18. Let $F(s) = m/(Km + n)$ be a positive real function. If $F(s)$ is an impedance, it can be realized by the network in Fig. P 3-18(a), while if $F(s)$ is an admittance, its realization will take the form of Fig. P 3-18(b). Let either of these two networks form the termination of a ladder each of whose branches consists of a single inductance or a single capacitance. Let the impedance of the ladder be $Z(s)$, and write $Z(s) = (m_1 + n_1)/(m_2 + n_2)$. Show that either m_1 or n_1 and either m_2 or n_2 have the factor m.

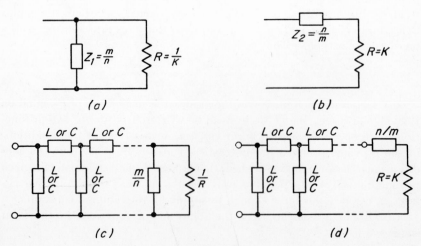

Fig. P 3-18

3-19. Let $U(-s^2)$ be the even part of an impedance $Z(s)$. Suppose $U(-s^2)$ has a factor $(s^2 + \omega_0^2)^2$. This will prevent the application of the Miyata realization procedure. Suppose the numerator and denominator of $Z(s)$ are multiplied by the surplus factor $s + k$, where k is a positive number. Show that it is always possible to find a positive number k such that either m_2 or n_2 has the factor $s^2 + \omega_0^2$, where m_2 and n_2 are the even and odd parts of the denominator of the augmented $Z(s)$ function.

3-20. Use the results of the previous two problems to show that, if $U(-s^2)$ has a factor $(s^2 + \omega_0^2)^2$, then a modification of the Miyata procedure is possible in which the function $U_a(-s^2)$ is $(s^2 + \omega_0^2)^2/D(-s^2)$ instead of $1/D(-s^2)$ as in Eq. (3-130). The realization will consist of the series connection of ladders such as those in Fig. P 3-18.

3-21. (a) Employ the technique of the previous set of problems to obtain a realization for the positive real function

$$Z(s) = \frac{3s^3 + 5s^2 + 4s + 6}{s^3 + 2s^2 + 2s + 1}$$

(b) Obtain realizations for the minimum functions in Prob. 3-3, using the same technique. Compare with the Bott-Duffin realization.

3-22. Let $Y(s)$ be the admittance of an RC one-port. Prove that

$$\arg Y(s) < \arg s \qquad \text{for} \qquad 0 < \arg s < \pi$$

3-23. The following functions are given as the real part of positive real functions. Find the positive real functions, using the Gewertz and the Bode methods.

(a) $\operatorname{Re}[Z(j\omega)] = \dfrac{(1 - \omega^2)^2}{1 + \omega^6}$

(b) $\operatorname{Re}[Z(j\omega)] = \dfrac{1}{1 + \omega^8}$

(c) $\operatorname{Re}[Z(j\omega)] = \dfrac{1 - 2\omega^2 + \omega^4}{1 - 2\omega^2 + \omega^4 + 4\omega^6}$

3-24. In the text it is shown that the numerator and denominator of the Richards function $F(s)$ given in Eq. (3-97) have a right half plane factor $(s - k)$. Show that *either* the Richards function *or* the positive real function $Z(s)$ given in Eq. (3-99) in terms of the Richards function, *must* have the factor $s + k$ in both numerator and denominator.

3-25. If $Z(s) = \dfrac{s^2 + a_1 s + a_0}{s^2 + b_1 s + b_0}$ is a minimum function, show that the value of k in the Bott-Duffin realization is

$$k = \frac{\omega_0}{X(\omega_0)} \sqrt{\frac{a_0}{b_0}}; \qquad X(\omega_0) > 0$$

$$k = -\omega_0 X(\omega_0) \sqrt{\frac{b_0}{a_0}}; \qquad X(\omega_0) < 0$$

where $Z(j\omega_0) = jX(\omega_0)$.

3-26. Let $Z(s)$ be a pr function and $U(-s^2)$ its even part. Suppose $U(-s^2)$ has a factor $(s^2 - a^2)^2$; that is to say, the real part of $Z(j\omega)$ becomes zero at an imaginary value of ω (a real value of s). By going through a development similar to that of the Brune cycle, find a "section" which will realize this factor in $U(-s^2)$.

3-27. Prove that whenever the ratio of two pr functions is real for $\mathrm{Re}\, s \geq 0$, it must be non-negative. Similarly for the product of two pr functions.

4

Properties of Two-Port Functions

The previous two chapters were devoted to the study of networks having a single pair of external terminals. We determined necessary and sufficient conditions that the driving-point functions of such networks must satisfy, and we established synthesis procedures by which functions satisfying the necessary conditions could be realized. We deferred the discussion of a very important general synthesis procedure (Darlington's) because this procedure is intimately related with the method of realization of a resistance-loaded lossless two-port.

The remainder of this book will be devoted to a study of networks having two pairs of external terminals, two-ports. Before we start discussing two-port realization techniques, we shall spend the present chapter in considering the properties of the functions that describe two-port behavior and in establishing necessary conditions satisfied by these functions.

4-1. Properties of general passive two-port functions

The functions which describe the external behavior of two-ports were defined in Chap. 1. For a complete description of the behavior a set of three functions is needed. The ones we shall use the most will be the open-circuit parameters (z's) and the short-circuit parameters (y's). However, the complete external behavior of a network is seldom specified. The transmission properties are usually specified in terms of one of the transfer functions. We shall be interested in determining the properties of all these functions. We shall initially consider the general two-port, putting no restrictions (other than the lumped, passive, bilateral ones) on the two-ports under consideration, either from the structural viewpoint or from the standpoint of permissible types of network elements.

137

Let us first consider the z parameters. We can establish some rather general properties of these functions by considering a theorem which we proved in Chap. 1. There we found that the z *matrix of a passive bilateral two-port is positive real*. This was expressed analytically in Eq. (1-66), which we shall rewrite as

$$z_{11}x_1^2 + 2z_{12}x_1x_2 + z_{22}x_2^2 = F_0 + sT_0 + \frac{V_0}{s} = F(s) \qquad (4\text{-}1)$$

The quantities F_0, T_0, and V_0 are the energy functions and hence are never negative. The right-hand side of this expression is a positive real function of s. Therefore the left-hand side is also pr for all real values of x_1 and x_2. It should be clear that this requirement will place restrictions on the permissible properties of the z parameters.

We already know that the z's are rational functions of s with real coefficients. The equation shows that a pole of any one of the z's will be a pole of $F(s)$. But since $F(s)$ is pr, it can have no poles in the right half plane. It follows that the z's are regular in the right half plane and any poles on the $j\omega$ axis are simple. Let k_{11}, k_{22}, and k_{12} be the residues of z_{11}, z_{22}, and z_{12}, respectively, at a pole on the $j\omega$ axis, and let k be the residue of $F(s)$ at this pole. We know that k must be real and nonnegative since $F(s)$ is pr. It follows that

$$k = k_{11}x_1^2 + 2k_{12}x_1x_2 + k_{22}x_2^2 \geq 0 \qquad (4\text{-}2)$$

This equation expresses the fact that the quadratic form involving the residues of the z parameters at a pole on the $j\omega$ axis must be positive semidefinite. Alternatively, we can state that *the matrix of the residues of the z parameters at poles on the $j\omega$ axis is positive semidefinite*.

In order to utilize this result, we need a theorem from matrix algebra. This theorem states: *Necessary and sufficient conditions that a nonsingular matrix be positive semidefinite are that the determinant of the matrix and all its principal cofactors be nonnegative*. We shall not digress here to prove this theorem; for a proof, refer to Guillemin (57).

When we use this theorem on the matrix of the quadratic form in Eq. (4-2), we get the following result:

$$k_{11} \geq 0 \qquad \qquad \text{(a)}$$
$$k_{22} \geq 0 \qquad \qquad \text{(b)} \quad (4\text{-}3)$$
$$k_{11}k_{22} - k_{12}^2 \geq 0 \qquad \text{(c)}$$

We already knew the first two of these, since z_{11} and z_{22} are driving-point impedance functions and hence positive real. The third expression is something new. We shall refer to this as the *residue condition*. It plays an important role in many synthesis procedures.

We established the residue condition by using the fact that the residue of a positive real function at a j-axis pole cannot be negative. We should expect that other properties of the positive real function $F(s)$ should also lead to restrictions on the z parameters. The outstanding property of a pr function is that its real part is never negative anywhere on the $j\omega$ axis. This fact should lead to some condition on the real parts of the z parameters. Let us write

$$\text{Re } z_{jk}(j\omega) = r_{jk} \qquad (4\text{-}4)$$

With this notation the real part of Eq. (4-1) can be written

$$\text{Re } [F(j\omega)] = r_{11}x_1^2 + 2r_{12}x_1x_2 + r_{22}x_2^2 \geq 0 \qquad (4\text{-}5)$$

This equation expresses the fact that *the matrix formed by the real parts of the z parameters on the j\omega axis is positive semidefinite.* It follows, therefore, that

$$r_{11} = \text{Re } [z_{11}(j\omega)] \geq 0 \qquad \text{(a)}$$

$$r_{22} = \text{Re } [z_{22}(j\omega)] \geq 0 \qquad \text{(b)} \quad (4\text{-}6)$$

$$r_{11}r_{22} - r_{12}^2 \geq 0 \qquad \text{(c)}$$

The last of these relationships expresses a fundamental restriction on a set of functions which are to be the z parameters of a two-port. It was first established by Gewertz (51). We shall refer to it as the *real-part condition*.

We know the properties of two of the three z parameters, z_{11} and z_{22}, rather completely, because they are positive real functions. The third one, z_{12}, is not necessarily positive real (but it may be). We *do* know that it is a real rational function of s, regular in the right half plane. It is further restricted by the real-part condition and the residue condition. There are no restrictions on the locations of its zeros; these may lie anywhere in the entire s plane.

The properties of the y parameters of a two-port may be established in a completely similar manner. The starting point is the theorem, which we established in Chap. 1, which states: *The y matrix of a passive bilateral two-port is positive real.* Proceeding with the analytical expression of this theorem, we shall find that the y parameters also satisfy the residue condition at j-axis poles and the real-part condition; we need only change the notation appropriately in Eqs. (4-3) and (4-6).

A glance at the residue condition shows that, if k_{12} has a nonzero value, then both k_{11} and k_{22} must be nonzero. That is, if z_{12} has a pole on the $j\omega$

axis, then both z_{11} and z_{22} must have a pole there also. Similarly, if y_{12} has a pole on the $j\omega$ axis, y_{11} and y_{22} must also have this pole. On the other hand, each of the driving-point functions may have a pole on the $j\omega$ axis which the others do not have. As an illustration, consider the network shown in Fig. 4-1(a). There are impedances Z_1 and Z_2 in series with the

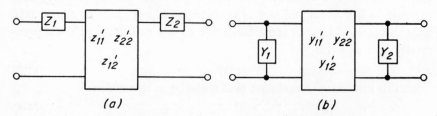

Fig. 4-1. Effect of series or shunt elements on two-port parameters.

input and output terminals, respectively. Let the z parameters of the network in the box be designated by primes, and suppose that they all have the same poles. For the z parameters of the entire network we can write

$$z_{11} = z'_{11} + Z_1 \qquad \text{(a)}$$

$$z_{22} = z'_{22} + Z_2 \qquad \text{(b)} \quad \text{(4-7)}$$

$$z_{12} = z'_{12} \qquad \text{(c)}$$

Thus Z_1 affects only z_{11}, while Z_2 affects only z_{22}. We say that the poles of Z_1 are the *private poles* of z_{11}. Similarly the poles of Z_2 are the private poles of z_{22}. It may be possible that Z_1 and Z_2 have some common poles, in which case z_{11} and z_{22} will have these poles, but not z_{12}. We label such poles *semiprivate poles* of z_{11} and z_{22}. In an entirely similar manner we can easily

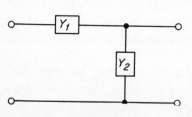

Fig. 4-2. L network.

be convinced with the aid of Fig. 4-1(b) that y_{11} and y_{22} may have private poles on the $j\omega$ axis.

In the preceding discussion we started by considering poles on the $j\omega$ axis. We found that, as a consequence of the residue condition, it is not possible for z_{12} to have a pole on the $j\omega$ axis which is not shared by z_{11} and z_{22}. Likewise, it is not possible for y_{12} to have a pole on the $j\omega$ axis not shared by y_{11} and y_{22}. However, the same conclusion is not true for poles in other parts of the s plane. As an example, consider the L network shown in Fig. 4-2. The y parameters of this network are

$$y_{11} = -y_{12} = Y_1 \qquad \text{(a)}$$

$$(4\text{-}8)$$

$$y_{22} = Y_1 + Y_2 \qquad \text{(b)}$$

Suppose that Y_1 and Y_2 are complementary admittances. This means that $Y_1 + Y_2 = G$, a constant. It follows that y_{22} will not have any of the poles of y_{12}. (The residue condition at j-axis poles is not violated by this example since Y_1 and Y_2 cannot be complementary admittances if Y_1 has poles on the $j\omega$ axis. See Sec. 6-6.)

Having examined the general properties of the z and y parameters, let us now turn our attention to the transfer functions of two-ports under various types of termination. We shall be interested in the transfer impedance $Z_{12}(s)$, the transfer admittance $Y_{12}(s)$, the transfer voltage ratio $T_{12}(s)$, and the insertion ratio $H(s)$. However, it is not necessary to single out each of these for individual study. It is necessary to study only one of these, say, $T_{12}(s)$, since the others can be expressed rather simply in terms of this one. For example, consider the sequence of networks in Fig. 4-3. The box is the same in each case. The function E_a/I_a in the

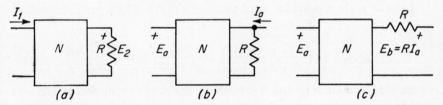

Fig. 4-3. Equivalence of a transfer impedance and a transfer voltage ratio.

second network is equal to the function $Z_{12} = E_2/I_1$ in the first network, by the reciprocity theorem. In the third network the current source has been replaced by the voltage-source equivalent. The voltage transfer ratio E_a/E_b is equal to $E_a/RI_a = Z_{12}/R$. We conclude that the transfer impedance function has the same properties as a transfer voltage ratio. The same conclusion is true for the other functions as well.[†]

The transfer voltage ratio can be expressed in terms of the z parameters or the y parameters according to Eq. (1-18). It is also a rational function. So we can write

† Note that in the case of Z_{12} or Y_{12} these statements apply only for a resistance-loaded network, normalized so that the termination is unity. For other cases, the constant multiplier of these functions is not restricted as the multiplier of T_{12} is. This is obvious from Eqs. (1-19) and (1-20).

$$T_{12}(s) = \frac{a_m s^m + a_{m-1} s^{m-1} + \ldots + a_1 s + a_0}{b_n s^n + b_{n-1} s^{n-1} + \ldots + b_1 s + b_0} \qquad (a)$$

$$T_{12}(s) = K \frac{s^m + a'_{m-1} s^{m-1} + \ldots + a'_1 s + a'_0}{s^n + b'_{n-1} s^{n-1} + \ldots + b'_1 s + b'_0} = K \frac{P(s)}{Q(s)} \qquad (b) \quad (4\text{-}9)$$

$$T_{12}(s) = \frac{z_{12}}{z_{11}} = \frac{-y_{12}}{y_{22}} \qquad (c)$$

We have written these three forms separately for ease of later reference. In the second form the highest power coefficients in numerator and denominator have been factored out and combined into a constant labeled K. We shall refer to this as the *gain constant*.

The poles of T_{12} are composed of:

1. Zeros of z_{11} which are not also zeros of z_{12}
2. Poles of z_{12} which are not also poles of z_{11}

It follows that poles of $T_{12}(s)$ lie in the left half plane or on the $j\omega$ axis. Those on the $j\omega$ axis can only be zeros of z_{11} and therefore are simple. [If a j-axis pole of $T_{12}(s)$ is a pole of z_{12} without being a pole of z_{11}, the residue condition will be violated.]

Let $s = j\omega_0$ be a zero of z_{11} (and a pole of T_{12}); then $1/z_{11}$ can be expanded in partial fractions. We can therefore write T_{12} as

$$T_{12}(s) = z_{12} \left(\frac{2k_0 s}{s^2 + \omega_0^2} + \frac{1}{z'_{11}} \right) = \frac{2s z_{12}}{s^2 + \omega_0^2} \left(k_0 + \frac{s^2 + \omega_0^2}{2s z'_{11}} \right) \qquad (4\text{-}10)$$

where $1/z'_{11}$ combines all the rest of the terms in the expansion of $1/z_{11}$. It is therefore regular at $s = j\omega_0$. If we now evaluate the residue of T_{12} at $s = j\omega_0$, we get

$$\text{Residue of } T_{12} \text{ at } j\omega_0 = k_0 z_{12}(j\omega_0)$$

$$= k_0 [r_{12}(\omega_0) + j x_{12}(\omega_0)] \qquad (4\text{-}11)$$

where we have written the real and imaginary parts of $z_{12}(j\omega_0)$ explicitly. Since $s = j\omega_0$ is a zero of z_{11}, the real part of z_{11} is zero at $s = j\omega_0$. Therefore, the real part of z_{12} must also be zero at that frequency; otherwise the real-part condition in Eq. (4-6) will be violated. Hence the last equation reduces to

$$\text{Residue of } T_{12}|_{s=j\omega_0} = j k_0 x_{12}(\omega_0) \qquad (4\text{-}12)$$

We can express the results of this discussion as follows: *The poles of $T_{12}(s)$ on the $j\omega$ axis are simple, and the residues there are imaginary.*

As far as the behavior of T_{12} at zero and infinity is concerned, we can easily establish that T_{12} cannot have a pole either at zero or at infinity. Take $s = 0$, for example. Suppose that z_{11} has a zero at $s = 0$, while z_{12}

has not. (This is the only way in which T_{12} can have a pole there.) If z_{12} is not zero at $s = 0$, it must either have a pole there or have a finite non-zero value. In the first case the residue condition will be violated, while in the second case the real-part condition will be violated. The same argument will prove the condition at infinity, as well. In terms of the polynomials in Eqs. (4-9), it follows that $b_0 \neq 0$ and $n \geq m$.

As for the zeros of $T_{12}(s)$, they are composed of the zeros of z_{12} (which are not also zeros of z_{11}) and the private poles of z_{11}. We have already seen that the private poles of z_{11} can be represented by a series impedance at the input terminals. It is clear that a pole of such an impedance will block transmission when the input is a voltage. We shall refer to a zero of any one of the transfer functions of a two-port as a *transmission zero*. As we have just seen, some of the zeros of transmission will depend on whether the input is a current or a voltage. When necessary we shall refer to *voltage-transmission zeros* and *current-transmission zeros*. Because the zeros of z_{12} are permitted to lie anywhere in the s plane, the same is true of the zeros of T_{12}.

We shall conclude this section with a summary of the general properties of the functions describing the behavior of passive bilateral two-ports.

1. Poles:
    (a) No poles of z_{12}, y_{12}, and T_{12} can lie in the right half plane.
    (b) In addition, no poles of T_{12} can lie at zero or infinity.
    (c) Poles of z_{12} and y_{12} on the $j\omega$ axis are simple with real residues.
    (d) Poles of T_{12} on the $j\omega$ axis are simple with imaginary residues.
    (e) The y parameters and the z parameters satisfy the residue condition $k_{11}k_{22} - k_{12}^2 \geq 0$ at all poles on $j\omega$ axis.

2. The zeros of z_{12}, y_{12}, and T_{12} may be multiple and can lie anywhere in the s plane.

3. The z and y parameters satisfy the real-part condition

$$r_{11}r_{22} - r_{12}^2 \geq 0$$

or

$$g_{11}g_{22} - g_{12}^2 \geq 0$$

4-2. Two-ports with no magnetic coupling

The two-ports under consideration in the last section were restricted only by the general requirements of being linear, lumped, passive, and bilateral. Neither the structure nor the permissible types of elements were restricted.

To see how the structure might affect the properties of the network functions, let us return to the consideration of pr functions for an instant. The Brune realization of pr functions always has a ladder structure. However, in some cases a transformer is needed in the realization. If we restrict the network to contain no mutual inductance, then we see that not all pr functions can be realized in a ladder structure. From a different point of view suppose that we require a one-port which is to contain no mutual inductance and which is to have a ladder structure. Then, clearly, the impedance function of such a one-port must be restricted in certain ways.

Similarly, if we require a two-port with no mutual inductance and further require that it have a specific structure, we should expect the two-port functions to have additional restrictions beyond the general ones we established in the last section.

Let us now restrict ourselves to two-ports with no mutual inductance and see what additional properties we can derive for the two-port functions. Two-ports can be classified broadly as balanced or unbalanced. An *unbalanced* two-port is characterized by having one terminal common to both the input and the output, such as a ladder network. This may also be called a *common-terminal* two-port. Any two-port which does not have such a common terminal is classified as a *balanced* structure.

A. *Unbalanced Two-ports*

We shall initially concern ourselves with unbalanced two-ports such as the one shown in Fig. 4-4. The noncommon input and output terminals

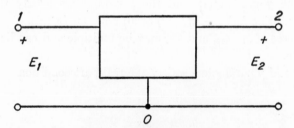

Fig. 4-4. Unbalanced two-port.

are labeled 1 and 2, respectively, while the common terminal is labeled 0. We wish to determine properties of the various two-port functions.

Suppose that we think of performing a tee-pi transformation at one of the internal nodes as shown in Fig. 4-5. This node will be eliminated from the network. The admittance functions of the branches of the equivalent pi will be

$$Y_1 = \frac{Y_b Y_c}{Y_a + Y_b + Y_c} \qquad \text{(a)}$$

$$Y_2 = \frac{Y_a Y_c}{Y_a + Y_b + Y_c} \qquad \text{(b)} \quad \text{(4-13)}$$

$$Y_3 = \frac{Y_a Y_b}{Y_a + Y_b + Y_c} \qquad \text{(c)}$$

The original admittances Y_a, Y_b, and Y_c are positive real functions so that all their coefficients are positive. After the transformation the resulting admittances are not necessarily pr, but their coefficients are still all positive since the transformation does not introduce any negative signs.

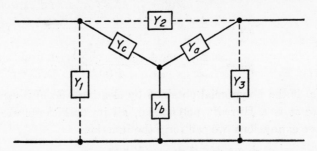

Fig. 4-5. Tee-pi transformation.

If there are more than three branches connected to a node, the simple tee-pi transformation cannot be performed. In this case we must resort to the more general *star-mesh* transformation. This is a generalization of the tee-pi transformation. For our purposes the important property of this transformation is the fact that the coefficients of the branch admittances are all positive since the transformation does not introduce negative signs.†

Following the procedure we have just outlined, it is possible to eliminate all the internal nodes of an unbalanced two-port, leaving only a pi structure between the three external nodes as shown in Fig. 4-6. All

† For a more complete discussion, see Guillemin (60).

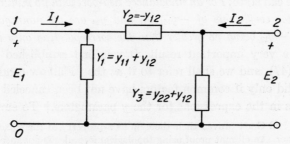

Fig. 4-6. Pi equivalent of two-port.

coefficients of the branches of the pi will be positive. Identifying the branches of the pi with the short-circuit parameters shown in the figure, we observe that all the coefficients of $-y_{12}$, $y_{11} + y_{12}$, and $y_{22} + y_{12}$ are positive. This assumes that no common factors have been canceled from the numerator and denominator of the branch admittances.

We can state the conclusion at which we have arrived in a more formal manner by considering the expressions for the short-circuit parameters in terms of the loop-impedance determinant and its cofactors as given in Table 1-2. Thus

$$-y_{12} = -\frac{\Delta_{12}}{\Delta} = \frac{a_0 + a_1 s + \ldots + a_n s^n}{P(s)} \qquad \text{(a)}$$

$$y_{22} = \frac{\Delta_{22}}{\Delta} = \frac{b_0 + b_1 s + \ldots + b_n s^n}{P(s)} \qquad \text{(b)} \quad \text{(4-14)}$$

$$y_{11} = \frac{\Delta_{11}}{\Delta} = \frac{c_0 + c_1 s + \ldots + c_n s^n}{P(s)} \qquad \text{(c)}$$

where $P(s)$ is the polynomial obtained by clearing $\Delta(s)$ of inverse powers of s. Since it is a Hurwitz polynomial, all its coefficients are positive. Using these expressions, we can form the functions

$$-y_{12} = \frac{a_0 + a_1 s + a_2 s^2 + \ldots + a_n s^n}{P(s)} \qquad \text{(a)}$$

$$y_{22} + y_{12} = \frac{(b_0 - a_0) + (b_1 - a_1)s + \ldots + (b_n - a_n)s^n}{P(s)} \qquad \text{(b)} \quad \text{(4-15)}$$

$$y_{11} + y_{12} = \frac{(c_0 - a_0) + (c_1 - a_1)s + \ldots + (c_n - a_n)s^n}{P(s)} \qquad \text{(c)}$$

According to the result we have established, none of the coefficients in the numerators of these expressions will be negative. Hence

$$a_i \geq 0$$
$$b_i \geq a_i \qquad i = 0, 1, \ldots, n \qquad \text{(4-16)}$$
$$c_i \geq a_i$$

In words we can state: *For an unbalanced two-port with no mutual inductance the numerator coefficients of* $-y_{12}$, y_{11} *and* y_{22} *are all nonnegative, the coefficients of* $-y_{12}$ *being no greater than the corresponding ones in* y_{11} *or* y_{22}.

This is a very important result. It was first established by Fialkow and Gerst (47), and we shall refer to it as the "Fialkow condition." The result is valid only if common factors have not been canceled from Δ and its cofactors in the expressions for the y parameters.† To emphasize this

† Fialkow and Gerst proved their theorem as a property of the cofactors of Δ in a rigorous manner. An elegant proof using topological formulas is advanced by Seshu in unpublished work. The proof given here was outlined by Lewis (78).

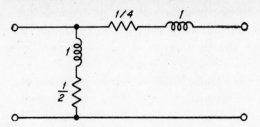

Fig. 4-7. Example to demonstrate Fialkow's condition.

fact, consider the network shown in Fig. 4-7. The y parameters of the network can be written by inspection. They are

$$-y_{12} = y_{22} = \frac{1}{s + \frac{1}{4}} \qquad \text{(a)}$$

$$y_{11} = \frac{2s + \frac{3}{4}}{s^2 + 3s/4 + \frac{1}{8}} = \frac{2s + \frac{3}{4}}{(s + \frac{1}{2})(s + \frac{1}{4})} \qquad \text{(b)}$$

(4-17)

As written, the constant term in the numerator of $-y_{12}$ is unity and is greater than the constant term in the numerator of y_{11}. However, the denominators of these two expressions are different, leading to the suspicion that some cancellation of factors has taken place. If we form the loop-impedance determinant and its cofactors, we shall find that Δ, Δ_{12}, and Δ_{22} have the common factor $s + \frac{1}{2}$. This factor has been canceled from y_{12} and y_{22}. If it is restored, we shall get

$$-y_{12} = y_{22} = \frac{s + \frac{1}{2}}{(s + \frac{1}{2})(s + \frac{1}{4})} \qquad \text{(a)}$$

$$y_{11} = \frac{2s + \frac{3}{4}}{(s + \frac{1}{2})(s + \frac{1}{4})} \qquad \text{(b)}$$

(4-18)

The Fialkow condition is now satisfied.

A similar condition can be derived for the coefficients of the z parameters. The pi structure in Fig. 4-6 can be replaced by its tee equivalent, and the positiveness of the coefficients of the branch impedances will be maintained. The branch impedances can then be related to the z parameters. If we consider the left side of Eqs. (4-14) to be z_{12}, z_{11}, and z_{22}, respectively, the conditions in Eqs. (4-16) will again follow. Hence we can make the following statement: *For an unbalanced two-port with no mutual inductance the numerator coefficients of z_{12}, z_{11}, and z_{22} are all nonnegative, the coefficients of z_{12} being no greater than the corresponding ones in z_{11} or z_{22}.* Again, common factors must not be canceled.

Let us now turn our attention to a consideration of the transfer function of unbalanced two-ports with no mutual inductance. If we substitute the expressions for the y parameters in Eqs. (4-14) into the last form in Eqs. (4-9), we shall get the first form in Eqs. (4-9), where now the a and b coefficients have the significance of being the numerator coefficients in $-y_{12}$ and y_{22}, respectively. We conclude that, *for an unbalanced two-port with no mutual inductance, the numerator coefficients of the transfer function are nonnegative and no greater than the corresponding denominator coefficients.*

Let us now restrict s to real positive values. Each term in the numerator of $T_{12}(\sigma)$ will be a positive number no greater than the corresponding term in the denominator. Hence the ratio can certainly never exceed unity. This leads to the condition

$$T_{12}(\sigma) \leq 1 \quad \text{for} \quad s = \sigma \geq 0 \qquad (4\text{-}19)$$

Furthermore it is clear that not all the a coefficients can be exactly equal to the corresponding b coefficients, since the transfer function would then be identically unity. It follows that $T_{12}(\sigma)$ cannot attain its maximum value of unity except possibly at $s = 0$ or at infinity, or both. This will occur when $a_0 = b_0$ or $a_n = b_n$, or both.

We can obtain further information about $T_{12}(s)$ if we consider the second form in Eqs. (4-9). It is clear that Fialkow's condition will put an upper limit on the permissible gain constant K. The transfer function is the product of K and P/Q. Hence, in order to satisfy the last equation, K can, at most, equal the reciprocal of the largest value attained by P/Q at any real positive value of s, including zero and infinity. Given a ratio P/Q, we can easily determine the value of the ratio at $s = 0$ and infinity. To see whether or not the value of P/Q evaluated at real positive values of s ever exceeds the larger of these two values, we would have to find the maxima of P/Q for positive real values of s. This involves differentiating P/Q to find the critical points and then evaluating the function at these critical points. We can express the condition on the gain constant analytically by writing

$$0 < K \leq K_0 \qquad (4\text{-}20)$$

where $1/K_0$ is the largest of the numbers

$$\frac{P(0)}{Q(0)} = \frac{a_0'}{b_0'} \qquad \text{(a)}$$

$$\lim_{s \to \infty} \frac{P(s)}{Q(s)} = 1 \quad \text{or} \quad 0 \qquad \text{(b)} \quad (4\text{-}21)$$

$$\frac{P(\sigma_i)}{Q(\sigma_i)} = \frac{1}{K_p} \qquad \text{(c)}$$

and the σ_i's are the positive roots of

$$\frac{d}{ds}\left[\frac{P(s)}{Q(s)}\right] = 0 \tag{4-22}$$

We have already seen that $T_{12}(\sigma)$ cannot equal unity anywhere but at zero or infinity. Hence, if the third number in Eqs. (4-21) is the largest (which means that $K_0 = K_p$), then K must be less than K_0. But if one of the other two numbers is the largest (which means that $K_0 = b_0'/a_0'$ or that $K_0 = 1$) then K can equal K_0.

Although Fialkow's condition restricts the gain constant K as just described, this restriction is not considered very important in many synthesis problems, since amplifiers can normally be used. Most realization techniques realize a given transfer function to within a constant multiplier with the expectation that the gain can be restored at a later stage. Nevertheless, synthesis procedures which yield large values of the gain constant are desirable in order to reduce the amount of subsequent amplification required.

Another important conclusion follows from Fialkow's condition. Since none of the numerator coefficients of the transfer function are negative, Descartes's rule of sign tells us that, *for an unbalanced two-port with no mutual inductance, none of the transmission zeros can lie on the positive real axis.* As a consequence, when attempting to find a realization for a given transfer function, we should hope to find an unbalanced realization provided that no transmission zeros occur on the positive real axis.

However, it is possible that a desired transfer function originally has some negative numerator coefficients, although it has no zeros on the positive real axis. We saw in the last chapter that it is always possible to make all the coefficients positive in such a case by the use of surplus factors. Of course, the number of surplus factors needed will depend on how close the zeros lie to the positive real axis.

We can summarize these results as follows: *For unbalanced two-ports with no mutual inductance*

1. Transmission zeros may lie anywhere except on the positive real axis.

2. For real positive values of s, the value of the transfer function lies between 0 and 1. The maximum value of unity can be attained only at zero or infinity, or both.

3. The numerator coefficients of the transfer function are positive (or zero) and no greater than the corresponding denominator coefficients, assuming no cancellations of factors.

B. *Balanced Two-ports*

Let us now turn our attention to balanced two-ports with no magnetic

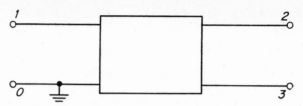

Fig. 4-8. Balanced two-port.

coupling. Consider the two-port shown in Fig. 4-8. Let us choose one terminal as a reference and use double subscripts to designate voltages. For the transfer voltage ratio we can write

$$\frac{E_{23}}{E_{10}} = \frac{E_{20}}{E_{10}} - \frac{E_{30}}{E_{10}} \qquad (4\text{-}23)$$

Each of the two functions on the right side is the transfer function of an unbalanced two-port. Because of the subtraction involved, some of the numerator coefficients of the balanced transfer function may be negative. However, the magnitude of a numerator coefficient is certainly no greater than the corresponding coefficient in the numerator of either one of the two functions on the right side. Each of these, in turn, is no greater than the corresponding denominator coefficient. We conclude that, *for the transfer function of a balanced two-port, the numerator coefficients may be negative but they can be no greater in magnitude than the corresponding denominator coefficients.*

If we again use Eqs. (4-14) to designate the y parameters of the two-port, this discussion leads to the conclusion

$$b_i \geq |a_i|$$
$$i = 0, 1, \ldots, n \qquad (4\text{-}24)$$
$$c_i \geq |a_i|$$

(The second of these is obtained by considering the right-to-left transfer voltage ratio, which is given by $-y_{12}/y_{11}$.)

If we again restrict s to real positive values, we know that each of the functions on the right side of Eq. (4-23) lies between the values of 0 and 1. Hence for a balanced two-port we get the condition

$$-1 \leq T_{12}(\sigma) \leq 1 \qquad \text{for } s = \sigma \geq 0 \qquad (4\text{-}25)$$

It should again be clear that the extreme values cannot be attained except at zero and infinity, by the same reasoning we used before.

We can summarize these results as follows: *For balanced two-ports with no mutual inductance*

1. Transmission zeros may lie anywhere, including the positive real axis.

2. For real positive values of s the value of the transfer function lies between -1 and $+1$. The extremities of the range can be attained only at zero or infinity, or both.

3. The numerator coefficients of the transfer function may be negative, but they are no greater in magnitude than the corresponding denominator coefficients, assuming no cancellation of factors.

C. *Ladder Networks*

In the previous parts of this section we observed in a very broad way how the structure of a network affects the properties of the transfer function. In particular, we found that the transmission zeros of an unbalanced two-port are forbidden to lie on the positive real axis. If we restrict the network structure even further, we should expect additional restrictions on the allowable locations of the transmission zeros.

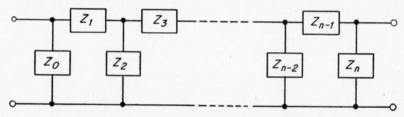

Fig. 4-9. Ladder two-port with no mutual inductance.

One of the simplest and most important network structures is the ladder, shown in Fig. 4-9. We shall now show that the transmission zeros of a ladder network are identical with poles of the series impedances or zeros of the shunt impedances.

In the first place consider the two-port formed by a shunt branch alone, say, the last branch in the ladder. For this two-port $z_{12} = Z_n$. Hence z_{12} will be zero only where $Z_n = 0$. Now consider the network in Fig. 4-10(b).

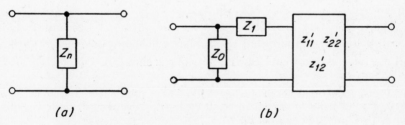

(a)   *(b)*

Fig. 4-10. Finding transmission zeros of a ladder network.

This is the ladder network with only two branches shown explicitly. The z parameters of the rest of the network are labeled z'_{11}, z'_{22}, and z'_{12}. The z_{12} function of the entire network will be

$$z_{12} = \frac{Z_0 z'_{12}}{Z_0 + Z_1 + z'_{11}} \tag{4-26}$$

(You were asked to establish this result in Prob. 1-2.) Our purpose is to determine the zeros of z_{12}. The equation shows that z_{12} can be zero in one of three ways:[†]

1. At a zero of Z_0, a shunt impedance;
2. At a pole of Z_1, a series impedance;
3. At a zero of z'_{12}

We can now repeat this procedure on the primed network and continue doing so until the last branch is reached. At each step we shall find that the zeros of the corresponding z_{12} can occur only in one of these three ways. For the last shunt branch we have already established that the zeros of z_{12} occur at the shunt-impedance zeros. It follows that z_{12} can be zero only at shunt-impedance zeros or series-impedance poles.

Since the branch impedances of the ladder are positive real functions, they will have no zeros or poles in the right half plane. It follows, then, that *the transmission zeros of a ladder network cannot lie in the right half plane.*

Let us return to the last equation and examine it in somewhat greater detail. One of the ways in which z_{12} can be zero is for Z_0 to be zero. However, suppose that $Z_1 + z'_{11}$ is simultaneously equal to zero. There will then be a cancellation, and z_{12} *will not become zero.* This condition, $Z_1 + z'_{11} = 0$, means that the impedance looking to the right beyond Z_0 becomes zero at a zero of the shunt-branch impedance. There would then appear to be two short circuits in parallel at the value of s in question, leading to a current division between the two branches. Thus current transmission will not be blocked. A network for which this is true is shown in Fig. 4-11(a). In this case z'_{11} and z'_{12} are simply the output shunt-branch impedance.

The second way in which z_{12} can be zero is for a series branch Z_1 to have a pole. But suppose that z'_{12} also has a pole at a pole of Z_1. Then z_{12} will not have a zero there. Such a network is shown in Fig. 4-11(b). The

[†] It may appear that z_{12} can also be zero if z'_{11} has a private pole. But we have seen that such poles represent series branches at the input of the (primed) network. Such a branch, then, constitutes part of Z_1.

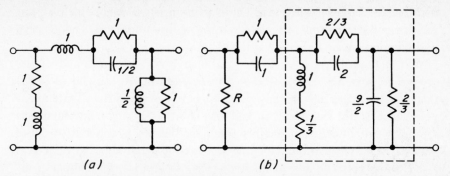

Fig. 4-11. Ladder networks which have no transmission zero at one shunt-impedance zero (a), or at one series-impedance pole (b).

primed network is enclosed in the dotted box. In the notation of Fig. 4-10 we have

$$Z_0 = R$$

$$Z_1 = \frac{1}{s + 1}$$

$$z'_{12} = \frac{\frac{2}{9}}{s + 1} \quad\quad\quad (4\text{-}27)$$

$$z'_{11} = \frac{2}{3} \frac{s + \frac{1}{3}}{s + 1}$$

These considerations demonstrate that, although the zeros of z_{12} for a ladder network necessarily occur at series-impedance poles or shunt-impedance zeros, not all such poles or zeros will be zeros of z_{12}.

A similar development in terms of the y parameters will lead to similar conclusions about the zeros of y_{12} for a ladder network. The details are left for you.

4-3. Lossless two-port functions

In the foregoing sections of this chapter we established the restrictions imposed on the functions describing the behavior of two-ports by various factors that influence this behavior. Thus the passive nature of the networks leads to the real-part condition on the z and y parameters and to the residue condition at j-axis poles. The structure of the network imposes restrictions on the permissible locations of the transmission zeros.

Let us now restrict ourselves to a consideration of lossless two-ports. We should expect this restriction to lead to further modifications in the permissible two-port functions. The starting point is again Eq. (4-1), in which the z parameters are related to the energy functions. The positive real function on the right side of the equation is now a reactance function. It follows that all the poles of the z parameters will be simple and will lie on the $j\omega$ axis. Of course, the residue condition will still be satisfied. Since all the poles are on the $j\omega$ axis, it is not possible for z_{12} to have a pole which is not shared by z_{11} and z_{22}. The two driving-point functions z_{11} and z_{22} are, of course, reactance functions but not z_{12}, since its residues may be negative (without violating the residue condition). Nevertheless $z_{12}(j\omega)$ must be imaginary at all frequencies; otherwise the real-part condition will be violated. Hence z_{12} must be an odd rational function, the ratio of an even and an odd polynomial.

The numerator of z_{12} will be an even polynomial in s, aside from a factor s when it is odd. Hence the zeros of z_{12} will occur in quadrantal symmetry according to the result we established in the last chapter. This means that, if there are any zeros in the interior of the left half plane, there must also be zeros in the right half plane.

In the case of an unbalanced two-port we already know that there can be no zeros of z_{12} on the positive real axis. It follows that there can be none on the negative real axis either, because of the quadrantal symmetry.

In the case of a ladder network we know that the transmission zeros lie at the zeros of shunt impedances and poles of series impedances. The branches of a lossless two-port are all reactive so that in this case the transmission zeros must all lie on the $j\omega$ axis. Recall, however, the discussion in the last section in which we demonstrated that not all series-impedance poles or shunt-impedance zeros are necessarily zeros of z_{12}. We found that there is no transmission zero at a shunt-impedance zero if the impedance looking to the right beyond the shunt branch also has a zero there. We also found that there is no transmission zero at a series-impedance pole if the z_{12} function of the remainder of the two-port beyond the series branch [that is, z'_{12} in the notation of Eq. (4-26)] also has a pole there. But, for a lossless two-port, z'_{12} cannot have a pole without z'_{11} also having the pole. Hence we can say that there will be no transmission zero at a series-impedance pole if the impedance looking to the right beyond the series impedance also has a pole there. We shall find these ideas very useful when synthesizing a ladder network.

So far we have talked about the zeros of z_{12} only. From Table 1-2 we find

$$y_{12} = -\frac{z_{12}}{z_{11}z_{22} - z_{12}^2} \qquad (4-28)$$

Let us see how the zeros of y_{12} can arise. It appears that y_{12} will have a zero at a zero of z_{12}, unless this coincides with a zero of z_{11} or z_{22}. In this case this factor will cancel from the expression on the right. A zero of y_{12} will occur also at a private pole of z_{11} or z_{22}, as you can see. Suppose that the z parameters have a common pole at $s = j\omega_0$. Then

$$z_{11} = \frac{2k_{11}s}{s^2 + \omega_0^2} + z_{11}' \qquad \text{(a)}$$

$$z_{22} = \frac{2k_{22}s}{s^2 + \omega_0^2} + z_{22}' \qquad \text{(b)} \quad \text{(4-29)}$$

$$z_{12} = \frac{2k_{12}s}{s^2 + \omega_0^2} + z_{12}' \qquad \text{(c)}$$

where the primed quantities account for the rest of the corresponding functions. So

$$z_{11}z_{22} - z_{12}^2 = \frac{4s^2(k_{11}k_{22} - k_{12}^2)}{(s^2 + \omega_0^2)^2} + z_{11}'z_{22}' - z_{12}'^2$$

$$+ \frac{2s(k_{11}z_{22}' + k_{22}z_{11}' - 2k_{12}z_{12}')}{s^2 + \omega_0^2} \qquad \text{(4-30)}$$

If the residue condition is satisfied with the equality sign $(k_{11}k_{22} - k_{12}^2 = 0)$, the first term on the right will vanish. Hence the function $z_{11}z_{22} - z_{12}^2$ will have only a simple pole at the pole of the z parameters. This means that y_{12} will be regular and nonzero at $s = j\omega_0$. However, if the residue condition is satisfied with the "greater than" sign, this function will have a double pole, which means that y_{12} will have a zero. Thus the zeros of y_{12} are, alternatively:

1. Zeros of z_{12}
2. Private poles of z_{11} or z_{22}
3. Poles of the z parameters at which $k_{11}k_{22} - k_{12}^2 > 0$

We shall use the residue condition very often in the following chapters. There should be a simple way of designating whether the equality sign or the inequality sign applies. We shall use the word *compact*† to mean that the residue condition is satisfied with the equality sign. The terms z *compact* and y *compact* will have the obvious significance of referring to poles of the z or the y parameters, respectively. We shall also use the term *compact pole* in an obvious way.

It is pertinent to inquire into the significance of noncompactness. Suppose that the z parameters of a two-port have a noncompact pole. We can consider z_{11} or z_{22}, or both, to have some excess residue at the pole,

---

† The term was first introduced by Dasher (39).

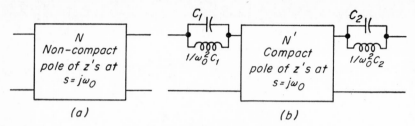

Fig. 4-12. Significance of compactness.

more than enough to satisfy the residue condition with the equality sign. Thus the noncompact network shown in Fig. 4-12 can be replaced by the second network, in which the excess residue is accounted for by the anti-resonant branches at the input and output. Actually only one of these branches is enough. In the same way a two-port with a noncompact admittance pole is equivalent to one with a compact pole, with resonant branches in shunt at the input or output to account for the excess residue.

Return now to a consideration of the zeros of y_{12}. We have seen that noncompact poles of the z parameters can be represented by series branches at the input or output. Likewise, private poles of z_{11} or z_{22} are also represented by such branches. Hence we find that the *zeros of y_{12} are either zeros of z_{12} or poles of the input or output series-branch impedances.*

Let us now turn to a consideration of the properties of transfer functions. The general results developed in the previous section still apply, but a few additional properties follow from the lossless character of the two-port. The network shown in Fig. 4-13 is a lossless two-port terminated in a

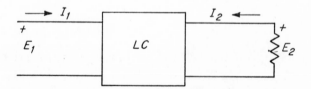

Fig. 4-13. Resistance-terminated lossless two-port.

resistance. In our preceding discussions we used the transfer voltage ratio function $T_{12}(s)$ as representative of all the transfer functions. However, if we include the terminating resistance as part of the network, our two-port will no longer be lossless. On the other hand, the T_{12} function for a network with no resistance, not even in the load, will be of only slight interest. (One case of importance appears in the Fialkow-Gerst synthesis of RLC two-ports in Chapter 8.)

The functions that are of much more interest are the transfer impedance $Z_{12}(s) = E_2/I_1$ and the transfer admittance $Y_{12}(s) = I_2/E_1$, with a resistance load. These functions are given by

$$Z_{12}(s) = \frac{z_{12}}{1 + z_{22}} \qquad \text{(a)}$$

$$\qquad\qquad\qquad\qquad (4\text{-}31)$$

$$Y_{12}(s) = \frac{y_{12}}{1 + y_{22}} \qquad \text{(b)}$$

where the z's and y's pertain to the lossless two-port not including the load and where the load resistance has been normalized to unity.

The forms of these two expressions are the same. Since the z and y parameters have similar properties, we should expect $Z_{12}(s)$ and $Y_{12}(s)$ also to have similar properties. From the properties of the z and y parameters we readily find that the denominators of Z_{12} and Y_{12} are strictly Hurwitz and that the numerators are normally even or odd polynomials. However, this condition on the numerator need not always be satisfied. It is possible for one or more left-half plane factors of the denominator to cancel with the numerator, thus leaving a polynomial in the numerator which is neither even nor odd. We conclude that the numerator of Z_{12} and Y_{12} must be either even or odd *except for possible factors representing zeros in the right-half plane.*

4-4. Magnitude and angle functions

In the preceding sections of this chapter we have discussed the properties of two-port functions—driving point and transfer. Until now we have assumed that the starting point is a rational function of s which is a realizable network function, and our problem is to obtain a network realization. In other words, we have not considered the approximation problem. In a practical situation a problem is presented in the form of some requirements on the behavior of the magnitude or angle (or both) of the transfer function over some interval of the $j\omega$ axis. The first problem is to obtain a function of ω satisfying necessary realizability criteria for a transfer function magnitude or angle, while at the same time approximating the prescribed behavior. After this a rational function of s must be found whose magnitude or phase coincides with the desired function.

In this section we shall study the properties of functions which, on the $j\omega$ axis, are to be the magnitude or angle of realizable transfer functions. We shall also establish methods of obtaining a realizable transfer function from a given magnitude or angle function. The approximation problem is in itself a rather extensive subject. We shall defer a discussion of this subject to a later chapter.

A. *Magnitude Function*

Let us designate by $F(s)$ any one of the transfer functions $Z_{12}(s)$, $Y_{12}(s)$, $T_{12}(s)$, and $H(s)$ (the insertion voltage ratio). The topics we discuss will be applicable to any of these functions. We shall exclude from consideration two-ports which include no resistance, not even in the termination. Let us designate the squared magnitude of $F(j\omega)$ as $G(\omega^2)$. Then we can write

$$G(\omega^2) = |F(j\omega)|^2 = F(j\omega)F^*(j\omega) = F(j\omega)F(-j\omega) \qquad (4\text{-}32)$$

Suppose that we now let s take on arbitrary values, rather than restricting it to the $j\omega$ axis. We then get

$$G(-s^2) = F(s)F(-s) \qquad (4\text{-}33)$$

This function is an even rational function of s. It becomes the squared magnitude of the transfer function when s is restricted to the $j\omega$ axis, but not for other values of s.

We shall refer to $G(-s^2)$ as the *magnitude squared* function. It is easy to establish the properties of this function. Because both the numerator and the denominator are even polynomials, both the poles and the zeros of $G(-s^2)$ occur in quadrantal symmetry. There can be no pole at zero or infinity. Any poles and zeros on the $j\omega$ axis must be of even multiplicity, the poles being no more than double.

The first step in forming the transfer function $F(s)$ from a given $G(\omega^2)$ is to replace ω^2 by $-s^2$. Since $F(s)$ can have no poles in the right half plane, we must assign all the left-half-plane poles of $G(-s^2)$ to $F(s)$. [Then all the right half plane poles of $G(-s^2)$ will belong to $F(-s)$.] Any poles or zeros of $G(-s^2)$ on the $j\omega$ axis must be split equally between $F(s)$ and $F(-s)$, which requires that they be of even order in $G(-s^2)$. When we come to the remainder of the zeros, we encounter some uncertainty. It is possible for $F(s)$ to have zeros in the right half plane. Hence we have some flexibility in assigning the zeros of $F(s)$.

Let us define a *minimum-phase* transfer function as one that has no zeros in the right half plane. We shall discuss such functions in greater detail in the next section. When the magnitude-squared function is given to us, it may also be stipulated that the transfer function be minimum-phase. In this case, the zeros of $F(s)$ can be uniquely assigned. It is usually easier to synthesize a minimum-phase transfer function than a nonminimum-phase one. Hence, if no stipulation is made, it is more advantageous to choose all the zeros of $F(s)$ in the left half plane.

B. *Angle Function*

Let us now turn to a consideration of the angle function. We can write

$$F(j\omega) = |F(j\omega)| \, \epsilon^{j\phi(\omega)}$$

$$F(-j\omega) = F^*(j\omega) = |F(j\omega)| \, \epsilon^{-j\phi(\omega)}$$

(4-34)

where $\phi(\omega)$ is the angle of $F(j\omega)$. Let us define a new function $A(j\omega)$ as follows:

$$A(j\omega) = \frac{F(j\omega)}{F(-j\omega)} = \epsilon^{j2\phi(\omega)}$$

(4-35)

This function has a magnitude of unity and an angle which is twice the angle of $F(j\omega)$. If we now let s take on arbitrary values rather than values on the $j\omega$ axis only, the above equation becomes

$$A(s) = \frac{F(s)}{F(-s)} = \epsilon^{2\phi_1(s)}$$

(4-36)

The function $\phi_1(s)$ is an odd function of s. It is not equal to the angle of $F(s)$. However, when $s = j\omega$, it reduces to $j\phi(\omega)$. We shall refer to $A(s)$ as the *A function* and to $\phi_1(s)$ as the *angle function*.

In order to determine the properties of $A(s)$, let us write the transfer function as the ratio of two polynomials and substitute into the last equation. Thus

$$F(s) = \frac{P_1(s)}{P_2(s)}$$

$$A(s) = \frac{F(s)}{F(-s)} = \frac{P_1(s)}{P_1(-s)} \frac{P_2(-s)}{P_2(s)}$$

(4-37)

If either of the polynomials $P_1(s)$ or $P_2(s)$ has zeros on the $j\omega$ axis, these will also be zeros of $P_1(-s)$ and $P_2(-s)$, respectively. Hence $A(s)$ will have no zeros or poles on the $j\omega$ axis. The zeros of $A(s)$ which are contributed by $P_2(-s)$ will lie in the right half plane. Those contributed by $P_1(s)$ may lie in the right or left. If $P_1(s)$ has zeros in the left half plane, then the corresponding zeros of $P_1(-s)$ will lie in the right half plane. This means that $A(s)$ may have poles in the right half plane. In summary each zero of $A(s)$ is the negative of one of its poles. The A function will have zeros in the right half plane, and it may also have poles there.

The angle function $\phi(\omega)$ is not a rational function of ω. We usually deal with the tangent of $\phi(\omega)$, which *is* a rational function. We shall refer to $\tan \phi(\omega)$ as the *tangent function*. To get a relationship between $A(j\omega)$ and $\tan \phi(\omega)$, we write

$$A(j\omega) = \epsilon^{j2\phi(\omega)} = \frac{\epsilon^{j\phi}}{\epsilon^{-j\phi}} = \frac{\cos\phi + j\sin\phi}{\cos\phi - j\sin\phi}$$

$$= \frac{1 + j\tan\phi}{1 - j\tan\phi} \qquad (4\text{-}38)$$

Suppose that $\tan\phi$ is given as a function of ω and we want to find the transfer function $F(s)$. The first step is to form the right-hand side of the last equation and then set $s = j\omega$. This gives us $A(s)$. We next consider the poles of $A(s)$; some of these are in the left half plane and some in the right. In the notation of Eq. (4-37) it may be possible that all the left-half-plane poles of $A(s)$ are zeros of $P_2(s)$, the right-half-plane poles being zeros of $P_1(-s)$. The negatives of the latter are zeros of $P_1(s)$. The transfer function, being $P_1(s)/P_2(s)$, is thus determined. However, it is not necessary that all the left-half-plane poles of $A(s)$ be the zeros of $P_2(s)$; some of them may be zeros of $P_1(-s)$. The negatives of these, which lie in the right half plane, will be zeros of $P_1(s)$, indicating that the transfer function is nonminimum-phase.

To illustrate these ideas, suppose that it is desired to find the transfer function when the following tangent function is given.

$$\tan\phi(\omega) = \frac{-13(\omega - \omega^3)}{2 - 10\omega^2 + 2\omega^4} \qquad (4\text{-}39)$$

The first step is to obtain $A(j\omega)$ according to Eq. (4-38). Thus

$$A(j\omega) = \frac{1 + j\tan\phi}{1 - j\tan\phi} = \frac{2\omega^4 - 10\omega^2 + 2 - j13\omega + j13\omega^3}{2\omega^4 - 10\omega^2 + 2 + j13\omega - j13\omega^3} \quad (4\text{-}40)$$

Replacing $j\omega$ by s yields

$$A(s) = \frac{2s^4 - 13s^3 + 10s^2 - 13s + 2}{2s^4 + 13s^3 + 10s^2 + 13s + 2} = \frac{(2s^2 - s + 2)(s^2 - 6s + 1)}{(2s^2 + s + 2)(s^2 + 6s + 1)}$$

$$(4\text{-}41)$$

After obtaining $A(s)$ a computational problem exists: we must find the poles and zeros. This involves factoring a high-order polynomial. (Only the denominator polynomial need be factored since the zeros of the numerator are the negatives of those of the denominator.) The result is shown on the far right of the last equation. There are two real poles and zeros and a pair of complex ones. All the zeros are in the right half plane while all the poles are in the left. We can assign any combination of the poles of $A(s)$ to $P_2(s)$, so long as the resulting transfer function has no pole at infinity. (Of course the complex pair must be kept together.) Any one of the following five alternatives can be obtained.

$$F_1(s) = \frac{K_1}{(2s^2 + s + 2)(s^2 + 6s + 1)} \qquad \text{(a)}$$

$$F_2(s) = \frac{K_2(a - s)}{(2s^2 + s + 2)(s + b)} \qquad \text{(b)}$$

$$F_3(s) = \frac{K_3(b - s)}{(2s^2 + s + 2)(s + a)} \qquad \text{(c)} \qquad \text{(4-42)}$$

$$F_4(s) = K_4 \frac{s^2 - 6s + 1}{2s^2 + s + 2} \qquad \text{(d)}$$

$$F_5(s) = K_5 \frac{2s^2 - s + 2}{s^2 + 6s + 1} \qquad \text{(e)}$$

In the second and third of these we have written $s + a$ and $s + b$ for the factors of $s^2 + 6s + 1$.

These transfer functions have the same angle for all $s = j\omega$, but the behavior of their magnitudes is quite different. The values of the gain constants permitted by Fialkow's condition will also be different. The second and third ones have a positive real transmission zero so that they require a balanced structure for their realization, while the other three might be realized by an unbalanced network. All these considerations will affect the choice in the formation of a transfer function from a given tangent function.

C. *Magnitude and Angle Functions of a Resistance-loaded Lossless Two-Port*

Since we shall be dealing to a considerable extent with the realization of resistance-terminated lossless two-ports, it will be worthwhile to discuss the additional restrictions imposed on the magnitude and angle functions by the lossless requirement. In the last section we observed that the transfer function of such a network has a Hurwitz denominator and an even or odd numerator. Hence we can write

$$F(s) = \frac{N_{12}(s)}{m + n} \qquad (4\text{-}43)$$

where m and n are the even and odd parts of a Hurwitz polynomial and N_{12} is an even or an odd polynomial. The magnitude-squared function can then be written

$$G(-s^2) = F(s)F(-s) = \frac{\pm N_{12}^2(s)}{m^2 - n^2} \qquad (4\text{-}44)$$

In this expression the minus sign applies when N_{12} is odd, since in this case $N_{12}(-s) = -N_{12}(s)$. It is clear that, for the type of network under consideration, all the zeros of $G(-s^2)$ are of even multiplicity. Hence, when

$G(-s^2)$ is given, we divide its zeros equally between $F(s)$ and $F(-s)$. As we mentioned in the last section, the zeros of the transfer function of a resistance-loaded lossless two-port will occur in quadrantal symmetry. Hence the only way in which $F(s)$ can be minimum-phase is to have all its zeros fall on the $j\omega$ axis.

Turn now to the A function. With $F(s)$ from Eq. (4-43) substituted into Eqs. (4-37), we get

$$A(s) = \pm \frac{m - n}{m + n} \qquad (4\text{-}45)$$

The minus sign applies when N_{12} is odd. We see that $A(s)$ and $F(s)$ have the same poles. The poles of $A(s)$ are all in the left half plane, while the zeros are all in the right.

To establish the requirements on $\tan \phi$ for a lossless two-port, turn again to Eq. (4-38). If we solve this for $j \tan \phi$ in terms of A and substitute Eq. (4-45), we get

$$j \tan \phi = \frac{A - 1}{A + 1} = -\frac{n}{m} \qquad \text{for } N_{12} \text{ even}$$

$$j \tan \phi = \frac{A - 1}{A + 1} = -\frac{m}{n} \qquad \text{for } N_{12} \text{ odd} \qquad (4\text{-}46)$$

Since $m + n$ is a Hurwitz polynomial, we can state that, *for a resistance loaded lossless two-port, $j \tan \phi$ must be the negative of a reactance function.* It is clear from this expression that the positive sign in Eq. (4-45) will apply when $\tan \phi$ is zero at $\omega = 0$, while the negative sign will apply when $\tan \phi$ is infinite there. You can demonstrate this result for the numerical example given in Eq. (4-39). The A function given in Eq. (4-41) has the form shown in Eq. (4-45). As predicted, if we assign all the poles of $A(s)$ to $F(s)$ we obtain a transfer function which is realizable as a lossless two-port with a resistance load. (At least, it satisfies necessary conditions of realizability in this form.) This is the first function in Eqs. (4-42).

Suppose that we start with a prescribed $\tan \phi$ function and the stipulation that the corresponding network is to be a lossless two-port with a resistance load. Of course, the given function must have one of the forms given in Eqs. (4-46). We form $A(s)$ according to Eq. (4-38), and then we assign all its poles to $F(s)$. We know whether or not the numerator of $F(s)$ is even or odd from the zero-frequency value of the given $\tan \phi$, according to Eqs. (4-46). However, the tangent function is not affected if we assign additional zeros to $F(s)$, provided that they have quadrantal symmetry. Thus we have a certain amount of control over the zeros of $F(s)$ without affecting the angle. Of course, there is a limit on the number of zeros we can insert in this manner since the final $F(s)$ should have no pole at infinity.

4-5. Minimum-phase and all-pass function

While discussing magnitude and angle functions in the last section, we encountered minimum- and nonminimum-phase transfer functions. The distinction between such functions is based solely on the permissible locations of the zeros. Thus we define a minimum-phase transfer function as one that has no zeros in the right half plane.

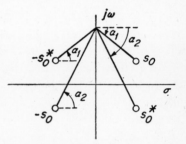

Fig. 4-14. Right half plane zeros and their images.

Let us compare the effects on the magnitude and phase of a transfer function from a pair of conjugate right-half-plane zeros and the pair in the left half plane which is the mirror image of the former. A quadruplet of such zeros is shown in Fig. 4-14. Let us write

$$P_a(s) = (s - s_0)(s - s_0^*) \qquad \text{(a)}$$
$$P_b(s) = (s + s_0)(s + s_0^*) \qquad \text{(b)} \qquad (4\text{-}47)$$

P_a has the two right-half-plane zeros, while P_b has the two left-half-plane zeros. When $s = j\omega$, the magnitudes of these two polynomials are the same, as evidenced by the figure. Using the notation in the figure, we find the angles of the two polynomials to be

$$\arg P_a(j\omega) = (\pi - \alpha_1) - (\pi + \alpha_2) = -(\alpha_1 + \alpha_2) \quad \text{(a)}\dagger$$
$$\arg P_b(j\omega) = \alpha_1 + \alpha_2 \qquad \text{(b)} \qquad (4\text{-}48)$$

For positive values of ω it is clear from the figure that $\alpha_1 + \alpha_2$, the angle contributed by the left-half-plane zeros, is always positive, ranging from zero at $\omega = 0$ to π at infinity. It follows from Eqs. (4-48), then, that the angle of $P_a(j\omega)$ is always negative for positive values of ω.

Consider the following two transfer functions:

$$F_1(s) = (s - s_0)(s - s_0^*)F(s) \qquad \text{(a)}$$
$$F_2(s) = (s + s_0)(s + s_0^*)F(s) \qquad \text{(b)} \qquad (4\text{-}49)$$

These two functions differ by the fact that $F_1(s)$ has a pair of complex

---

† We have chosen to write the angle of $s - s_0^*$ as $-(\pi + \alpha_2)$ rather than $\pi - \alpha_2$ in order that the angle contributed by the complex pair be zero at $\omega = 0$ rather than 2π. For a more complete discussion see Balabanian and LePage (3).

zeros in the right half plane, while in $F_2(s)$ these are replaced by their left-half-plane images. Both functions may have additional zeros in the right-half plane which are not explicitly shown. If we multiply and divide the first one by $(s + s_0)(s + s_0^*)$, we shall get

$$F_1(s) = F_2(s) \frac{(s - s_0)(s - s_0^*)}{(s + s_0)(s + s_0^*)} = F_2(s)F_{a1}(s) \qquad (4\text{-}50)$$

where

$$F_{a1}(s) = \frac{(s - s_0)(s - s_0^*)}{(s + s_0)(s + s_0^*)} \qquad (4\text{-}51)$$

From the results of the preceding discussion it is clear that the magnitude of $F_{a1}(j\omega)$ is unity. Its zeros are in the right half plane, while its poles are in the left half plane, being mirror images of its zeros. Let us define an *all-pass function* to be a transfer function whose zeros are all in the right half plane and whose poles are the negatives of its zeros. Then $F_{a1}(s)$ in Eq. (4-51) is an all-pass function. Using Eqs. (4-48), we easily find that

$$\arg F_{a1}(j\omega) = -2(\alpha_1 + \alpha_2) < 0 \qquad \omega > 0 \qquad (4\text{-}52)$$

Thus the angle of the all-pass function is never positive for positive frequencies.

Using Eqs. (4-50) and (4-52), we can now write

$$\arg F_1(j\omega) = \arg F_2(j\omega) + \arg F_{a1}(j\omega) = \arg F_2(j\omega) - 2(\alpha_1 + \alpha_2)$$
$$< \arg F_2(j\omega) \qquad \text{for all } \omega > 0 \qquad (4\text{-}53)$$

In words, at positive frequencies the angle of the function having right-half-plane zeros is less than that of the function in which one pair of such zeros is replaced by its left-half-plane image.

This procedure of expressing a transfer function as the product of two others may now be repeated. At each step a pair of complex zeros or a real zero from the right half plane may be replaced by their left-half-plane images and the resulting function multiplied by an all-pass function. A sequence of functions, of which F_1 and F_2 are the first two, will be obtained. Each member in the sequence will have fewer right-half-plane zeros than the preceding one. The last member in this sequence will have no right-half-plane zeros, and we shall label it $F_m(s)$, the subscript implying "minimum-phase." From Eq. (4-53) and similar results for the other functions, we can write

$$\arg F_1(j\omega) < \arg F_2(j\omega) < \arg F_3(j\omega)$$
$$< \ldots < \arg F_m(j\omega) \qquad \omega > 0 \qquad (4\text{-}54)$$

Each of the transfer functions in this sequence will have the same magnitude, but the angles will become progressively larger. The minimum-phase function will have the largest angle of all.

At each step in the above procedure a second-order or first-order all-pass function is obtained (the order refers to the number of poles). Let us designate by $F_a(s)$ the product of all these all-pass functions. Then the original nonminimum-phase function can be written

$$F_1(s) = F_m(s)F_a(s) \qquad (4\text{-}55)$$

Thus a nonminimum-phase function can always be written as the product of a minimum-phase function and an all-pass function.

A word of explanation is necessary about the terminology. We have seen that the angle of a minimum-phase function is larger than that of a corresponding nonminimum-phase function. Why, then, do we call it *minimum*-phase? In this book we have defined all transfer functions as ratios of an output quantity to an input quantity. We could, instead, define them as ratios of input to output. The angle of the latter will be the negative of the angle of the former. Hence, in Eq. (4-52) the negative sign would be absent, and the inequality would be reversed. Similarly the inequalities in Eq. (4-54) would be reversed, and the minimum-phase function *would* have the smallest angle. The concept of minimum-phase and nonminimum-phase originated with Bode (16), who does, indeed, define transfer functions as ratios of input to output quantities. We shall continue to use this terminology since it is so well established, in spite of the apparent contradiction of the words "minimum phase" by the property of largest angle.

Since the zeros of an all-pass function are the negatives of its poles, such a function can be written as

$$F_a(s) = \frac{m - n}{m + n} \qquad (4\text{-}56)$$

where m and n are the even and odd parts of a Hurwitz polynomial. If we glance back at Eq. (4-45), we shall find that an all-pass transfer function has the same form as the A function of a lossless two-port.

Let us inquire whether or not an all-pass function can be the transfer function of a resistance-terminated lossless two-port. The last equation shows that the numerator is not an even or an odd polynomial. However, all the zeros are in the right half plane. In Sec. 4-3 we found that such a situation is possible if left-half-plane zeros of the transfer function have been canceled. Thus an all-pass function satisfies the necessary conditions for being the transfer function of an LC two-port with a resistance load.

PROBLEMS

4-1. Figure P 4-1 shows a two-port at each pair of terminals of which an ideal transformer is connected. The secondaries of the transformers are connected in series. Show that the driving-point impedance looking into the series-connected secondaries is

$$Z(s) = x_1^2 z_{11} + 2 x_1 x_2 z_{12} + x_2^2 z_{22}$$

where x_1 and x_2 are the turns ratios of the ideal transformers. This interpretation of the quadratic form on the right was first suggested by Brune.

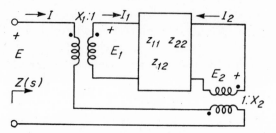

Fig. P 4-1

4-2. Show that the residue condition for the z parameters of a transformer will be satisfied with the equality sign if the coefficient of coupling is unity. In analogy with a close-coupled transformer Dasher introduced the term *compact* two-port to refer to any two-port for which the residue condition is satisfied with the equality sign.

4-3. (a) Let the z parameters of a lossless two-port have a compact pole at $s = 0$. Show that the y parameters will also have a pole at $s = 0$.

(b) Repeat if the pole is at infinity.

4-4. Show that any zeros of z_{12} and of y_{12} of a lossless two-port that are not shared by both must lie on the $j\omega$ axis and must be either simple or double.

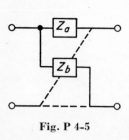

Fig. P 4-5

4-5. Given two real rational functions z_{12} and $z_{11} = z_{22}$, both regular in the right-half s plane. Show that if the real-part conditions in Eqs. (4-6) and the residue conditions in Eqs. (4-3) for all j-axis poles are satisfied then the impedances Z_a and Z_b of the symmetrical lattice shown in Fig. P 4-5 realizing these functions are positive real. This establishes the fact that a symmetrical lattice will realize any given set of realizable symmetrical z parameters.

4-6. Let N represent a two-port which is both structurally and electrically symmetrical with z parameters $z_{11} = z_{22}$ and z_{12}, and y parameters

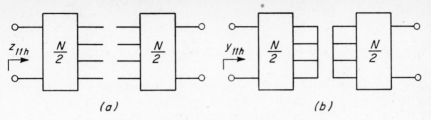

Fig. P 4-6. Bartlett's bisection theorem.

$y_{11} = y_{22}$ and y_{12}. Consider bisecting the two-port at its structural line of symmetry. At the junction of the two halves some terminals will be created. Assume that, before the bisection, none of the leads, from which these terminals are formed, were crossed. Now consider the two cases shown in Fig. P 4-6, in which these terminals are left open and are short-circuited, respectively. Designate by z_{11h} and y_{11h} the input impedance and the input admittance in the two cases (the subscript stands for half). Prove that

$$z_{11h} = z_{11} + z_{12} \quad ; \quad \frac{1}{y_{11h}} = z_{11} - z_{12}$$

or

$$\frac{1}{z_{11h}} = y_{11} + y_{12} \quad ; \quad y_{11h} = y_{11} - y_{12}$$

Recalling the expressions for the arm impedances of a symmetrical lattice, this leads to the result

$$z_{11h} = Z_b$$

$$\frac{1}{y_{11h}} = Z_a$$

if the original network is to be equivalent to a symmetrical lattice. One method of proof, due to Brune,† consists in first applying voltages $E_1 = E_2 = E$ at the terminals of the original network and then $E_1 = -E_2 = E$. These correspond to the two cases above.

4-7. Let $F(j\omega) = |F(j\omega)|\epsilon^{j\phi}$ be a transfer function. The following tangent functions are given. Find the corresponding $F(s)$. If there is more than one choice, find all of them.

(a) $\tan \phi = \dfrac{-\omega}{\omega^2 + 2}$

(b) $\tan \phi = \dfrac{8\omega^3 + 2\omega}{\omega^4 - 17\omega^2 - 24}$

(c) $\tan \phi = \dfrac{-\omega^3}{\omega^4 - 4\omega^2 + 24}$

† O. Brune, "Note on Bartlett's Bisection Theorem," *Phil. Mag., 14*, p. 806, Nov. 1932.

(d) $\tan \phi = \dfrac{2 - 3\omega^2}{4\omega - \omega^3}$

4-8. (a) Figure P 4-8 shows an L network. Assume that there is no magnetic coupling between the arms. Let $T_{12}(s) = E_2/E_1$. Prove that for Re $s \geq 0$, whenever $T_{12}(s)$ is real, it must be positive and no greater than unity.

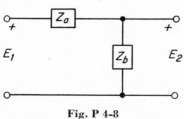

Fig. P 4-8

(b) Using this result, prove the same condition for a ladder network which has no magnetic coupling between branches. Assuming that any minimum-phase T_{12} function can be realized as a ladder network (this will be shown in Chap. 8), this establishes the result that whenever a minimum-phase transfer function is real for any right-half-plane values of s, it must be positive and no greater than unity.

4-9. Let $F(s)$ be the transfer function of a passive two-port with no positive real zeros but with complex zeros in the right half plane. It has already been proved that $|F(s)| \leq 1$ for real positive values of s. Show that, if $F(s)$ has n poles, then $|F(s)| \leq 1$ for arg $s \leq \pi/2n$.

4-10. Show that if a shunt-branch impedance of a ladder network is zero at $s = 0$ or infinity, then the open-circuit transfer impedance of the network must also have a zero there, even though the impedance looking to the right beyond the shunt branch also is zero at $s = 0$ or infinity, respectively.

4-11. Let

$$F(s) = K \frac{s^k(s^m + a_{m-1}s^{m-1} + \ldots + a_1s + a_0)}{s^n + b_{n-1}s^{n-1} + \ldots + b_1s + b_0}$$

be a minimum-phase transfer function. Show that the net change in angle as ω goes from zero to infinity is $(m - n)\pi/2$. This is also $-\pi/2$ times the sum of the order of the zero of $F(s)$ at zero and that at infinity.

5

Realization of Lossless Two-Ports

In the previous chapter we concentrated on establishing necessary conditions for realizability of the various functions describing the behavior of two-ports in general and of lossless two-ports in particular. We saw how the structure of the network affects the behavior. We are now ready to discuss the problem of realization, assuming that the prescribed function (or functions) satisfies the necessary conditions of realizability. We shall discuss the realization problems in increasing order of complexity.

5-1. Symmetrical two-ports

An often occuring problem, and one which is relatively easy to handle, is the following: We are asked to provide a coupling network to be inserted in the plate circuit of a pentode amplifier tube, its output feeding into the grid circuit of a second tube. Making the usual approximations, we consider the first tube to be a current source and the grid to ground impedance of the second tube to be infinite. So the response that is prescribed for the coupling network is the ratio of open-circuit voltage to input current, z_{12}.

If the coupling network is to be lossless, the prescribed z_{12} will be required to have simple poles restricted to the $j\omega$ axis and its residues will have to be real. Since z_{11} and z_{22} are not prescribed, we shall have great latitude in choosing these functions. They must, of course, be reactance functions, and they must be chosen to satisfy the residue requirement.

One simple solution to the problem is to assume that the network is symmetrical ($z_{11} = z_{22}$). In the case of a symmetrical lossless two-port the residue condition reads

$$k_{11}^2 - k_{12}^2 = (k_{11} - k_{12})(k_{11} + k_{12}) \geq 0 \qquad (5\text{-}1)$$

where k_{11} is positive, while k_{12} may be positive or negative. This condition can be satisfied only if $k_{11} \geq |k_{12}|$.

In the given problem only z_{12} is prescribed. It remains for us to find $z_{11} = z_{22}$ such that the residue condition is satisfied. In the preceding chapter we established that noncompactness leads to an extra series branch at the input or output. Such a branch is redundant as far as z_{12} is concerned, since z_{12} will in no way be affected. For this reason it is better to choose a compact set of z parameters. We go through the following procedure, then, in synthesizing a lossless two-port for a prescribed z_{12} function: We first expand the given function in partial fractions; some of the residues k_{12j} will be positive, some negative. The partial-fraction expansion of z_{11} will be the same as that of z_{12}, but with the negative residues made positive, that is, $k_{11j} = |k_{12j}|$. Analytically, let us write

$$z_{12} = z_{12p} - z_{12n} \tag{5-2}$$

Here we have grouped all the terms in the expansion of z_{12} with positive residue in z_{12p} and all those with negative residue in $-z_{12n}$. Note that z_{12p} and z_{12n} are individually reactance functions. Now we write

$$z_{22} = z_{11} = z_{12p} + z_{12n} \tag{5-3}$$

We now have a set, z_{12} and $z_{11} = z_{22}$, which satisfies the necessary realizability criteria for a symmetrical lossless two-port. It is easy to show that a symmetrical lattice will realize any given set of realizable symmetrical z parameters (see Prob. 4-5). Such a lattice is shown in Fig. 5-1. It

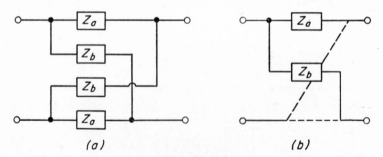

Fig. 5-1. Symmetrical lattice.

is usually drawn in the second form to avoid confusion. The z parameters of the lattice are given (see Prob. 1-3) by

$$z_{11} = z_{22} = \tfrac{1}{2}(Z_b + Z_a)$$
$$z_{12} = \tfrac{1}{2}(Z_b - Z_a) \tag{5-4}$$

If we solve this set of equations for Z_a and Z_b, we shall get

$$Z_a = z_{11} - z_{12} \qquad \text{(a)}$$
$$Z_b = z_{11} + z_{12} \qquad \text{(b)}$$
$$(5\text{-}5)$$

Finally, using Eqs. (5-2) and (5-3), these become

$$Z_a = 2z_{12n}$$
$$Z_b = 2z_{12p}$$
$$(5\text{-}6)$$

Thus Z_a and Z_b will be realizable reactance functions which we can realize in any of the equivalant forms discussed in Chap. 2. Note that the two lattice arms have no common poles. If we had not satisfied the residue condition with the equality sign at one of the poles, then this pole would have appeared in both Z_a and Z_b, leading to more complicated lattice arms.

As an example of this procedure, let the prescribed function be

$$z_{12} = \frac{2s}{(s^2 + 1)(s^2 + 2)(s^2 + 3)} = \frac{s}{s^2 + 1} + \frac{s}{s^2 + 3} - \frac{2s}{s^2 + 2} \quad (5\text{-}7)$$

This function has simple poles restricted to the $j\omega$ axis, and its residues are real. Incidentally the zeros are at zero and infinity, and so they are also on the $j\omega$ axis. We now form z_{11} and the lattice impedances.

$$z_{11} = \frac{s}{s^2 + 1} + \frac{s}{s^2 + 3} + \frac{2s}{s^2 + 2}$$

$$Z_a = z_{11} - z_{12} = \frac{4s}{s^2 + 2} \qquad (5\text{-}8)$$

$$Z_b = z_{11} + z_{12} = \frac{2s}{s^2 + 1} + \frac{2s}{s^2 + 3}$$

The resulting network is shown in Fig. 5-2.

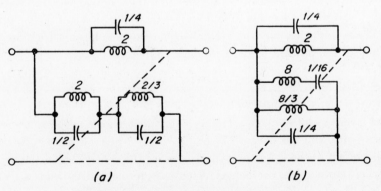

Fig. 5-2. Realization of numerical example.

The main disadvantage of this realization is the balanced structure of the resulting network. It is usually desirable to have an unbalanced network. This leads us to inquire into the possibility of converting a lattice into an equivalent unbalanced two-port. We know that this will not always be possible because unbalanced two-ports cannot have transmission zeros in parts of the s plane where balanced two-ports can. Nevertheless, whenever a conversion *is* possible, it would be well to have procedures for carrying out the conversion.

5-2. Conversion of symmetrical lattice to unbalanced form

In the preceding section we discussed the synthesis of a prescribed loss-less z_{12} function in terms of a symmetrical lattice. A symmetrical lattice arises in other synthesis techniques as well, such as in the design of all-pass networks and in conventional filter design. The disadvantage of such a balanced structure can be overcome if an unbalanced equivalent of the lattice can be found. Our purpose now is to discuss ways of breaking down the lattice step by step until the entire lattice is unbalanced. We should not expect this to be possible in all cases since the lossless lattice is the most general symmetrical lossless two-port. We have already taken the first step in this direction; we showed in the preceding chapter that the transmission zeros of a lossless ladder must lie on the $j\omega$ axis. If the zeros of the prescribed z_{12} are not all on the $j\omega$ axis, we should at least not expect to find a ladder equivalent of the lattice.

Furthermore, the Fialkow-Gerst theorem gives us necessary conditions for the realizability of more general unbalanced two-ports. Thus, if the given z_{12} has real transmission zeros, no unbalanced equivalent of the lattice will exist. As a matter of fact, even if there are no real transmission zeros, we might not be able to find an unbalanced equivalent of the lattice because the sufficiency of the Fialkow-Gerst theorem has not been demonstrated for the problem under consideration here.

Let us now embark on the task of converting the lattice to an equivalent unbalanced form. Suppose the two arms of the lattice have a common series impedance, as illustrated in Fig. 5-3. Let us form the tee equivalent of the lattice (see Prob. 1-4). The tee equivalent, shown in the second part of the figure, will not necessarily be physically realizable since it involves a subtraction in the shunt branch. However, the central tee in the figure, omitting the two Z_0's, can be converted back into a realizable lattice. The result is shown in Fig. 5-3(c). By this process any impedances which the series and crossarms of the lattice may have in common can be removed and placed in series at the input and output terminals, leaving a central lattice with simpler arms.

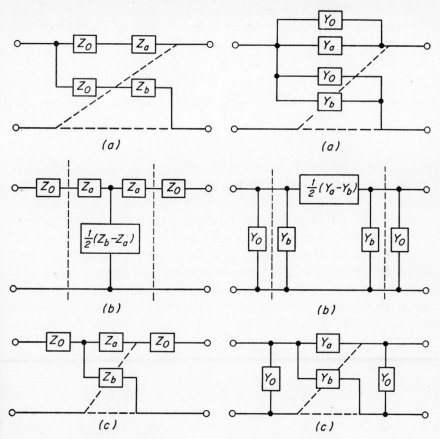

Fig. 5-3. Decomposition of lattice—series arm removal.

Fig. 5-4. Decomposition of lattice—shunt arm removal.

The situation dual to the one we just discussed immediately comes to mind. Suppose the two arms of the lattice have a common shunt admittance, as illustrated in Fig. 5-4. Let us form the equivalent of the lattice, as shown in the second part of the figure. Again this involves a subtraction in one of the branches and, hence, may not be physically realizable. Nevertheless a realizable network is obtained when the central pi, not including the Y_0's, is converted back into a lattice. The result is shown in the last part of the figure. In this fashion any admittances which the arms of the lattice may have in common can be removed and placed in shunt at the input and output terminals, leaving a central lattice with simpler arms.

After the completion of either one of these steps, it may be that conditions are right for the application of the other step. In such a case these two steps may be applied alternately until the complete lattice is unbal-

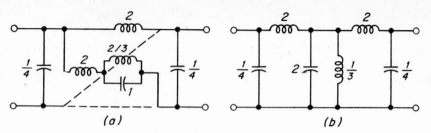

Fig. 5-5. Unbalancing a simple lattice.

anced. The resulting two-port will be a ladder. Of course, this requires all the zeros of the original z_{12} to lie on the $j\omega$ axis.

In the numerical example given in Eq. (5-7) the transmission zeros occur at zero and infinity, and so we should expect that a ladder realization is possible. Let us see if we can obtain such a realization by applying the two steps we have just discussed. In the second form of the lattice realization given in Fig. 5-2 the capacitance $C = \frac{1}{4}$ that appears as a parallel component of both arms may be removed and placed in shunt across the terminals, as in Fig. 5-4. The remaining impedance in the crossarm can then be converted to the first Foster form. The result is shown in Fig. 5-5(a). The algebra involved proceeds as follows: Starting with the crossarm impedance in Eqs. (5-8), we write

$$Z_b = \frac{2s}{s^2 + 1} + \frac{2s}{s^2 + 3} = \frac{4s(s^2 + 2)}{(s^2 + 1)(s^2 + 3)}$$

$$Y_b = \frac{1}{Z_b} = \frac{(s^2 + 1)(s^2 + 3)}{4s(s^2 + 2)} = \frac{1}{4}s + \frac{3}{8s} + \frac{s/8}{s^2 + 2} \qquad (5\text{-}9)$$

$$Y_b' = Y_b - \frac{1}{4}s = \frac{3}{8s} + \frac{s/8}{s^2 + 2} = \frac{2s^2 + 3}{4s(s^2 + 2)}$$

$$Z_b' = \frac{1}{Y_b'} = \frac{4s(s^2 + 2)}{2s^2 + 3} = 2s + \frac{s}{s^2 + \frac{3}{2}}$$

The crossarm and the series arm now have a common series inductance which can be removed as a series branch, as in Fig. 5-3. Since this inductance constitutes the whole of the lattice series arm, a short circuit will be left when it is removed, placing the remaining crossarms in parallel. Subtracting $2s$ from Z_b' yields

$$Z_b'' = Z_b' - 2s = \frac{s}{s^2 + \frac{3}{2}} \qquad \text{(a)}$$

$$\qquad\qquad\qquad\qquad\qquad\qquad\qquad (5\text{-}10)$$

$$Y_b'' = s + \frac{3}{2s} \qquad \text{(b)}$$

The complete ladder equivalent is shown in Fig. 5-5(b).

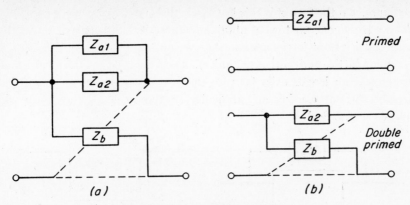

Fig. 5-6. Decomposition of lattice.

Suppose that at a particular stage of the development neither of the two steps in Fig. 5-3 or 5-4 is possible. Consider Fig. 5-6(a), and recall the expressions for y_{11} and y_{12} of the symmetrical lattice (see Prob. 1-3). These can be written

$$y_{11} = \tfrac{1}{2}(Y_b + Y_{a2}) + \tfrac{1}{2}Y_{a1} = y_{11}'' + y_{11}'$$

$$y_{12} = \tfrac{1}{2}(Y_b - Y_{a2}) - \tfrac{1}{2}Y_{a1} = y_{12}'' + y_{12}'$$

$$(5\text{-}11)$$

The primed and double-primed parameters refer to the networks in Fig. 5-6(b). The parallel connection of these two networks will be equivalent to the original. However, if they are connected in parallel directly as in Fig. 5-7(a), then the series arms of the lattice will be short-circuited.

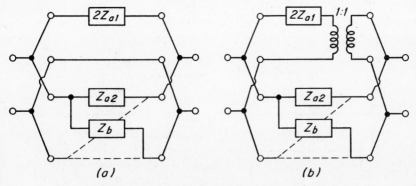

Fig. 5-7. Incorrect and correct methods of parallel connection.

Hence the over-all y parameters of this parallel connection will not be the sum of the y parameters of the individual networks. This difficulty can be overcome by the use of a 1:1 ideal transformer as shown in part (b) of the figure. On the face of it this last figure does not leave us very confident that we have gone far toward obtaining a practical unbalanced equivalent of the lattice. But let us assume that we are now able to unbalance the remaining lattice (possibly as a ladder). Then the need for the ideal transformer will no longer exist because the two networks can be paralleled directly without causing any difficulty. A redrawing of the figure will look like Fig. 5-8(a).

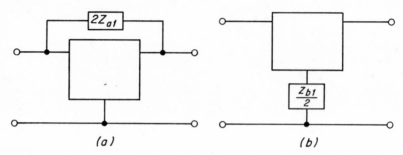

Fig. 5-8. Steps in unbalancing a lattice.

Another equivalence can be established from a consideration of Fig. 5-9 and the expressions for the z parameters of the lattice (see Prob. 1-3). These may be written

$$z_{11} = \tfrac{1}{2}Z_{b1} + \tfrac{1}{2}(Z_{b2} + Z_a) = z'_{11} + z''_{11}$$
$$z_{12} = \tfrac{1}{2}Z_{b1} + \tfrac{1}{2}(Z_{b2} - Z_a) = z'_{12} + z''_{12}$$

(5-12)

The primed and double-primed parameters refer to the two-ports of Fig. 5-9(b). The series connection of these two will be equivalent to the original. However, if this connection is made directly as in Fig. 5-10(a), one of the series arms of the lattice will be short-circuited so that it will not be

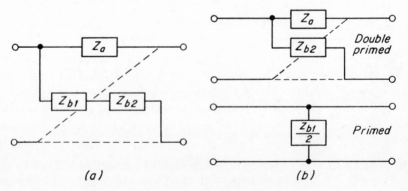

Fig. 5-9. Alternative decomposition of lattice.

permissible to add the individual z parameters in order to obtain the over-all z parameters. Again the difficulty is overcome by the use of an ideal transformer as in Fig. 5-10(b). If it is possible to replace the remaining

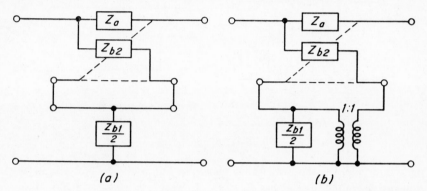

Fig. 5-10. Incorrect and correct methods of series correction.

lattice with an unbalanced equivalent, there will then be no need for the ideal transformer and so it can be removed. The resulting network, after redrawing, looks like Fig. 5-8(b).

We have now presented four distinct steps that can be used in convert-ing a lattice into an equivalent unbalanced form. These are illustrated in Figs. 5-3, 5-4, and 5-8. For future reference let us renumber these steps in a different order from that originally presented.

Step 1. Removal in shunt of any common admittance of the lattice arms as in Fig. 5-4

Step 2. Removal of a bridging branch as in Fig. 5-8(a)

Step 3. Removal in series of any common impedance of the lattice arms as in Fig. 5-3

Step 4. Removal of a branch as the leg of tee as in Fig. 5-8(b)

After the application of any one of these steps, conditions may be appropriate for the application of any one of the others. Some ingenuity may be required in the application of this procedure in a practical situation.

As a simple example, consider the lattice shown in Fig. 5-11. This lattice occurs quite frequently in network synthesis. Let us contemplate the removal of the capacitance C_1 as a bridging element. Anticipating that the rest of the lattice will eventually be unbalanced, we can dispense with the ideal transformer. The remaining lattice shown in the second of the figures has series inductance in both arms. Suppose we remove L_1 according to step 3. The series arm of the remaining lattice will now be a short circuit, thus placing the remaining crossarms in parallel. The com-

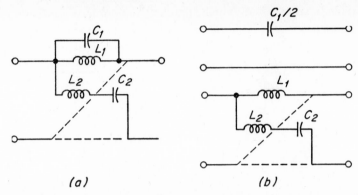

Fig. 5-11. Simple lattice.

plete equivalent is the bridged tee shown in Fig. 5-12(a). This will involve a negative inductance unless $L_1 \le L_2$. In any case the tee of inductances can be replaced by an equivalent transformer.

Alternatively we can remove the inductance L_1 as a bridging element. The remaining lattice can now be converted to an equivalent tee with

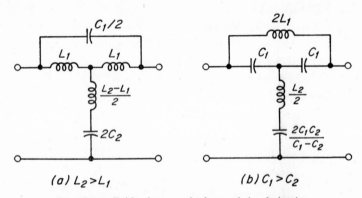

Fig. 5-12. Bridged tee equivalents of simple lattice.

capacitance C_1 in the two series arms. The result is shown in Fig. 5-12(b). This will be possible only if C_1 is larger than C_2.

Let us now consider a moderately complicated illustration of the process of unbalancing a lattice. The lattice shown in Fig. 5-13 has the branch impedances

$$Z_a = \frac{2s(4s^2 + 1)}{4s^4 + 6s^2 + 1} \qquad \text{(a)}$$

$$(5\text{-}13)$$

$$Z_b = \frac{(4s^2 + 1)(s^2 + 1)}{s(3s^2 + 1)} \qquad \text{(b)}$$

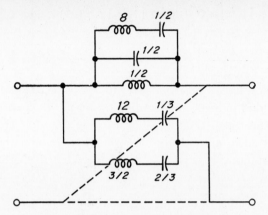

Fig. 5-13. Lattice to be unbalanced.

If we compute the open-circuit transfer impedance, we shall find

$$z_{12} = \frac{2(4s^2 + 1)(s^2 + 0.238)(s^4 + 0.762s^2 + 1.069)}{s(3s^2 + 1)(4s^4 + 6s^2 + 1)} \qquad (5\text{-}14)$$

This is seen to have no zeros on the real axis so that an unbalanced realization is not out of the question. On the other hand, not all the zeros are on the $j\omega$ axis. Hence we should not expect the possibility of a ladder equivalent.

The lattice impedances do not behave the same at zero and infinite frequency. Suppose that we write

$$Z_b = \frac{1}{s} + \frac{2s(2s^2 + 1)}{3s^2 + 1} = Z_{b1} + Z_{b2} \qquad (5\text{-}15)$$

and remove $Z_{b1}/2$ according to step 4. Both arms of the remaining lattice will now have an impedance zero at $s = 0$. Their reciprocals can be written

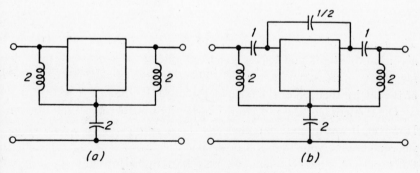

Fig. 5-14. Decomposition of lattice.

$$Y_a = \frac{4s^4 + 6s^2 + 1}{2s(4s^2 + 1)} = \frac{1}{2s} + \frac{s(2s^2 + 1)}{4s^2 + 1} = Y_{a1} + Y_{a2}$$

$$Y_{b2} = \frac{3s^2 + 1}{2s(2s^2 + 1)} = \frac{1}{2s} + \frac{s}{2(2s^2 + 1)} = Y_{b3} + Y_{b4}$$

(5-16)

Both admittances have a pole at $s = 0$ with the same residue. This permits removal of a shunt inductance according to step 1. The partial decomposition of the lattice takes the form shown in Fig. 5-14(a). The ideal transformer is omitted in anticipation of a complete decomposition. Both remaining admittances, Y_{a2} and Y_{b4}, now have zeros at $s = 0$. Their reciprocals can be written

$$Z_{a2} = \frac{4s^2 + 1}{s(2s^2 + 1)} = \frac{1}{s} + \frac{2s}{2s^2 + 1} = Z_{a3} + Z_{a4}$$

$$Z_{b4} = \frac{2(2s^2 + 1)}{s} = \frac{1}{s} + \frac{4s^2 + 1}{s} = Z_{b5} + Z_{b6}$$

(5-17)

The residue of Z_{b4} at $s = 0$ is larger than that of Z_{a2}. The form of Eqs. (5-17) now suggests removal of a series branch according to step 3. This will be a capacitance of value unity.

The remaining admittance Y_{a4} has a pole at infinity which the remaining crossarm admittance Y_{b6} does not have. We can consider removing this pole as a bridging branch according to step 2. Thus

$$Y_{a4} = \frac{2s^2 + 1}{2s} = s + \frac{1}{2s} = Y_{a5} + Y_{a6}$$

(5-18)

The bridging element is a capacitance of value $\frac{1}{2}$ (not of value unity since the bridging impedance is to be $2Z_{a5}$). At this stage the decomposition is shown in Fig. 5-14(b).

The impedances of the remaining lattice are now

$$Z_{a6} = 2s$$

$$Z_{b6} = \frac{4s^2 + 1}{s} = 2s + \frac{2s^2 + 1}{s}$$

(5-19)

The removal of a series branch consisting of an inductance of value 2 according to step 3 now leaves a short circuit in the series arm, thus placing the two crossarms in parallel. The complete unbalanced equivalent of the lattice then takes the form of Fig. 5-15.

On the surface, the procedure we went through was straightforward. However, it was by judicious choice of the steps that we came to a successful conclusion. Note that the original lattice arms both have an admittance pole at $s^2 = -\frac{1}{4}$. Thus we may be tempted initially to carry out

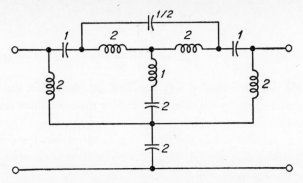

Fig. 5-15. Unbalanced equivalent of lattice.

step 1 and remove a series-resonant circuit at the start. You can easily show that, starting in this manner, the decomposition eventually will be blocked.

In a later chapter we shall discuss a realization procedure of a symmetrical two-port which was first advanced by Ozaki in connection with *RC* two-ports. It applies equally well to the lossless case. This procedure is related to the lattice unbalancing which we have discussed in this section, but all the guesswork is eliminated.

5-3. Synthesis for a prescribed Y_{12}, Z_{12}, or T_{12}

In Sec. 5-1 we considered the problem of realizing a given open-circuit transfer impedance. We shall now consider the more important and more complicated problems illustrated in Fig. 5-16. The problem is to synthesize

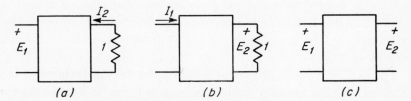

Fig. 5-16. Synthesis problems.

a lossless network to be inserted between a resistive load (normalized to 1 ohm) and a voltage source or a current source. The prescribed functions are $Y_{12} = I_2/E_1$ or $E_2/I_1 = Z_{12}$. The expressions for Y_{12} and Z_{12} in terms of the z and y parameters, respectively, are

$$Y_{12} = \frac{y_{12}}{1 + y_{22}} \qquad \text{(a)}$$

$$\text{(5-20)}$$

$$Z_{12} = \frac{z_{12}}{1 + z_{22}} \qquad \text{(b)}$$

To be specific, let us consider only the first problem. We should expect the second problem to be handled in a similar manner, since the forms of the two equations are so similar.

We already established in the preceding chapter that the denominator of Y_{12} is a Hurwitz polynomial, while the numerator is an even or an odd polynomial. Thus we can write

$$-Y_{12}(s) = \frac{N_{12}(s)}{m(s) + n(s)} \qquad \text{(5-21)}$$

where N_{12} is an even or odd polynomial, while m and n are the even and odd parts of a Hurwitz polynomial, respectively. This equation can be rewritten in two ways, depending on whether N_{12} is even or odd. Thus

$$-Y_{12} = \frac{N_{12}/m}{1 + n/m} \qquad -y_{12} = \frac{N_{12}}{m}$$

$$N_{12} \text{ odd} \qquad \text{(5-22)}$$

$$y_{22} = \frac{n}{m}$$

$$-Y_{12} = \frac{N_{12}/n}{1 + m/n} \qquad -y_{12} = \frac{N_{12}}{n}$$

$$N_{12} \text{ even} \qquad \text{(5-23)}$$

$$y_{22} = \frac{m}{n}$$

The identification with the y parameters is made by comparing these equations with Eq. (5-20). In either of these cases, from the given Y_{12} we are able to determine two of the y parameters. Our problem is now reduced to the realization of a lossless two-port when two of the y parameters are prescribed. The procedure to be used will depend on the locations of the zeros of N_{12}.

The case of a prescribed transfer impedance Z_{12} can be handled in a completely similar manner. Again two cases will result; Eqs. (5-22) and (5-23) will apply just as well to z_{12} and z_{22}. Again the procedure to be followed in the realization will depend on the locations of the transmission zeros.

For completeness we shall include a consideration of the open-circuit voltage transfer function, although this problem is not so important as the previous two in the case of lossless two-ports. For the network of Fig. 5-16(c) the prescribed function is

$$T_{12} = \frac{E_2}{E_1} = -\frac{y_{12}}{y_{22}} = \frac{z_{12}}{z_{11}} \tag{5-24}$$

From the properties of the z or y parameters we can establish that $T_{12}(s)$ is an even rational function all of whose poles are simple and lie on the $j\omega$ axis, all the residues being imaginary. The zeros are not restricted except for the quadrantal symmetry requirement. Thus we can write

$$T_{12}(s) = \frac{N_{12}(s)}{m(s)} \tag{5-25}$$

where both N_{12} and m are even polynomials.

If a function T_{12} satisfying these necessary conditions is prescribed, we need to divide both numerator and denominator by an odd polynominal and identify, say, the y parameters y_{12} and y_{22}.

$$T_{12} = \frac{N_{12}}{m} = \frac{N_{12}/n}{m/n} = \frac{-y_{12}}{y_{22}}$$

$$-y_{12} = \frac{N_{12}}{n} \tag{5-26}$$

$$y_{22} = \frac{m}{n}$$

The polynomial n must be chosen so that its zeros are simple, lie on the $j\omega$ axis, and separate the zeros of m. This will ensure that the ratio m/n will be a reactance function.

We are now at the same stage in the solution of this problem as we were in the solution of the previous two. We have two z or y parameters prescribed. Again the realization procedure will depend on the locations of the zeros of N_{12}.

A possible realization procedure is to assume a symmetrical network. However, two of the three z or y parameters are now prescribed, rather than just z_{12} or y_{12}. We must first determine, whether or not a symmetrical network is possible under such conditions.

Let us carry out the discussion in terms of a given $Y_{12}(s)$; similar results follow when Z_{12} or T_{12} is the given function. In most problems the absolute transmission level is not of vital importance. That is to say, we shall be satisfied to realize the given $Y_{12}(s)$ to within a constant multiplier, counting on our ability subsequently to raise the transmission level by means of amplifiers. Nevertheless it is desirable to obtain as high a gain constant as possible in order to reduce the amount of amplification that must be supplied.

From the given transfer admittance $Y_{12}(s)$ we form the functions y_{12} and

y_{22}, as already described. Suppose the residue k_{12} is greater in magnitude than k_{22} at one of the poles. Then, in order to satisfy the residue condition, k_{11} must be larger than k_{22}. This means that the network cannot be symmetrical. However, if it is permitted to sacrifice transmission gain, the residue of y_{12} can be made as small as we please by reducing the constant multiplier of $Y_{12}(s)$. Thus we can always achieve the result $k_{22} \geq |k_{12}|$ at all the poles. The residue condition can now be satisfied by choosing $k_{11} = k_{22}$. This leads to a symmetrical network—and we have already discussed a realization technique for symmetrical networks.

With such a technique the transmission gain (constant multiplier of Y_{12}) is determined from the start, a fact which is not true for some other techniques, as we shall see. The method has two serious disadvantages. One of these, the low transmission level, we have already mentioned. The second disadvantage develops from the fact that a symmetrical network normally requires more elements than a nonsymmetrical one, although it is not possible to state this in a quantitative way.

5-4. Transmission zeros on $j\omega$ axis—ladder development

In the previous section we described how to determine two of the three z or y parameters from a given transfer function. It remains now actually to realize a lossless two-port from these two functions. Since the permissible locations of the transmission zeros of a two-port depend on its structure, we should expect to need different realization techniques, depending on the locations of the transmission zeros. In this section we shall consider the case in which all transmission zeros lie on the $j\omega$ axis.

For definiteness let us assume that we have y_{12} and y_{22} as realizable functions of s. Both functions have the same poles, and in addition y_{22} may have private poles as well. The zeros of these functions will, in general, be different. Since the transmission zeros lie on the $j\omega$ axis, we shall seek a ladder realization. For a ladder network the transmission zeros necessarily occur at series-impedance poles or shunt-impedance zeros.

In Chap. 2 we discussed the Cauer ladder development of a reactance function. The procedure consisted in removing, completely, the pole at infinity, thus forcing the remaining function to have a zero at infinity. This zero was then completely removed by inverting and removing the pole of the reciprocal function. Suppose that, instead of forcing a zero of the remaining function to occur at infinity, we wished to force this zero to occur at some other point on the $j\omega$ axis. Would we be able to do it? To answer this question, consider the sketch of a susceptance function shown

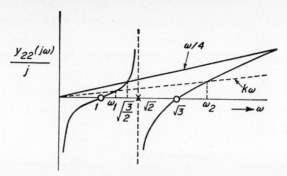

Fig. 5-17. Plot of susceptance.

in Fig. 5-17. This is the same function as Y_b given in Eq. (5-9). The function has one internal pole and two internal zeros. Suppose that this is to be the y_{22} function of a two-port. We can write

$$y_{22}(s) = \frac{(s^2+1)(s^2+3)}{4s(s^2+2)} = \frac{1}{4}s + \frac{2s^2+3}{4s(s^2+2)} \qquad (5\text{-}27)$$

The pole at infinity has a residue of $\frac{1}{4}$. If we remove this pole completely, the zero which was at $\omega = \sqrt{3}$ will move out to infinity, as Eq. (5-27) shows. The zero which was at $\omega = 1$ will also move and will now fall at $\omega = \sqrt{\frac{3}{2}}$. Suppose, instead, that we remove only part of the pole at infinity; i.e., suppose we subtract from y_{22} a quantity ks, where $0 < k \leq \frac{1}{4}$. In terms of Fig. 5-17 we subtract the dotted line whose slope is k from the susceptance curve. The zeros at $\omega = 1$ and $\sqrt{3}$ move to the locations ω_1 and ω_2. Figure 5-18(a) shows the variation of ω_1 and ω_2 as we change the amount of the pole that we remove. (Not to scale.)

This figure shows that by partially removing the pole at infinity we

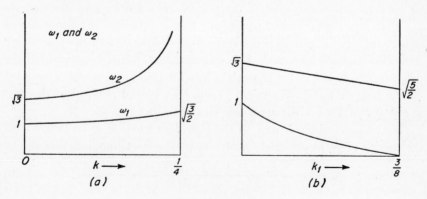

Fig. 5-18. Shifting of zeros.

can shift a zero anywhere in the range from $\omega = \sqrt{3}$ to infinity and anywhere in the range from $\omega = 1$ to $\sqrt{\frac{3}{2}}$. In the ladder development of y_{22} these zeros are realized as poles of impedance by means of an antiresonant series branch. Thus, if we are required to have a transmission zero in one of the above ranges, this procedure will realize the required zero, *provided that the pole of impedance is completely removed.* The partial network will look like Fig. 5-19.

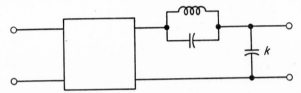

Fig. 5-19. Partial realization of ladder.

You might wonder whether or not the shunt capacitance of value k will give a transmission zero at infinity. The answer is "no." Even though this shunt impedance has a zero at infinity, the impedance looking beyond that point into the network also has a zero at infinity, since this capacitance constitutes only a *partial* removal of the admittance pole. The phenomenon now becomes clear: when we partially remove a pole and realize this as a branch of the ladder, this serves to shift the zeros and no transmission zero is created. A transmission zero *is* created when a pole is completely removed.

At this point we are still a little unhappy because, in the example under consideration, there is a finite frequency range to which we are not able to shift a zero. But we have not exhausted all avenues of procedure. We considered the partial removal of the pole at infinity only. Suppose that we consider removal of part of the pole at zero. In the previous case we saw that, when we removed part of the pole at infinity, both zeros moved toward infinity. It was as if the zeros were sucked toward the pole which was being partially removed. As a matter of fact, complete removal of the pole would suck one of the zeros right into the position previously occupied by the pole (infinity). We might expect that partial removal of the pole at $s = 0$ would move the zeros toward the origin.

Let us now subtract from y_{22} the term k_1/s where k_1 is no bigger than the residue of y_{22} at the origin, which is $\frac{3}{8}$. The remaining function will be

$$y'_{22} = y_{22} - \frac{k_1}{s} = \frac{s^4 + 4(1 - k_1)s^2 + (3 - 8k_1)}{4s(s^2 + 2)} \tag{5-28}$$

The locations of the two zeros will depend on the value of k_1. Figure 5-18(b) shows how these locations move toward zero, one of them actually reaching $\omega = 0$ when the pole is completely removed. However, the combination of partially removing the poles at zero and at infinity still leaves a frequency range (from $\sqrt{\frac{3}{2}}$ to $\sqrt{\frac{5}{2}}$) to which a zero cannot be shifted. This range falls on both sides of the internal pole at $\omega = \sqrt{2}$. Based on our recently acquired experience, if this pole is now partially removed, the zeros will shift toward the pole, thus tending to cover the range not previously attainable. We can write

$$y_{22}'' = y_{22} - \frac{k_2 s}{s^2 + 2} = \frac{s^4 + 4(1 - k_2)s^2 + 3}{4s(s^2 + 2)} \tag{5-29}$$

The largest possible value of k_2 is $\frac{1}{8}$, which is twice the residue of y_{22}. You can easily determine that varying the value of k_2 will cause the zero at $\omega = \sqrt{3}$ to be shifted as far as the pole at $\omega = \sqrt{2}$. The zero at $\omega = 1$ will be shifted as far as $\omega = \sqrt{\frac{3}{2}}$. Thus there will still be a range, $\sqrt{\frac{3}{2}} < \omega < \sqrt{2}$, to which no zeros can be shifted by partial removal of any of the poles. We seem to have met an impasse.

What we have been doing is to shift an admittance zero by removal of a shunt branch. This zero has then been realized by a series branch. But why not shift the zeros by means of a series branch and then realize them by means of a shunt branch? Why not, indeed; let us do so. Formally,

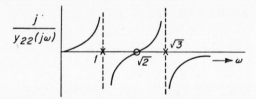

Fig. 5-20. Sketch of reciprocal of susceptance in Fig. 5-17.

we take the reciprocal of y_{22}. This is shown plotted in Fig. 5-20. Suppose that we partially remove the pole at $\omega = 1$. Then we can write

$$\frac{1}{y_{22}(s)} = \frac{4s(s^2 + 2)}{(s^2 + 1)(s^2 + 3)} - \frac{k_3 s}{s^2 + 1} = \frac{(4 - k_3)\left(s^2 + \dfrac{8 - 3k_3}{4 - k_3}\right)}{(s^2 + 1)(s^2 + 2)} \tag{5-30}$$

where the maximum value of k_3 is 2, which is twice the residue of $1/y_{22}$ at $s = j1$. As k_3 goes from 0 to $\frac{3}{4}$, the internal zero of $1/y_{22}$ moves from $\omega = \sqrt{2}$ to $\omega = \sqrt{\frac{3}{2}}$, thus covering the range to which we were previously unable to shift a zero.

We can summarize the procedure we have been describing as follows:

We start with one driving point and one transfer function from the set of y or z parameters. The driving-point function is developed into a ladder in a special way. A pole (or possibly more than one) of the driving-point function or of its reciprocal is partially removed, thus forcing a zero of the remaining function to occur at one of the prescribed transmission zeros. The reciprocal of the remaining function will have a pole at this transmission zero. The transmission zero is realized by completely removing this pole. The process is now repeated until all the transmission zeros are realized. The y_{12} (or z_{12}) function will automatically have the correct pole locations. Another way of describing this is to say that the procedure consists in removing series and shunt branches which alternately shift the zeros and then realize them. The over-all y_{12} (or z_{12}) will have the prescribed zeros and poles, but we have no control over the gain constant; we have to accept whatever gain constant the procedure gives us.

In many cases the zero shifting step will not be necessary. This will be true whenever a driving-point function (either the original one or one of the intermediate functions in the ladder development) has a zero at one of the transmission zeros. For instance, there may be a transmission zero at infinity. If the original driving-point function has a pole at infinity, this may be completely removed, leaving a remainder function with a zero at infinity, which is precisely the location of the transmission zero. The transmission zero is realized by taking the reciprocal of this remainder function and completely removing its pole at infinity.

When there are several transmission zeros, the network we obtain will depend on the order in which these transmission zeros are realized and also on which poles we use to do the zero shifting. Consider again the example of Eq. (5-27), and assume that we want to shift a zero to a point between $\omega = 1$ and $\omega = \sqrt{\tfrac{3}{2}}$. To do this, we can use either the pole at infinity (as we did in the example) or the pole at $\omega = \sqrt{2}$. The first will give a shunt capacitance in the network, while the second will give a resonant shunt branch. There is no clear-cut criterion for deciding which pole to use except for the fact that zero shifting with a pole at zero or infinity will require but a single element, whereas shifting with an internal pole will require two.

To illustrate these ideas, let it be required to synthesize a lossless two-port which, when terminated in a resistance load (normalized to unity), will have a transfer impedance

$$Z_{12}(s) = K \frac{(s^2 + 4)(s^2 + 9)}{s^5 + s^4 + 7s^3 + 4s^2 + 10s + 3} \tag{5-31}$$

Since the numerator is an even polynomial, we divide numerator and denominator by the odd part of the denominator. Then we identify z_{12} and z_{22} according to Eqs. (5-23). The result is

$$z_{22} = \frac{(s^2 + 1)(s^2 + 3)}{s(s^2 + 2)(s^2 + 5)} \qquad (a)$$

$$z_{12} = \frac{K(s^2 + 4)(s^2 + 9)}{s(s^2 + 2)(s^2 + 5)} \qquad (b)$$

(5-32)

(Note that the Fialkow condition requires $K \leq \frac{1}{12}$ for an unbalanced network.) There are two pairs of finite j-axis transmission zeros and one at infinity. Suppose we begin by realizing the one at infinity. Since z_{22} has a zero at infinity, its reciprocal $y_1 = 1/z_{22}$ will have a pole there. Complete removal of this pole will realize the desired transmission zero. The remainder admittance function will be

$$y_2 = y_1 - s = \frac{s(s^2 + 2)(s^2 + 5)}{(s^2 + 1)(s^2 + 3)} - s = \frac{s(3s^2 + 7)}{(s^2 + 1)(s^2 + 3)} \qquad (5-33)$$

The partial network realization is shown in Fig. 5-21(a). We next want to

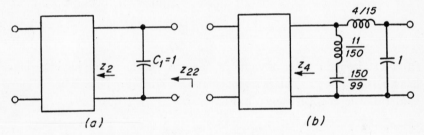

Fig. 5-21. Partial ladder development of numerical example.

realize the transmission zero at $s^2 = -9$ (or $\omega = 3$). We shall do this by partially removing the pole of $z_2 = 1/y_2$ at infinity in the form of a series inductance L, such that the remainder z_3 has a zero at $s = j3$.

$$z_3(s) = z_2(s) - Ls$$

$$z_3(j3) = z_2(j3) - j3L = 0$$

$$L = \frac{z_2(j3)}{j3} = \left.\frac{(s^2 + 1)(s^2 + 3)}{j3s(3s^2 + 7)}\right|_{s=j3} = \frac{4}{15} \qquad (5-34)$$

With this value of L we find the remaining impedance to be

$$z_3(s) = \frac{(s^2 + 1)(s^2 + 3)}{s(3s^2 + 7)} - \frac{4}{15}s = \frac{(s^2 + 9)(3s^2 + 5)}{15s(3s^2 + 7)}$$

This has a zero at the desired location. Its reciprocal will have a pole which we can completely remove, leaving a remainder y_4.

$$y_3 = \frac{15s(3s^2 + 7)}{(s^2 + 9)(3s^2 + 5)} = \frac{\frac{150}{11}s}{s^2 + 9} + \frac{\frac{15}{11}s}{s^2 + \frac{5}{3}}$$

$$y_4 = y_3 - \frac{\frac{150}{11}s}{s^2 + 9} = \frac{\frac{15}{11}s}{s^2 + \frac{5}{3}}$$

$$z_4 = \frac{11(s^2 + \frac{5}{3})}{15s} \qquad (5\text{-}35)$$

The removed pole is realized as a resonant shunt branch. The realization up to this point is shown in Fig. 5-21(b).

The remaining transmission zero is at $s = j2$. In order to shift a zero to this point, we evaluate $z_4(j2)$ and set this equal to $L_1 s$, also evaluated at $j2$, where L_1 represents the partial removal of the pole of z_4 at infinity.

$$z_4(j2) - j2L_1 = 0$$

$$L_1 = \frac{z_4(j2)}{j2} = \frac{s^2 + \frac{5}{3}}{j2(\frac{15}{11}s)}\bigg|_{s=j2} = \frac{77}{180}$$

$$z_5(s) = z_4(s) - L_1 s = \frac{s^2 + \frac{5}{3}}{\frac{15}{11}s} - \frac{77}{180}s = \frac{11(s^2 + 4)}{36s}$$

$$y_5 = \frac{36s/11}{s^2 + 4} \qquad (5\text{-}36)$$

After a series inductance of value $\frac{77}{180}$ is removed, the remaining impedance has a zero at $s = j2$. This is removed as an admittance pole. The complete ladder development is shown in Fig. 5-22.

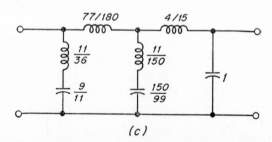

(c)

Fig. 5-22. Complete realization of numerical example.

In this problem the series branches of the ladder were used to remove a pole partially, while the shunt branches removed poles completely. Removal of the series branches were just *zero-shifting* steps, while removal of the shunt branches were *zero-producing* steps. We can vary the procedure by interchanging the roles of the series and shunt branches.

Let us start again by considering $y_1 = 1/z_{22}$. Figure 5-23 shows a sketch of this function. We wish to shift the zero from $s = j\sqrt{5}$ to $s = j2$

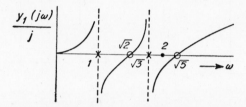

Fig. 5-23. Plot of susceptance.

by partial removal of the pole at $s = j\sqrt{3}$. We start by evaluating $y_1(j2)$.

$$y_1(j2) = \frac{s(s^2 + 2)(s^2 + 5)}{(s^2 + 1)(s^2 + 3)}\bigg|_{s=j2} = -j\frac{4}{3}$$

We now set this equal to $ks/(s^2 + 3)$, when $s = j2$. This determines k.

$$\frac{ks}{s^2 + 3}\bigg|_{s=j2} = y_1(j2) = -j\frac{4}{3}$$

$$k = \frac{2}{3} \tag{5-37}$$

The zero-shifting step now requires a resonant shunt branch. The element values are

$$L_1 = \frac{1}{k} = \frac{3}{2}$$

$$C_1 = \frac{1}{3L_1} = \frac{2}{9} \tag{5-38}$$

The remainder function will be

$$y_2(s) = y_1(s) - \frac{\frac{2}{3}s}{s^2 + 3} = \frac{s(s^2 + 4)(3s^2 + 7)}{3(s^2 + 1)(s^2 + 3)}$$

$$z_2(s) = \frac{3(s^2 + 1)(s^2 + 3)}{s(s^2 + 4)(3s^2 + 7)} = \frac{\frac{9}{20}s}{s^2 + 4} + \frac{3(11s^2 + 15)}{20s(3s^2 + 7)} \tag{5-39}$$

The zero of y_2 at $s = j2$ is completely removed as an impedance pole, leaving a remainder

$$z_3(s) = z_2(s) - \frac{9s/20}{s^2 + 4} = \frac{3(11s^2 + 15)}{20s(3s^2 + 7)} \tag{5-40}$$

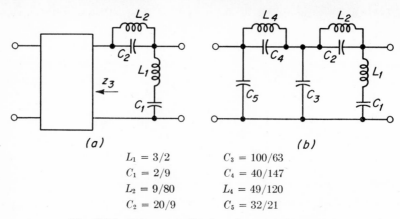

$$L_1 = 3/2 \qquad\qquad C_3 = 100/63$$
$$C_1 = 2/9 \qquad\qquad C_4 = 40/147$$
$$L_2 = 9/80 \qquad\qquad L_4 = 49/120$$
$$C_2 = 20/9 \qquad\qquad C_5 = 32/21$$

Fig. 5-24. Alternate realization of numerical example.

The partial realization is shown in Fig. 5-24(a).

Let us now realize the transmission zero at $s = j3$ by partially removing the pole of $y_3 = 1/z_3$ at infinity, thus shifting the zero that appears at $s = j\sqrt{\frac{7}{3}}$ to $s = j3$. The following steps are self-explanatory.

$$y_3(j3) = \frac{20s(3s^2 + 7)}{3(11s^2 + 15)}\Big|_{s=j3} = j\,\frac{100}{21}$$

$$sC_3\big|_{s=j3} = y_3(j3) = j\,\frac{100}{21}$$

$$C_3 = \frac{100}{63}$$

$$y_4(s) = y_3(s) - \frac{100s}{63} = \frac{160s(s^2 + 9)}{63(11s^2 + 15)}$$

$$z_4(s) = \frac{63(11s^2 + 15)}{160s(s^2 + 9)} = \frac{147s/40}{s^2 + 9} + \frac{21}{32s} \qquad (5\text{-}41)$$

The zero is shifted to $s = j3$ by removal of a shunt capacitiance C_3. It is then realized by removing a resonant series branch. There remains an impedance $z_5 = 21/32s$ which has a zero at infinity, and this is precisely where the remaining transmission zero is. The zero is realized by removal of a shunt capacitance of value $C_5 = \frac{32}{21}$. The complete realization is shown in Fig. 5-24(b).

We have now obtained two different realizations of the original transfer function. This by no means exhausts the possibilities. Other realizations are possible by changing the order of removal of transmission zeros and by changing the poles used for zero shifting. The number of circuit elements needed will not be the same for all cases, as a count of the elements in Figs. 5-22 and 5-24 will show.

It is a simple matter to determine the gain constant achieved without calculating z_{12} from the network. It is enough to find the asymptotic value of z_{12} as s goes to zero or infinity. For example, Fig. 5-24(b) reduces to a parallel connection of C_1, C_3, and C_5 at low frequencies. Thus,

$$z_{12} \to \frac{1}{(C_1 + C_3 + C_5)s} = \frac{3}{10s} \quad \text{as} \quad s \to 0$$

From Eq. (5-32) we see that $z_{12} \to 36K/10s$ as $s \to 0$. Hence the realization of Fig. 5-24(b) will give a constant multiplier $K = \frac{1}{12}$. If we check the realization of Fig. 5-22, we find that this also gives the constant multiplier $\frac{1}{12}$, which is the maximum value permitted by the Fialkow condition.

In the synthesis procedure we have been discussing, only two of the three parameters are prescribed. The realization process we go through gives us no control over the third parameter; we must accept what we get. The third parameter may even have poles not contained in the other two. In the realization of Fig. 5-22, for example, we can readily see that z_{11} has a pole at infinity, whereas the prescribed functions z_{22} and z_{12} have no pole at infinity. Similarly in the alternate realization of Fig. 5-24 we shall find that z_{11} has a private pole at $s^2 = -3$. (This is most easily established by evaluating each branch impedance at $s^2 = -3$ and then calculating z_{11}.) Note that in this realization the first zero-shifting step was performed by partially removing an admittance pole at $s^2 = -3$. Similarly in the first realization a zero-shifting step was performed by using an admittance pole at infinity. In both cases the resulting z_{11} has a private pole at the admittance pole used in the zero shifting. This is not an accident but a general condition.

In addition to the introduction of extraneous poles in the far-end driving-point function, the ladder development does not guarantee that the residue condition will be satisfied with the equality sign at all the poles. As an exercise you can find the z_{11} functions in the two-ports of Figs. 5-22 and 5-24. The residue condition is satisfied with the equality sign at all poles in the first case, but not in the second.

There is one major difficulty with the Cauer ladder development we have just discussed. This has not become apparent in the examples we have used because of the simple numerical values involved. Because many of the steps involve subtraction of two quantities, extreme accuracy is required in the numerical values. Significant figures are lost as we progress toward the end of a problem. Thus, even though the final answer is required to only two or three digits, we must know the initial coefficients in the prescribed function to many more places. You will become aware of this peculiarity of the method as you gain some experience in the realization technique.

5-5. Parallel-ladders realization

In the last section we described a complete synthesis procedure for a prescribed transfer function whenever the transmission zeros are on the $j\omega$ axis. Let us now turn our attention to the realization of a network when the transmission zeros are not restricted to the $j\omega$ axis (but do have quadrantal symmetry). We shall require only that there be no zeros on the real axis in order that we can seek an unbalanced realization.

Specifically the starting point is a transfer-admittance function $Y_{12}(s) = I_2/E_1$. The y_{12} and y_{22} functions are formed from the given function according to Eqs. (5-22) and (5-23). Again we have two of the three y parameters, but now the transmission zeros are not on the $j\omega$ axis.

Since we know a realization procedure for transmission zeros restricted to the $j\omega$ axis, we might try decomposing the given y parameters into components so that the transmission zeros of each component lie on the $j\omega$ axis. The components can then be realized individually and interconnected to give the over-all realization. With this idea in mind, consider the parallel connection of two-ports shown in Fig. 5-25. The over-all y_{22}

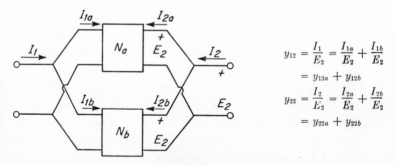

$$y_{12} = \frac{I_1}{E_2} = \frac{I_{1a}}{E_2} + \frac{I_{1b}}{E_2}$$
$$= y_{12a} + y_{12b}$$
$$y_{22} = \frac{I_2}{E_2} = \frac{I_{2a}}{E_2} + \frac{I_{2b}}{E_2}$$
$$= y_{22a} + y_{22b}$$

Fig. 5-25. Parallel connection of two-ports.

function is equal to the sum of the y_{22} functions of the individual two-ports, and similarly for the y_{12} function. This statement is quite evidently also true when more than two networks are connected in parallel. The broad outlines of a realization procedure become clear: we should break the given functions into the sum of several functions. If each of these components has transmission zeros only on the $j\omega$ axis, we can obtain a ladder realization for each. The parallel combination of these ladders will give us the desired realization. This procedure was first developed by Guillemin (56).

Let us examine this process in detail. For definiteness, let y_{12} be the ratio of an even to an odd polynomial. Then we can write

$$-y_{12} = \frac{a_0 + a_1 s^2 + \ldots + s^{2k}}{n(s)}$$

$$= \frac{a_0}{n(s)} + \frac{a_1 s^2}{n(s)} + \ldots + \frac{s^{2k}}{n(s)}$$

or
$$y_{12} = a_0 y_{12a} + a_1 y_{12b} + \ldots + y_{12(k+1)} \tag{5-42}$$

The original y_{12} is written with a gain constant of unity. The component y_{12}'s are also defined with a gain constant of unity, since the a coefficients are shown explicitly. The particular breakdown of $-y_{12}$ that we have indicated ensures that all the zeros of each component is on the $j\omega$ axis— in fact, they are all at zero or infinity. If each of the components $a_j y_{12j}$ is to be realizable, we must require the a coefficients to be positive. Suppose that we let the y_{22} function which is to be associated with each component be a fraction of the original y_{22}, say, $y_{22j} = A_j y_{22}$. Since the y_{22} function of a parallel combination of two-ports is the sum of the individual y_{22} functions, the fractions must be chosen in such a way that their sum is equal to unity. That is,

$$A_a + A_b + \ldots + A_{k+1} = 1 \tag{5-43}$$

We already know how to develop each of the component two-ports in a ladder, since all the transmission zeros of each are on the $j\omega$ axis. However, as we noted in the previous section, we have no control over the constant multiplier that we achieve for each y_{12}. These will undoubtedly be different from the a coefficients that we had at the start. Hence, if we connect these ladders in parallel, the over-all y_{12} function will be quite different from the original one.

Let us designate the y parameters of the realized networks by primes, and let the gain constant of the jth ladder which is obtained by the realization be B_j. In this notation we have $y'_{12j} = B_j y_{12j}$. We can change the gain constant of each ladder to the value we desire by appropriately changing the admittance level of each. But this will also change the y_{22} of each ladder so that the sum in Eq. (5-43) will no longer be unity. It really will not greatly concern us if, instead of realizing the original y_{12} exactly, we realize it to within a constant multiplier. This flexibility, then, provides us with one additional parameter, which we can adjust to achieve the result we want. Thus, after realizing each ladder, let us change the admittance level of the jth one by Ka_j/B_j, where K is still unknown. We can now write the over-all y_{12} function which we have realized as

$$y_{12}' \text{ (realized)} = \frac{Ka_0}{B_a} y_{12a}' + \frac{Ka_1}{B_b} y_{12b}' + \ldots + \frac{K}{B_{k+1}} y_{12(k+1)}'$$

$$= Ky_{12} \quad \text{(prescribed)} \tag{5-44}$$

Just as we mentioned, changing the admittance level will change the y_{22} of each ladder also. The over-all y_{22} function becomes

$$y_{22}' \text{ (realized)} = \frac{Ka_0}{B_a} y_{22} + \frac{Ka_1}{B_b} y_{22} + \ldots + \frac{K}{B_{k+1}} y_{22}$$

$$= K \left(\frac{a_0}{B_a} + \frac{a_1}{B_b} + \ldots + \frac{1}{B_{k+1}} \right) y_{22} \text{ (prescribed)} \tag{5-45}$$

Since we want the realized function (y_{22}') to equal the prescribed function (y_{22}), we must require

$$\frac{1}{K} = \frac{a_0}{B_a} + \frac{a_1}{B_b} + \ldots + \frac{1}{B_{k+1}} \tag{5-46}$$

Let us now summarize the procedure we have just described.

1. Write the numerator of the given y_{12} as a sum of terms each of which has zeros on the $j\omega$ axis only. Designate the gain constant of the jth term by a_j. These terms will form the numerators of component y_{12} functions, the denominators of which are the same as the denominator of the original y_{12}.

2. Develop the prescribed y_{22} into several ladder networks, each one of which realizes the zeros of one of the component y_{12} functions.

3. Calculate the gain constant of the realized y_{12} function of each ladder; label the jth one B_j.

4. Compute the quantity

$$\frac{1}{K} = \frac{a_0}{B_a} + \frac{a_1}{B_b} + \ldots + \frac{1}{B_{k+1}} \tag{5-47}$$

5. Change the admittance level of the jth ladder by Ka_j/B_j.

6. Connect the ladders in parallel at both input and output.

This procedure will realize the original transfer admittance to within a constant multiplier K. The number of ladders we shall need will depend on the degree of the numerator of y_{12}. In the decomposition we have discussed, a ladder is needed for each power of s, the total number being one more than the degree. This is extremely wasteful of elements. However, this decomposition is not the only one possible. The only criterion is to write the numerator polynomial of y_{12} as a sum of polynomials each of which has zeros only on the $j\omega$ axis. One possible breakdown, for instance, is to group the powers of s in the numerator of y_{12} in pairs. This will reduce the number of ladders by a factor of 2 (slightly less when there are an odd number of terms in the numerator).

As an example of this procedure, suppose the prescribed functions are

$$y_{22} = \frac{(s^2 + 1)(s^2 + 3)}{s(s^2 + 2)} = s + \frac{3}{2s} + \frac{s/2}{s^2 + 2}$$

$$-y_{12} = K \frac{s^4 + 3s^2 + 5}{s(s^2 + 2)} = K\left(s + \frac{5}{2s} - \frac{3s/2}{s^2 + 2}\right)$$

(5-48)

To satisfy the Fialkow condition, K must be no larger than $\frac{3}{5}$. The numerator of y_{12} can be written as the sum of several terms, each of whose zeros are exclusively on the $j\omega$ axis, in many ways. A few are listed here.

$$\begin{aligned} s^4 + 3s^2 + 5 &= (s^2 + 1)(s^2 + 2) + 3 \\ &= (s^2 + \tfrac{3}{2})^2 + \tfrac{11}{4} \\ &= (s^2 + \tfrac{5}{2})(s^2 + \tfrac{1}{2}) + \tfrac{15}{4} \\ &= (s^4) + (3s^2) + (5) \end{aligned}$$

(5-49)

The last breakdown will lead to three ladders, while the others require only two.

The first breakdown illustrates a simplifying technique which is quite useful. The two component y_{12} functions will be

$$-y_{12a} = \frac{s^2 + 1}{s} \qquad \text{(a)}$$

$$-y_{12b} = \frac{1}{s(s^2 + 2)} \qquad \text{(b)}$$

(5-50)

Note that the multiplier of $-y_{12a}$ is 1, while that of $-y_{12b}$ is 3. In each of these, one of the poles of the original y_{12} is missing. Thus y_{12a} does not have a pole at $s^2 = -2$, while y_{12b} does not have a pole at infinity. This means that in the corresponding ladders these will be private poles of y_{22a} and y_{22b}, respectively, and so each ladder will be simpler. Such a simplification will result whenever it is possible to decompose the numerator of y_{12} such that some of the terms in the decomposition have one or more factors which are also factors of the denominator. These factors will then cancel in the corresponding y_{12j}.

Let us now develop the two ladders. As already mentioned, the pole at $s^2 = -2$ is a private pole of y_{22} in ladder a. We can remove it completely from y_{22}. Thus

$$y_1 = y_{22} - \frac{\tfrac{1}{2}s}{s^2 + 2} = \frac{2s^2 + 3}{2s}$$

(5-51)

The only transmission zero of ladder a occurs at $s^2 = -1$. We can shift the zero of y_1 to this point by partial removal of the pole at $s = 0.$ Thus

$$y_1(j1) = \frac{1}{j2} = \frac{k}{s}\Big|_{s=j1} = \frac{k}{j1}$$

or $k = \tfrac{1}{2}$

$$y_2 = y_1 - \frac{1}{2s} = \frac{s^2 + 1}{s}$$

$$z_2 = \frac{1}{y_2} = \frac{s}{s^2 + 1}$$

Upon complete removal of this pole as a series branch the ladder is complete. It is shown in Fig. 5-26(a).

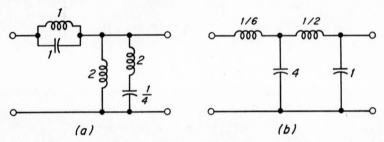

Fig. 5-26. Component ladder realizations numerical example.

The transmission zeros of ladder b are all at infinity so that the formal Cauer division process will give these zeros. However, we shall carry through the steps as alternate zero shifting and zero removal to emphasize this concept. Since y_{22} has a private pole at infinity, we can remove this initially. The following steps are self-explanatory:

$$y_3 = y_{22} - s = \frac{2s^2 + 3}{s(s^2 + 2)}$$

$$z_3 = \frac{s(s^2 + 2)}{2s^2 + 3} = \frac{s}{2} + \frac{\tfrac{1}{4}s}{s^2 + \tfrac{3}{2}}$$

$$z_4 = z_3 - \frac{s}{2} = \frac{\tfrac{1}{4}s}{s^2 + \tfrac{3}{2}} \qquad \text{zero removal}$$

$$y_4 = \frac{4}{s}(s^2 + \tfrac{3}{2}) = 4s + \frac{6}{s}$$

$$y_5 = y_4 - 4s = \frac{6}{s} \qquad \text{zero removal}$$

$$z_5 = \frac{s}{6} \qquad \text{zero removal}$$

The resulting ladder is shown in Fig. 5-26(b).

We are now ready to perform the third step in the procedure, which involves the determination of the gain constants of the ladders. For this purpose it is not necessary to compute the entire y_{12} function. It is necessary to determine only the asymptotic behavior as s goes to zero or infinity.

For ladder b assume a 1-volt source applied to end 1 and the output short-circuited. As $s \to 0$, the ladder consists essentially of the series inductances only. Thus $-y'_{12b} \to 3/2s$. In Eq. (5-50) $-y_{12b}$ approaches $1/2s$ as $s \to 0$. Hence $B_b = 3$. In a similar manner we easily find $B_a = 1$.

The next step is to compute K from Eq. (5-47). Thus

$$\frac{1}{K} = \tfrac{1}{1} + \tfrac{3}{3} = 2$$

$$K = \tfrac{1}{2} \tag{5-52}$$

Finally we change the admittance levels of the ladders as follows:

Ladder a. Multiply C's and divide L's by $\tfrac{1}{2} \cdot \tfrac{1}{1} = \tfrac{1}{2}$.

Ladder b. Multiply C's and divide L's by $\tfrac{1}{2} \cdot \tfrac{3}{3} = \tfrac{1}{2}$.

When this is done and the two ladders are connected in parallel, Fig. 5-27 results.

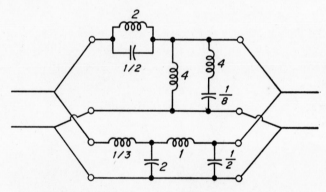

Fig. 5-27. Parallel-ladders realization of numerical example.

Let us now turn to a consideration of the requirement that the numerator coefficients of $-y_{12}$ be positive. If the originally given y_{12} does not satisfy this requirement, we can always use surplus factors to achieve this form, as discussed in previous chapters, provided only that y_{12} has no real zeros. For our present application the surplus factors will be of the form $s^2 + \omega_i^2$. The number of factors needed will depend on how close the zeros of y_{12} are to the real axis.

As an illustration, let us consider the polynomial $P(s)$, having the zeros illustrated in Fig. 5-28. It can be written as

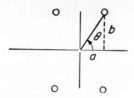

Fig. 5-28. Zeros of $P(s)$.

$$P(s) = (s^2 + 2as + a^2 + b^2)(s^2 - 2as + a^2 + b^2)$$
$$= s^4 + 2(b^2 - a^2)s^2 + (a^2 + b^2)^2 \qquad (5\text{-}53)$$

All the coefficients of $P(s)$ will be positive if $b^2 - a^2 \geq 0$, which means $\theta \geq 45°$.

Suppose that $\theta < 45°$ so that $P(s)$ has a negative coefficient. Let us multiply $P(s)$ by $P_1(s) = s^2 + \omega_0^2$, which is an even polynomial with one pair of j-axis zeros. Then

$$P(s)P_1(s) = s^6 + [\omega_0^2 - 2(a^2 - b^2)]s^4$$
$$+ [(a^2 + b^2)^2 - 2\omega_0^2(a^2 - b^2)]s^2 + \omega_0^2(a^2 + b^2) \qquad (5\text{-}54)$$

In order to have no negative coefficients, we must satisfy the condition

$$2(a^2 - b^2) \leq \omega_0^2 \leq \frac{(a^2 + b^2)^2}{2(a^2 - b^2)} \qquad (5\text{-}55)$$

Thus we require ω_0^2 to fall within a certain range. For this range to exist, the right-hand side of the inequality must be greater than the left-hand side. That is,

$$\frac{(a^2 + b^2)^2}{2(a^2 - b^2)} \geq 2(a^2 - b^2)$$

or

$$\frac{b}{a} = \tan \theta \geq \frac{1}{\sqrt{3}}$$

or, finally,

$$\theta \geq 30° \qquad (5\text{-}56)$$

We conclude that, if the original quadruplet of zeros lies no closer to the real axis than lines making 30°, then multiplication of $P(s)$ by $s^2 + \omega_0^2$ will result in all the coefficients becoming positive, the value of ω_0^2 lying in the range given by Eq. (5-55). If the zeros lie closer to the real axis than 30°, we shall need a higher-order multiplying polynomial. In this case we can try $P_1 = (s^2 + \omega_0^2)(s^2 + \omega_1^2)$. We shall find that this will permit the original zeros to lie closer to the positive real axis, the range being $\theta \geq 24.2°$. It is not difficult to appreciate that the closer the zeros of $P(s)$ are to the positive real axis the more multiplying factors $s^2 + \omega_i^2$ are needed to make all the resulting coefficients positive. If there are any zeros of $P(s)$ on the positive real axis, no finite number of such factors will be enough.

A disadvantage of the use of surplus factors is that the degree of the numerator of y_{12} is increased, thereby necessitating a greater number of ladders in the realization. Furthermore, the order of y_{22} is also increased, thus increasing the complexity of each ladder. Both these effects lead to an increase in the number of elements.

You will wonder whether a realization similar to parallel ladders is possible when the prescribed function is $Z_{12}(s)$. You would expect the analogous realization to be a *series* connection of ladders. Unfortunately, this is not possible, except for some trivial cases, unless we admit ideal transformers. The trouble is that a series connection of two unbalanced two-ports is not an unbalanced two-port unless at least one of them is a tee network. If we admit ideal transformers, then a series-ladders realization can be obtained in a completely analogous manner. As a matter of fact we may perform the impedance-level adjustment by varying the turns ratios of the ideal transformers.

There are at least two other major synthesis procedures that we could very well discuss at this stage. Both these were initially developed for RC networks but apply equally well to the lossless networks under discussion here. One of these procedures, due to Dasher (39), may be viewed as an extension of the ladder-network realization for j-axis transmission zeros. The two-port is obtained as a cascade connection of sections each of which realizes one pair of complex transmission zeros. The individual sections are bridged tees, twin tees, or bridged twin tees. The method is restricted to transmission zeros which lie no closer to the real axis than lines making an angle of 45° with the real axis.

The second procedure is due to Ozaki (94) and applies to symmetrical two-ports. The transmission zeros are restricted to the same part of the plane as in the Dasher method. The realization consists in alternate removals of branches from both ends of the two-port, similar to the steps in the decomposition of the lattice which we discussed in Sec. 5-2. We shall discuss both these procedures in the chapter on RC two-ports. It will there become evident how they apply to the lossless case as well.

PROBLEMS

5-1. Discuss the realization of a lossless two-port when the three parameters y_{11}, y_{22}, and y_{12} are prescribed under the special conditions that $k_{11} \geq k_{12}$ and $k_{22} \geq k_{12}$, where the k's are residues of the corresponding y's. Illustrate by means of an example.

5-2. Consider the symmetrical lattice of Fig. P 5-2.

(a) Compute the z and y parameters.

(b) Show that they are compact.

(c) Show that Fialkow's condition will be satisfied under any one of three conditions:

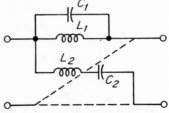

(1) $\dfrac{L_2}{L_1} \geq 1$

(2) $\dfrac{C_1}{C_2} \geq 1$

(3) $\dfrac{L_2}{L_1} + \dfrac{C_1}{C_2} \geq 1$

Fig. P 5-2

5-3. The unbalanced equivalents of the lattice for the first two conditions in the previous problem were given as the bridged-tee networks in Fig. 5-12. To obtain an unbalanced equivalent if the third condition is satisfied, decompose the y parameters that you found in the previous problem into two sets. Assign a fraction $k < 1$ of the finite pole together with all the pole at the origin to one set, and assign the remainder of the finite pole together with the pole at infinity to the other set. Show that each set can be realized as a tee network so that the twin-tee network of Fig. P 5-3 results. Determine the range of values of k. Is there a preferred value for k?

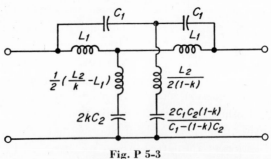

Fig. P 5-3

5-4. The following functions are the squared magnitudes of the transfer admittance of resistance-loaded lossless two-ports. Obtain a ladder or parallel-ladders realization of each two-port.

(a) $|Y_{12}(j\omega)|^2 = \dfrac{-\omega^2 + 2\omega^4 - \omega^6}{1 + \omega^8}$

(b) $|Y_{12}(j\omega)|^2 = \dfrac{1 - 4\omega^2 + \omega^4}{1 - 2\omega^2 + \omega^4 + 4\omega^6}$

(c) $|Y_{12}(j\omega)|^2 = \dfrac{(\omega^4 - \omega^2 + 1)^2}{(\omega^4 - 4\omega^2 + 3)^2 + \omega^2(\omega^4 - 6\omega^2 + 8)^2}$

5-5. The following two z parameters are given:

$$z_{11} = \frac{16s^4 + 9s^2 + 1}{s(26s^4 + 21s^2 + 3)}$$

$$z_{12} = \frac{(4s^2 + 1)(s^2 + 1)}{s(26s^4 + 21s^2 + 3)}$$

(a) Obtain a ladder realization in which the zero shifting is done with the series branches and the zero removal with shunt branches. This will be a so-called "mid-series" ladder.

(b) Obtain a ladder realization in which the zero shifting is done with the shunt branches and the zero removals with the series branches. This is a "mid-shunt" ladder.

5-6. Obtain a ladder realization for the following sets of functions. The transmission zeros may be realized in any order.

(a) $\quad z_{11} = \dfrac{(s^2 + 4)(s^2 + 16)}{s(s^2 + 9)(s^2 + 25)}$ $\qquad$ (b) $\quad z_{11} = \dfrac{s(s^2 + 16)(s^2 + 36)}{(s^2 + 1)(s^2 + 25)}$

$\quad z_{12} = \dfrac{(s^2 + 1)(s^2 + 36)}{s(s^2 + 9)(s^2 + 25)}$ $\qquad\qquad z_{12} = \dfrac{s(s^2 + 4)}{(s^2 + 1)(s^2 + 25)}$

5-7. Suppose the functions given in Prob. 5-6 are y_{11} and $-y_{12}$. Obtain ladder realizations.

5-8. The open-circuit transfer impedance of a lossless coupling network is given as

$$z_{12} = \frac{s^4 + s^2 + 1}{s(s^2 + 1)(s^2 + 3)(s^2 + 5)}$$

(a) Obtain a symmetrical-lattice realization.

(b) Obtain an unbalanced equivalent of the lattice.

5-9. The following function is to be the transfer impedance of a lossless two-port terminated in a resistance:

$$Z_{12}(s) = \frac{K(s^2 + 4)(s^2 + 9)}{s^5 + s^4 + 7s^3 + 4s^2 + 10s + 3}$$

For a suitable value of K obtain a symmetrical network realizing this function. Compare with the realizations given in Sec. 5-4.

5-10. Obtain a realization of the following nonminimum-phase transfer-admittance function in the form of a resistance-loaded lossless two-port:

$$Y_{12}(s) = \frac{2s^2 - s + 2}{s^2 + 6s + 1}$$

5-11. The transfer admittance of a resistance-terminated lossless two-port is given as follows:

$$Y_{12}(s) = K \frac{(s^2 + 9)(s^4 + 3s^2 + 5)}{(s^2 + 1)(s^2 + 3)(s^2 + 5) + s(s^2 + 2)(s^2 + 4)}$$

There is a pair of transmission zeros on the $j\omega$ axis, as well as a quadruplet of complex zeros. The normal way of obtaining a parallel-ladders realization involves expanding the numerator and taking consecutive pairs of terms as the numerators of the component y_{12}'s. In this case three ladders will be required.

(a) Obtain a parallel-ladder realization by first breaking down the quartic factor into two terms with zeros on the $j\omega$ axis. The numerators of the two component y_{12}'s will then be these terms multiplied by $s^2 + 9$. This realization will require two ladders.

(b) Obtain a realization by first removing the j-axis transmission zeros as in a ladder development. The remainder is then realized as a pair of parallel ladders.

(c) Compare the number of elements required in the two realizations, and discuss the general applicability of these special procedures.

6

Insertion-Loss Synthesis

In the previous chapter we considered the realization of lossless two-ports for problems of increasing complexity. The first problem was that of a prescribed open-circuit transfer impedance. The problem of next greater complexity involved the specification of the transfer admittance $Y_{12}(s)$ or the transfer impedance $Z_{12}(s)$ of a resistance-loaded lossless two-port. No realization procedure was discussed in the latter case for transmission zeros not restricted to the $j\omega$ axis. (Discussion of the Dasher procedure was deferred.)

Normally the $Z_{12}(s)$ or $Y_{12}(s)$ functions are not prescribed; these are obtained from the specification of a desired magnitude or angle function. However, when the prescribed behavior is the magnitude function, a different realization technique will become available if we do not compute $Z_{12}(s)$ or $Y_{12}(s)$ from the prescribed magnitude. Instead, from the fact that no power will be dissipated in a lossless network, the transfer-function magnitude squared can be related to the real part of the driving-point function. This will eventually lead to the open-circuit or short-circuit parameters of the two-port. The same technique applies when there is a finite load resistance at both the input and the output.

6-1. Darlington synthesis

Consider the network shown in Fig. 6-1. This is a lossless two-port terminated in a resistance. We shall often refer to such a network as a *Darlington network*. Since the network is lossless, the real power input to the network must equal the power delivered to the load resistance for sinusoidal driving functions. If we equate the expressions for these two quantities, we get

$$|I_1|^2 \operatorname{Re}[Z(j\omega)] = \frac{|E_2|^2}{R}$$

$$\frac{\operatorname{Re} Z(j\omega)}{R} = \frac{1}{R^2}\left|\frac{E_2}{I_1}\right|^2 = \frac{|Z_{12}(j\omega)|^2}{R^2}$$

Finally, normalizing with respect to R, we can write

$$|Z_{12}(j\omega)|^2 = \operatorname{Re}[Z(j\omega)] \tag{6-1}$$

In words, this result says that the magnitude squared of the transfer impedance of a lossless two-port terminated in a 1-ohm resistance is

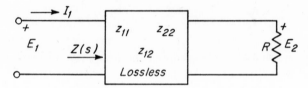

Fig. 6-1. Darlington network.

numerically equal to the real part of the driving-point impedance at all frequencies. This is a very important result. We already know how to find an impedance function when its real part is given. Hence, from a prescribed $|Z_{12}(j\omega)|^2$ for a Darlington network, we can find the input impedance $Z(s)$. The problem is now reduced to the realization of a positive real function. However, the methods of synthesis of pr functions, which we discussed in Chap. 3, are not useful in this problem because we require that the whole network be lossless except for the terminating resistance. We need a new method. The realization procedure we shall now discuss is due to Darlington (35).

Darlington's idea is marvelously simple. Consider again Fig. 6-1. At this stage it is the driving-point impedance $Z(s)$ which is known. Glance back at Eq. (1-23), which gives an expression for the driving-point impedance in terms of the z parameters of the lossless network. Using Table 1-2, we can replace $|z|$ by z_{11}/y_{22} so that we can rewrite this expression as

$$Z(s) = \frac{Rz_{11} + |z|}{R + z_{22}} = z_{11}\frac{1 + 1/Ry_{22}}{1 + z_{22}/R} = \frac{m_1 + n_1}{m_2 + n_2} \tag{6-2}$$

At the far right we have written the impedance in its usual form in terms of the even and odd part of its numerator and denominator. This can be rewritten in one of two ways as follows.

$$Z(s) = \frac{m_1}{n_2}\frac{1 + n_1/m_1}{1 + m_2/n_2} \qquad \text{case A} \tag{6-3}$$

$$Z(s) = \frac{n_1}{m_2} \frac{1 + m_1/n_1}{1 + n_2/m_2} \qquad \text{case B} \qquad (6\text{-}4)$$

Both these equations look something like Eq. (6-2). We can formally make the identifications

	Case A	Case B	
(a)	$z_{11} = \dfrac{m_1}{n_2}$	$z_{11} = \dfrac{n_1}{m_2}$	
(b)	$\dfrac{z_{22}}{R} = \dfrac{m_2}{n_2}$	$\dfrac{z_{22}}{R} = \dfrac{n_2}{m_2}$	(6-5)
(c)	$Ry_{22} = \dfrac{m_1}{n_1}$	$Ry_{22} = \dfrac{n_1}{m_1}$	

We know that $m_1 + n_1$ and $m_2 + n_2$ are Hurwitz polynomials, so that m_1/n_1 and m_2/n_2 (and their reciprocals) are reactance functions. But z_{11} in Eqs. (6-5) is the ratio of the odd part of one polynomial to the even part of the other. We have not yet established whether or not this is a realizable reactance function. We shall now digress in order to do this.

Consider again the bilinear transformation in Eq. (3-17), which is illustrated in Fig. 3-4. The right half of the Z plane is mapped into the W-plane unit circle. When $s = j\omega$, Z takes on values in the right half plane or on the jX axis, and these fall inside, or on the circumference of, the W-plane unit circle. Thus, if $Z(s)$ is pr, we can write

$$|W(j\omega)|^2 \le 1 \qquad (a)$$
$$(6\text{-}6)$$
where
$$W(s) = \frac{Z - 1}{Z + 1} \qquad (b)$$

We can see that the poles of $W(s)$ are the zeros of $Z(s) + 1$. These cannot lie in the right-half s plane, since this would require Re $Z(s)$ to be negative for a value of s with positive real part.

The converse property is also true. If we had a $W(s)$ which was regular in the right-half s plane and satisfied Eqs. (6-6), then the $Z(s)$ obtained from the transformation would be pr [for otherwise Eqs. (6-6) would be violated, contradicting the assumption].

Using the expression involving m's and n's for Z, we can write W as

$$W(s) = \frac{(m_1 - m_2) + (n_1 - n_2)}{(m_1 + m_2) + (n_1 + n_2)} \qquad (a)$$
$$(6\text{-}7)$$
$$|W(j\omega)|^2 = \left| \frac{\dfrac{m_1 + n_1}{m_2 + n_2} - 1}{\dfrac{m_1 + n_1}{m_2 + n_2} + 1} \right|^2_{s=j\omega} = \left. \frac{(m_1 - m_2)^2 - (n_1 - n_2)^2}{(m_1 + m_2)^2 - (n_1 + n_2)^2} \right|_{s=j\omega} \le 1 \qquad (b)$$

Now consider the function

$$Z_m(s) = \frac{m_1 + n_2}{m_2 + n_1} \tag{6-8}$$

Here the odd parts of the two polynomials in $Z(s)$ have been interchanged. (The subscript stands for mixed.) If we use this function in the transformation of Eqs. (6-6), we shall get a new W function which we shall call W_m. This function will have the same denominator as W, and the square of its magnitude for $s = j\omega$ will be identical with Eq. (6-7b). You can verify this by carrying out the required operations. Thus W_m will be regular in the right-half s plane, and its magnitude will be less than 1 for $s = j\omega$. Hence $Z_m(s)$ is positive real. It follows from this that both $m_1 + n_2$ and $m_2 + n_1$ are Hurwitz polynomials. Therefore m_1/n_2 and m_2/n_1, and their reciprocals, are reactance functions.

We have now established that all the functions in Eqs. (6-5) individually are realizable reactance functions. However, this set is a mixed one involving both the z and y parameters. We need to find z_{12} in order to have a complete set of parameters. Let us first find an expression for $|z|$. Two different expressions will result, depending on whether we use the forms appropriate for case A or those for case B. Thus

$$|z| = \frac{z_{11}}{y_{22}} = R\,\frac{n_1}{n_2} \qquad \text{case A} \qquad \text{(a)}$$
$$\tag{6-9}$$
$$|z| = R\,\frac{m_1}{m_2} \qquad \text{case B} \qquad \text{(b)}$$

Using this expression for $|z|$ and Eqs. (6-5) for z_{11} and z_{22}, we can now find z_{12}.

$$z_{12} = \sqrt{z_{11}z_{22} - |z|}$$

$$\frac{z_{12}}{\sqrt{R}} = \frac{\sqrt{m_1 m_2 - n_1 n_2}}{n_2} = \frac{\sqrt{N(-s^2)}}{n_2} \qquad \text{case A} \qquad \text{(6-10)}$$

$$\frac{z_{12}}{\sqrt{R}} = \frac{\sqrt{-(m_1 m_2 - n_1 n_2)}}{m_2} = \frac{\sqrt{-N(-s^2)}}{m_2} \qquad \text{case B} \qquad \text{(6-11)}$$

Here we have used the notation $N(-s^2)$ for the numerator of the even part of $Z(s)$, as in Chap. 3.

We can also obtain expressions for y_{11} and y_{12}, using the relationships between the y and z parameters. The complete results are tabulated in Table 6-1.

Consider the expression for z_{12}. We know that z_{12} must be a rational function. This means that the polynomial $\pm N(-s^2)$ must have zeros, in terms of s^2, of even multiplicity only. Since $Z(s)$ is a positive real function,

Table 6-1

Case A No pole or zero of $Z(s)$ at $s = 0$	
$z_{11} = \dfrac{m_1}{n_2}$	$y_{11} = \dfrac{m_2}{n_1}$
$\dfrac{z_{22}}{R} = \dfrac{m_2}{n_2}$	$Ry_{22} = \dfrac{m_1}{n_1}$
$\dfrac{z_{12}}{\sqrt{R}} = \dfrac{\sqrt{m_1 m_2 - n_1 n_2}}{n_2}$	$\sqrt{R}y_{12} = \dfrac{\sqrt{m_1 m_2 - n_1 n_2}}{n_1}$
Case B Pole or zero of $Z(s)$ at $s = 0$	
$z_{11} = \dfrac{n_1}{m_2}$	$y_{11} = \dfrac{n_2}{m_1}$
$\dfrac{z_{22}}{R} = \dfrac{n_2}{m_2}$	$Ry_{22} = \dfrac{n_1}{m_1}$
$\dfrac{z_{12}}{\sqrt{R}} = \dfrac{\sqrt{-(m_1 m_2 - n_1 n_2)}}{m_2}$	$\sqrt{R}y_{12} = \dfrac{\sqrt{-(m_1 m_2 - n_1 n_2)}}{m_1}$

we are guaranteed that any real negative s^2 zeros occur with even multiplicity. The requirement of a rational z_{12} forces us to demand that all other zeros occur with even multiplicity also. This statement does not apply to a zero at the origin because, if s^2 is a factor of $N(-s^2)$, taking the square root will not lead to an irrational function. For an arbitrary positive real function there is no guarantee that all the zeros of $N(-s^2)$ will be of even multiplicity. The situation is remedied by multiplying numerator and denominator of $Z(s)$ by a Hurwitz polynomial $P_0 = m_0 + n_0$ just as we discussed in connection with the Miyata realization in Chap. 3. Thus

$$Z(s) = \frac{m_1 + n_1}{m_2 + n_2} \frac{m_0 + n_0}{m_0 + n_0} \tag{6-12}$$

If we now form the revised polynomial $N(-s^2)$, we find

$$N(-s^2) = (m_1 m_2 - n_1 n_2)(m_0^2 - n_0^2) \tag{6-13}$$

It is now clear how to choose the polynomial $m_0^2 - n_0^2$; all the factors of the original $N(-s^2)$ which occur with odd multiplicity will be factors of $m_0^2 - n_0^2$. We already know that, to find the Hurwitz polynomial $m_0 + n_0$ from the polynomial $m_0^2 - n_0^2$, we take all the left-half-plane zeros of the latter and assign them to $m_0 + n_0$.

The question arises as to the significance of the two cases A and B, When should you use the one or the other? The denominator of z_{12} is odd or even, respectively, in cases A and B. Hence the numerator must be even or odd, respectively, because z_{12} is an odd rational function. If the original $N(-s^2)$ has s^2 as a factor, then case B will be appropriate, otherwise case A. In terms of $Z(s)$ this means that case B applies when $Z(s)$ has a pole or zero at $s = 0$; otherwise, case A.

To illustrate these results, consider the impedance

$$Z_1(s) = \frac{s^2 + s + 1}{s^2 + s + 4}$$

$$N(-s^2) = s^4 + 4s^2 + 4 = (s^2 + 2)^2$$

$$z_{12} = \sqrt{R}\,\frac{\sqrt{N(-s^2)}}{n_2} = \sqrt{R}\,\frac{s^2 + 2}{s}$$

Here $N(-s^2)$ does not have a factor s^2, so that case A applies. As a second example, take

$$Z_2(s) = \frac{s^3 + 4s^2 + 4s}{s^3 + 5s^2 + 8s + 4}$$

$$N(-s^2) = -s^2(s^2 - 4)^2$$

$$z_{12} = \sqrt{R}\,\frac{\sqrt{-N(-s^2)}}{m_2} = \sqrt{R}\,\frac{s(s^2 - 4)}{5s^2 + 4}$$

In this case $N(-s^2)$ does have a factor s^2, so that case B applies. Furthermore it has a negative sign, so that $-N$ is a positive quantity, as it should be. No auxiliary polynomial is necessary in these two cases.

Let us assume now that the impedance functions under consideration have been augmented by appropriate auxiliary polynomials, so that $N(-s^2)$ (or $-N$) is a complete square. We now have a complete set of z or y parameters, and it remains to determine whether this set satisfies the conditions of realizability of a lossless two-port. These conditions are that z_{11} and z_{22} must be reactance functions and the residue condition $k_{11}k_{22} - k_{12}^2 \geq 0$ must be satisfied at all the poles. We have already established the first condition. It remains to look at the residue condition.

One way of finding the residue of a rational function is to evaluate the numerator divided by the derivative of the denominator at a pole of the function. For the z parameters of case A and case B given in Table 6-1, we get

$$\textit{Case A} \qquad\qquad\qquad\qquad \textit{Case B}$$

$$k_{11} = \frac{m_1}{n_2'}\bigg|_{n_2=0} \qquad\qquad k_{11} = \frac{n_1}{m_2'}\bigg|_{m_2=0} \qquad\qquad (a)$$

$$k_{22} = \frac{Rm_2}{n_2'}\bigg|_{n_2=0} \qquad\qquad k_{22} = \frac{Rn_2}{m_2'}\bigg|_{m_2=0} \qquad\qquad (b)\ \ (6\text{-}14)$$

$$k_{12} = \frac{\sqrt{R}\,\sqrt{m_1 m_2 - n_1 n_2}}{n_2'}\bigg|_{n_2=0} \qquad k_{12} = \frac{\sqrt{R}\,\sqrt{n_1 n_2 - m_1 m_2}}{m_2'}\bigg|_{m_2=0} \qquad (c)$$

where the primes indicate differentiation with respect to s. These expressions show that the residue condition is satisfied with the equality sign at all finite poles. This compact nature of the two-port is an outstanding characteristic of the Darlington procedure. The formulas we have used for the residues do not apply to a pole at infinity; hence the residue condition at infinity must be investigated independently. You can readily verify the same result for the y parameters.

In Chap. 4 we showed that, at a compact nonzero pole of the z parameters, $|z| = z_{11}z_{22} - z_{12}^2$ will have only a simple pole. By going through a similar process you can show that, if the z parameters have a compact pole at infinity, then $|z|$ will be regular there. Now consider again Eq. (6-2) for the driving-point impedance. If all the poles of the z parameters are compact, then $Z(s)$ will be regular at these poles on the $j\omega$ axis. If $Z(s)$ has a finite nonzero j-axis pole, say, at $s = j\omega_0$, then $s^2 + \omega_0^2$ will be a factor of both m_2 and n_2 and hence will be a private pole of z_{11}, according to Table 6-1.

To determine whether the residue condition is satisfied at the pole at infinity, consider case A in Table 6-1. The residue of z_{11} at infinity will be the ratio of the coefficients of the highest-power terms of m_1 and n_2; that of z_{22} will be the corresponding ratio of m_2 and n_2. If both z_{11} and z_{22} have a pole at infinity, m_1 and m_2 are of the same degree and they are of higher degree (by 1) than n_2. There are two cases to consider. (1) n_1 is of the same degree as n_2; then $Z(s)$ is regular at infinity, and the degree of n_1n_2 is lower than the degree of m_1m_2. In this case, looking at the expression for z_{12} shows that the pole at infinity will be compact. (2) n_1 is of higher degree than n_2; it will also be of higher degree (by 1) than m_1 and m_2. Thus $Z(s)$ will have a pole at infinity, and this pole will not be compact. Similar conclusions follow for case B.

Table 6-1 shows that in case B the z and y parameters consist of the ratio of an odd to an even polynomial. Superficially, then, it would appear that $s = 0$ will be a zero of these functions, and not a pole. However, in case B, $Z(s)$ has a pole or a zero at $s = 0$. This means that the constant term in either the denominator or the numerator of $Z(s)$ will be missing. Thus either m_2 or m_1 will have a factor s^2. Suppose it is m_2; then, instead of having a zero at $s = 0$, the z parameters will have a pole there. Let us examine the residue condition in this case. We can write

$$k_{11}k_{22} - k_{12}^2 = \frac{Rn_1n_2}{m_2'^2} - R\frac{n_1n_2 - m_1m_2}{m_2'^2}\bigg|_{m_2=0}$$

$$= \frac{Rm_1m_2}{m_2'^2}\bigg|_{m_2=0}$$

At all the other zeros of m_2 this reduces to zero. However, since m_2 has a factor s^2, m_2' has a factor s. Hence the above result will be nonzero. Writing

$$m_2 = b_2 s^2 + b_4 s^4 + \ldots + b_{2n} s^{2n}$$

we shall find

$$k_{11} k_{22} - k_{12}^2 = \frac{R m_1(0)}{4 b_2} > 0$$

In a similar manner suppose that m_1 has a factor s^2. Then, evaluating the residue condition for the y parameters, we shall find that there is a noncompact pole at $s = 0$.

In summary: (1) If $Z(s)$ has a pole at $s = 0$, the z's have a noncompact pole there. (2) If $Z(s)$ has a zero at $s = 0$, the y's have a noncompact pole there. (3) If $Z(s)$ has neither a pole nor a zero at $s = 0$, then both the z's and the y's will have a compact pole there. The same statements are true if we replace the point $s = 0$ by the point $s = \infty$. (See Sec. 6-5.)

We can summarize the discussion in this section as follows: The squared magnitude of the transfer impedance, $|Z_{12}(j\omega)|^2$, of a resistance-loaded lossless two-port is specified. This implies the real part of the driving-point impedance. The driving-point impedance $Z(s)$ is constructed from the real part by the Gewertz or Bode procedure. From this the z parameters of the two-port are constructed. It is guaranteed that these are compact at all the poles except possibly the pole at infinity and the pole at the origin. The pole at infinity will be compact if $Z(s)$ is regular there. If $Z(s)$ has any j-axis poles, these will be private poles of z_{11}.

An exactly analogous procedure can be carried out, starting with the driving-point admittance. An expression for $Y(s)$ in terms of the y parameters will be the same as Eq. (6-2), with y's replacing z's and G replacing R. It is

$$Y(s) = \frac{G y_{11} + |y|}{G + y_{22}} \tag{6-15}$$

A development similar to the one just presented will again lead to Table 6-1, but with the z's and y's interchanged.

At this point it will probably be worthwhile to illustrate some of the ideas we have been discussing. Suppose that we are to find the lossless two-port realizing a given $|Z_{12}(j\omega)|^2$ when terminated in a unit resistance. The given function is

$$|Z_{12}(j\omega)|^2 = \frac{1 + \omega^2}{1 - \omega^2 + \omega^4} \tag{6-16}$$

This is equal to the even part of $Z(s)$ when we replace ω^2 by $-s^2$. Hence

$$U(-s^2) = \frac{1 - s^2}{1 + s^2 + s^4} = \frac{1 - s^2}{(1 + s + s^2)(1 - s + s^2)} \tag{6-17}$$

The denominator is easily factored and the left-half-plane poles of $U(-s^2)$ found. Using the Gewertz or the Bode method, we find $Z(s)$ to be

$$Z(s) = \frac{2s + 1}{s^2 + s + 1} \tag{6-18}$$

Our next step is to determine the z parameters according to Table 6-1. However, $N(-s^2)$, the numerator of the given $U(-s^2)$, is not a complete square, as it should be to make z_{12} rational. To make it a complete square, we multiply numerator and denominator of Eq. (6-17) by $1 - s^2$. This reduces to

$$U(-s^2) = \frac{1 - s^2}{1 + s^2 + s^4} \frac{1 - s^2}{1 - s^2} = \frac{(1 - s^2)^2}{1 - s^6} \tag{6-19}$$

The auxiliary polynomial $m_0 + n_0$ is easily found from the factor $1 - s^2$ to be $m_0 + n_0 = s + 1$, so that the modified $Z(s)$ is

$$Z(s) = \frac{2s + 1}{s^2 + s + 1} \frac{s + 1}{s + 1} = \frac{2s^2 + 3s + 1}{s^3 + 2s^2 + 2s + 1} \tag{6-20}$$

Since $N(-s^2)$ does not have a factor s^2, case A applies. From Table 6-1 we get

$$z_{11} = \frac{m_1}{n_2} = \frac{2s^2 + 1}{s(s^2 + 2)} = \frac{1}{2s} + \frac{\frac{3}{2}s}{s^2 + 2} \tag{a}$$

$$\frac{z_{22}}{R} = \frac{m_2}{n_2} = \frac{2s^2 + 1}{s(s^2 + 2)} = \frac{1}{2s} + \frac{\frac{3}{2}s}{s^2 + 2} \tag{b} \tag{6-21}$$

$$\frac{z_{12}}{\sqrt{R}} = \frac{\sqrt{N}}{n_2} = \frac{1 - s^2}{s(s^2 + 2)} = \frac{1}{2s} - \frac{\frac{3}{2}s}{s^2 + 2} \tag{c}$$

We see that $z_{11} = z_{22}/R$. With $R = 1$ the two-port will be symmetrical. In such a case we already know a realization procedure in terms of a symmetrical lattice. There are two transmission zeros on the real axis so that an unbalanced realization is not possible. The partial-fraction expansion shows that both poles are compact, as they should be.

6-2. Prescribed insertion ratio

One of the most important problems in network synthesis involves the realization of a two-port to be inserted between a resistive load and a physical source with a finite nonzero source resistance, as illustrated in Fig. 6-2. The function that describes the behavior of the two-port is the ratio of the load voltage E_2 to the source voltage E_0, $T(s) = E_2/E_0$ (or its reciprocal). However, as discussed in Chap. 1, it is sometimes more convenient to deal with the insertion voltage ratio, $H(s) = E_2/E_{20}$, or the

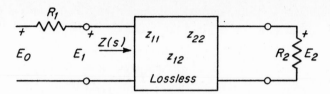

Fig. 6-2. Lossless two-port inserted between source and load.

transmission coefficient, $H'(s) = E_2/E'_{20}$. The relationship among these functions, which was given in Eq. (1-40), is repeated here for convenience.

$$T(s) = \frac{E_2}{E_0} = \frac{R_2}{R_1 + R_2} H(s) = \sqrt{\frac{R_2}{4R_1}} H'(s) \qquad (6\text{-}22)$$

They differ from each other by a multiplicative constant which depends on the termination. For equal terminations H and H' are equal, and they are equal to twice $T(s)$. In discussing general procedures for which the multiplying constant is unimportant, we shall refer to these three functions interchangeably. The function which is usually prescribed is the *insertion loss*, defined as one-half the logarithm of the insertion power ratio. If we write for the insertion voltage ratio

$$H(j\omega) = \frac{E_2}{E_{20}} = \epsilon^{-\alpha(\omega) - j\beta(\omega)} \qquad (6\text{-}23)$$

then the insertion loss is α. Prescribing the insertion loss amounts to prescribing the magnitude of $H(j\omega)$. In a later chapter we shall discuss the approximation procedure involved in getting an even rational function in ω, which $|H(j\omega)|^2$ must be, from specifications of the desired loss. For the moment, let us assume that we have an $|H(j\omega)|^2$ satisfying the necessary condition given in Eq. (1-34).

The expression for $T(s)$ in terms of the z parameters of the two-port involves these parameters in a very complicated way, as shown in Eq. (1-24). With a given $T(s)$ we shall not be able to recognize the z parameters, as we did in the last section. However, if we can obtain the impedance $Z(s)$ from the prescribed $|T(j\omega)|^2$, we can use the results of the Darlington procedure to obtain the z parameters of the two-port. Our purpose, then, is to find the driving-point impedance $Z(s)$ from the prescribed $|T(j\omega)|^2$. The necessary steps become clear if we glance at the expressions involving the insertion ratio, the reflection coefficient and the driving-point impedance first given in Chap. 1. These are repeated here for convenience

$$|\rho(j\omega)|^2 + \frac{4R_1}{R_2}|T(j\omega)|^2 = 1 \qquad (a)$$

$$\rho(s) = \frac{R_1 - Z(s)}{R_1 + Z(s)} \qquad (b) \quad (6\text{-}24)$$

$$\frac{Z(s)}{R_1} = \frac{1 - \rho}{1 + \rho} \qquad (c)$$

The squared magnitude of the reflection coefficient is determined from the prescribed insertion power ratio, using the first of these expressions. We must then determine $\rho(s)$, whereupon $Z(s)$ follows from the last expression. Finally Table 6-1 gives the z or y parameters of the two-port.

Let us now consider in detail the procedure we have outlined. By considering the expression for the voltage transfer function $T(s) = E_2/E_0$ as given in Eq. (1-24), it is easy to establish that it is the ratio of an odd or even polynomial to a Hurwitz polynomial. Let us write

$$T(s) = \frac{1}{2}\sqrt{\frac{R_2}{R_1}} \frac{N_{12}(s)}{m(s) + n(s)} \qquad (a)$$

$$\qquad\qquad\qquad\qquad\qquad\qquad\qquad (6\text{-}25)$$

$$T(s)T(-s) = \pm\frac{R_2}{4R_1}\frac{N_{12}^2(s)}{m^2 - n^2} \qquad (b)$$

where $N_{12}(s)$ is either even or odd and the minus sign applies when $N_{12}(s)$ is odd. The constant $R_2/4R_1$ is included here in order to simplify subsequent expressions. In Eq. (6-24a) let us replace ω^2 by $-s^2$ and substitute the last equation. The result will be

$$\rho(s)\rho(-s) = 1 - \frac{4R_1}{R_2}T(s)T(-s) = 1 \mp \frac{N_{12}^2(s)}{m^2 - n^2} \qquad (6\text{-}26)$$

Now the reflection coefficient can also be written as a ratio of two polynomials,

$$\rho(s) = \frac{m_r + n_r}{m + n} \qquad (6\text{-}27)$$

If we consider the expression for $\rho(s)$ in terms of the input impedance, we can see that the poles of $\rho(s)$ are the zeros of the positive real function $R_1 + Z(s)$ and, hence, they lie in the left-half s plane. However, its zeros are the zeros of $R_1 - Z(s)$, and consequently they do not necessarily lie in the left half plane. Thus the numerator polynomial of $\rho(s)$ is not necessarily Hurwitz.

Using the last equation, we can form the function $\rho(s)\rho(-s)$ and equate it to the preceding equation. Thus

$$\frac{m_r^2 - n_r^2}{m^2 - n^2} = 1 \mp \frac{N_{12}^2}{m^2 - n^2} = \frac{m^2 - n^2 \mp N_{12}^2}{m^2 - n^2} \qquad (6\text{-}28)$$

Starting from a prescribed $T(s)T(-s)$ function in the form of the ratio of two even polynomials as in Eqs. (6-25), we form the right-hand side of Eq. (6-28). This gives us $\rho(s)\rho(-s)$. From this we need to find $\rho(s)$. The denominator presents no new problems: we need to find the Hurwitz polynomial $m + n$ from the polynomial $m^2 - n^2$, whose zeros occur in quadrantal symmetry. The zeros of the numerator also occur in quadrantal symmetry. However, since the zeros of $\rho(s)$ are not necessarily in the left half plane, we have some flexibility in choosing them. Any j-axis zeros of $\rho(s)\rho(-s)$ must be divided equally between $\rho(s)$ and $\rho(-s)$, and so there will be no choice in these. There will be a choice in assigning the complex zeros of $\rho(s)\rho(-s)$. From a quadruplet of zeros we can assign either the right-half-plane pair or the left-half-plane pair to $\rho(s)$.

Besides the zeros and poles we must choose the multiplying constant of $\rho(s)$. Of course, this will be the square root of the multiplying constant of $\rho(s)\rho(-s)$. But we have a choice of the plus sign or the minus sign. A glance at Eq. (6-24c) shows that a reversal of the sign of $\rho(s)$ simply inverts the driving-point impedance function. The network corresponding to one choice of sign will be the inverse of that corresponding to the second choice of sign.

Having determined $\rho(s)$, we now determine $Z(s)$ from Eq. (6-24c). The result is

$$Z(s) = R_1 \frac{(m - m_r) + (n - n_r)}{(m + m_r) + (n + n_r)} = \frac{m_1 + n_1}{m_2 + n_2} \tag{6-29}$$

We can now use Table 6-1 to calculate the z or y parameters. As a matter of fact, we can rewrite that table in terms of the even and odd parts of the numerator and denominator of $\rho(s)$, which are related to m_1, m_2, n_1, and n_2 through Eq. (6-29). The result is shown in Table 6-2. We have used Eq. (6-28) to simplify the expressions for z_{12} and y_{12}. Also, R in Table 6-1 becomes R_2 in Table 6-2.

Table 6-2

Case A $N_{12}(s)$ even		Case B $N_{12}(s)$ odd	
$z_{11} = R_1 \dfrac{m - m_r}{n + n_r}$	$y_{11} = \dfrac{1}{R_1} \dfrac{m + m_r}{m - n_r}$	$z_{11} = R_1 \dfrac{n - n_r}{m + m_r}$	$y_{11} = \dfrac{1}{R_1} \dfrac{n + n_r}{m - m_r}$
$z_{22} = R_2 \dfrac{m + m_r}{n + n_r}$	$y_{22} = \dfrac{1}{R_2} \dfrac{m - m_r}{n - n_r}$	$z_{22} = R_2 \dfrac{n + n_r}{m + m_r}$	$y_{22} = \dfrac{1}{R_2} \dfrac{n - n_r}{m - m_r}$
$z_{12} = \sqrt{R_1 R_2} \dfrac{N_{12}}{n + n_r}$	$y_{12} = -\dfrac{1}{\sqrt{R_1 R_2}} \dfrac{N_{12}}{n - n_r}$	$z_{12} = \sqrt{R_1 R_2} \dfrac{N_{12}}{m + m_r}$	$y_{12} = -\dfrac{1}{\sqrt{R_1 R_2}} \dfrac{N_{12}}{m - m_r}$

There are two very important special cases that are worth considering separately. An important type of two-port is a *symmetrical* one. This is characterized by $z_{11} = z_{22}$ or $y_{11} = y_{22}$, and we obviously also require that $R_1 = R_2$. A glance at the table shows that this requirement will be met only if $m_r = 0$ in case A and $n_r = 0$ in case B. Using this fact in Eq. (6-28), we get

$$m^2 - n^2 = (N_{12}^2 - n_r^2) \qquad N_{12} \text{ even} \qquad \text{(a)}$$

$$m^2 - n^2 = (-N_{12}^2 + m_r^2) \qquad N_{12} \text{ odd} \qquad \text{(b)}$$

(6-30)

Finally, putting these into Eq. (6-25b), we get

$$\frac{1}{T(s)T(-s)} = 4\left[1 - \left(\frac{n_r}{N_{12}}\right)^2\right] \qquad N_{12} \text{ even} \qquad \text{(a)}$$

$$\frac{1}{T(s)T(-s)} = 4\left[1 - \left(\frac{m_r}{N_{12}}\right)^2\right] \qquad N_{12} \text{ odd} \qquad \text{(b)}$$

(6-31)

In either case the reciprocal of $T(s)T(-s)$, aside from a constant multiplier, is 1 minus the square of an odd rational function of s. If we had used the insertion ratio instead of $T(s)$, the constant would have been 1.

Using the conditions $m_r = 0$ for case A and $n_r = 0$ for case B in Eq. (6-29), we find that the driving-point impedance is

$$Z = R_1 \frac{m + (n - n_r)}{m + (n + n_r)}; \qquad \text{case A, symmetrical} \quad \text{(a)}$$

$$Z = R_1 \frac{(m - m_r) + n}{(m + m_r) + n}; \qquad \text{case B, symmetrical} \quad \text{(b)}$$

(6-32)

These expressions show that, for a symmetrical network, either the even parts (case A) or the odd parts (case B) of the numerator and denominator of the driving-point impedance are the same.

Another type of important two-port is the one we shall label *anti-metrical* (Darlington called this an "inverse-impedance network"). The distinguishing characteristic of this two-port is the fact that the open-circuit input impedance at one port is the reciprocal, with respect to R_1R_2, of the short-circuit impedance at the other port. That is,

$$\frac{z_{11}}{y_{22}} = \frac{z_{22}}{y_{11}} = R_1R_2$$

Using Table 6-2, this equation leads to

$$R_1R_2 \frac{n - n_r}{n + n_r} = R_1R_2 \qquad \text{case A} \qquad \text{(a)}$$

$$R_1R_2 \frac{m - m_r}{m + m_r} = R_1R_2 \qquad \text{case B} \qquad \text{(b)}$$

(6-33)

These equations can be satisfied only if $n_r = 0$ in case A and $m_r = 0$ in case B. With these conditions substituted into Eq. (6-28), we can solve for $m^2 - n^2$. Finally, using this result in Eqs. (6-25), we shall get

$$\frac{1}{T(s)T(-s)} = \frac{4R_1}{R_2}\left[1 + \left(\frac{m_r}{N_{12}}\right)^2\right] \qquad N_{12} \text{ even} \qquad (a)$$

$$\frac{1}{T(s)T(-s)} = \frac{4R_1}{R_2}\left[1 + \left(\frac{n_r}{N_{12}}\right)^2\right] \qquad N_{12} \text{ odd} \qquad (b)$$
$$(6\text{-}34)$$

Thus, for an antimetrical two-port, the reciprocal of $T(s)T(-s)$, aside from a constant multiplier, is equal to 1 plus the square of an even rational function of s. In the case of equal terminations the constant becomes 4, which is the same as the constant in the symmetrical case.

For the driving-point impedance, we find that Eqs. (6-32) are valid in the antimetric case as well, except that case A and case B are interchanged.

For these two cases, the symmetrical and antimetrical, we can consolidate the above results and write

$$\frac{1}{T(s)T(-s)} = K[1 \mp \phi(s)^2] \tag{6-35}$$

In the symmetrical case $K = 4$, ϕ is an odd rational function, and the minus sign applies. In the antimetrical case $K = 4R_1/R_2$, $\phi(s)$ is an even rational function, and the plus sign applies.

Let us illustrate some of the topics we have been discussing by means of an example. Suppose the squared magnitude of a voltage ratio is given as

$$|T(j\omega)|^2 = \frac{\frac{1}{4}}{1 + \omega^6} \tag{6-36}$$

Assume that the two terminations are equal. Analytically continuing this function and putting it in the form of Eq. (6-35), we get

$$\frac{1}{T(s)T(-s)} = 4(1 - s^6) = 4[1 - (s^3)^2] \tag{6-37}$$

Thus the given function is appropriate for a symmetrical two-port, so that $m_r = 0$. In addition $N_{12}(s) = 1$, and $n_r = s^3$. Hence, aside from a choice of sign, the numerator of $\rho(s)$ is determined. It remains to determine the denominator. Formally, using Eq. (6-26), we get

$$\rho(s)\rho(-s) = 1 - 4T(s)T(-s) = 1 - \frac{1}{1 - s^6} = \frac{-s^6}{1 - s^6} \tag{6-38}$$

Hence the numerator of $\rho(s)$ is either s^3 or $-s^3$. To find the denominator, we must find the factors of $1 - s^6$ and assign all the left-half-plane factors to $\rho(s)$. In this simple case the factors are easily found.

$$1 - s^6 = [(1 + s)(1 + s + s^2)][(1 - s)(1 - s + s^2)] \tag{6-39}$$

Finally
$$\rho(s) = \frac{\pm s^3}{s^3 + 2s^2 + 2s + 1} \tag{6-40}$$

Using this, we can form $Z(s)$ and the z and y parameters. The results are

$$Z(s) = R_1 \frac{s^3 + 2s^2 + 2s + 1 \mp s^3}{s^3 + 2s^2 + 2s + 1 \pm s^3} \tag{a}$$

$$z_{11} = z_{22} = R_1 \frac{2s^2 + 1}{s^3 + 2s \pm s^3} \tag{b} \quad (6\text{-}41)$$

$$z_{12} = \frac{R_1}{s^3 + 2s \pm s^3}$$

$$y_{11} = y_{22} = \frac{1}{R_1} \frac{2s^2 + 1}{s^3 + 2s \mp s^3} \tag{c}$$

$$y_{12} = \frac{-1/R_1}{s^3 + 2s \mp s^3}$$

If we choose $n_r = s^3$, the y parameters will simplify, while if we choose $n_r = -s^3$, the z parameters will simplify. Thus

$$\underline{n_r = s^3} \qquad\qquad \underline{n_r = -s^3}$$

$$y_{11} = y_{22} = \frac{1}{R_1}\left(s + \frac{1}{2s}\right) \qquad z_{11} = z_{22} = R_1\left(s + \frac{1}{2s}\right)$$

$$y_{12} = -\frac{1}{R_1}\frac{1}{2s} \qquad\qquad z_{12} = \frac{R_1}{2s}$$

In this simple case the realization is obtained by recognizing these expressions as the y and z parameters of a symmetrical pi and symmetrical tee, respectively. The result is shown in Fig. 6-3.

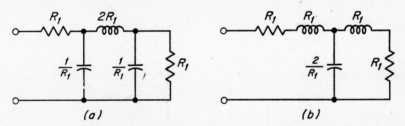

(a)   *(b)*

Fig. 6-3. Realization of numerical example.

This figure serves to point out a practical consideration in the choice of the sign of $\rho(s)$. The realization in part (a) of the figure is desirable because of the shunt capacitances at the input and output. These capacitances can be adjusted to take account of any stray capacitances in the physical realization. We can always guarantee a shunt capacitance at the input terminals whenever the reflection coefficient has a magnitude of unity at infinity. This possibility becomes clear from a consideration of Eq. (6-24c). If the plus sign is chosen for $\rho(s)$, then $\rho(\infty) = +1$ and so

$Z(s)$ has a zero at infinity, which is realized as a shunt capacitance. On the other hand, choice of the minus sign will cause a pole of $Z(s)$ at infinity.

6-3. Cauer realization of lossless two-ports

In the previous two sections we discussed the procedures for obtaining a complete set of z or y parameters of a lossless two-port starting from a prescribed $|Z_{12}(j\omega)|^2$ or $|Y_{12}(j\omega)|^2$ or $|T(j\omega)|^2$. We are now faced with the problem of realizing a lossless two-port when a realizable set of z or y parameters is given. The procedure we shall discuss in this section is due to Cauer (32).

Suppose we are given a set of three rational functions, z_{11}, z_{22} and z_{12}, all of whose poles are simple and lie on the $j\omega$ axis. The residues k_{11} and k_{22} are positive, but the residues k_{12} are not necessarily positive. Nevertheless, the residues satisfy the condition $k_{11}k_{22} - k_{12}^2 \geq 0$. We have already shown that these conditions are necessary if z_{11}, z_{22}, and z_{12} are to be the z parameters of a lossless two-port. Our present purpose is to show that these conditions are sufficient as well. We do this by constructing a two-port from the given functions.

Cauer's realization procedure was developed as an extension of Foster's synthesis of reactance functions. The first step in the Foster synthesis is to expand a given reactance function in partial fractions. Each term in the expansion is realized as a component network, the over-all network being the series or parallel connection of these components. In the present case we have not one function but three. Again we expand each one in partial fractions. The poles lie at zero, at infinity, or at finite points on the $j\omega$ axis. We can write the partial-fraction expansion of a typical set of z parameters as

$$
\begin{aligned}
z_{11} &= \left[\frac{k_{11}^{(0)}}{s}\right] + \left[k_{11}^{(\infty)}s\right] + \left[\frac{2k_{11}^{(1)}s}{s^2 + \omega_1^2}\right] \\
\frac{z_{22}}{R_2} &= \left[\frac{k_{22}^{(0)}}{s}\right] + \left[k_{22}^{(\infty)}s\right] + \left[\frac{2k_{22}^{(1)}s}{s^2 + \omega_1^2}\right] \\
\frac{z_{12}}{\sqrt{R_2}} &= \left[\frac{k_{12}^{(0)}}{s}\right] + \left[k_{12}^{(\infty)}s\right] + \left[\frac{2k_{12}^{(1)}s}{s^2 + \omega_1^2}\right]
\end{aligned}
\qquad (6\text{-}42)
$$

R_2 is the terminating resistance. The brackets merely serve to group the terms having the same poles and have no other significance. Only one pair of finite j-axis poles has been explicitly shown; any more such poles merely add to the complexity of the algebra but do not affect the procedure in any way.

In case $z_{11} = z_{22}$ the two-port can be realized as a symmetrical lattice. We have already discussed this case and the possibility of obtaining an unbalanced equivalent of the lattice. Let us now consider the general case. If we can realize the parameters in each of the brackets as a two-port, the complete realization can be obtained as a series connection of these components. You will remember that in Chap. 5 we discussed the fact that a series connection of unbalanced two-ports may require ideal transformers. Keeping this in mind, consider Fig. 6-4, in which Z is a capacitance, an inductance, or an antiresonant circuit and the transformer is ideal. The z parameters of the two-port are given in the figure.

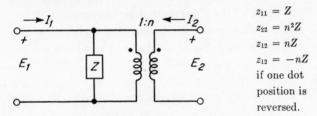

$$z_{11} = Z$$
$$z_{22} = n^2 Z$$
$$z_{12} = nZ$$
$$z_{12} = -nZ$$
if one dot position is reversed.

Fig. 6-4. Component two-port for compact pole.

We see that the sign of z_{12} will depend on the relative winding directions of the transformer windings. Alternatively, we may, by convention, always take the dots as shown in the figure but consider the turns ratio n to be an algebraic quantity. Thus a negative turns ratio will mean that one of the dots should be reversed.

In order to discuss all three of the poles of Eqs. (6-42) simultaneously, let $g(s)$ represent one of the following three functions:

$$g(s) = \frac{1}{s} \qquad \text{(a)}$$

$$g(s) = s \qquad \text{(b)} \qquad \text{(6-43)}$$

$$g(s) = \frac{2s}{s^2 + \omega_1^2} \qquad \text{(c)}$$

The parameters in any one of the brackets in Eq. (6-42) can now be represented as

$$z_{11} = k_{11}g(s) \qquad \text{(a)}$$

$$z_{22} = k_{22}g(s) \qquad \text{(b)} \qquad \text{(6-44)}$$

$$z_{12} = k_{12}g(s) \qquad \text{(c)}$$

If these parameters are to be realized by the two-port in Fig. 6-4, they should be equal to the corresponding ones given in the figure. Thus

$$k_{11}g(s) = Z \qquad \text{(a)}$$

$$k_{22}g(s) = n^2 Z \qquad \text{(b)} \quad \text{(6-45)}$$

$$k_{12}g(s) = nZ \qquad \text{(c)}$$

By taking the ratio of these last equations in pairs we find

$$\frac{k_{22}}{k_{11}} = n^2 \qquad \text{(a)}$$

$$\qquad\qquad\qquad\qquad\qquad \text{(6-46)}$$

$$\frac{k_{22}}{k_{12}} = n \qquad \text{(b)}$$

For these two values of n to be equal, we must have $k_{11}k_{22} - k_{12}^2 = 0$. This requires all the poles of the z parameters to be compact.

For the Darlington network we showed that all the poles of the z parameters, except possibly the poles at infinity and zero, will be compact. Thus we see that the present procedure will apply. The case of a possible noncompact pole will be discussed shortly. Hence a series connection of three networks like that in Fig. 6-4 will realize Eqs. (6-42) when all the poles are compact. This realization is shown in Fig. 6-5.

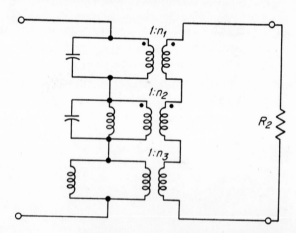

Fig. 6-5. Cauer realization.

The value of n for each component two-port is computed from Eqs. (6-46). You can see that the sign of n for a particular transformer will be the same as the sign of k_{12} for the component two-port. In case the original z parameters have more poles, there will be one additional component two-port for each pair of j-axis poles.

The realization we have obtained is not very appealing because of the presence of the ideal transformers. However, note that, except for the case of the pole at zero, which requires just a capacitance, the other transformers have one side shunted with an inductance. Figure 6-6(a) shows

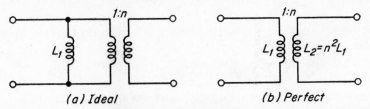

Fig. 6-6. Perfect transformer and its equivalent.

an ideal transformer with a shunt inductance L_1 on one side. From the second pair of terminals this looks like an inductance $n^2 L_1$. But this is precisely the relation between the primary and secondary inductances of a perfect (unity coupling) transformer. Hence this figure is equivalent to the perfect transformer shown in part (b) of the figure. Thus the ideal transformers in Fig. 6-5, together with their shunt inductances, can be replaced by physical transformers having unity coupling coefficient and a primary inductance equal to the corresponding shunt inductance. This leaves only one ideal transformer in the realization.

There would be no need for even this ideal transformer, which is associated with the pole at zero, if the corresponding n were equal to unity. For this to be true, Eqs. (6-46) show that we must have $k_{11} = k_{22} = k_{12}$ for the pole at zero. So far, we have behaved as if the terminating resistance had a value of 1 ohm. Let us return to Eqs. (6-42), keeping R_2 arbitrary. Equating the first terms in the three equations after multiplying the second and third one by R_2 and $\sqrt{R_2}$, respectively, we shall get

$$R_2 = \frac{k_{12}^2}{k_{22}^2} \tag{6-47}$$

If the pole at zero is compact, this value of R_2 is also equal to k_{11}/k_{22}. If this were the termination presented to the two-port, the ideal transformer could be eliminated. However, for a terminating resistance of 1 ohm to appear as the value given in this equation will require an ideal transformer at the output. The secondary-to-primary turns ratio of this transformer must be the square root of the reciprocal of the value of R_2 in Eq. (6-47). But this is precisely the turns ratio of the transformer we just eliminated, according to Eq. (6-46b). Thus the net effect has been to remove the ideal transformer from the interior of the network and to place it at the output.

Let us briefly summarize the procedure to be followed in this realization of a lossless two-port when the three z parameters are specified:

1. Expand the z-parameters in partial fractions.

2. Compute the transformer turns ratio for each component two-port, using Eq. (6-46b). The ideal transformer belonging to the pole at zero is moved to the output.

3. Compute the value of the capacitances from

$$C_0 = \frac{1}{k_{11}^{(0)}} \qquad \text{pole at } s = 0$$

$$C_i = \frac{1}{2k_{11}^{(i)}} \qquad \text{poles at } s = \pm j\omega_i$$

4. Compute the value of the inductances from

$$L_{1\infty} = k_{11}^{(\infty)} \qquad \text{pole at } \infty$$

$$L_{1i} = \frac{2k_{11}^{(i)}}{\omega_i^2} \qquad \text{poles at } s = \pm j\omega_i$$

$$L_{2i} = n_i^2 L_{1i}$$

The complete realization for any number of finite poles, in addition to poles at zero and infinity, is shown in Fig. 6-7.

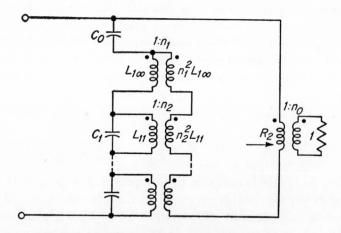

Fig. 6-7. Cauer realization of lossless two-port.

Up to this point we assumed that the z parameters with which we were dealing were obtained from a given magnitude squared function so that the poles were compact. It may happen that a set of z parameters arises in a different manner so that all the poles may not be compact. In other words, we may have $k_{11}k_{22} - k_{12}^2 > 0$ at some of the poles. The method just discussed can still be used with some modification. We can assume that the excess in the residue condition is due to an excess in k_{11} from the

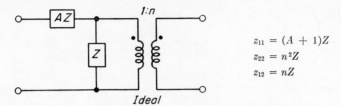

$$z_{11} = (A + 1)Z$$
$$z_{22} = n^2 Z$$
$$z_{12} = nZ$$

Fig. 6-8. Component two-port for noncompact pole.

value needed to make the pole compact. Consider the component two-port shown in Fig. 6-8. Instead of Eqs. (6-46), we shall have

$$\frac{k_{22}}{k_{11}} = \frac{n^2}{A + 1} \qquad (a)$$
$$\frac{k_{22}}{k_{12}} = n \qquad (b)$$

(6-48)

from which we find

$$k_{11}k_{22} - k_{12}^2 = A k_{12}^2 > 0 \qquad (6\text{-}49)$$

The first two steps of the previous procedure for compact poles will remain unchanged. Before proceeding to the third step we must determine the value of A at each pole. This is accomplished with the aid of Eq. (6-48a). The fraction of the total residue k_{11} at each pole that belongs to the shunt branch in Fig. 6-8 is $1/(A + 1)$. To compute the element values in step 4, then, the same relationships can be used if k_{11} is replaced by $k_{11}/(A + 1)$.

The complete realization will look like Fig. 6-5 except that there will be additional elements in series with the input port representing the excess of the residues of z_{11}. This is shown in Fig. 6-9. If the pole at infinity is not compact, then there will be an inductance in series with the input port. If we add a fraction of this inductance to the primary inductances of each perfect transformer, the coupling of each will be reduced from unity. In such a case, except for the transformer at the output, this realization requires only physical transformers with less than perfect coupling (in addition to inductance and capacitance) and, hence, loses some of its objectionable properties.

A completely analogous procedure could be followed if a set of three y parameters were specified. Again these would be expanded into partial fractions and a grouping into components made. The realization would be obtained as a parallel combination of the component two-ports. Perfect

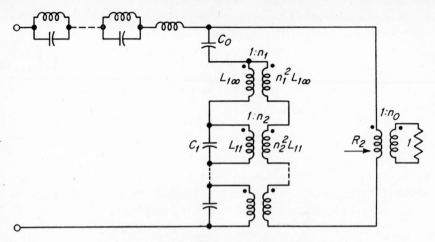

Fig. 6-9. Cauer realization for noncompact poles.

transformers would again be involved. As a matter of fact, from a given set of z parameters we could construct the corresponding y parameters, using the relations in Table 1-1. Even though the two-port realization is z-compact, it may not be y-compact. Thus, although the transformers in the first realization are perfect, those in the second realization need not be. The details of the realization of a set of y parameters are left to you.

The realization procedure we have just discussed constitutes a sufficiency proof for the realizability of a set of z or y parameters which satisfy the necessary conditions stated at the beginning of this section. However, it is not a desirable realization both from the point of view of network structure and because of the necessity of such a large number of transformers.

6-4. Darlington realization of a lossless two-port

In the previous section we discussed a realization procedure which showed that a given set of three z or y parameters satisfying necessary conditions of realizability can always be realized. However, the realization, at best, needs as many physical transformers as there are pairs of poles. At worst, these transformers must be perfectly coupled, except for one at the output, which must be ideal.

An alternative realization has been given by Darlington (35). The procedure is an extension of the ladder-development idea discussed in Chap. 5. The starting point is the input impedance of the resistance-loaded lossless two-port. The transmission zeros of the two-port are the same as the zeros of the even part of $Z(s)$, as clearly seen in Table 6-1. Suppose that all the transmission zeros lie on the $j\omega$ axis. We know that, when only two z parameters are specified (say, z_{22} and z_{12}), a ladder realization can be obtained by the zero-shifting technique. However, when all three z parameters are prescribed, as in the present case, a ladder realization may not be possible even though all the transmission zeros lie on the $j\omega$ axis. This will be clear if you recall that we had no control over the far-end impedance, say, z_{11}, when using the zero-shifting procedure.

In addition to this consideration is the fact that there may also be other transmission zeros, not on the $j\omega$ axis. Darlington's procedure, which we shall now discuss, utilizes more complicated sections, other than series or shunt branches, to realize the transmission zeros. Four types of section are needed; these are shown in Fig. 6-10. The branches in the

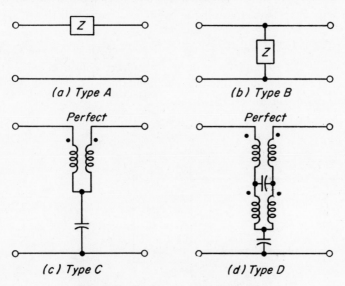

Fig. 6-10. Darlington canonic sections.

first two types consist of single inductance or capacitance, or series-tuned circuits or parallel-tuned circuits. The third type of section is a Brune section, while the fourth type is a generalization of this. The type C section realizes transmission zeros on the $j\omega$ axis and on the real axis (see Prob. 3-26), while type D sections realize complex zeros.

Starting from a given $Z(s)$, we know that sections of type A and type B can be removed to realize poles and zeros of $Z(s)$ on the $j\omega$ axis. After all such poles and zeros have been removed (including any at zero and infinity), we are left with a positive real function. The even part of this function will have three types of zeros: real, imaginary, and complex. A typical even part will be

$$U(-s^2) = \frac{(s^2 + \omega_0^2)^2(s^2 - a^2)^2(s^4 + b_1 s^2 + b_0)^2}{D(-s^2)} \tag{6-50}$$

(If the real and complex zeros are not initially double, we use surplus factors to achieve this form.)

We must now show that removal of a type C section with appropriate element values will leave an impedance of lower rank and with an even part having the same zeros as before, except for a pair of imaginary ones or a pair of real ones which are realized by the section. Finally we must show that removal of a type D section will leave an impedance of still lower rank and with an even part which is missing a quadruplet of complex zeros. Successive removals of such sections will reduce the rank of the original impedance to zero, and the result will realize all the transmission zeros.

We have already seen in Chap. 3 that removal of a type C (Brune) section will leave an impedance of lower rank. We need to show that the even part of the remainder function will have the same zeros as the original function (except for the pair realized).

Let $Z(s)$ in Fig. 6-11 be a positive real function whose even part has at least one pair of zeros on the $j\omega$ axis.

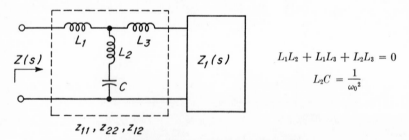

$$L_1 L_2 + L_1 L_3 + L_2 L_3 = 0$$

$$L_2 C = \frac{1}{\omega_0^2}$$

Fig. 6-11. Removal of type C section.

If we solve for $Z_1(s)$ in terms of Z directly from the figure, we shall get

$$Z_1(s) = \frac{1}{\dfrac{1}{Z(s) - sL_1} - \dfrac{s/L_2}{s^2 + \omega_0^2}} - sL_3 \tag{6-51}$$

Recall from the discussion of the Brune realization in Chapter 3 that L_1 is chosen to produce a zero of $Z - sL_1$ at $s = j\omega_0$. Hence, writing

$$Z(s) - sL_1 = \frac{m_1 + n_1}{m_2 + n_2} - sL_1 = \frac{(m_1 - sL_1 n_2) + (n_1 - sL_1 m_2)}{m_2 + n_2} \tag{6-52}$$

we see that both the odd and even parts of the numerator on the right must have the factor $s^2 + \omega_0^2$.

Now let us rewrite Eq. (6-51) as the ratio of two polynomials, using Eq. (6-52). The result is

$$Z_1(s) =$$

$$\frac{[(m_1 - sL_1n_2) + (L_2 + L_3)Cs^2m_1 - L_3sn_2] + (n_1 - sL_1m_2) + (L_2 + L_3)s^2n_1 - L_3sm_2}{[(L_2Cs^2 + 1)m_2 - sC(n_1 - L_1sm_2)] \quad + \quad [(L_2Cs^2 + 1)n_2 - sC(m_1 - L_1sn_2)]} \tag{6-53}$$

The m's and n's belong to $Z(s)$. After considerable algebraic manipulation, we shall find the even part of this expression to be

$$U_1(-s^2) = \frac{m_1m_2 - n_1n_2}{\left(m_2 - sC\dfrac{n_1 - sL_1m_2}{s^2L_2C + 1}\right)^2 - \left(n_2 - sC\dfrac{m_1 - L_1sn_2}{s^2L_2C + 1}\right)^2} \tag{6-54}$$

The numerator is the same as that of the even part of $Z(s)$. However, we can show that each term in parentheses in the denominator has a factor $s^2 + \omega_0^2$. To see this, remember that $Z(s) - sL_1$ has this factor so that its reciprocal has a pole at $s = j\omega_0$. Return to Eq. (6-51). In the denominator of the first term L_2 is chosen so that this pole is completely subtracted, leaving a result which is regular at $s = j\omega_0$. Let us write an expression for that denominator, using Eq. (6-52) and the value of ω_0^2.

$$\frac{1}{Z - L_1s} - \frac{sC}{s^2L_2C + 1} = \frac{m_2 + n_2}{(m_1 - sL_1n_2) + (n_1 - sL_1m_2)} - \frac{sC}{s^2L_2C + 1}$$

$$= \frac{\left(m_2 - sC\dfrac{n_1 - sL_1m_2}{s^2L_2C + 1}\right) + \left(n_2 - sC\dfrac{m_1 - sL_1n_2}{s^2L_2C + 1}\right)}{(m_1 - sL_1n_2) + (n_1 - sL_1m_2)} \tag{6-55}$$

We have already established that each term in the denominator has the factor $s^2 + \omega_0^2$. Hence, since the entire expression is to be regular at $s = j\omega_0$, each term in the numerator must also have this factor. But these terms are the same as those in the denominator of Eq. (6-54), which proves the statement we made.

We see, then, that a factor $(s^2 + \omega_0^2)^2$ will cancel from the numerator of Eq. (6-54). This shows that the even part of the terminating impedance $Z_1(s)$ has the same zeros as the even part of the original impedance, except for the double zeros at $s^2 = -\omega_0^2$, which are realized by the type C section.

The previous argument will be unchanged if we set $\omega_0^2 = -a^2$. Hence the type C section will realize a pair of zeros on the real axis as well. Since the product L_2C of the shunt-branch elements in Fig. 6-11 is equal to $1/\omega_0^2$, the condition $\omega_0^2 = -a^2$ will require L_2 or C to be negative. However, a negative L_2 does not cause any difficulty. You can easily show that the inductance tee network of the type C section is equivalent to a perfectly coupled transformer in this case, as well as when L_1 or L_3 is negative. In the present case one of the winding directions will be reversed.

We must go through a similar process to show that a type D section will realize a quadruplet of complex transmission zeros, leaving an impedance of reduced rank whose even part has the same zeros as the original one except for the quadruplet. This is a straightforward procedure, but the algebra becomes extremely laborious. The details are left to you as an exercise.

In this fashion an arbitrary positive real function will be realized as a lossless two-port, consisting of a cascade connection of the four types of section, terminated in a resistance. In view of the fact that the input impedance of such a two-port can be uniquely formed from a given set of three z parameters, the Darlington procedure constitutes an alternative general realization technique when all three z parameters are specified. Whereas the Cauer technique requires perfectly coupled transformers in every case, the Darlington synthesis may avoid transformers in certain fairly important cases. (We shall discuss these in the next section). Furthermore, since the transmission zeros are realized separately by separate portions of the over-all network, adjustments of the element values of one section in a practical realization can be made without affecting the alignment of the other sections.

6-5. Low-pass ladder realization

Having discussed general realization techniques in the previous two sections, let us now discuss some special cases, which nevertheless are important. Let us restrict ourselves to transmission zeros lying on the $j\omega$ axis only. Generally it will not be possible to obtain a ladder realization (type A and B sections only) when all three z parameters are prescribed even though all transmission zeros are on the $j\omega$ axis. However, we have already seen in Chap. 3 that, when the even part of an impedance (and, hence, z_{12}) has zeros only at zero, or infinity, or both, a ladder realization can be obtained, the arms consisting of single L's and C's. Thus, to obtain a ladder realization, it is sufficient that the transmission zeros lie at zero or infinity. But this is not a necessary condition. In this section we shall discuss necessary and sufficient conditions for the realization of special kinds of ladder networks.

The words *passband*, *low-pass*, *high-pass*, etc., have an intuitive significance in filter theory. In image parameter filter theory a passband is said to exist when the image attenuation is zero and the image impedance is purely real. Of course, the actual attenuation (not the image attenuation) is not zero in the passband. It seems intuitively true that the character of a response will not be drastically changed if the poles and zeros of the z parameters are displaced slightly from the positions demanded by the above definitions. Thus, for slight changes in the locations of the critical points, we should expect a low-pass network to remain low-pass.

We do not wish to restrict the significance of a passband to filter functions alone. The magnitude of the transfer function or its angle may be arbitrarily prescribed over an interval of the $j\omega$ axis. We shall call this interval the passband no matter what the shape of the prescribed function.

Very roughly, the property that distinguishes a low-pass network from another is that low-frequency sinusoids are transmitted (with their amplitude or angle modified in a prescribed way), while high-frequency sinusoids are not (or are transmitted much less). Thus a low-pass two-port should have no transmission zero at $s = 0$. Although it is desirable to have a transmission zero at infinity, this is not necessary. That is, some transmission can be tolerated at infinite frequency, but this transmission should be small compared with the transmission at low frequencies.

In the above discussion no restriction is made on the structure of the two-port. If we restrict ourselves to a ladder network, we can make more precise definitions of low-pass and high-pass. In a ladder network there is only a single path from the input port to the output. Hence, for a low-pass ladder, if we are to have no transmission zero at $s = 0$, we must require that the series arm impedances have a zero at $s = 0$. This means there should be no series capacitance in the series branches. Thus, the series branches can consist of a single inductance or of any reactive network shunted by an inductance, e.g., an antiresonant circuit. Also, we must require that the shunt arm impedances have a pole at $s = 0$. This means there should be no parallel inductance in the shunt branches. Thus, the shunt branches can consist of a single capacitance, or any reactive

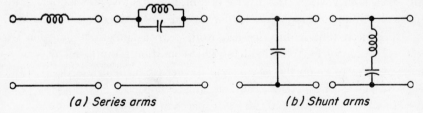

(a) Series arms   (b) Shunt arms

Fig. 6-12. Series and shunt arms of low-pass ladder.

network in series with a capacitance, e.g., a resonant circuit. Some simple permissible branches are shown in Fig. 6-12.

Based on this discussion, we can give the following definition: *A low-pass ladder is one that has no transmission zero at* $s = 0$ *and* z_{12} *or* y_{12} *(or both) have at least a simple zero at infinity.* We have already seen a special case when all the transmission zeros are at infinity; the ladder has only inductance in the series arm and only capacitance in the shunt arm, each element realizing one of the transmission zeros.

Two other special low-pass ladders are shown in Fig. 6-13. The first is called a *mid-series* ladder; it has the characteristic that all the series

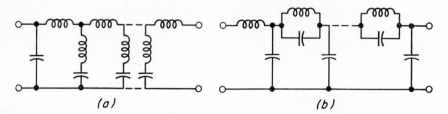

Fig. 6-13. Mid-series and mid-shunt low-pass ladders.

branches are single inductances. Thinking in terms of the Cauer ladder development, the series branches serve to shift the zeros by partial removal of an impedance pole at infinity. The transmission zeros are then realized by the shunt branches.

The second ladder is the dual of the first and is called a *mid-shunt* ladder. It is characterized by each shunt branch being a single capacitance. The shunt capacitances serve to shift the zeros by partially removing an admittance pole at infinity. The transmission zeros are then realized by the series branches. The general low-pass ladder is a mixed mid-series and mid-shunt type.

Similar to the definition of a low-pass ladder, we can give the following definition: *A high-pass ladder is one that has no transmission zero at infinity and* z_{12} *or* y_{12} *(or both) have at least a simple zero at* $s = 0$. Each branch of a high-pass ladder will be the inverse of a branch of a low-pass ladder. Mid-series and mid-shunt high-pass ladders can also be defined in a similar way.

Darlington (35) in his classical work gave a sufficient condition for the realization of low-pass ladders. This condition requires all the transmission zeros to lie on the $j\omega$ axis and farther from the origin than all the poles of the z parameters. However, this condition is not necessary. It remained for Fujisawa (50) to state necessary and sufficient conditions for the realization of such ladders. We shall now discuss these conditions.

Consider the consequences of the definition of a low-pass ladder. Since there is to be no transmission zero at $s = 0$, Table 6-1 shows that case A will apply. A glance at the table shows that both the z and y parameters will have a compact pole at $s = 0$. This means that the input impedance $Z(s)$ can have no pole or zero at $s = 0$. The zeros of the even part of $Z(s)$ must all lie on the $j\omega$ axis since these are the transmission zeros. Hence we can write

$$N(-s^2) = m_1m_2 - n_1n_2 = K(s^2 + \omega_1^2)^2(s^2 + \omega_2^2)^2 \ldots (s^2 + \omega_k^2)^2 \qquad (6\text{-}56)$$

Let us examine various types of impedance function to determine whether their even part can have this form. We see that the degree of $N(-s^2)$ is a multiple of 4. We quickly find that, when the numerator and denominator of $Z(s)$ are of the same degree, either the degree of $N(-s^2)$ is not a multiple of 4 or z_{12} and y_{12} both have a pole at infinity. We conclude that the input impedance of a low-pass resistance-loaded ladder cannot be of the same degree in numerator and denominator. It remains to consider impedances having a pole or zero at infinity.

A glance at the expression for $Z(s)$ in terms of the z parameters will show that there are two ways in which $Z(s)$ can have a pole on the $j\omega$ axis: (1) *The z's have a noncompact pole* or (2) z_{11} *has a private pole.* Since all the poles of the z parameters except the one at infinity are compact, $Z(s)$ can have no pole on the finite $j\omega$ axis due to the first reason, but it may have one at infinity. From the relationships between the z and y parameters we can determine that all the y's will have a zero at infinity if the z's have a noncompact pole there. Thus, even though z_{12} has a pole at infinity, y_{12} will have a zero there, satisfying the condition for a low-pass ladder. In this case Table 6-1 will show that m_1 and m_2 are both of lower degree than n_1 so that the highest power of s in the numerator of $Z(s)$ is odd. For the second alternative, if z_{11} has a private pole at infinity, the relationships among z's and y's show that y_{22} will also have a private pole at infinity. Thus both z_{12} and y_{12} will have a zero at infinity, and the condition for a low-pass ladder is satisfied. Again Table 6-1 will show that in this case both n_1 and n_2 are of lower degree than m_1 so that the highest power in the numerator of $Z(s)$ is even.

Let us examine $N(-s^2)$ when $Z(s)$ has a pole at infinity and the highest power in the numerator is even. The simplest case is a second-degree polynomial over a first degree.

$$Z(s) = \frac{s^2 + a_1s + a_0}{s + b_0} \qquad \text{(a)}$$

$$N(-s^2) = (b_0 - a_1)s^2 + a_0b_0 \qquad \text{(b)}$$

$$(6\text{-}57)$$

Since N is only quadratic, it cannot have a double pair of roots on the finite $j\omega$ axis. This means that we must have $a_1 = b_0$.

The next higher-order impedance of this type will be a fourth-degree polynomial over a third degree. In this case $N(-s^2)$ will be of the sixth degree, and so it can have only one pair of double zeros on the $j\omega$ axis. Again the coefficient of the highest power of s in N must vanish. This coefficient is equal to the difference between a_{k-1} and b_{k-2}, where k is the degree of the numerator. Continuing in this fashion, we shall always find that, *when the highest power in the numerator of* $Z(s)$ *is even, the coefficients of the next to the highest power in the numerator and the denominator are equal* (assuming the highest powers are written with the same coefficient). You can verify this fact for higher-order impedances.

For $Z(s)$ to have a zero at infinity, $Y(s)$ must have a pole. In this case Eq. (6-15) shows that either (1) *the y parameters have a noncompact pole at infinity* or (2) y_{11} *has a private pole at infinity*. By reasoning similar to the above, we find that, in the first case, all the z's will have a zero at infinity and the highest power in the denominator of $Z(s)$ will be odd. When y_{11} has a private pole at infinity, so does z_{22} and the highest power in the denominator of $Z(s)$ is even. In both cases the condition for a low-pass ladder is satisfied.

The preceding discussion, by the very nature of the subject under consideration, has involved a considerable amount of detail and may have appeared laborious. Let us summarize the pertinent results for the purpose of consolidating our ideas.

Low-pass ladder—Definition:

1. No transmission zero at $s = 0$.
2. Either z_{12} or y_{12} (or both) has at least a simple zero at infinity.

Consequences:

1. $Z(s)$ has neither a pole nor a zero at $s = 0$.
2. $Z(s)$ has either a pole or a zero at infinity.
3. With pole of $Z(s)$ at infinity:
   (a) If degree of numerator is even, then:
      (1) z_{11} and y_{22} have a private pole at infinity.
      (2) Coefficients of next to highest-power terms in numerator and denominator are equal.
   (b) If degree of numerator is odd, then:
      (1) z parameters have a noncompact pole at infinity; y parameters have a zero at infinity.

    (2) Coefficients of next to highest-power terms in numerator and denominator may or may not be equal. If they are equal, this implies that z_{11} and z_{22} have a semiprivate pole at infinity.

  4. With zero of $Z(s)$ at infinity:

    (a) If degree of denominator is even, then:

      (1) y_{11} and z_{22} have a private pole at infinity.

      (2) Coefficients of next to highest-power terms in numerator and denominator are equal.

    (b) If degree of denominator is odd, then:

      (1) y parameters have a noncompact pole at infinity;
         z parameters have a zero at infinity.

      (2) Coefficients of next to highest-power terms in numerator and denominator may or may not be equal. If they are equal, this implies that y_{11} and y_{22} have a semiprivate pole at infinity.

The consequences listed under 3(b)(2) and 4(b)(2) in this summary were not developed in the preceding discussion. Demonstration of their validity is left to you as an exercise.

From the discussion just completed we find that a necessary condition for the driving-point impedance $Z(s)$ of a low-pass ladder network is: $Z(s)$ *has a pole or a zero at infinity.* An additional useful condition can be stated, utilizing the definition of a low-pass ladder. Looking at Table 6-1, we can state that, since z_{12} or y_{12} must have at least a simple zero at infinity, then n_1 or n_2 (*or both*) *must have at least one more zero* (*counting the one at $s = 0$*) *than there are finite transmission zeros.*

Both the conditions just given are necessary for the realizability of a low-pass Darlington ladder, but they are not sufficient. On the other hand, we mentioned that a sufficient condition is for all the transmission zeros to be greater in magnitude than all the finite zeros of n_2, but this condition is not necessary. It remained for Fujisawa to discover a condition which, combined with the others discussed above, forms a set of necessary and sufficient conditions. We shall list all these conditions for easy reference.

Necessary and sufficient conditions for the realizability of a low-pass resistance-terminated lossless ladder network:

1. Transmission zeros [zeros of $N(-s^2)$] restricted to the $j\omega$ axis.
2. $Z(s)$ has a pole or zero at infinity.
3. n_1 or n_2 (or both) have at least one more zero than there are finite transmission zeros.

4. Let the transmission zeros be denoted $s_i = j\omega_i$, and write $\omega_1 < \omega_2 < \ldots < \omega_k$. Then, if n_1 satisfies condition 3, any value ω_i has at least i zeros of m_1 between the origin and itself; and if n_2 satisfies condition 3, ω_i has at least i zeros of m_2 between the origin and itself. Stated differently, this condition says that one or both of the polynomials m_1 and m_2 have at least i zeros on the positive $j\omega$ axis which are no larger in magnitude than the transmission zero ω_i, for any value of i.

We have yet to prove that the last condition is necessary and that, given functions satisfying all four conditions, a low-pass ladder can be realized.

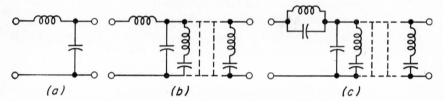

Fig. 6-14. Simple low-pass ladders.

Consider the simple low-pass ladders shown in Fig. 6-14. You can easily show that the realizability conditions are satisfied for these simple cases. Fujisawa used a proof by mathematical induction to show that the four conditions which we listed are necessary for realizability. Thus suppose that the conditions are satisfied for the network shown in Fig. 6-15(a). It suffices to show that the conditions are still satisfied if we

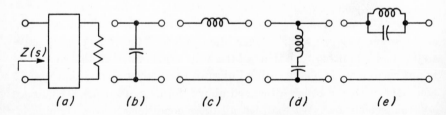

Fig. 6-15. Branches of low-pass ladder.

cascade at the input the other networks shown in the figure. We shall demonstrate the method when the section in part (d) is cascaded at the input of the two-port. The procedure will be identical when the other sections are cascaded.

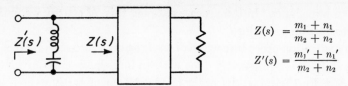

$$Z(s) = \frac{m_1 + n_1}{m_2 + n_2}$$

$$Z'(s) = \frac{m_1' + n_1'}{m_2 + n_2}$$

Fig. 6-16. Notation for cascade connection.

Let us designate by primes the quantities involved after the cascade connection. The notation is shown in Fig. 6-16. Let ω_0 be the resonant frequency of the shunt branch. Then

$$Z'(s) = \cfrac{1}{\cfrac{ks}{s^2 + \omega_0^2} + \cfrac{1}{Z(s)}} = \cfrac{1}{\cfrac{ks}{s^2 + \omega_0^2} + \cfrac{m_2 + n_2}{m_1 + n_1}}$$

$$= \frac{(s^2 + \omega_0^2)m_1 + (s^2 + \omega_0^2)n_1}{[(s^2 + \omega_0^2)m_2 + ksn_1] + [n_2(s^2 + \omega_0^2) + ksm_1]} = \frac{m_1' + n_1'}{m_2' + n_2'} \quad (6\text{-}58)$$

and $\qquad N'(-s^2) = m_1'm_2' - n_1'n_2' = (s^2 + \omega_0^2)^2(m_1m_2 - n_1n_2) \quad (6\text{-}59)$

The shunt branch does not affect the behavior of the network at infinity, so that the behavior of Z' is the same as the behavior of Z at infinity. The first two conditions are thus satisfied. If the numerator and denominator of Z' have no common factors, n_1' and n_2' have one more zero on the positive $j\omega$ axis than n_1 and n_2, respectively, and there is one additional transmission zero on the positive $j\omega$ axis, so that condition 3 is also satisfied. Since the new transmission zero coincides with the new zero of m_1', condition 4 is also satisfied for m_1' if it was originally satisfied for m_1.

If the numerator and denominator of $Z'(s)$ have a common factor, this factor must be $s^2 + \omega_0^2$, which we can cancel. Then

$$Z'(s) = \frac{m_1 + n_1}{\left(m_2 + \cfrac{ksn_1}{s^2 + \omega_0^2}\right) + \left(n_2 + \cfrac{ksm_1}{s^2 + \omega_0^2}\right)} = \frac{m_1 + n_1}{m_2'' + n_2''} \quad (6\text{-}60)$$

$$N''(-s^2) = m_1m_2'' - n_1n_2'' = m_1m_2 - n_1n_2 \quad (6\text{-}61)$$

Thus conditions 3 and 4 are satisfied in this case also.

The details of the proof when the other sections are cascaded at the input are left to you.

We have now established that the four realizability conditions are necessary. It remains to prove that, when a driving-point function is given satisfying the above four necessary conditions, we can always construct a low-pass lossless ladder two-port terminated in a resistance which realizes the given impedance. In the process of doing this, of course, we must out-line a realization procedure.

The realization procedure we shall use is again a zero-shifting technique, but the shifting is consistently done with an impedance or admittance pole at infinity. Furthermore the order of realization of transmission zeros is not completely arbitrary because we must ensure that the removal of a branch leaves an impedance which satisfies the necessary conditions.

To start with, suppose that $Z(s)$ has a pair of conjugate j-axis poles. We have already shown that this can result only from a private pole of z_{11}. Hence we can realize this pole as a branch in series with the rest of the network as shown in Fig. 6-17(a). Since the pole is to be completely re-

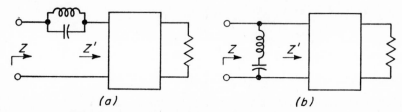

Fig. 6-17. Steps in the realization of a lossless ladder.

moved in the series branch, this pole of $Z(s)$ will become a transmission zero. The remaining impedance will be

$$Z'(s) = Z(s) - \frac{ks}{s^2 + \omega_0^2} = \frac{m_1 - \dfrac{ksn_2}{s^2 + \omega_0^2}}{s^2 + \omega_0^2} + \frac{n_1 - \dfrac{ksm_2}{s^2 + \omega_0^2}}{s^2 + \omega_0^2} = \frac{m_1' + n_1'}{m_2' + n_2'} \quad (6\text{-}62)$$

and
$$N'(-s^2) = m_1'm_2' - n_1'n_2' = \frac{m_1m_2 - n_1n_2}{(s^2 + \omega_0^2)^2} \quad (6\text{-}63)$$

In Eq. (6-62) we have divided both numerator and denominator by $s^2 + \omega_0^2$ because we know that $Z'(s)$ has no pole at $s = j\omega_0$. $Z'(s)$ has the same behavior at infinity as $Z(s)$. The remaining transmission zeros are on the $j\omega$ axis. n_2' has one fewer zero on the positive $j\omega$ axis than n_2, but then there is one fewer transmission zero there also. m_2' obviously satisfies condition 4 if m_2 does. Thus Z' satisfies the four necessary conditions, and it is simpler than $Z(s)$.

Next assume that $Z(s)$ has a pair of conjugate j-axis zeros. This is possible only if y_{11} has a private pole, which can be realized as a resonant branch in parallel with the input terminals, as shown in Fig. 6-17(b).

Following the pattern above, you can show that the remaining impedance satisfies the necessary conditions.

These two steps have been zero removals. After all finite j-axis poles and zeros of $Z(s)$ have been exhausted, we come to the necessity of zero shifting. Suppose that $Z(s)$ has a pole at infinity. We know that this is possible under two conditions, and we shall treat these separately.

Case A. The highest power in the numerator is even.

Then z_{11} has a private pole at infinity, which means that there is a transmission zero at infinity. This pole can be completely removed as a series inductance whose value is the residue of $Z(s)$ at infinity. You can see this by looking at Eq. (6-2), which shows that $Z(s) \to z_{11}$ as s approaches a private pole of z_{11}.

Suppose that we remove an inductance L from $Z(s)$. Then

$$Z'(s) = Z(s) - Ls = \frac{(m_1 - Lsn_2) + (n_1 - Lsm_2)}{m_2 + n_2} = \frac{m_1' + n_1'}{m_2 + n_2} \qquad (6\text{-}64)$$

$$N'(-s^2) = m_1'm_2 - n_1'n_2 = m_1m_2 - n_1n_2 \qquad (6\text{-}65)$$

The remaining impedance has the same finite transmission zeros, and so condition 1 is satisfied. If L is less than or equal to the residue of $Z(s)$ at infinity, $Z'(s)$ is positive real. In the present case L is equal to the residue of $Z(s)$ at infinity. Recall that the coefficients of the next to the highest-power terms in the numerator and denominator must be equal in this case. This ensures that, when we subtract the entire residue at infinity, $Z'(s)$ will have a zero there, so that condition 2 is satisfied. The denominator has not changed, which means that the highest power in the denominator of Z' is odd, which in turn means that the new y parameters have a non-compact pole at infinity. Recalling the expression for y_{12} in Table 6-1, we see that n_1' *does not* satisfy condition 3. However, $n_2' = n_2$ *does*, so that condition 3 is satisfied. Since $m_2' = m_2$, condition 4 is also satisfied.

To summarize, when $Z(s)$ has a pole at infinity and the highest power in the numerator is even, we remove the pole as a series inductance whose value is equal to the residue of $Z(s)$ at infinity. This shifts a zero of $Z'(s)$ to the transmission zero at infinity.

Case B. The highest power in the numerator of $Z(s)$ is odd.

Then the z parameters have a noncompact pole at infinity. In this case $Z(s) \to 1/y_{11} = z_{11} - z_{12}^2/z_{22}$ as s approaches a noncompact impedance pole. Again we remove a series inductance L, but its value will depend on the transmission zero to which we want to shift. Equations (6-64) and (6-65) will still apply, but the value of L is still to be determined. The remaining impedance, $Z'(s)$, will still have a pole at infinity so that conditions 1 and 2 are again satisfied. Also, $n_2' = n_2$ still satisfies condition 3; but now n_1' also satisfies this condition since its order is not reduced from that of n_1. So we must determine whether m_1' satisfies condition 4. (We already know that $m_2' = m_2$ does.) Write

$$m_1' = m_1 - Lsn_2 = n_2\left(\frac{m_1}{n_2} - Ls\right) = n_2(z_{11} - Ls) \qquad (6\text{-}66)$$

Except for common zeros of m_1 and n_2 (if any), the zeros of m_1' will be those of $z_{11} - Ls$. A sketch of a typical z_{11} is shown in Fig. 6-18. The squares

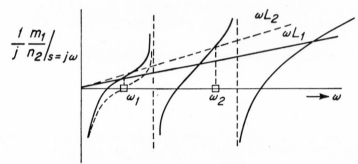

Fig. 6-18. Sketch of $\frac{1}{j} z_{11}(j\omega)$.

indicate the locations of transmission zeros. In this particular case only two finite transmission zeros are possible on the positive ω axis. Notice that we have made m_1 satisfy condition 4, but just barely. The value of L to remove from $Z(s)$ becomes apparent from a consideration of the figure. If we subtract the solid line with slope L_1 from z_{11}, we cause a zero of the curve to shift to ω_1. Subtracting the dotted line with slope L_2 will cause another zero of the curve to shift to ω_2. But the first zero will now move beyond ω_1, thus causing condition 4 to be violated. Therefore the value of L needed is the smallest value that will cause a zero of z_{11} to shift to one of the transmission zeros. That is, z_{11} should equal Ls, evaluated at one of the transmission zeros. However, according to Prob. 6-3, the value of $Z(s)$ is equal to that of z_{11} at a transmission zero. The process is thus clear: Evaluate

$$L_i = \frac{Z(j\omega_i)}{j\omega_i} \qquad (6\text{-}67)$$

at all the transmission zeros $j\omega_i$. The value of L desired is

$$L = \text{minimum } L_i \qquad (6\text{-}68)$$

Any larger value of L will cause condition 4 to be violated.

When condition 4 is satisfied with a greater margin of safety than in this illustration, we can relax the choice of L given by the last equation. Thus, if ω_1 in Fig. 6-18 is moved out beyond the last zero of m_1, then we can use either value of L as computed from Eq. (6-67) without violating condition 4. This means that the transmission zeros can then be realized in either order.

Based on this discussion, we can readily appreciate that, the larger the magnitude of the transmission zeros relative to the magnitude of the zeros of m_1, the greater the flexibility in the order of realization of the transmission zeros. In the limit, when condition 4 is satisfied but with no margin, as in the illustration, there is a unique order in which the transmission zeros must be realized. This completes the discussion of zero shifting when $Z(s)$ has a pole at infinity.

After the completion of the previous step we shall have generated a zero of $Z'(s)$ on the finite $j\omega$ axis. This is then removed as a series-resonant branch in parallel with the rest of the network. However, after the removal of the inductance in case A (i.e., when the highest power in the numerator of $Z(s)$ is even), $Z(s)$ (we have dropped the prime since we are treating it as a fresh impedance) will have a zero at infinity. Furthermore, the y parameters will have a noncompact pole at infinity. If we take the reciprocal and talk about $Y(s)$, we shall have the exact dual of case B (i.e., when the highest power in the numerator of $Z(s)$ is odd). The discussion there will apply intact merely by an interchange of symbols, y's for z's, subscripts 1 for 2 on the m's and n's, and vice versa, C for L. Equations (6-67) and (6-68) will also apply, with these replacements, so that the value of shunt capacitance that should be removed is calculated from

$$C_i = \frac{Y(j\omega_i)}{j\omega_i} \qquad \text{(a)}$$
$$C = \text{minimum } C_i \qquad \text{(b)}$$
$$(6\text{-}69)$$

We have seen that the following sequence takes place: If $Z(s)$ has a pole at infinity and the highest power in the numerator is even, we remove an inductance equal in value to the residue of $Z(s)$ at infinity. This makes the remaining impedance zero at infinity. The remaining admittance, then, has a pole at infinity caused by a noncompact pole of y parameters. We next remove a shunt capacitance whose value is given by Eqs. (6-69). Finally the transmission zero is realized as a parallel-resonant branch in series with the remainder.

There remains one more consideration. When case B is encountered and a transmission zero is realized by means of a series-resonant branch, the remaining admittance will have a pole at infinity. This may be caused by a private pole of y_{11}. A discussion which is the dual of case A will now apply, showing that this pole of $Y(s)$ is completely removed as a shunt capacitance. The remaining impedance then will have a pole at infinity due to a noncompact pole of z's, and we are back to case B.

As an illustration of the realization procedure, consider the following impedance function:

$$Z(s) = \frac{1}{5} \frac{s^4 + s^3 + 3s^2 + 2s + 1}{s^3 + s^2 + \frac{2}{5}s + \frac{1}{5}} \qquad \text{(a)}$$
$$N(-s^2) = m_1 m_2 - n_1 n_2 = 4(s^2 + \tfrac{1}{2})^2 \qquad \text{(b)}$$

(6-70)

We first check to determine whether or not this function satisfies the necessary conditions for a low-pass ladder, and we find that it does. (Do this.) Observe that $Z(s)$ has a pole at infinity and the highest power in the numerator is even. Thus z_{11} has a private pole at infinity. As we would expect, the coefficients of the next to the highest-power terms in numerator and denominator are the same. The residue of $Z(s)$ at infinity is $1/5$; if we subtract an inductance $L_1 = 1/5$, we get

$$Z_1(s) = Z(s) - \frac{1}{5}s = \frac{1}{5} \frac{\frac{13}{5}s^2 + \frac{9}{5}s + 1}{s^3 + s^2 + \frac{2}{5}s + \frac{1}{5}} \qquad (6\text{-}71)$$

$Z_1(s)$ has a zero at infinity, and the highest power in the denominator is odd. Hence the y parameters have a noncompact pole at infinity. We need to remove a shunt capacitance whose value is calculated from Eqs. (6-69). Since there is only one (positive) transmission zero, we get

$$C_1 = \frac{Y_1(j/\sqrt{2})}{j/\sqrt{2}} = \frac{5}{3} \qquad (6\text{-}72)$$

and

$$Y_2(s) = Y_1(s) - \frac{5}{3}s = \frac{10}{3} \frac{(s^2 + \tfrac{1}{2})(s + 3)}{13s^2 + 9s + 5} \qquad (6\text{-}73)$$

We have shifted a zero to the desired location. We now remove this zero as a pole of $Z_2(s) = 1/Y_2(s)$. The residue of $Z_2(s)$ at $s = 1/\sqrt{2}$ is $9/20$ so that

$$Z_3(s) = \frac{3}{10} \frac{(13s^2 + 9s + 5)}{(s^2 + \tfrac{1}{2})(s + 3)} - \frac{\frac{9}{10}s}{s^2 + \tfrac{1}{2}} = \frac{3}{s + 3} \qquad (6\text{-}74)$$

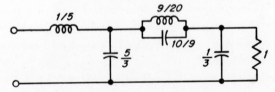

Fig. 6-19. Realization of numerical example.

$Y_3(s)$ is now recognized as a capacitance $C = \frac{1}{3}$ in parallel with $R = 1$. The complete realization is shown in Fig. 6-19.

This completes the discussion of the realization of low-pass Darlington ladder networks. Through the appropriate frequency transformation (see Chapter 9) the same discussion can be applied to high-pass and bandpass networks as well.

6-6. Complementary networks—constant-resistance filter pairs

In Chap. 5 we discussed two-port realization techniques when only one of the terminations has a finite nonzero value. The procedures were relatively simple because of the simple expressions relating Z_{12} or Y_{12} with the open-circuit or short-circuit parameters. When both terminations are finite, the complexity of the procedure increases considerably, as demonstrated in this chapter.

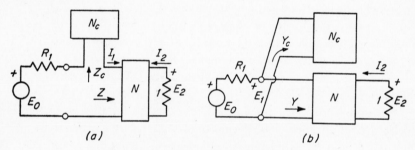

Fig. 6-20. Constant-resistance filter pairs.

Consider Fig. 6-20(a), in which a source with its series resistance R_1 is to be connected to a unit load resistance through a network in order to obtain a prescribed E_2/E_0 function. The dual situation is shown in Fig. 6-20(b). In our previous discussions we have set $Z_c = 0$ and $Y_c = 0$, respectively. But now suppose that we can find a Z_c such that

$$Z + Z_c = K \qquad (6-75)$$

Then the current I_1 will be proportional to E_0 so that we may consider the prescribed function to be $E_2/I_1 = Z_{12}$ instead of E_2/E_0. The network N can be found by the methods of Chap. 5. Of course, we still have the task of realizing the network N_c as well.

Two impedances are said to be complementary when their sum is a constant (independent of frequency). Thus Z and Z_c in Eq. (6-75) are complementary impedances. A similar definition applies to admittances. Before continuing the discussion of the present problem let us determine the restrictions on two impedances if they are to be complementary. Let Z_a and Z_b be the two impedances, and expand them in partial fractions.

$$Z_a = K_a + k_{a\infty}s + \frac{k_{a0}}{s} + \frac{k_{a1}}{s - s_1} + \cdots \quad \text{(a)}$$

$$Z_b = K_b + k_{b\infty}s + \frac{k_{b0}}{s} + \frac{k_{b1}}{s - s_1} + \cdots \quad \text{(b)} \quad \text{(6-76)}$$

$$Z_a + Z_b = (K_a + K_b) + (k_{a\infty} + k_{b\infty})s$$
$$+ \frac{k_{a0} + k_{b0}}{s} + \frac{k_{a1} + k_{b1}}{s - s_1} + \cdots \quad \text{(c)}$$

If the sum of Z_a and Z_b is to be a constant, there must be no poles on the right side of the last equation. If either Z_a or Z_b has a pole which is not also a pole of the other, this pole will appear in the sum. Thus, if two impedances are to be complementary, they must have the same poles. We anticipated this fact in writing the partial-fraction expansions in Eqs. (6-76). Looking at the last equation, we can see that the only way in which $Z_a + Z_b$ can be a constant is for the residues of Z_a to be the negatives of the residues of Z_b at all the poles. But we know that the residues of positive real functions are positive at all j-axis poles. This means that Z_a and Z_b can have no poles on the $j\omega$ axis, including zero and infinity, if they are to be complementary.

We established in the previous chapter that, at internal poles, the residues of RL admittances and RC impedances are positive, while those of RL impedances and RC admittances are negative. Hence the complement of an RL impedance is an RC impedance, and the complement of an RL admittance is an RC admittance.

One other condition must be satisfied if an impedance is to be the complement of another. Let Z_a be given, and let Z_b be the desired complementary impedance. We can write

$$Z_b(s) = K - Z_a(s)$$
$$\text{Re } Z_b(j\omega) = K - \text{Re } Z_a(j\omega) \quad \text{(6-77)}$$

It is clear that K must be greater than the maximum value of the real part of $Z_a(j\omega)$ for Z_b to be positive real.

In summary, we have found that any minimum-reactance impedance function will have a complement for a suitably chosen value of K. Similarly any minimum-susceptance admittance function will have a complement.

Let us now return to the problem illustrated in Fig. 6-20(a). Assume that Z_c is the complement of Z. If a function $|E_2/E_0|^2$ is given, we may assume that the given function is $|Z_{12}(j\omega)|^2$ within a constant multiplier, since I_1 is proportional to E_0. Hence this function is equal to the real part of $Z(j\omega)$. Since Z_c is the complement of Z, for a suitable value of K we can write

$$\operatorname{Re} Z_c(j\omega) = K - \operatorname{Re} Z(j\omega) \qquad (6\text{-}78)$$

There is no reason why we cannot consider the complementary network N_c to be itself a lossless two-port terminated in a resistance. If we designate the transfer impedance of this complementary network Z_{12c}, then we shall have

$$|Z_{12c}(j\omega)|^2 = \operatorname{Re} Z_c(j\omega) \qquad (6\text{-}79)$$

and, finally, substituting from the previous equation,

$$|Z_{12c}(j\omega)|^2 = K - |Z_{12}(j\omega)|^2 \qquad (6\text{-}80)$$

In this manner, from the given magnitude squared function, we determine both Z_{12} and Z_{12c}, following which we realize both as lossless two-ports with a resistance load.

Alternatively, we may contemplate the situation in Fig. 6-20(b) and consider the given $|E_2/E_0|^2$ function to be $|Y_{12}(j\omega)|^2$ to within a constant multiplier because E_1 will be proportional to E_0. A discussion similar to the preceding one will apply, but with Z's replaced by Y's.

Broadly speaking, the transmission properties of the two complementary networks will be inverse with respect to each other. That is, a passband of one will correspond to a stopband of the other, and vice versa. Thus, if network N is a low-pass filter, network N_c will be high-pass. The combination of the two as in Fig. 6-20(a) or (b) is called a *constant-resistance filter pair*.

An additional restriction will exist if we require both N and N_c to be ladder networks. Suppose that network N is a low-pass ladder. Then, as we saw in the previous section, the impedance Z must have a pole or a zero at infinity. However, if we wish to find the complement of Z, a pole at infinity is not possible. Hence Z must have a zero at infinity. We can write Z and its complement as

$$Z(s) = \frac{a_0 + a_1 s + \ldots + a_{k-1}s^{k-1}}{1 + b_1 s + \ldots + b_k s^k} \qquad (a)$$

$$Z_c(s) = K - Z(s) \qquad (6\text{-}81)$$

$$= \frac{(K - a_0) + (Kb_1 - a_1)s + \ldots + (Kb_{k-1} - a_{k-1})s^{k-1} + Kb_k s^k}{1 + b_1 s + \ldots + b_k s^k} \qquad (b)$$

If $Z_c(s)$ is to be the impedance of a high-pass Darlington ladder, it must have a zero at $s = 0$ (see Prob. 6-4). To satisfy this condition, we must have $K = a_0$. Looking at $Z(s)$ will show that a_0 is the zero-frequency value of Z. Since the imaginary part is zero at $s = 0$, this is also the zero-frequency value of the real part of $Z(j\omega)$. We also have the condition that K must be no less than the maximum value of Re $Z(j\omega)$. These conditions can be satisfied simultaneously only if the maximum value of the real part of $Z(j\omega)$ occurs at $\omega = 0$. We conclude that a *high-low constant-resistance filter pair both of which are ladders is realizable only if the maximum value of* Re $Z(j\omega)$ *occurs at* $\omega = 0$. Z *is the impedance of the low-pass network.*

As an illustration of these ideas, let a given magnitude squared function be

$$G(\omega^2) = \frac{1}{1 + \omega^6} \qquad (6\text{-}82)$$

The realization sought is a double-loaded lossless network. We shall assume that a realization in the form of Fig. 6-20(b) is to be obtained so that the given function is considered to be $|Y_{12}(j\omega)|^2$. The maximum value of the given function is unity. For the complementary function we shall have

$$|Y_{12c}(j\omega)|^2 = 1 - \frac{1}{1 + \omega^6} = \frac{\omega^6}{1 + \omega^6} \qquad (6\text{-}83)$$

We have already met this particular function once before in the numerical example in Sec. 6-2. From the results of that example the two transfer functions can be written

$$-Y_{12}(s) = \frac{1}{s^3 + 2s^2 + 2s + 1} \qquad \text{(a)}$$

$$-Y_{12c}(s) = \frac{s^3}{s^3 + 2s^2 + 2s + 1} \qquad \text{(b)}$$

$$(6\text{-}84)$$

Next we form the corresponding y parameters.

$$-y_{12} = \frac{1}{s(s^2 + 2)} \qquad \text{(a)}$$

$$y_{22} = \frac{2s^2 + 1}{s(s^2 + 2)} \qquad \text{(b)}$$

$$(6\text{-}85)$$

and

$$-y_{12c} = \frac{s^3}{2s^2 + 1} \qquad \text{(a)}$$

$$y_{22c} = \frac{s(s^2 + 1)}{2s^2 + 1} \qquad \text{(b)}$$

$$(6\text{-}86)$$

The zeros of y_{12} are all at infinity. Hence a low-pass ladder can be obtained by the Cauer development of y_{22}. Similarly all the zeros of y_{12c} are at $s = 0$, and so a high-pass-ladder realization can be obtained for the complementary network. We should expect this result since the maximum value of the given magnitude squared function does occur at $\omega = 0$. The com-

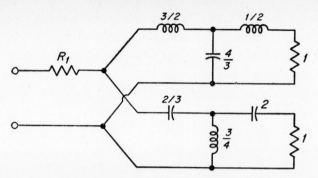

Fig. 6-21. Constant-resistance filter pair.

plete realization is shown in Fig. 6-21. You can carry out the continued-fraction expansions as an exercise.

PROBLEMS

6-1. The following parameters are given

(a) $z_{11} = 7 \dfrac{s(s^2 + 3)}{(s^2 + 1)(s^2 + 6)}$ (b) $y_{11} = \dfrac{6s^2 + 2}{s(s^2 + 1)}$

$z_{22} = \dfrac{17}{20} \dfrac{s(s^2 + 2)}{(s^2 + 1)(s^2 + 6)}$ $y_{22} = \dfrac{3s^2 + 2}{s(s^2 + 1)}$

$z_{12} = \dfrac{s(s^2 - 3.45)}{(s^2 + 1)(s^2 + 6)}$ $-y_{12} = \dfrac{2}{s(s^2 + 1)}$

Obtain a lossless two-port realizing each of these sets of parameters.

6-2. An important type of two-port is one that might be termed *semisymmetrical*. It is characterized by $z_{11} = K_0 z_{22}$, where K_0 is a positive number. When $K_0 = 1$, this is the symmetrical case. Show that Eq. (6-35) will still apply in this case, and determine the value of K, the type of function ϕ, and the choice of sign.

6-3. Let $Z(s) = (m_1 + n_1)/(m_2 + n_2)$ be the driving-point impedance of a resistance-terminated lossless two-port. Let $s = j\omega_0$ be a transmission zero, more exactly, a zero of $m_1 m_2 - n_1 n_2$. Prove that $Z(j\omega_0) = z_{11}(j\omega_0)$ or $[1/y_{11}(j\omega_0)]$. That is, the value of the driving-point impedance evaluated at the transmission zero is the same whether the output is terminated, is short-circuited, or is left open.

6-4. Using the frequency transformation $p = 1/s$, derive the realizability conditions for a high-pass Darlington ladder. By a high-pass ladder we mean: (1) one that has no transmission zero at infinity, and (2) either z_{12} or y_{12} (or both) have at least a simple zero at $s = 0$.

6-5. The following function is the impedance of a resistance-terminated lossless two-port. Obtain a low-pass ladder realization.

$$Z(s) = \frac{6s^7 + \frac{5}{2}s^6 + 28s^5 + \frac{43}{4}s^4 + \frac{71}{2}s^3 + \frac{25}{2}s^2 + 13s + 4}{24s^6 + 10s^5 + 88s^4 + 33s^3 + 58s^2 + 18s + 4}$$

6-6. The squared magnitude of the transfer impedance for a low-pass Darlington network is prescribed as follows:

$$|Z_{12}(j\omega)|^2 = \frac{1}{1 + \omega^2 + \omega^4}$$

Find the transfer impedance of the complementary network, and realize the filter pair.

6-7. The square of the transfer voltage ratio, $T(s) = E_2/E_0$, of a double loaded Darlington network is given as follows. Realize the network for a convenient value of K.

$$|T(j\omega)|^2 = K \frac{1 + \omega^2}{1 - \omega^2 + \omega^4}$$

6-8. Figure P 6-8(a) shows a lossless network with a resistance load. In Fig. P 6-8(b) the two pairs of terminals of the lossless network have been interchanged. The driving-point impedance in the first case is

$$Z_1(s) = \frac{m_1 + n_1}{m_2 + n_2}$$

(a) Find expressions for the driving point impedance Z_2 appropriate for case A or case B (defined in Eqs. 6-5 in the text).

(b) Comment on the relationships between $Z_1(s)$ and $Z_2(s)$ under the conditions $m_1 = m_2$ and $n_1 = n_2$.

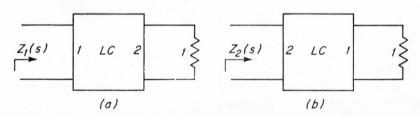

(a)   (b)

Fig. P 6-8

6-9. Consider the functions given in Problem 3-23 (as the real part of a positive real function) to be the magnitude squared of the transfer impedance of a resistance-loaded lossless network. Find the corresponding transfer impedances and realize the networks.

7

Realization of RC Two-Ports

If we direct our attention to the realization of arbitrary transfer functions, it will become apparent that we have just scratched the surface. So far we have handled only the situation in which the transmission zeros occur in quadrantal symmetry. This leads to a realization in terms of a lossless coupling network. If we remove this restriction from the locations of transmission zeros, lossless networks will no longer be adequate for the realization.

Before we undertake to discuss the most general situation, let us stay in the realm of networks with two kinds of elements. The transformation $s^2 \rightarrow p$ served us well in establishing properties and synthesis techniques of driving-point functions of RC networks from those of reactance functions. We can expect the same transformation to be useful in obtaining realizations of RC two-ports from the results of the previous two chapters. However, in the present case characteristic differences will crop up which will need special methods of handling.

Much of the motivation for our interest in RC networks comes from the special requirements of control systems. The frequency range of interest in such systems is very low. Hence any inductances that may arise in a realization will be of large value. This requires a large physical size and weight, rendering the realization undesirable. In this chapter we shall discuss the realization of RC two-ports.

7-1. Properties of RC two-port parameters

First let us consider the open-circuit impedance and short-circuit admittance parameters of an RC two-port. As far as the driving-point functions (z_{11}, z_{22}, y_{11}, y_{22}) are concerned, we have already established in

249

Chap. 2 that their properties follow immediately from the corresponding properties of reactance functions. Thus

$$Z_{RC}(s) = \frac{1}{p} Z_{LC}(p) \qquad (a)$$
$$\text{(7-1)}$$
$$Y_{RC}(s) = p Y_{LC}(p) \qquad (b)$$

with the transformation $s = p^2$. These results were established simply from a consideration of the mesh impedance determinant and cofactors of an RC network. Although the transfer admittance y_{12} is not a driving-point function, it is given in terms of the mesh impedance determinant and its cofactor by $\Delta_{12}(s)/\Delta(s)$. Thus Eq. (7-1b) applies to y_{12} as well as to y_{11} and y_{22}. In a similar way Eq. (7-1a) applies to the transfer impedance z_{12} as well as to the driving-point impedances z_{11} and z_{22}. It is therefore a simple matter to determine the realizability conditions on the set of z or y parameters of an RC two-port from the corresponding properties of lossless two-ports.

Consider a set of open-circuit parameters of a lossless network.

$$z_{11}(p) = k_{11}^{(\infty)} p + \frac{k_{11}^{(0)}}{p} + \frac{k_{11}^{(1)} p}{p^2 + a_1} \qquad (a)$$

$$z_{22}(p) = k_{22}^{(\infty)} p + \frac{k_{22}^{(0)}}{p} + \frac{k_{22}^{(1)} p}{p^2 + a_1} \qquad (b) \quad \text{(7-2)}$$

$$z_{12}(p) = k_{12}^{(\infty)} p + \frac{k_{12}^{(0)}}{p} + \frac{k_{12}^{(1)} p}{p^2 + a_1} \qquad (c)$$

The complex-frequency variable has been designated by p for later convenience. We have shown only one finite pole explicitly; additional poles will introduce additional terms like the last one. Also, in order to have the result in a natural form after transformation, we have written the residue and the pole location in an unnatural form here. Using Eqs. (7-1) and the transformation $p^2 = s$, we get

$$z_{11}(s) = k_{11}^{(\infty)} + \frac{k_{11}^{(0)}}{s} + \frac{k_{11}^{(1)}}{s + a_1} \qquad (a)$$

$$z_{22}(s) = k_{22}^{(\infty)} + \frac{k_{22}^{(0)}}{s} + \frac{k_{22}^{(1)}}{s + a_1} \qquad (b) \quad \text{(7-3)}$$

$$z_{12}(s) = k_{12}^{(\infty)} + \frac{k_{12}^{(0)}}{s} + \frac{k_{12}^{(1)}}{s + a_1} \qquad (c)$$

This is the partial-fraction expansion of a typical set of z parameters of an RC two-port. It immediately follows that the residue condition

$$k_{11} k_{22} - k_{12}^2 \geq 0 \qquad \text{(7-4)}$$

must be satisfied by the z parameters of an RC two-port at all their poles.

(Although the z parameters are regular at infinity, we sometimes refer to the infinite-frequency values $k_{11}^{(\infty)}$, $k_{22}^{(\infty)}$, and $k_{12}^{(\infty)}$ as residues at infinity.) We already know that the poles of the driving-point functions are negative real and simple. In order to satisfy the residue condition, we conclude that the poles of z_{12} must also be negative real and must coincide with common poles of z_{11} and z_{22}. The residues of z_{12} must be real but not necessarily positive.

From our discussion of RC functions in Chap. 2 we know that the functions in Eqs. (7-3) can refer just as well to y_{11}/s, y_{22}/s, and y_{12}/s, respectively. Thus a typical set of short-circuit admittance parameters of an RC two-port will be

$$y_{11} = k_{11}^{(\infty)}s + k_{11}^{(0)} + \frac{k_{11}^{(1)}s}{s + a_1} \qquad \text{(a)}$$

$$y_{22} = k_{22}^{(\infty)}s + k_{22}^{(0)} + \frac{k_{22}^{(1)}s}{s + a_1} \qquad \text{(b)} \quad \text{(7-5)}$$

$$y_{12} = k_{12}^{(\infty)}s + k_{12}^{(0)} + \frac{k_{12}^{(1)}s}{s + a_1} \qquad \text{(c)}$$

The k's are the residues of y_{11}/s, y_{22}/s, and y_{12}/s, and they must satisfy the residue condition. (Although the y's are regular at the origin, we sometimes refer to the zero-frequency values as the residues at the origin.)

The structure of an RC two-port will impose additional restrictions on the z and y parameters. For instance, we showed in Chap. 4 that the transmission zeros of a ladder network fall at series-branch impedance poles or shunt-branch impedance zeros. It follows that for an RC ladder the transmission zeros must lie on the negative real axis of the s plane. Of course, Fialkow's condition for unbalanced two-ports applies to RC two-ports as well.

Let us now consider the functions $Z_{12}(s)$, the transfer impedance, and $Y_{12}(s)$, the transfer admittance, of a resistance-terminated RC two-port, and the voltage transfer function $T_{12}(s)$. With the terminating resistance assumed unity, these functions are given by

$$Z_{12}(s) = \frac{z_{12}}{1 + z_{22}} \qquad \text{(a)}$$

$$Y_{12}(s) = \frac{y_{12}}{1 + y_{22}} \qquad \text{(b)} \quad \text{(7-6)}$$

$$T_{12}(s) = \frac{z_{12}}{z_{11}} = \frac{-y_{12}}{y_{22}} \qquad \text{(c)}$$

The poles of $Y_{12}(s)$ are the zeros of $1 + y_{22}$. Since y_{22} is an RC admittance function, so also is $1 + y_{22}$, and hence its zeros are simple and lie on the negative real axis. A similar statement can be made concerning the zeros of $1 + z_{22}$. On the other hand, the zeros of z_{12} and of y_{12} may lie anywhere in the s plane. Hence we conclude that the transfer impedance, the transfer admittance, and the voltage transfer functions of RC networks must have simple negative real poles. The zeros may lie anywhere, but they are restricted by the structure of the network.

7-2. Synthesis for prescribed $Y_{12}(s)$, $Z_{12}(s)$, or $T_{12}(s)$

Having established the properties of the transfer functions, the next step is to determine a set of z or y parameters when a transfer function satisfying the necessary conditions is prescribed. Suppose that $Y_{12}(s)$ is prescribed as the ratio of two polynomials. Let us write it in the form

$$- Y_{12}(s) = \frac{N_{12}(s)}{P(s)} = \frac{N_{12}(s)}{P_1(s) + P_2(s)} = \frac{N_{12}/P_2}{1 + P_1/P_2} \qquad (7\text{-}7)$$

In the case of a lossless network we separated the denominator into its even and odd parts. Subsequent division of numerator and denominator by the even or odd part permitted the identification of y_{12} and y_{22}. We cannot do this in the RC case because the y parameters are not odd rational functions. What we must do is decompose the denominator into two polynomials P_1 and P_2 such that the ratio P_1/P_2 is an RC admittance function. This permits us to identify the y parameters as

$$y_{22} = \frac{P_1(s)}{P_2(s)} \quad \text{(a)} \qquad - y_{12} = \frac{N_{12}(s)}{P_2(s)} \quad \text{(b)} \qquad (7\text{-}8)$$

The determination of the polynomials P_1 and P_2 is an added task which was not present in the case of lossless networks. Our problem can be stated as follows: Given a polynomial $P(s)$ all of whose zeros are negative real and simple, find two other polynomials $P_1(s)$ and $P_2(s)$ all of whose zeros are also negative real and simple, such that $P_1 + P_2 = P$. Furthermore the zeros of P_1 and P_2 must alternate. This problem can be solved in several ways.

In Fig. 7-1 two polynomials P and P_a are plotted against negative values of σ. The two polynomials are of the same degree, having simple negative real zeros which alternate. The zero-frequency value of P is greater than that of P_a. Their difference, $P_b = P - P_a$, is also sketched. We see that the zeros of P_b alternate both with the zeros of P_a and with those of P. Let us write

$$P(s) = s^n + a_{n-1}s^{n-1} + \ldots + a_1 s + a_0 \qquad \text{(a)}$$
$$P_a(s) = K(s^n + b_{n-1}s^{n-1} + \ldots + b_1 s + b_0) \qquad \text{(b)} \qquad (7\text{-}9)$$

There are two cases to consider corresponding to the two parts of the figure

1. Starting from $\sigma = 0$ and moving down the negative-σ axis, of the two polynomials $P(s)$ and $P_a(s)$, the first zero encountered belongs to P.

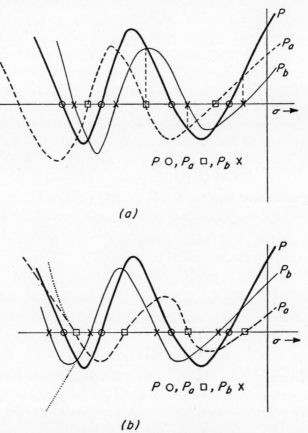

(a)

(b)

Fig. 7-1. Sketch of polynomials.

It follows that P_b will have a zero closer to the origin than will P_a. From Eqs. (7-9) the zero-frequency values of the two polynomials are $P(0) = a_0$ and $P_a(0) = Kb_0$. In addition, the constant terms a_0 and b_0 represent the products of the zeros of $P(s)$ and $P_a(s)$, respectively. The following two relationships can now be written from a consideration of the figure:

$$a_0 < b_0 \quad \text{(a)} \qquad a_0 > Kb_0 \quad \text{(b)} \qquad (7\text{-}10)$$

These inequalities can both be satisfied only if $K < 1$. Hence, when we take the difference between P and P_a, the highest-power terms cannot cancel. This means that P_b will have the same degree as P_a and P.

2. The first zero encountered on the negative-σ axis belongs to P_a. It follows that this zero is smaller (in magnitude) than the first zero of P_b,

as Fig. 7-1(b) shows. In the present case, noting the zero-frequency values and the locations of the zeros, the inequalities corresponding to Eqs. (7-10) are

$$a_0 > b_0 \qquad\qquad \text{(a)}$$
$$a_0 > Kb_0 \qquad\qquad \text{(b)}$$
(7-11)

These do not require K to be strictly less than 1; they can be satisfied with $K = 1$. In the latter case the highest-power term will disappear in the difference polynomial, leading to a polynomial P_b having one zero fewer than P_a or P.

Let us now return to the problem of the decomposition of the denominator polynomial in Eq. (7-7). In factored form the denominator polynomial is

$$P(s) = (s + \sigma_1)(s + \sigma_2) \ldots (s + \sigma_n) \qquad\qquad (7\text{-}12)$$

where the zeros have been written in ascending order so that

$$0 < \sigma_1 < \sigma_2 < \ldots < \sigma_n \qquad\qquad (7\text{-}13)$$

The polynomial $P_a(s)$, of the same degree as $P(s)$, is formed by arbitrarily choosing n zeros that alternate with those of $P(s)$. Thus

$$P_a(s) = K(s + \sigma_{a1})(s + \sigma_{a2}) \ldots (s + \sigma_{an}) \qquad\qquad (7\text{-}14)$$

We have two choices corresponding to the two cases considered above.

1. We can choose $\sigma_{aj} > \sigma_j$. This requires us to choose K so as to satisfy Eqs. (7-10). Thus

$$K\sigma_{a1}\sigma_{a2} \ldots \sigma_{an} < \sigma_1\sigma_2 \ldots \sigma_n \qquad\qquad (7\text{-}15)$$

With P_a determined, we find P_b as the difference between P and P_a. The construction guarantees that the zeros of P_a and P_b are simple and alternate on the negative-σ axis. Since P_b has a zero closer to the origin than P_a, the ratio P_b/P_a will be an RC admittance function. Thus, in the notation of Eqs. (7-8), $P_b = P_1$ and $P_a = P_2$, and y_{22} will be regular at infinity.

2. We can choose $\sigma_{aj} < \sigma_j$. In this case the zero closest to the origin belongs to P_a so that P_a/P_b will be an RC admittance. Thus the identification $y_{22} = P_a/P_b$ is made. Any value of $K \leq 1$ will satisfy Eqs. (7-11). With $K = 1$, P_b will have one zero fewer than P_a, and so y_{22} will have a pole at infinity.

Thus, starting with a prescribed transfer admittance function $Y_{12}(s)$, we obtain the two short-circuit parameters, y_{22} and y_{12}, in the manner just described. In a completely similar manner we can obtain the two open-circuit parameters z_{12} and z_{22} from a prescribed transfer impedance function $Z_{12}(s)$. If the prescribed function is the voltage transfer function $T_{12}(s)$, the procedure is even simpler. Given a function

$$T_{12}(s) = \frac{N_{12}(s)}{P(s)} \tag{7-16}$$

satisfying the necessary conditions, we need to divide numerator and denominator by a polynomial $Q(s)$ having simple negative real zeros which alternate with those of $P(s)$. Ensuring proper behavior at zero and infinity as well, we now identify P/Q and N_{12}/Q with z_{11} and z_{12}, respectively, or y_{22} and $-y_{12}$, respectively.

Thus, starting with one of the transfer functions, we now know how to form two of the open-circuit or short-circuit parameters. The procedure which we utilize to obtain a realization will depend on the locations of the transmission zeros.

7-3. Unbalanced symmetrical realization

In Chap. 5 we discussed realization techniques of lossless two-ports for prescribed transfer functions. There we saw that it is always possible to obtain a realization in terms of a symmetrical network at the possible expense of transmission gain. We discussed a realization in terms of a symmetrical lattice which could be later replaced by an unbalanced equivalent under some conditions. Four steps were involved in the lattice decomposition, corresponding to Figs. 5-3, 5-4, and 5-8. The conditions under which an unbalanced equivalent of the lattice can be found were not completely clear. This procedure applies equally well here with the transformation $p^2 = s$.

In the present section we shall discuss a realization procedure due to Ozaki (94). An unbalanced symmetrical structure is obtained without going through the intermediate step of a lattice realization. We shall see that a sufficient condition for the realization, although not necessary, is that the transfer function be minimum-phase.

The starting point is any one of the transfer functions $Y_{12}(s)$, $Z_{12}(s)$, or $T_{12}(s)$. From these we can obtain two of the z or y parameters, say y_{12} and y_{22}, as discussed in the last section. By accepting a low value of the gain constant we can always make each residue of y_{22} at least as large as the magnitude of the corresponding residue of y_{12}. A symmetrical set of functions will result if we choose the residues of y_{11} equal to those of y_{22}. Thus we can start the realization from a set of symmetrical y functions satisfying the residue condition. In the next section we shall show that choosing the poles of y_{22} in a certain way will yield the maximum value for the gain constant in a symmetrical realization.

Suppose that, initially, all the admittance poles are not compact. Then we can write

$$y_{22} = y_{11} = y'_{11} + Y_1 \qquad \text{(a)}$$
$$y_{12} = y'_{12} \qquad \text{(b)}$$

$$(7\text{-}17)$$

where the primed quantities form a set of compact y parameters and Y_1 is the excess in y_{11} after all the poles are made compact. A realization of the original parameters consists of the parallel connection of the two subnetworks shown in Fig. 7-2. This corresponds to step 1 in the lattice decomposition discussed in Chap. 5 and shown in Fig. 5-4.

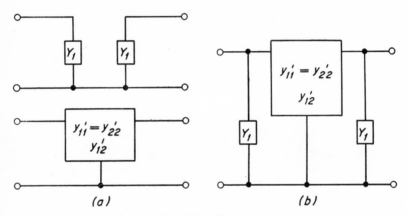

Fig. 7-2. Partial realization—step 1.

We now have a set of compact y parameters (the primed ones). The partial-fraction expansion of these parameters will have the form

$$y'_{11} = k_\infty s + k_0 + \sum_{i=1}^{n} \frac{k_{ip}s}{s + \sigma_{ip}} + \sum_{i=1}^{m} \frac{k_{in}s}{s + \sigma_{in}} = \frac{P_p(s)}{Q_p(s)} + \frac{P_n(s)}{Q_n(s)} \qquad \text{(a)}$$

$$(7\text{-}18)$$

$$-y'_{12} = k_\infty s + k_0 + \sum_{i=1}^{n} \frac{k_{ip}s}{s + \sigma_{ip}} - \sum_{i=1}^{m} \frac{k_{in}s}{s + \sigma_{in}} = \frac{P_p(s)}{Q_p(s)} - \frac{P_n(s)}{Q_n(s)} \qquad \text{(b)}$$

Some of the residues of $-y'_{12}$ are positive and some negative. We have grouped all the positive ones and labeled them with the subscript p and the negative ones with the subscript n. We shall call these groups the "positive" part and "negative" part, respectively. The constant term represents behavior at $s = 0$ and hence is never negative. Similarly the residue at infinity is never negative. In particular cases these may be zero. Note that the negative part of the y parameters has no constant term and no pole at infinity and therefore is of the same degree in numerator and denominator.

At each step in the decomposition process we must make sure that Fialkow's condition is satisfied by the numerator coefficients of $-y'_{12}$. If the transmission zeros are all in the left half plane (or on the $j\omega$ axis), the numerator coefficients of $-y'_{12}$ will necessarily be nonnegative. It is apparent from the fact that some of the residues of $-y'_{12}$ are negative while all the residues of y'_{11} are positive that the numerator coefficients of y'_{11} will be no smaller than the corresponding ones in y'_{12}.

The next step corresponds to step 2 in the lattice decomposition shown in Fig. 5-8(a). Suppose that we can remove an admittance Y_2 from the positive part of $-y'_{12}$ and y'_{11} and still maintain the numerator of the remaining y_{12} a Hurwitz polynomial. This might require quite a bit of trial and error, and we shall not even be certain of success. If it is possible to perform this step, then we can write

$$y'_{11} = y''_{11} + Y_2 \qquad \text{(a)}$$
$$y'_{12} = y''_{12} - Y_2 \qquad \text{(b)} \qquad \text{(7-19)}$$

A realization of the primed parameters can be obtained as a parallel connection of the networks shown in Fig. 7-3.

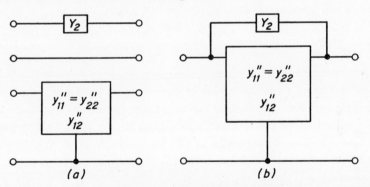

Fig. 7-3. Partial realization—step 2.

We can now proceed with the double-primed parameters. (If no Y_2 can be removed as above, we proceed with the single-primed parameters.) Let us write the parameters in terms of the positive and negative parts as follows:

$$y''_{11} = \frac{P''_p}{Q''_p} + \frac{P''_n}{Q''_n} \qquad \text{(a)}$$
$$-y''_{12} = \frac{P''_p}{Q''_p} - \frac{P''_n}{Q''_n} \qquad \text{(b)} \qquad \text{(7-20)}$$

Using the relationships between the z and y parameters, we now find the z parameters to be

$$z_{11}'' = \frac{y_{11}''}{|y''|} = \frac{1}{4}\frac{Q_n''}{P_n''} + \frac{1}{4}\frac{Q_p''}{P_p''} \qquad (a)$$

$$z_{12}'' = \frac{-y_{12}''}{|y''|} = \frac{1}{4}\frac{Q_n''}{P_n''} - \frac{1}{4}\frac{Q_p''}{P_p''} \qquad (b)$$

$$(7\text{-}21)$$

This is an extremely interesting result! We see that, aside from a factor of 1/4, the positive part of the z parameters is the reciprocal of the negative part of the y parameters. Likewise, the negative part of the z parameters is the reciprocal of the positive part of the y's.

Several cases must now be considered, depending on the behavior of the y'' parameters.

Case A. No pole of y'' parameters at infinity

This means that the positive part of the y'' parameters, as well as the negative part, will be of the same degree in numerator and denominator. This is apparent from a consideration of Eqs. (7-18). Now suppose that we expand the z parameters in Eqs. (7-21) in partial fractions. Both the p and the n parts will have a constant term. Because of the subtraction involved in z_{12}'', it immediately follows that the constant term of the z parameters will be noncompact. Hence we can write

$$z_{11}'' = z_{11}^{(3)} + R_3 \qquad (a)$$

$$z_{12}'' = z_{12}^{(3)} \qquad (b)$$

$$(7\text{-}22)$$

(Superscripts will be used to avoid the use of triple and quadruple primed quantities.) Here R_3 is the excess in the constant term after it has been made compact. A realization for this set of parameters can be obtained as a series connection of two networks as shown in Fig. 7-4. In the present case $Z_3 = R_3$. This corresponds to the lattice-decomposition step shown in Fig. 5-3.

Case B. Zero of y parameters at $s = 0$

This means that the y's have a factor s which is a factor both of the positive part and of the negative part. That is, s is a factor of both P_p'' and P_n'' in Eqs. (7-20). It follows from Eqs. (7-21) that both the p and n parts of the z'' parameters will have a pole at $s = 0$ and this pole will be noncompact. Hence we can write

$$z_{11}'' = z_{11}^{(3)} + \frac{1}{sC_3} \qquad (a)$$

$$z_{12}'' = z_{12}^{(3)} \qquad (b)$$

$$(7\text{-}23)$$

where $1/sC_3$ is the excess remainder after the pole at $s = 0$ is made compact. A realization for this set of parameters again takes the form of Fig. 7-4, where now $Z_3 = 1/sC_3$.

Case C. The y'' parameters have a common zero at $s = -\sigma_0$

This will require that both P_p'' and P_n'' have a factor $s + \sigma_0$, which, in turn, requires the z'' parameters to have a noncompact pole at $s = -\sigma_0$. Hence we can write

$$z_{11}'' = z_{11}^{(3)} + \frac{k}{s + \sigma_0} \qquad \text{(a)}$$

$$z_{12}'' = z_{12}^{(3)} \qquad \qquad \text{(b)}$$

(7-24)

The quantity $k/(s + \sigma_0)$ is the excess after the pole has been made compact. The realization again takes the form of Fig. 7-4, where $Z_3 = k/(s + \sigma_0)$.

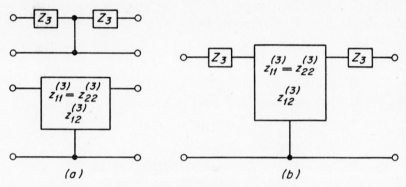

Fig. 7-4. Partial realization—step 3.

The three possible behaviors of the y'' parameters are not mutually exclusive. It may be that all three of these cases apply simultaneously. In such a case Z_3 in Fig. 7-4 will be a series combination of a resistance, a capacitance, and a parallel RC.

After this partial realization we are left with a set of compact z param-

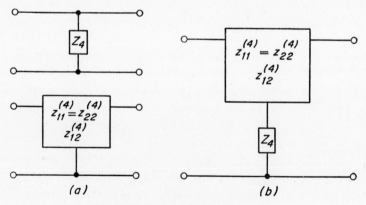

Fig. 7-5. Partial realization—step 4.

eters. Suppose now that we can remove an impedance Z_4 from the positive part of $z_{12}^{(3)}$ and $z_{11}^{(3)}$ while still maintaining the numerator of the remaining z_{12} a Hurwitz polynomial. Then we can write

$$z_{11}^{(3)} = z_{11}^{(4)} + Z_4 \qquad \text{(a)}$$
$$z_{12}^{(3)} = z_{12}^{(4)} + Z_4 \qquad \text{(b)}$$

(7-25)

A realization of this set of parameters is obtained as the series connection of two networks as shown in Fig. 7-5. This corresponds to step 4 in the lattice decomposition shown in Fig. 5-8(b). Such a decomposition may not be possible, in which case we proceed with the $z^{(3)}$ parameters.

The next step depends on the behavior of the z parameters. Three cases can be identified analogous to the three cases discussed for the y parameters.

Case A. No pole of z parameters at $s = 0$

Then the y's will have a noncompact constant term.

Case B. Zero of z parameters at infinity

Then the y's will have a noncompact pole at infinity.

Case C. Common zero of the z parameters at $s = -\sigma_0$.

Then the y's will have a noncompact pole at $s = -\sigma_0$.

In any one of these cases the y parameters will take the form shown in Eqs. (7-17), and the realization takes the form of Fig. 7-2, where

$$Y_1 = G \qquad \text{case A} \qquad \text{(a)}$$
$$Y_1 = sC \qquad \text{case B} \qquad \text{(b)} \quad \text{(7-26)}$$
$$Y_1 = \frac{k}{s + \sigma_0} \qquad \text{case C} \qquad \text{(c)}$$

This step completes a cycle of realization. We can now repeat the cycle until we are left with a set of y parameters which does not permit any further reduction. The partial-fraction expansions for such a set will look like Eqs. (7-18), in which k_0 and k_∞ are not zero and the y's do not have a common zero.

We must now seek some other type of decomposition—something different from the steps we have performed till now. Ozaki suggested that we seek a parallel connection of two subnetworks. Thus we decompose the set of y parameters into two subsets. If this decomposition is to be useful, each of the two subsets must be amenable to further reductions by one of the previous steps. For instance, if one of the component y_{12} functions has no pole at infinity or has a zero at $s = 0$, then the reduction step 3 shown in Fig. 7-4 can be performed.

In addition to this requirement, the component y_{12} functions must satisfy two other conditions. In order to satisfy Fialkow's condition, the numerator coefficients of the $-y_{12}$ functions must be nonnegative. A sufficient condition for this requirement is that the numerators be Hurwitz polynomials. The second condition on the component y_{12}'s involves the residues. We must require that *the residues of the two component y_{12}'s have the same sign at each pole which is shared by both.* The reason for this requirement becomes clear from the following consideration. Designate the components by subscripts a and b. Before reduction the y parameters are compact. The residue of the over-all y_{11} at a pole is the sum of the residues of the component y_{11}'s at the same pole, and similarly for y_{12}. Hence we can write

$$(k_{11a} + k_{11b})^2 - (k_{12a} + k_{12b})^2 = 0 \qquad \text{(a)}$$

or $\qquad\qquad\qquad\qquad\qquad\qquad\qquad\qquad\qquad\qquad\qquad$ (7-27)

$$(k_{11a}^2 - k_{12a}^2) + (k_{11b}^2 - k_{12b}^2) + 2(k_{11a}k_{11b} - k_{12a}k_{12b}) = 0 \qquad \text{(b)}$$

The first two terms in parentheses cannot be negative. In fact, the component y's must be compact so that these two terms are zero. If k_{12a} and k_{12b} have opposite signs, it will be impossible to satisfy the last equation.

We have now established the conditions that must be satisfied if a decomposition into two parallel networks is to be obtained. Let us proceed then to a discussion of the decomposition procedure. Suppose that we write

$$-y_{12} = \frac{P(s)}{Q(s)} = \frac{P_1(s)}{Q(s)} + \frac{P_2(s)}{Q(s)} \qquad \text{(a)}$$

$$-y_{12a} = \frac{P_1}{Q} \qquad\qquad \text{(b)} \quad \text{(7-28)}$$

$$-y_{12b} = \frac{P_2}{Q} \qquad\qquad \text{(c)}$$

The numerator polynomial has been written as the sum of two polynomials. We shall now show that it is always possible to find two polynomials P_1 and P_2 which satisfy the following conditions:

1. The zeros of P_1 and P_2 are either in the left half plane or on the $j\omega$ axis.
2. The signs of the residues of y_{12a} and y_{12b} are the same as the signs of the corresponding residues of y_{12}.
3. Each of the polynomials P_1 and P_2 will have one of the following properties:
   (a) P_1 or P_2 will be of lower degree than P. This means that y_{12a} or y_{12b} has no pole at infinity, which permits a further reduction according to Fig. 7-4, with $Z_3 = R$.

(b) P_1 or P_2 will have a factor s. This means that y_{12a} or y_{12b} will have a zero at $s = 0$, which also permits a further reduction according to Fig. 7-4, with $Z_3 = 1/sC$.

(c) P_1 or P_2 (or both) have a common factor with $Q(s)$. This means that y_{12a} or y_{12b} (or both) will have one pole fewer than y_{12} and hence will be a simpler function.

We shall refer to this statement as the *Ozaki separation theorem* and to the three conditions just listed as the "Ozaki conditions."

To show that the contemplated decomposition is always possible, note that the factors of the numerator of y_{12} must have one of the following forms.

(A) $s^2 + \omega_0^2$ pair of j-axis zeros

(B) $(s + \sigma_0)^2 + \omega_0^2$ pair of complex left-half-plane zeros

(C) $s + \sigma_0$ negative-real-axis zero

We shall take each of these in turn and see how the decomposition is accomplished.

A. $$P(s) = (s^2 + \omega_0^2)P_0(s)$$

$$P_1 = s^2 P_0 \qquad -y_{12a} = \frac{s^2 P_0}{Q} \qquad \text{(a)}$$

$$\qquad\qquad\qquad\qquad\qquad\qquad\qquad\qquad\qquad (7\text{-}29)$$

$$P_2 = \omega_0^2 P_0 \qquad -y_{12b} = \frac{\omega_0^2 P_0}{Q} \qquad \text{(b)}$$

It is a simple matter to show that the three Ozaki conditions are satisfied.

B. $$P = [(s + \sigma_0)^2 + \omega_0^2]P_0$$

Let $f(s) = (s + \sigma_0)^2 + \omega_0^2$. When s is real, $f(s)$ is the equation of a parabola. Figure 7-6 shows a sketch of this parabola in the solid curve.

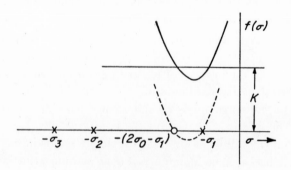

Fig. 7-6. Sketch of $f(\sigma)$.

Also shown are the poles of y_{12}, which lie on the negative real axis. Suppose that we now subtract a positive real constant from $f(\sigma)$. Then

$$f_1(\sigma) = f(\sigma) - K = (\sigma + \sigma_0)^2 + \omega_0^2 - K \qquad (7\text{-}30)$$

As K increases from zero, the vertex of the parabola will get lower and lower. When $K = \omega_0^2$, the vertex will be resting on the σ axis. For larger values of K the parabola will intersect the σ axis in two places. For some value of K the parabola will pass through one of the poles of $y_{12}(s)$, say, $s = -\sigma_1$. To find the other intersection point, divide the right side of Eq. (7-30) by $s + \sigma_1$. The second factor of $f_1(s)$ is found to be $s + 2\sigma_0 - \sigma_1$. Thus we can write

$$f_1(s) = (s + \sigma_1)(s + 2\sigma_0 - \sigma_1) \qquad \text{(a)}$$
$$f(s) = f_1(s) + K = (s + \sigma_1)(s + 2\sigma_0 - \sigma_1) + K \quad \text{(b)}$$

$$(7\text{-}31)$$

Hence

$$P = (s + \sigma_1)(s + 2\sigma_0 - \sigma_1)P_0 + KP_0 \qquad \text{(a)}$$

$$P_1 = (s + \sigma_1)(s + 2\sigma_0 - \sigma_1)P_0 \qquad \text{(b)} \quad (7\text{-}32)$$

$$P_2 = KP_0 \qquad \text{(c)}$$

It is left for you to show that P_1 and P_2 satisfy the Ozaki conditions.

There is still a question of determining the value of K. If we let K increase still further, the vertex of the parabola will go still lower. One or the other arm of the parabola will eventually intersect the σ axis at the other poles of y_{12}. However, now the signs of P_1 and P_2 will not be the same at all the poles of y_{12} so that the second Ozaki condition will not be satisfied. We conclude that the value of K to use is the smallest value that will cause the parabola to intersect the σ axis at one of the poles of y_{12}. Another difficulty becomes apparent if we assume that the point $-\sigma_1$ in Fig. 7-6 is not a pole of y_{12}. Then we will have to increase K until the left branch of the parabola goes through $-\sigma_2$. But now the right branch of the parabola intersects the positive σ axis, thus putting a zero of $P_1(s)$ in the right half plane. This means that we cannot permit K to increase so much. The situation is remedied by using the value of K needed to make the parabola intersect the σ axis at the origin.

To summarize, let $y_{12}(s)$ have poles at $-\sigma_i$, $i = 1, 2, \ldots, n$. In Eq. (7-30) we set $\sigma = 0, -\sigma_1, -\sigma_2, \ldots, -\sigma_n$ and find the corresponding value of K which will make $f_1(\sigma) = 0$. The smallest of these values is the one we must use. In other words, compute the numbers

$$K_0 = \sigma_0^2 + \omega_0^2 \qquad \text{(a)}$$

$$K_i = (\sigma_0 - \sigma_i)^2 + \omega_0^2 \qquad i = 1, 2, \ldots, n \qquad \text{(b)}$$

$$(7\text{-}33)$$

where the $-\sigma_i$'s are the poles of y_{12}. The value of K to be used in Eqs. (7-32) is the smallest of these numbers.

C. $$P(s) = (s - \sigma_0)P_0(s)$$

The appropriate decomposition of $P(s)$ will depend on the location of σ_0 relative to the poles of y_{12}. Figure 7-7 shows the three possible situations.

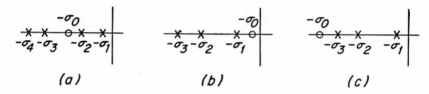

(a)   (b)   (c)

Fig. 7-7. Possible locations of σ_0.

Suppose that σ_0 falls between two poles of y_{12}, say, σ_i and σ_{i+1}. That is, $\sigma_{i+1} > \sigma_0 > \sigma_i$. It will then be possible to decompose $P(s)$ into two polynomials one of which has a factor $s + \sigma_i$ and the other a factor $s + \sigma_{i+1}$. Thus

$$P(s) = (s + \sigma_0)P_0 = K_1(s + \sigma_i)P_0 + K_2(s + \sigma_{i+1})P_0 \qquad (7\text{-}34)$$

which requires that

$$s + \sigma_0 = K_1(s + \sigma_i) + K_2(s + \sigma_{i+1}) \qquad (7\text{-}35)$$

The two constants K_1 and K_2 can easily be determined by equating coefficients of like powers of s on the two sides of this equation. We find

$$K_1 = \frac{\sigma_{i+1} - \sigma_0}{\sigma_{i+1} - \sigma_i} \qquad (a)$$
$$\qquad\qquad\qquad\qquad\qquad\qquad (7\text{-}36)$$
$$K_2 = \frac{\sigma_0 - \sigma_i}{\sigma_{i+1} - \sigma_i} \qquad (b)$$

Thus the two polynomials are

$$P_1(s) = K_1(s + \sigma_i)P_0(s) \qquad (a)$$
$$\qquad\qquad\qquad\qquad\qquad\qquad (7\text{-}37)$$
$$P_2(s) = K_2(s + \sigma_{i+1})P_0(s) \qquad (b)$$

where $P_0(s) = P(s)/(s + \sigma_0)$ and K_1 and K_2 are given in the preceding equation. It is left to you to show that P_1 and P_2 satisfy the Ozaki conditions.

The second possibility is that $-\sigma_0$ is closer to the origin than $-\sigma_1$, the pole of y_{12} which is closest to the origin. Then, proceeding as before, we shall find the two component polynomials to be

$$P_1(s) = K_1(s + \sigma_1)P_0(s) \qquad K_1 = \frac{\sigma_0}{\sigma_1} \qquad \text{(a)}$$

$$(7\text{-}38)$$

$$P_2(s) = K_2 s P_0(s) \qquad K_2 = 1 - \frac{\sigma_0}{\sigma_1} \qquad \text{(b)}$$

The details of this procedure, as well as a demonstration that P_1 and P_2 satisfy the Ozaki conditions, are left to you.

Finally we have the possibility that $-\sigma_0$ is farther from the origin than $-\sigma_n$, the pole of y_{12} which is farthest from the origin. We shall find the component polynomials to be

$$P_1(s) = (s + \sigma_n)P_0(s) \qquad\qquad \text{(a)}$$
$$P_2(s) = (\sigma_0 - \sigma_n)P_0(s) \qquad\qquad \text{(b)}$$

$$(7\text{-}39)$$

Having decomposed the over-all y_{12} into the sum of two component y_{12}'s, we form the component y_{11}'s by making $k_{11} = |k_{12}|$ at each pole. The two sets of y parameters are simpler than the original one and permit further reduction, as discussed previously.

This completes the proof of Ozaki's theorem. For future reference we will tabulate all the relationships we have developed.

Formulas for Ozaki Separation Theorem

$$-y_{12} = \frac{P(s)}{Q(s)} = \frac{P_1 + P_2}{Q} \qquad \text{(a)}$$

$$-y_{12a} = \frac{P_1(s)}{Q(s)} \qquad \text{(b)} \qquad (7\text{-}28)$$

$$-y_{12b} = \frac{P_2(s)}{Q(s)} \qquad \text{(c)}$$

Case A. $P(s) = (s^2 + \omega_0^2)P_0(s)$

$$P_1(s) = s^2 P_0(s) \qquad \text{(a)}$$
$$P_2(s) = \omega_0^2 P_0(s) \qquad \text{(b)} \qquad (7\text{-}29)$$

Case B. $P(s) = [(s + \sigma_0)^2 + \omega_0^2]P_0(s)$

$$P_1 = (s + \sigma_m)(s + 2\sigma_0 - \sigma_m)P_0(s) \qquad \text{(b)}$$
$$P_2 = KP_0(s) \qquad \text{(c)} \qquad (7\text{-}32)$$

where K = smallest one of the following numbers:

$$K_0 = \sigma_0^2 + \omega_0^2 \qquad \text{(a)}$$
$$K_i = (\sigma_0 - \sigma_i)^2 + \omega_0^2 \qquad i = 1, 2, \ldots, n \quad \text{(b)} \qquad (7\text{-}33)$$

where σ_i is a pole of y_{12} and σ_m either is zero or is the pole which gives the smallest K_i.

Case C. $P(s) = (s + \sigma_0)P_0(s)$

1. *$-\sigma_0$ lies between two poles of y_{12}, $-\sigma_i$ and $-\sigma_{i+1}$.*

$$P_1(s) = K_1(s + \sigma_i)P_0(s) \qquad \text{(a)}$$
$$P_2(s) = K_2(s + \sigma_{i+1})P_0(s) \qquad \text{(b)} \qquad (7\text{-}37)$$

$$K_1 = \frac{\sigma_{i+1} - \sigma_0}{\sigma_{i+1} - \sigma_i} \qquad \text{(a)}$$

$$K_2 = \frac{\sigma_0 - \sigma_i}{\sigma_{i+1} - \sigma_i} \qquad \text{(b)} \qquad (7\text{-}36)$$

2. *σ_0 is smaller than σ_1, the closest pole of y_{12} to origin.*

$$P_1(s) = K_1(s + \sigma_1)P_0(s) \qquad K_1 = \frac{\sigma_0}{\sigma_1} \qquad \text{(a)}$$
$$P_2(s) = K_2 s P_0(s) \qquad K_2 = 1 - \frac{\sigma_0}{\sigma_1} \quad \text{(b)} \qquad (7\text{-}38)$$

3. *σ_0 is larger than σ_n, the farthest pole of y_{12} from origin.*

$$P_1(s) = (s + \sigma_n)P_0(s) \qquad \text{(a)}$$
$$P_2(s) = (\sigma_0 - \sigma_n)P_0(s) \qquad \text{(b)} \qquad (7\text{-}39)$$

At this point an illustrative example will serve to clarify some of the concepts developed in the preceding pages. Suppose that we start with the following set of y parameters:

$$-y_{12} = \frac{(s^2 + 2s + 5)(s + 4)}{(s + 1)(s + 2)} = s + 10 + \frac{5s}{s + 2} - \frac{12s}{s + 1} \quad \text{(a)}$$

$$y_{22} = y_{11} = \frac{s^3 + 30s^2 + 61s + 20}{(s + 1)(s + 2)} = s + 10 + \frac{5s}{s + 2} + \frac{12s}{s + 1} \quad \text{(b)}$$

(7-40)

The set is symmetrical and compact, and y_{12} is minimum-phase, with one pair of complex zeros and one real zero. There are no common zeros of y_{11} and y_{12}, and both the constant term and the pole at infinity are present. Hence reduction step 3 is not possible. Let us now apply the Ozaki separation theorem, decomposing the factor due to the complex zeros. Considering Eqs. (7-32) and (7-33), we can write

$$P(s) = [(s + 1)^2 + 4](s + 4)$$

$$\sigma_0 = 1 \qquad \omega_0^2 = 4$$

$$\sigma_1 = 1 \qquad \sigma_2 = 2$$

$$K_0 = 5 \qquad K_1 = 4 \qquad K_2 = 5$$

The smallest value of K is 4, which occurs for the pole $s = -1$. We can now write P_1 and P_2 as

$$P_1 = (s + 1)(s + 1)(s + 4)$$

$$P_2 = 4(s + 4)$$

Hence

$$-y_{12a} = \frac{(s + 1)(s + 4)}{s + 2} = s + 2 + \frac{s}{s + 2} \quad \text{(a)}$$

$$y_{11a} = \frac{(s + 1)(s + 4)}{(s + 2)} = s + 2 + \frac{s}{s + 2} \quad \text{(b)}$$

$$-y_{12b} = \frac{4(s + 4)}{(s + 1)(s + 2)} = 8 + \frac{4s}{s + 2} - \frac{12s}{s + 1} \quad \text{(c)}$$

(7-41)

$$y_{11b} = \frac{4(6s^2 + 135 + 4)}{(s + 1)(s + 2)} = 8 + \frac{4s}{s + 2} + \frac{12s}{s + 1} \quad \text{(d)}$$

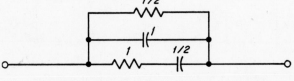

Fig. 7-8. Realization of component network.

Although y_{11a} and y_{11b} appear first as the ratio of two polynomials in these equations, it is the right-hand side which is first formed from the corresponding y_{12} function. The a parameters can be immediately recognized as a degenerate pi and realized as shown in Fig. 7-8. As for the b parameters, we see that they have no pole at infinity. Hence the corresponding z parameters will have a noncompact constant term, permitting the removal of a resistance by step 3. So let us form the z parameters.

$$z_{11b} = \frac{y_{11b}}{|y_b|} = \frac{6s^2 + 13s + 4}{48s(3s + 4)} = \frac{1}{24} + \frac{1}{48s} + \frac{\frac{1}{24}}{3s + 4} \quad \text{(a)}$$

$$z_{12b} = \frac{-y_{12b}}{|y_b|} = \frac{s + 4}{48s(3s + 4)} = \frac{1}{48s} - \frac{\frac{1}{24}}{3s + 4} \quad \text{(b)}$$

(7-42)

After removal of a resistance $R = 1/24$, the remaining z's will have no constant term. This implies that the corresponding y's will have a noncompact pole at infinity. Designating the network remaining after removal of R with a prime, we can form the y parameters as follows:

$$y_{11b}' = \frac{z_{11b}'}{|z_b'|} = 30s + 24$$

$$-y_{12b}' = \frac{z_{12b}'}{|z_b'|} = 6s + 24$$

The excess in the pole at infinity can now be removed as $C = 24$ by step 1. In the remaining set, $y_{11} = -y_{12}$. This characterizes a degenerate pi similar to that of Fig. 7-8. The complete realization is shown in Fig. 7-9(a), the ladder being the b network.

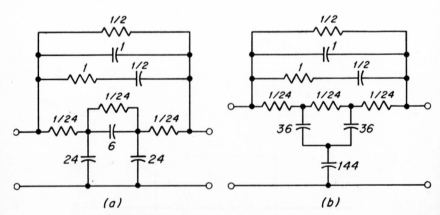

Fig. 7-9. Realization of numerical example.

The realization we have obtained is certainly not unique. One possible variation is obtained as follows. After removal of the 1/24 resistance in the b network, we can try to use step 4 in the reduction procedure. Suppose that we subtract K/s from z'_{12b}. The remainder will be

$$z''_{12b} = \frac{1}{48s} - \frac{\frac{1}{24}}{3s+4} - \frac{K}{s} = \frac{(1-144K)s + 4(1-48K)}{48s(3s+4)}$$

To maintain positive numerator coefficients, we must keep $K \leq 1/144$. Let us choose $K = 1/144$ and subtract $1/144s$ from both z'_{11b} and z'_{12b}. Following this, we form the y parameters.

$$y''_{11b} = 24 + 36s$$

$$-y''_{12b} = 24$$

This set is immediately realized as a pi structure leading to the over-all realization shown in Fig. 7-9(b). This realization is inferior to the preceding one since it requires a greater value of total capacitance.

Another realization can be obtained by initially decomposing the other factor in the original y_{12}. Equations (7-39) would be applicable in that case. This is left for you as an exercise.

Let us now take stock of what we have accomplished. Starting from a prescribed transfer function, we obtained a set of two y or z parameters. In order to obtain a realization, we imposed two major restrictions: (1) we assumed a symmetrical network, thereby possibly reducing the transmission gain and possibly increasing the number of elements required, and (2) we assumed a minimum-phase function in order to guarantee positive numerator coefficients. It would be extremely useful if we could remove these restrictions. Lucal (80) has done some work in this direction.

The minimum-phase condition is certainly a sufficient condition for positive numerator coefficients of $-y_{12}$, but it is not necessary. Thus it may be possible for the numerator coefficients of $-y_{12}$ to be positive even though there are zeros in the right half plane. However, it is not at all certain in such a case that the Ozaki separation theorem can be applied. Nevertheless it is possible to find realizations for some nonminimum-phase functions. For example, y_{12} in the following set of y parameters is non-minimum-phase:

$$-y_{12} = \frac{s^3 + s^2 + s + 2}{(s+1)(s+2)} = \left(s - \frac{s}{s+1} \right) + \left(1 - \frac{2s}{s+2} \right)$$

$$y_{11} = \left(s + \frac{s}{s+1} \right) + \left(1 + \frac{2s}{s+2} \right)$$

(7-43)

However, by decomposing the parameters as indicated by the parentheses into a and b networks, the realization shown in Fig. 7-10 is obtained. (Do this.)

So we see that, although sufficient, it is not necessary to have a minimum-phase function. Complete necessary and sufficient realizability conditions for unbalanced RC two-ports are still unknown at this date.

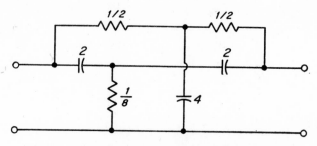

Fig. 7-10. Realization of nonminimum-phase function.

The other restriction we imposed—that of symmetry—is also sufficient but not necessary. To demonstrate this, consider the following y parameters:

$$-y_{12} = s + 2 - \frac{s}{s+1} = \frac{s^2 + 2s + 2}{s+1} \qquad (a)$$

$$y_{22} = s + 2 + \frac{2s}{s+1} = \frac{s^2 + 5s + 2}{s+1} \qquad (b) \quad (7\text{-}44)$$

$$y_{11} = s + 2 + \frac{s/2}{s+1} = \frac{s^2 + 7s/2 + 2}{s+1} \qquad (c)$$

Imagine that the y_{12} and y_{22} functions result from a prescribed $Y_{12}(s)$. We then choose y_{11} to make the poles compact. This set is nonsymmetrical but minimum-phase. Let us now apply the Ozaki separation theorem. Using Eqs. (7-32) and (7-33), which apply in this case, we find

$$-y_{12a} = s + 1$$

$$y_{22a} = s + 1 \qquad (7\text{-}45)$$

$$y_{11a} = s + 1$$

$$-y_{12b} = 1 - \frac{s}{s+1} = \frac{1}{s+1}$$

$$y_{22b} = 1 + \frac{2s}{s+1} = \frac{3s+1}{s+1} \qquad (7\text{-}46)$$

$$y_{11b} = 1 + \frac{s/2}{s+1} = \frac{3s/2+1}{s+1}$$

The first set can be immediately realized as a degenerate pi network as shown in Fig. 7-11(a). The second set of y's have no pole at infinity. Hence the corresponding z parameters will have a non-compact constant term. Forming the z parameters, we get

$$z_{12b} = \frac{2}{9s}$$

$$z_{22b} = \frac{2}{9s} + \frac{2}{3} \tag{7-47}$$

$$z_{11b} = \frac{2}{9s} + \frac{1}{3}$$

This set can be immediately recognized as a tee network. The complete realization is shown in Fig. 7-11(b).

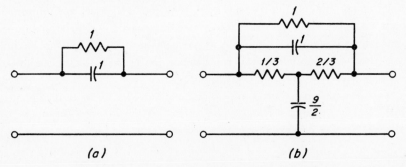

(a)   (b)

Fig. 7-11. Realization of nonsymmetrical two-port.

This example demonstrates that symmetry is not a necessary condition for realizability in the type of structure we have been discussing. However, suppose that we start from a given transfer function and obtain the y_{12} and y_{22} functions. (Assume no transmission zeros on the positive real axis.) We then determine a y_{11} function that satisfies the residue condition, so that all three y parameters are known. We have seen that, if y_{12} is minimum-phase and the set is symmetrical, we can always obtain an unbalanced realization. We have also seen by example that neither the symmetry condition nor the minimum-phase condition is necessary. However, if we relax the symmetry condition, we shall find that the minimum-phase condition is no longer even sufficient. That is to say, we may have a set of three minimum-phase nonsymmetrical y parameters for which we cannot find an unbalanced realization [see Lucal (80)]. Similarly, we might not be able to obtain a realization for a symmetrical nonminimum-phase set of y parameters.

7-4. Maximizing the gain constant

One of the disadvantages of the symmetrical realization discussed in the last section is the relatively low value of the gain constant which we are forced to accept. Any method that will improve this situation will be most welcome. Bower and Ordung (19) have described such a method.

Let us review the procedure for obtaining the parameters y_{12} and y_{22} from a given $Y_{12}(s)$. With $-Y_{12}$ given as the ratio of two polynomials, N_{12}/P, we decompose P into the sum of two polynomials P_1 and P_2 such that the ratio has poles and zeros that alternate. There is considerable flexibility in the choice of the polynomials P_1 and P_2, and we should be able to use this flexibility to choose these polynomials in such a way as to satisfy some independently specified requirement. Such a requirement might be maximum gain. In Chap. 4 we discussed the restrictions on the gain constant of an unbalanced two-port. Those results of course apply here. However, the symmetry condition imposes additional restrictions, as we shall see.

Since the gain constant is of importance here, let us write it explicitly. Thus

$$-Y_{12}(s) = K\frac{Q(s)}{P(s)} = K\frac{Q}{P_1 + P_2} = K\frac{Q/P_2}{1 + P_1/P_2} = \frac{-y_{12}}{1 + y_{22}} \tag{7-48}$$

Let us designate the residues of Q/P_2 as k_{12} so that the residues of $-y_{12}$ will be Kk_{12}. For a symmetrical network the residue condition will become

$$k_{22}^2 - (Kk_{12})^2 \geq 0$$

or

$$\left|\frac{Kk_{12}}{k_{22}}\right| \leq 1, \qquad K \leq \frac{k_{22}}{|k_{12}|} \tag{7-49}$$

The gain constant must satisfy this result at all the poles. The left-hand side of this expression can be interpreted very simply as follows: Let $s = -\sigma_i$ be a pole of the y parameters, and multiply numerator and denominator of the right-hand side of Eq. (7-48) by $s + \sigma_i$. The result is

$$Y_{12}(s) = \frac{(s + \sigma_i)y_{12}(s)}{(s + \sigma_i) + (s + \sigma_i)y_{22}(s)} \tag{7-50}$$

Now evaluate this expression at $s = -\sigma_i$. The numerator is immediately recognized as the residue of y_{12} at that pole, while the second term of the denominator is recognized as the corresponding residue of y_{22}. Since the first term in the denominator vanishes, we get

$$-Y_{12}(-\sigma_i) = \frac{Kk_{12}^{(i)}}{k_{22}^{(i)}} \tag{7-51}$$

Combining this with Eq. (7-49), we get

$$|Y_{12}(-\sigma_i)| \leq 1 \tag{7-52}$$

This condition tells us that the magnitude of the transfer function evaluated at any one of the poles which we choose for the y parameters must be no greater than unity. The value of the gain constant must be small enough to satisfy this condition at all the poles of y_{22}.

It is obvious that the ratio $Q(s)/P(s)$ will be different for different values of s. If we can choose the poles of the y parameters at those values of s which make this ratio small, then K can be relatively large and still satisfy the last equation.

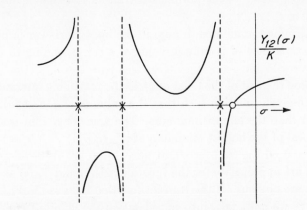

Fig. 7-12. Sketch of normalized transfer admittance.

In Fig. 7-12 a typical RC transfer function is sketched as a function of σ. The poles of the function are the zeros of $P(s)$. Recalling the procedure for finding the poles of y_{22} from the given Y_{12}, we note that these must lie between the poles of $Y_{12}(s)$. Qualitatively speaking, according to our statement in the preceding paragraph, we want to locate these poles so that $|Y_{12}/K|$ evaluated at these points is small. More exactly, we can write

$$|Y_{12}(-\sigma_i)| = K\left|\frac{Y_{12}(-\sigma_i)}{K}\right| \leq 1 \qquad K \leq \frac{1}{|Y_{12}(-\sigma_i)/K|} \tag{7-53}$$

where $s = -\sigma_i$ are the poles of the y parameters. In other words, K cannot exceed the reciprocal of the normalized transfer admittance evaluated at each of the poles of y_{22}.

In the interval from the origin to the first pole $|Y_{12}/K|$ takes on values as small as you please, so that, as far as the pole of the y parameters in this interval is concerned, an arbitrarily large value of K can be achieved.

However, in the next two intervals $|Y_{12}/K|$ reaches a minimum value. It is evident, then, that the maximum value of K will result if Eq. (7-53) is satisfied with the equality sign at the value of s corresponding to the largest minimum of $|Y_{12}/K|$.

Remember that Fialkow's condition also places a restriction on the permissible value of K based on the behavior of $Y_{12}(\sigma)$ for positive values of σ. However, this restriction will automatically be satisfied (show this) if K is chosen as outlined.

In summary, to achieve a maximum gain constant, perform the following steps:

1. Make a sketch of the normalized transfer function against negative real values of s.

2. Determine the minima, if any, in the intervals between poles.

3. Choose a pole of y_{22} at the value of s corresponding to the largest minimum.

4. Choose the rest of the poles of y_{22} in the remaining intervals between poles of the given function such that the value of $|Y_{12}/K|$ at these points is no larger than the largest minimum. The value of K that is achieved is the reciprocal of the largest minimum of $|Y_{12}/K|$.

We have used the transfer admittance $Y_{12}(s)$ in this development, but the results are appropriate for the functions $Z_{12}(s)$ and $T_{12}(s)$ as well. The differences are obvious. If the transfer function involved is $Y_{12}(s)$, then in step 2 above we must take into consideration the infinite-frequency value as well. It may be that this is the largest minimum. Similarly, if the function is Z_{12}, we must include the zero-frequency value. If the function is T_{12}, we must consider both the zero-frequency value and the infinite-frequency value, since either one of these may be larger.

As an example, consider the function

$$Z_{12}(s) = K \frac{s^2 + s + 3}{(s + 1)(s + 5)} \qquad (7\text{-}54)$$

A sketch of the function is shown in Fig. 7-13. For negative values of σ there is a single extreme point which occurs at $s = -2.06$. The value $|Z_{12}/K|$ at this point is 1.66. (The maximum value of the function for positive σ is unity, and it occurs at infinity.) The zero-frequency value is lower than this, so that the largest gain constant that can be achieved in a symmetrical realization is $K = 1/1.66 = 0.603$. It is apparent from the figure that the maximum is quite broad so that the value of K is not changed appreciably by choosing the pole at $s = -2$, instead of -2.06. The value of K achieved will be 3/5. The other pole must be chosen be-

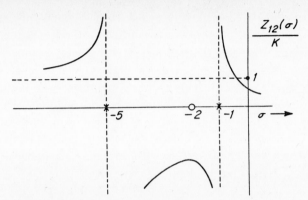

Fig. 7-13. Sketch of normalized transfer impedance.

tween the origin and -1, at a point for which $|Z_{12}/K| \leq 5/3$. To determine the permissible range, we can solve for the roots of $Z_{12}/K = 5/3$. Thus

$$\frac{s^2 + s + 3}{(s + 1)(s + 5)} = \frac{5}{3}$$

The solution of this equation gives a value $s = -0.621$ in the desired interval. A value of s in the range $-0.621 \leq s < 0$ can be chosen as the second pole of the z parameters. However, if we choose $s = -0.621$, this pole, like the one at $s = -2$, will also be compact.

Recall that in the decomposition of the denominator of Z_{12} into two polynomials P_1 and P_2 we can assign part of the highest-power term to each polynomial. The fraction that must be assigned to P_1 and to P_2 is dictated by the requirement that the infinite-frequency value of z_{12} not exceed that of z_{11}. These two values will be equal if we choose the highest-power term of P_1 to be Ks^2, while that of P_2 is $(1 - K)s^2$. This choice will ensure that the constant term in the expansion of the z parameters will be compact. Thus we can write

$$P_2 = \tfrac{2}{5}(s + 0.621)(s + 2) \tag{7-55}$$

The polynomial P_1 is now obtained by subtracting this polynomial from the denominator of Z_{12}. Thus

$$P_1 = P - P_2 = \tfrac{3}{5}(s + 1.04)(s + 7.21)$$

Finally the z parameters can be written

$$z_{12} = \frac{3}{2}\frac{s^2 + s + 3}{(s + 0.621)(s + 2)} = \frac{3}{2} + \frac{5.445}{s + 2} - \frac{3.01}{s + 0.621}$$

$$z_{11} = z_{22} = \frac{3}{2}\frac{(s + 1.04)(s + 7.21)}{(s + 0.621)(s + 2)} = \frac{3}{2} + \frac{5.445}{s + 2} + \frac{3.01}{s + 0.621} \tag{7-56}$$

These functions constitute a compact set of symmetrical z parameters, and a realization can be obtained according to the method discussed in the last section. Because the parameters are already compact, it is not necessary to remove an initial series branch consisting of the excess residue of z_{11} and z_{22} over z_{12}. This assures a realization with fewer elements.

This example has served to illustrate the principle that, after choosing the critical pole which serves to establish the gain constant, choice of the remaining poles (as well as the infinite-frequency value) such that they are all compact will yield a realization with a minimum number of elements. This fact was pointed out by Belove (13).

7-5. Extension to nonsymmetrical unbalanced forms

In Sec. 7-3 we discussed a realization technique for which sufficient conditions are symmetry and the minimum-phase property. However, we saw that these conditions are not necessary.

Consider again the y parameters of the numerical example given in Eqs. (7-44) for a nonsymmetrical network. Let us calculate the branch admittances of the equivalent pi network shown in Fig. 7-14. These are

$$y_a = y_{11} + y_{12} = \frac{3s/2}{s+1} \qquad \text{(a)}$$

$$y_c = y_{22} + y_{12} = \frac{3s}{s+1} \qquad \text{(b)} \quad \text{(7-57)}$$

$$y_b = -y_{12} = \frac{s^2 + 2s + 2}{s+1} \qquad \text{(c)}$$

It is apparent that y_a and y_c are RC admittance functions, but not y_b. If we take the ratio of y_a to y_c, we get

$$\frac{y_{11} + y_{12}}{y_{22} + y_{12}} = \frac{1}{2} \qquad \text{(7-58)}$$

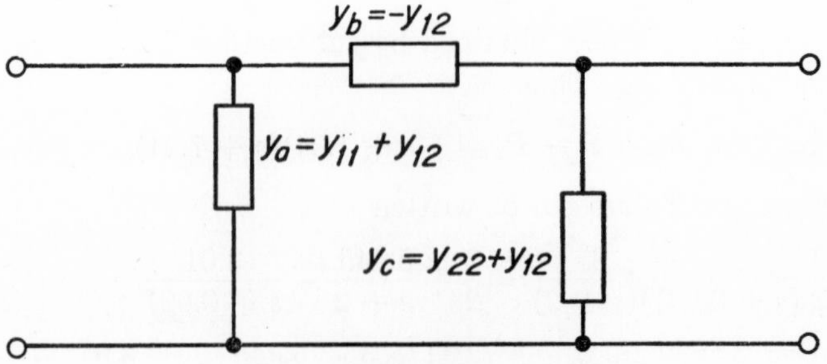

Fig. 7-14. Pi equivalent.

This equation says that the two shunt branches of the pi equivalent differ only by a constant multiplier. For the example under consideration it is possible to obtain an unbalanced realization, as shown in Fig. 7-11. This result motivates us to investigate unsymmetrical networks which satisfy the condition

$$\frac{y_{11} + y_{12}}{y_{22} + y_{12}} = \frac{y_a}{y_c} = a \qquad (7\text{-}59)$$

where a is a real positive constant. Note that for symmetrical networks the constant is unity. We assume of course that the other conditions of realizability in an unbalanced network are satisfied, including Fialkow's condition.

In terms of y_a, y_b, and y_c, the admittances y_{11} and y_{12} are given by

$$y_{11} = y_a + y_b \qquad \text{(a)}$$
$$y_{22} = y_c + y_b \qquad \text{(b)}$$

(7-60)

Since the residues of y_{11}/s and y_{22}/s are nonnegative, we can write

$$k_a + k_b \geq 0$$
$$k_c + k_b \geq 0$$

(7-61)

where the k's are the residues of $1/s$ times the corresponding y. Another relationship involving the residues is obtained by evaluating Eq. (7-59) at any of the poles of the y parameters. The result is

$$\frac{k_a}{k_c} = \frac{k_{11} + k_{12}}{k_{22} + k_{12}} = a \qquad (7\text{-}62)$$

Note that these are residues at poles of y_a and y_c, which do not necessarily include all poles of y_{11}, y_{22}, and y_{12}. This result means that k_a and k_c are either both positive or both negative. To eliminate the ambiguity, consider the sum $y_a + y_c = y_{11} + y_{22} + 2y_{12}$. The residues will be related by

$$k_a + k_c = k_{11} + k_{22} + 2k_{12} \qquad (7\text{-}63)$$

If k_{12} is positive, then the left-hand side will also be positive. Suppose that k_{12} is negative. From the residue condition we know that

$$|k_{12}| \leq \sqrt{k_{11}k_{22}} \qquad (7\text{-}64)$$

If we substitute $-\sqrt{k_{11}k_{22}}$ for k_{12} in Eq. (7-63), the equality will become an inequality as follows:

$$k_a + k_c \geq k_{11} + k_{22} - 2\sqrt{k_{11}k_{22}} = (\sqrt{k_{11}} - \sqrt{k_{22}})^2 \geq 0 \qquad (7\text{-}65)$$

Consequently, since both the sum and the ratio of k_a and k_c are always nonnegative, both $k_a \geq 0$ and $k_c \geq 0$. This guarantees that y_a and y_c are RC admittance functions.

We have dealt here with the pi equivalent and the y parameters. Similar results follow for the tee equivalent and the z parameters. For example, using the z-y relationships in Eq. (7-59), we get

$$\frac{z_{22} - z_{12}}{z_{11} - z_{12}} = \frac{z_a}{z_c} = a \qquad (7\text{-}66)$$

where z_a and z_c are the series-branch impedances of the tee. In a similar way we can show that these are RC impedances. Note that z_{22} and z_{11} replace y_{11} and y_{22}, respectively.

The next step is to show that the Ozaki realization procedure can be adapted to the present case. We shall follow the same sequence of steps as we did in the symmetrical case. Let us first group the terms in the partial-fraction expansion of the y parameters according as the residues of $-y_{12}$ are positive or negative. Thus

$$-y_{12} = y_{12p} - y_{12n} \qquad \text{(a)}$$

$$y_{11} = y_{11p} + y_{11n} \qquad \text{(b)} \quad (7\text{-}67)$$

$$y_{22} = y_{22p} + y_{22n} \qquad \text{(c)}$$

These correspond to Eqs. (7-18), with the difference that the residues of y_{11} and y_{22} are not necessarily the same as the corresponding ones of $-y_{12}$. Let us now substitute these into Eq. (7-59). From the result we can express the following relationships among the residues:

$$k_{11p} = k_{12p} + a(k_{22p} - k_{12p}) \qquad \text{(a)}$$
$$k_{11n} = -k_{12n} + a(k_{22n} + k_{12n}) \qquad \text{(b)} \qquad (7\text{-}68)$$

From the first of these equations an important result follows. Suppose that $k_{22p} < k_{12p}$ at one of the poles. The residue condition then requires that $k_{11p} > k_{12p}$ at that pole. But the second term in Eq. (7-68, a) will be negative so that this requirement cannot be satisfied. It follows that if the y parameters satisfy Eq. (7-59) then the residues of y_{11} and y_{22} are necessarily at least as large as the corresponding positive residues of $-y_{12}$. These include the residue at infinity and the constant term. At compact poles this requires $k_{11p} = k_{22p} = k_{12p}$.

In the first step of the realization the y parameters are made compact. This involves removal of enough of k_{11p} and k_{22p} so as to make the remainders equal to k_{12p}. Suppose that we write

$$k_{11p} = k_{12p}(1 + x_1) \qquad \text{(a)}$$
$$k_{22p} = k_{12p}(1 + x_2) \qquad \text{(b)} \qquad (7\text{-}69)$$

so that the amount of the residue that is removed at each pole of the positive part of y_{11} is $x_1 k_{12p}$, while the corresponding quantity for y_{22} is $x_2 k_{12p}$. Using these expressions in the first of Eqs. (7-68), we find that $x_2 = x_1/a$. Thus, if we let Y_1 be the admittance that is subtracted from y_{11}, then the admittance that is subtracted from y_{22} is Y_1/a. The partial realization is shown in Fig. 7-15(a). This corresponds to Fig. 7-2 in the symmetrical case.

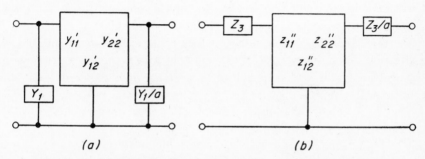

Fig. 7-15. Partial realization of unbalanced nonsymmetrical two-port.

The second step in the realization is the same as the second step in the symmetrical case. It involves the removal of a bridging branch as in Fig. 7-3. This step can be performed if an admittance Y_2 can be subtracted from the positive part of $-y_{12}$ and still maintain a Hurwitz polynomial in the numerator of the remaining y_{12}.

The third step is to form the z parameters. Then, following the same reasoning that we used for the y parameters we can show that, whenever the positive and negative parts of the y parameters have similar terms in their partial-fraction expansions, then the positive parts of z_{11} and z_{22} will have excess residues. These can then be subtracted and realized as series impedances as illustrated in Fig. 7-15(b). If Z_3 denotes the impedance at the input terminals, the impedance at the output terminals will be Z_3/a. The details of this development are left to you.

Step 4, which is illustrated in Fig. 7-5, remains unchanged.

Finally, if none of the above steps can be performed, the Ozaki separation theorem can be applied. After $-y_{12}$ is separated into two components, we assign the residues of the component y_{11} and y_{22} functions so that they are the same fraction of the residues of the initial y_{11} and y_{22} as the residues of the component y_{12}'s are of the initial y_{12}. Alternate application of some or all of these steps will lead to a complete realization.

This realization technique will be illustrated in connection with the cascade synthesis in Sec. 7-10.

7-6. Realization in a tree structure

Let us now view in perspective the ideas we have been discussing in the early parts of this chapter. Starting from a realizable transfer function $(Z_{12}, Y_{12}, \text{ or } T_{12})$, we have seen that it is always possible to obtain a symmetrical realization if we accept a low value of gain. This realization can always take the form of a lattice. We found the minimum-phase condition to be sufficient (but not necessary) to permit an unbalanced symmetrical realization. Finally, we were able to generalize the unbalanced symmetrical realization, obtaining a network having the same structure as the symmetrical one. This will usually lead to a higher gain constant than the symmetrical realization.

In this section we shall discuss a realization procedure which leads to a network having the maximum realizable gain constant. The procedure is due to Fialkow and Gerst (45).

A. *Unbalanced Realization*

We shall first treat transfer functions which have no zeros on the positive real axis but may have zeros anywhere else, including the right half plane. Suppose that the given function is $T_{12}(s)$, the voltage transfer ratio. We saw in Chap. 4 that it is always possible to write such a function in the form

$$T_{12}(s) = \frac{a_0 + a_1 s + a_2 s^2 + \ldots + a_m s^m}{b_0 + b_1 s + \ldots + b_n s^n} = \frac{P(s)}{Q(s)} \tag{7-70}$$

None of the numerator coefficients is negative and each one is no greater than the corresponding denominator coefficient; that is, $a_i \leq b_i$ for all i. Sometimes this may require the use of surplus factors.

Consider initially the first-order transfer function

$$T_{12} = \frac{a_1 s + a_0}{b_1 s + b_0} \tag{7-71}$$

This function can be realized by the L network shown in Fig. 7-16, whose

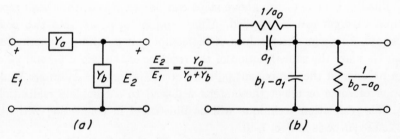

Fig. 7-16. Realization of first-order transfer functions.

transfer ratio is also given in the figure. By comparing this with the last equation, we find

$$Y_a = a_1 s + a_0 \qquad \text{(a)}$$
$$Y_b = (b_1 - a_1)s + (b_0 - a_0) \qquad \text{(b)}$$

(7-72)

The final realization is shown in part (b) of the figure. Note that the admittance level can be multiplied by any constant value without modifying the transfer function.

Now let us turn our attention back to the nth-order function in Eq. (7-70). Our objective will be to obtain two simpler transfer functions from the nth-order function with the expectation that realizations of these simpler functions, when connected in parallel, will realize the original function. If the two simpler functions are of the first order, we realize them by L networks, as we have just shown. If they are of higher order, we reduce each one of them again until we have only first-order functions. This is the scheme we plan to explore.

Let us decompose the denominator polynomial into the sum of two polynomials Q_a and Q_b. The next step is to decompose the numerator also into the sum of two polynomials P_a and P_b. Finally, let us divide numerator and denominator by another polynomial G. We do not yet know what the properties of the various polynomials should be. The requirements on them will be established as we proceed. The formal result of these steps will be

$$T_{12}(s) = \frac{P_a(s)/G(s) + P_b(s)/G(s)}{Q_a(s)/G(s) + Q_b(s)/G(s)} \qquad (7\text{-}73)$$

According to our plan, we are seeking a realization which is the parallel connection of two networks. Since the y parameters of two parallel-connected two-ports is the sum of the component y parameters, we can write for the transfer ratio of the parallel combination

$$T_{12}(s) = \frac{-(y_{12a} + y_{12b})}{y_{22a} + y_{22b}} \qquad (7\text{-}74)$$

where the subscripts refer to the two networks. A comparison of the last two equations shows that we can make the following formal identifications:

$$-y_{12a} = \frac{P_a(s)}{G(s)} \qquad y_{22a} = \frac{Q_a(s)}{G(s)} \qquad \text{(a)}$$
$$-y_{12b} = \frac{P_b(s)}{G(s)} \qquad y_{22b} = \frac{Q_b(s)}{G(s)} \qquad \text{(b)}$$

(7-75)

Furthermore, the voltage ratios of the individual two-ports can be formed from the individual y parameters, and we get

$$T_{12a} = \frac{-y_{12a}}{y_{22a}} = \frac{P_a(s)}{Q_a(s)} \qquad \text{(a)}$$

$$T_{12b} = \frac{-y_{12b}}{y_{22b}} = \frac{P_b(s)}{Q_b(s)} \qquad \text{(b)}$$

(7-76)

From the known properties of transfer ratios and y parameters of unbalanced RC two-ports we can now establish the required properties of the polynomials. If y_{22a} and y_{22b} are to be RC admittance functions, we must require that Q_a and Q_b have negative real zeros only. Furthermore, $G(s)$ must also have only negative real zeros which alternate with those of both Q_a and Q_b. Thus we decompose $Q(s)$ into two polynomials Q_a and Q_b as discussed in Sec. 7-2 so that their zeros are negative real and separate each other. Then we choose $G(s)$ so that it is of the same degree as Q_b and its zeros separate those of both Q_a and Q_b.

Now consider the requirements on the component polynomials P_a and P_b. Since T_{12a} and T_{12b} are to be transfer functions of unbalanced RC two-ports, none of the coefficients of P_a and P_b should be negative, while each one should be no greater than the corresponding coefficient of Q_a or Q_b, respectively. This decomposition of $P(s)$ is always possible since its coefficients, in turn, are no greater than the corresponding ones of $Q(s)$.

We have now succeeded in obtaining two transfer functions from the original one. The same procedure can now be applied to each of these in turn. If we are to make any progress by this technique, however, the component transfer functions should be of lower order than the original one so that, after successive applications of the decomposition procedure, we shall arrive at first-order transfer functions which we know how to realize. This result can be achieved in the following way:

In decomposing $Q(s)$ assign all the highest-power term to Q_a and all the constant term to Q_b. Hence Q_b will be one degree lower than Q, while Q_a will have a factor s. We can force P_a also to have a factor s by assigning the entire constant term of P to P_b. Thus, in the ratio P_a/Q_a, the factor s cancels, leaving a function of lower order than the original T_{12}. Of course, other factors may also cancel, reducing the order even more. The ratio P_b/Q_b will also be of lower order than T_{12}. (If P and Q are of the same degree, we assign the entire highest-power term of P to P_a.)

Having obtained two transfer functions of lower order than the original one, we must now realize each of these functions and then connect the resulting networks in parallel. However, we need to exercise some care at this point. Let us assume that a realization of T_{12a} is obtained. This network may not have the required y_{22a}. You will recall that, in forming T_{12a} from y_{22a} and y_{12a}, a factor s was canceled. This factor plays no part in the realization of T_{12a}; yet it should appear in y_{22a}. This discrepancy is corrected in the following way: Suppose that the box (not including the series impedance Z_a) shown in Fig. 7-17(a) realizes the function T_{12a}.

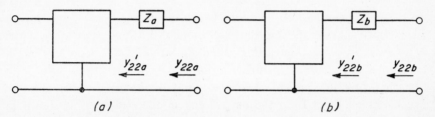

Fig. 7-17. Network modification which leaves transfer ratio invariant.

The impedance placed in the output lead does not modify the transfer ratio but does modify both y_{22a} and y_{12a}. Looking at the network, we can write

$$\frac{1}{y_{22a}} = Z_a + \frac{1}{y'_{22a}} \tag{7-77}$$

where the prime applies to the box alone. We can now substitute for y_{22a} from Eq. (7-75). Remember that $Q_a(s)$ has a factor s so that we can write $Q_a = sQ_1$. This means that $1/y_{22a}$ has a pole at the origin. Hence we can write

$$\frac{1}{y_{22a}} = \frac{G(s)}{sQ_1} = \frac{k_0}{s} + \frac{G_1(s)}{Q_1(s)} \tag{7-78}$$

where $G_1(s) = G(s)/s - G(0)Q_1(s)/sQ_1(0)$. This leads to the identifications

$$Z_a(s) = \frac{k_0}{s} \tag{a}$$
$$\tag{7-79}$$
$$y'_{22a} = \frac{Q_1(s)}{G_1(s)} \tag{b}$$

Remember that $G(s)$ is of lower degree than $Q_a(s)$ so that $1/y_{22a}$ has a zero at infinity. Hence $1/y'_{22a}$ also has a zero at infinity, which means that y'_{22a} has a pole at infinity. Similar results follow for the second network in the figure. We can write

$$\frac{1}{y_{22b}} = Z_b + \frac{1}{y'_{22b}} = \frac{G(s)}{Q_b} = k_1 + \frac{G_2(s)}{Q_b(s)} \tag{7-80}$$

where $G_2(s) = G(s) - Q_b(s)/y_{22b}(\infty)$. It follows that

$$Z_b = k_1 = \frac{1}{y_{22b}(\infty)} \tag{a}$$
$$\tag{7-81}$$
$$y'_{22b} = \frac{Q_b(s)}{G_2(s)} \tag{b}$$

It is possible to write the right-hand side of Eq. (7-80) because $Q_b(s)$ and $G(s)$ are of the same degree. Thus k_1 is the infinite-frequency value of $1/y_{22b}$. With this removed as a series resistance, y'_{22b} will have a pole at infinity.

Before connecting the networks which are to realize T_{12a} and T_{12b} in parallel, we connect the impedances Z_a and Z_b in the output leads of the two networks, respectively. If T_{12a} and T_{12b} are of the first order, the job is complete. If they are of higher order, the cycle is repeated until only first-order functions are left. The resulting structure has the form of a tree which branches out from the output end of the structure, as shown in Fig. 7-18.

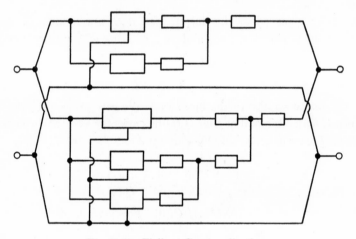

Fig. 7-18. Fialkow-Gerst realization.

The preceding discussion has been carried out on the basis of a prescribed open-circuit voltage transfer ratio. However, with a slight modification the synthesis can be applied when a resistance termination is prescribed. Let the given function be $Y_{12}(s)$ (which equals $-T_{12}$ for a unity-resistance load). We again decompose the denominator into the sum of two polynomials with negative real zeros, with the requirement that their ratio be an RC admittance. This time each polynomial should share the highest-power term. Just as we mentioned in the discussion of Sec. 7-2, we now divide numerator and denominator of Y_{12} by one of these two polynomials. The result can be written

$$-Y_{12} = \frac{P(s)}{Q(s)} = \frac{P}{Q_a + Q_b} = \frac{P/Q_b}{1 + Q_a/Q_b} \qquad (7\text{-}82)$$

In the now familiar way we make the identifications

$$-y_{12} = \frac{P}{Q_b} \qquad \text{(a)}$$

$$y_{22} = \frac{Q_a}{Q_b} \qquad \text{(b)}$$

(7-83)

These are the y parameters of the desired two-port exclusive of the load. Their ratio is the voltage transfer ratio which the two-port would have if the load were not present. Thus

$$T'_{12}(s) = \frac{-y_{12}}{y_{22}} = \frac{P(s)}{Q_a(s)} \qquad (7\text{-}84)$$

We now apply the previous realization procedure to this function, remembering that the required y_{22} must also be achieved. This is ensured by writing

$$\frac{1}{y_{22}} = \frac{Q_b}{Q_a} = k + \frac{Q'_b}{Q_a} = Z + \frac{1}{y'_{22}} \qquad (7\text{-}85)$$

The realization will then take the form shown in Fig. 7-19. The series resistance of value k will not affect T'_{12} but is needed in order to guarantee the correct y_{22} and y_{12}.

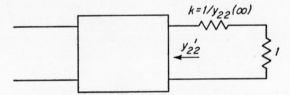

Fig. 7-19. Realization for finite-load resistance.

To illustrate the procedures we have discussed, let us synthesize the following transfer function in a resistance-terminated two-port:

$$-Y_{12}(s) = K \frac{s^2 + 2s + 2}{3s^2 + 9s + 5} \qquad (7\text{-}86)$$

The first step is to decompose the denominator polynomial. One possible breakdown is the following:

$$-Y_{12} = \frac{K(s^2 + 2s + 2)}{(2s+1)(s+2) + (s+1)(s+3)} = \frac{K \dfrac{s^2 + 2s + 2}{(s+1)(s+3)}}{1 + \dfrac{(2s+1)(s+2)}{(s+1)(s+3)}} \qquad (7\text{-}87)$$

This leads to the functions

$$-y_{12} = K \frac{s^2 + 2s + 2}{(s+1)(s+3)} \qquad \text{(a)}$$

$$y_{22} = \frac{(2s+1)(s+2)}{(s+1)(s+3)} \qquad \text{(b)} \quad \text{(7-88)}$$

$$T'_{12} = \frac{-y_{12}}{y_{22}} = K \frac{s^2 + 2s + 2}{2s^2 + 5s + 2} \qquad \text{(c)}$$

Finally

$$\frac{1}{y_{22}} = \frac{(s+1)(s+3)}{(2s+1)(s+2)} = \frac{1}{2} + \frac{\frac{3}{2}s + 2}{(2s+1)(s+2)}$$

so that

$$k = \tfrac{1}{2} \qquad \text{(a)}$$
$$\qquad\qquad\qquad\qquad\qquad\qquad\qquad \text{(7-89)}$$
$$y'_{22} = 2 \frac{(2s+1)(s+2)}{3s+4} \qquad \text{(b)}$$

The complete synthesis will consist of a resistance of $\frac{1}{2}$ connected in the output lead of the realization of T'_{12} and terminated in a unity resistance.

The first step in the realization of T'_{12} is to establish the permissible value of K. This constant must be small enough to guarantee that the value of T'_{12} is no greater than unity for any point on the positive real axis (including zero and infinity). Thus the value of K will be controlled by the largest value attained by the normalized transfer function (i.e., with K replaced by unity) for positive real values of s. To find this largest value, we calculate the zero-frequency value and the infinite-frequency value of the normalized transfer function. We also determine the peaks attained by this function along the positive-σ axis. The value of K can be no greater than the reciprocal of the largest of these numbers.

In the present example we find by differentiating the function that there are no peaks along the positive real axis. Thus K can be no bigger than unity, which is the reciprocal of the zero-frequency value. Let us choose the maximum possible value for K, namely, $K = 1$.

In the next step we must decompose both numerator and denominator of T'_{12}. Because the function we are considering is relatively simple, we shall keep the arbitrary choices of coefficient in literal form in order to obtain some insight into practical factors that may affect our choice. Thus let us write

$$T'_{12} = \frac{(s^2 + 2s) + 2}{(2s^2 + as) + [(5-a)s + 2]} \qquad \text{(7-90)}$$

We then divide numerator and denominator by a polynomial $G(s)$, which will be linear in this case. Note, however, that this factor fixes the pole of y'_{22}, which is already fixed in Eqs. (7-89). Hence $G(s) = s + \frac{4}{3}$.

$$-y_{12a} = \frac{s^2 + 2s}{s + \frac{4}{3}} \qquad -y_{12b} = \frac{2}{s + \frac{4}{3}} \qquad \text{(a)}$$

$$y_{22a} = \frac{2s^2 + as}{s + \frac{4}{3}} \qquad y_{22b} = \frac{(5 - a)s + 2}{s + \frac{4}{3}} \qquad \text{(b)} \quad \text{(7-91)}$$

$$T_{12a} = \frac{s + 2}{2s + a} \qquad T_{12b} = \frac{2}{(5 - a)s + 2} \qquad \text{(c)}$$

The number a is certainly no greater than 5; for T_{12a} to be a realizable transfer ratio, it must also be no smaller than 2. The range of a is further narrowed by the requirement that y_{22a} and y_{22b} must be RC admittance functions, which requires that the first critical point of these functions be a zero and that the zeros and poles alternate. Applying these requirements to y_{22a} and y_{22b} leads to the condition

$$\frac{8}{3} < a < \frac{7}{2} \tag{7-92}$$

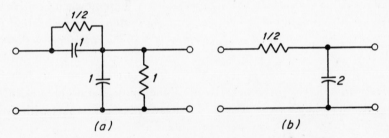

Fig. 7-20. Component realizations of numerical example.

Let us choose $a = 3$. With this choice each of the functions T_{12a} and T_{12b} is realized as an L network as shown in Fig. 7-20.

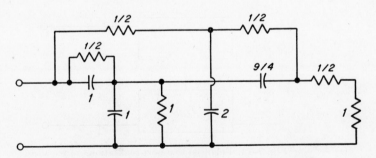

Fig. 7-21. Complete realization of numerical example.

It remains to determine the impedances Z_a and Z_b. We find these by expanding $1/y_{22a}$ and $1/y_{22b}$. Thus

$$\frac{1}{y_{22a}} = \frac{s + \frac{4}{3}}{s(2s + 3)} = \frac{4}{9s} + \frac{\frac{1}{9}}{2s + 3} \qquad \text{(a)}$$

$$\frac{1}{y_{22b}} = \frac{s + \frac{4}{3}}{2s + 2} = \frac{1}{2} + \frac{\frac{1}{6}}{s + 1} \qquad \text{(b)}$$

$$(7\text{-}93)$$

Hence $Z_a = 4/9s$ and $Z_b = \frac{1}{2}$. The complete realization is shown in Fig. 7-21. Because of the relatively low order of the original transfer function, this has the form of the familiar twin-tee network. (It also has the general form shown in Fig. 7-18.)

B. Balanced Realization

The preceding discussion has served to show that any minimum-phase or nonminimum-phase transfer function (with negative real and simple poles), with the sole exception of one having positive real zeros, can be realized in an unbalanced structure, with the gain constant specified beforehand up to the maximum realizable value.

We shall now consider a technique which will apply when positive real zeros are also present. This will constitute an alternative realization to a symmetrical lattice. In Chap. 4 we showed that the transfer function of a balanced two-port can be expressed as the difference between two unbalanced transfer functions. Thus the numerator coefficients of a balanced transfer function may be negative, but they must be no greater in size than the denominator coefficients. If such a transfer function with simple negative real poles is given, we can express it as

$$T_{12}(s) = \frac{P(s)}{Q(s)} = \frac{P_1}{Q} - \frac{P_2}{Q} = T_{12a} - T_{12b} \qquad (7\text{-}94)$$

The polynomials P_1 and P_2 are formed by grouping all the positive coefficients of P into P_1 and all the negative coefficients into P_2. Each of

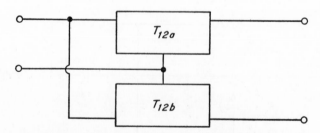

Fig. 7-22. Balanced two-port realization.

the two functions T_{12a} and T_{12b} is realizable by the method just described. The complete realization is then obtained by connecting the realizations of the two component functions in the manner shown in Fig. 7-22, as you can readily verify.

As an example, consider the open-circuit voltage ratio

$$T_{12} = K \frac{4 - s}{(s + 1)(s + 2)} \qquad (7\text{-}95)$$

We find that the maximum realizable value of K is 1/2. Let us choose K to be this value and write

$$T_{12} = \frac{2}{s^2 + 3s + 2} - \frac{s/2}{s^2 + 3s + 2} = T_{12a} - T_{12b}$$

$$T_{12a} = \frac{2}{s^2 + 3s + 2} \qquad \qquad \text{(a)}$$
$$\qquad\qquad\qquad\qquad\qquad\qquad\qquad (7\text{-}96)$$
$$T_{12b} = \frac{s/2}{s^2 + 3s + 2} \qquad \qquad \text{(b)}$$

We must now realize each of functions T_{12a} and T_{12b}. For T_{12a} we get

$$T_{12a} = \frac{\dfrac{0}{s + a} + \dfrac{2}{s + a}}{\dfrac{s^2 + bs}{s + a} + \dfrac{(3 - b)s + 2}{s + a}} \qquad (7\text{-}97)$$

Hence we make the identifications

$$y_{12c} = 0 \qquad\qquad -y_{12d} = \frac{2}{s + a}$$

$$y_{22c} = \frac{s^2 + bs}{s + a} \qquad\qquad y_{22d} = \frac{(3 - b)s + 2}{s + a}$$

$$T_{12c} = 0 \qquad\qquad T_{12d} = \frac{2}{(3 - b)s + 2}$$

The subscripts c and d refer to the two component networks which together realize T_{12a}. For y_{22c} and y_{22d} to be RC admittance functions, we must require the conditions

$$a < b$$
$$\frac{2}{3 - b} < a \qquad (7\text{-}98)$$

These conditions will be satisfied by $b = 7/4$, $a = 5/3$.

One other point needs explanation. The transfer voltage ratio of the c network is zero, while its y_{22} function is not. This may be realized by a degenerate tee whose shunt-branch admittance is y_{22c}, whose output series branch is a short circuit, and whose input branch is open circuit. When the c and d networks are then connected in parallel, the result is to place the shunt branch of the c network across the output terminals of the d network.

The remainder of the realization is now straightforward. The resulting network is shown in Fig. 7-23. You are urged to carry out the remaining details. In realizing T_{12b} the denominator was decomposed into $s^2 + 3s/2$

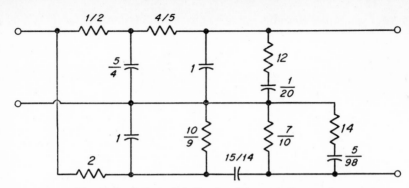

Fig. 7-23. Balanced realization of numerical example.

and $3s/2 + 2$. The polynomial $G(s)$ by which numerator and denominator are divided was chosen to be $s + \frac{7}{5}$.

7-7. Ladder realization

The realization technique discussed in the preceding section is applicable to any realizable RC transfer function. It would appear, then, that there is no further purpose to be served in pursuing the subject of RC synthesis. This, however, is not the case. We should always be "in the market" for alternative realization procedures and equivalent networks, with the hope of improving network structure and reducing the required number of elements.

The locations of the transmission zeros are not taken into account in the Fialkow-Gerst synthesis technique, except to the extent of determining the existence of positive real zeros. But, from our knowledge of the necessary locations of the transmission zeros of certain simple network structures, we may be tempted to seek such structures when the function under consideration has zeros in the appropriate parts of the plane. As a case in point, we know that the transmission zeros of RC ladder networks necessarily lie on the negative real axis. Hence let us seek a ladder realization when the transmission zeros are all negative real.

The situation here is completely analogous to the case of a lossless network with transmission zeros restricted to the $j\omega$ axis. The Cauer ladder-development technique applies equally well here. Since we spent considerable time discussing this procedure in Chap. 5, it is not necessary to dwell on it further here. It will suffice merely to give an illustration which will point up any peculiarities of the RC situation as compared with the lossless case.

Suppose the following two y parameters are obtained from a prescribed Y_{12} function:

$$y_{22} = \frac{(s+1)(s+3)}{(s+\frac{3}{2})(s+4)} \qquad \text{(a)}$$

$$-y_{12} = K \frac{s+\frac{5}{2}}{(s+\frac{3}{2})(s+4)} \qquad \text{(b)}$$

(7-99)

The transmission zeros lie at $s = -5/2$ and at infinity. A sketch of $y_{22}(\sigma)$ is shown in Fig. 7-24. You will recall that the realization procedure consists

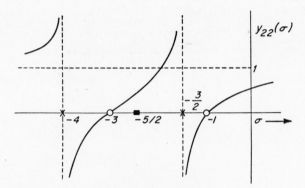

Fig. 7-24. Sketch if $y_{22}(\sigma)$.

in partially removing a pole of y_{22} (or its reciprocal) such that the remainder has a zero at the desired transmission zero. The transmission zero is then realized by completely removing a series-impedance pole or a shunt-admittance pole. The order of removal of transmission zeros is arbitrary, and the different choices constitute alternative realizations.

Suppose we first attack the transmission zero at infinity. The sketch of y_{22} (as well as previous knowledge) indicates that the infinite-frequency value of y_{22} is greater than its zero-frequency value. Hence we cannot subtract $y_{22}(\infty)$ from y_{22}, for the purpose of creating a zero, without leaving an unrealizable remainder. On the other hand, the infinite-frequency value of an RC impedance is less than its zero-frequency value. So we take the reciprocal of y_{22} and subtract its infinite-frequency value, which is unity.

$$z_2 = \frac{1}{y_{22}} - 1 = \frac{(s+\frac{3}{2})(s+4)}{(s+1)(s+3)} - 1 = \frac{\frac{3}{2}(s+2)}{(s+1)(s+3)} \qquad (7\text{-}100)$$

Thus the network realization starts out with a series resistance of value unity. The remaining impedance z_2 has a zero at infinity; so our next step is to invert and completely remove the pole at infinity from $y_2 = 1/z_2$, thus creating the desired transmission zero.

$$y_2 = \frac{1}{z_2} = \frac{(s+1)(s+3)}{\frac{3}{2}(s+2)} = \frac{\frac{4}{3}(s+\frac{3}{2})}{s+2} + \frac{2}{3}s \quad \text{(a)}$$

$$(7\text{-}101)$$

$$y_3 = y_2 - \frac{2}{3}s = \frac{4}{3}\frac{s+\frac{3}{2}}{s+2} \quad \text{(b)}$$

The network realization up to this point is shown in Fig. 7-25.

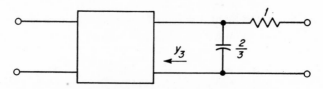

Fig. 7-25. Partial ladder realization.

The transmission zero at $s = -5/2$ still remains to be realized. The sketch of the function $y_3(\sigma)$ shown in Fig. 7-26 shows that it is impossible

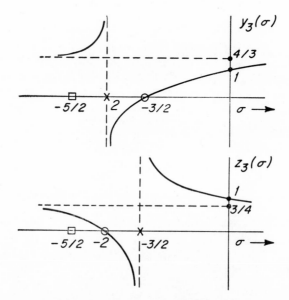

Fig. 7-26. Sketches of $y_3(\sigma)$ and $z_3(\sigma)$.

to shift a zero to $s = -5/2$; so we consider its reciprocal $z_3 = 1/y_3$. This is also sketched in Fig. 7-26. In order to shift the zero from -2 to $-5/2$, we need to subtract a constant from z_3 which is the value of z_3 at $s = -5/2$. Hence we first compute $z_3(-5/2)$. This is

$$z_3\left(-\frac{5}{2}\right) = \frac{3}{4}\left(\frac{s+2}{s+\frac{3}{2}}\right)\bigg|_{s=-5/2} = \frac{3}{8}$$

Then
$$z_4 = z_3 - \frac{3}{8} = \frac{3\,s + \frac{5}{2}}{8\,s + \frac{3}{2}}$$

$$y_4 = \frac{1}{z_4} = \frac{16s/15}{s + \frac{5}{2}} + \frac{8}{5}$$

The transmission zero at $s = -5/2$ is now realized as a shunt branch. This leaves a remainder function $y_5 = 8/5$, which is realized as a series resistance of value $5/8$. The complete realization is shown in Fig. 7-27(a).

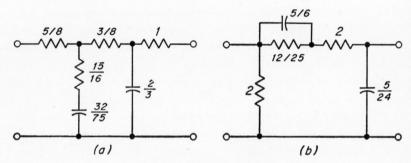

Fig. 7-27. Ladder realizations.

An alternative realization can be obtained by removing the transmission zeros in the opposite order. The result is shown in Fig. 7-27(b). The details are left for you as an exercise. Note that the finite transmission zero is produced in a series branch in this case.

The same realization technique applies, of course, when the given functions are z_{12} and z_{22}, provided only that the transmission zeros are all on the negative real axis. As discussed in Chap. 5 for the LC case, however, we have no control over the achieved transmission level and over the third parameter (y_{11} or z_{11}). In the illustration of Fig. 7-27(a), for example, we find that the zero-frequency value of $-y_{12}$ is $1/2$; from Eqs. (7-99), it is $5K/12$. This means that the value of K which we have realized is $K = 6/5$. The alternative realization of part (b) of the figure yields a value $K = 30/31$. On the other hand, the low gain constant in this case is compensated by the reduction in the total number of elements from six to five.

7-8. Parallel-ladders realization

If the transmission zeros of a given transfer function do not all lie on the negative real axis, then a ladder network will not be realizable. In this section we shall discuss an alternative to the Fialkow-Gerst synthesis when there are no transmission zeros on the positive real axis.

The starting point is a prescribed transfer admittance $Y_{12}(s)$ or an open-circuit voltage ratio $T_{12}(s)$, from which we obtain the two short-circuit parameters y_{12} and y_{22}. Since the transmission zeros do not all lie on the negative real axis, a ladder realization is not possible. However, if we can decompose the y parameters in such a way that the transmission zeros of each component all lie on the negative real axis, then each component can be realized as a ladder. The parallel connection of the components will constitute the complete realization.

This technique is identical with the method described in Sec. 5-4 for the realization of lossless two-ports. It was first described by Guillemin (56). We require only that the numerator coefficients of $-y_{12}$ be positive. A sufficient condition for this requirement is that the numerator of $-y_{12}$ be a Hurwitz polynomial, but this is not necessary. We have already seen how the use of surplus factors will lead to positive coefficients in case some of the zeros of y_{12} are in the right half plane.

It is not necessary at this point to repeat the development carried out in Sec. 5-4. It will be sufficient to give a numerical illustration. For this purpose let us resynthesize the transfer admittance given in Eq. (7-86) for which a Fialkow-Gerst realization was obtained in Fig. 7-21. The given function is

$$-Y_{12}(s) = K\frac{s^2 + 2s + 2}{3s^2 + 9s + 5} \tag{7-102}$$

Let us decompose the denominator into the same two polynomials we did before. The given function can then be written

$$-Y_{12} = K\frac{\dfrac{s^2 + 2s + 2}{(s + 1)(s + 3)}}{1 + \dfrac{(2s + 1)(s + 2)}{(s + 1)(s + 3)}} \tag{7-103}$$

from which we identify the following functions:

$$-y_{12} = K\frac{s^2 + 2s + 2}{(s + 1)(s + 3)} \tag{a}$$

$$y_{22} = \frac{(2s + 1)(s + 2)}{(s + 1)(s + 3)} \tag{b}$$

$$\tag{7-104}$$

The next step is to decompose the numerator of y_{12} into two polynomials each of which has zeros exclusively on the negative real axis. One such decomposition is the following:

$$s^2 + 2s + 2 = [s(s + 1)] + (s + 2) \tag{7-105}$$

With this decomposition the two component y_{12} functions become

$$-y_{12a} = \frac{s}{s+3} \tag{a}$$

$$-y_{12b} = \frac{s+2}{(s+1)(s+3)} \tag{b}$$

(7-106)

In the a function the factor $s + 1$ cancels. Hence $s = -1$ can be considered a private pole of y_{22a}. Thus we first remove this pole.

$$y_{22} = \frac{s/2}{s+1} + \frac{3s+4}{2(s+3)} \tag{a}$$

$$y_1 = y_{22} - \frac{s/2}{s+1} = \frac{3s+4}{2(s+3)} \tag{b}$$

(7-107)

The only zero of y_{12a} occurs at the origin. In order to shift a zero of y_1 to the origin, we should remove its zero-frequency value, which is 2/3. Thus

$$y_2 = y_1 - \frac{2}{3} = \frac{5s/6}{s+3}$$

$$z_2 = \frac{1}{y_2} = \frac{18}{5s} + \frac{6}{5}$$

(7-108)

The pole of z_2 at the origin is then realized as a series capacitance. The remainder of the function is then simply a resistance. The complete realization is shown in Fig. 7-28(a).

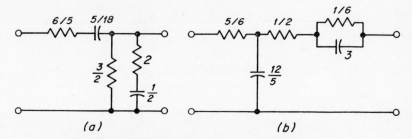

Fig. 7-28. Component ladders in numerical example.

Now let us turn to the b ladder. We see that y_{22} already has a zero at $s = -2$, which is one of the zeros of y_{12b}. Hence we invert and remove completely the pole of the reciprocal function at this point.

$$z_3 = \frac{1}{y_{22}} = \frac{(s+1)(s+3)}{(2s+1)(s+2)} = \frac{\frac{1}{3}}{s+2} + \frac{s+\frac{4}{3}}{2s+1}$$

$$z_4 = z_3 - \frac{\frac{1}{3}}{s+2} = \frac{s+\frac{4}{3}}{2s+1}$$

(7-109)

The other zero of y_{12b} is at infinity. To create a zero of z_4 at infinity, we must subtract its infinite-frequency value, which is 1/2. Thus

$$z_5 = z_4 - \frac{1}{2} = \frac{\frac{5}{6}}{2s + 1} \qquad \text{(a)}$$

$$y_5 = \frac{12s}{5} + \frac{6}{5} \qquad \text{(b)}$$

(7-110)

The pole of y_5 at infinity is removed as a shunt capacitance, leaving a remainder whose reciprocal is realized as a series resistance. The complete ladder is shown in Fig. 7-28(b).

The next step is to calculate the constant multipliers of y_{12a} and y_{12b} directly from the networks. In the notation of Sec. 5-4 we find $B_a = 5/6$ and $B_b = 1$ from the asymptotic behavior at infinity and zero, respectively. Finally, using Eq. (5-47), we find

$$K = \frac{1}{1 + 1/\frac{5}{6}} = \frac{5}{11} \qquad (7\text{-}111)$$

Hence the admittance levels of the ladders must be changed by the following factors:

Ladder a:

$$\frac{\frac{5}{11}}{\frac{5}{6}} = \frac{6}{11}$$

Ladder b:

$$\frac{5}{11}$$

The resulting network is shown in Fig. 7-29. This network together with the gain constant $K = 5/11$ is to be compared with the network of Fig. 7-21

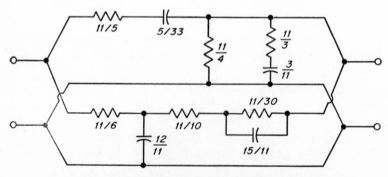

Fig. 7-29. Parallel ladders realization of numerical example.

and the corresponding gain constant of unity. We find that the Fialkow-Gerst realization of this example is superior both in the required number of elements and in the achieved gain constant.

7-9. Cascade realization—Dasher

In the preceding sections we have presented several realization procedures for an unbalanced RC two-port when a transfer function is prescribed. One of these is a symmetrical structure, and a sufficient condition for the realizability is the requirement of no right-half-plane transmission zeros. The technique can be used whether the two-port is resistance-terminated or is open-circuited and whether the driving function is a voltage source or a current source. The parallel-ladders technique overcomes the restriction on right-half-plane transmission zeros but cannot be applied when the prescribed function is the transfer impedance $Z_{12}(s)$. Both these realizations suffer from the affliction of low transmission gain and excessive number of elements. The Fialkow-Gerst procedure overcomes the low-gain problem. However, this method, along with the other two, suffers from another disadvantage which we have not yet discussed. In these realizations there is no single element or group of elements that control the locations of each transmission zero. In a physical realization (when the network is actually built) it may be necessary to adjust the elements to compensate for the inaccuracy of element values. But each element affects the performance of the network at all frequencies, and so no independent adjustments are possible.

When the transmission zeros are restricted to the negative real axis, a ladder realization can be obtained. This realization has the feature that some of the branches are *zero-shifting* branches, while others, which alternate with the former, are *zero-producing* branches. Each transmission zero is practically controlled by a single branch of the network. Thus adjustment of element values of one branch in order to shift a transmission zero slightly does not adversely affect the network performance at other frequencies.

It would be useful to have a realization technique, even when transmission zeros are complex, that incorporates the desirable features of the ladder network. What we want is a cascade connection of component two-ports, or *sections*, such that each section realizes a pair of complex transmission zeros, just as the branches of a ladder realize real transmission zeros. Figure 7-30 shows the desired structure. This idea is reminiscent of the Darlington synthesis of a positive real function as a cascade connection of lossless two-ports terminated in a resistance. Darlington's type C (Brune section) and type D sections are used to realize a pair of imaginary or real zeros and a quadruplet of complex zeros, respectively. In the initial realization of a type C, or Brune, section, negative elements appear. However, we find that the section as a whole constitutes a compact two-port with no negative elements.

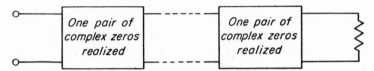

Fig. 7-30. Cascade realization.

This same idea was used by Dasher (39) in his cascade synthesis of RC two-ports. The starting point is again a transfer function with negative real poles (Z_{12}, Y_{12}, or T_{12}). From this function two of the three z or y parameters are determined. The remainder of this chapter will be devoted to a discussion of cascade realization.

To be specific, suppose that y_{22} and y_{12} are given as a realizable set of RC parameters. We want to develop the driving-point function in a ladderlike cascade connection of simple two-ports such that the transmission zeros are all realized. If there are any negative real transmission zeros, we know how to handle them. Let us assume that the negative real transmission zeros have been realized and all the remaining zeros of y_{12} are complex or lie on the $j\omega$ axis. Let us designate by $y(s)$ the driving-point admittance of the remaining network. Each pair of complex or imaginary transmission zeros is to be realized by a section in cascade with the rest of the network. Let us designate by a subscript c (standing for "component") the y and z parameters of the zero-producing section.

Since the section is to realize a pair of complex zeros, $s_0 = -\sigma_0 + j\omega_0$ and its complex conjugate, the numerator of y_{12c}, must be a quadratic. The simplest function will be obtained if we assign a single finite pole to y_{12c}. Thus

$$-y_{12c} = \frac{k[(s + \sigma_0)^2 + \omega_0^2]}{s + \sigma_c} = k\left(s + k_{0c} - \frac{k_{12}s}{s + \sigma_c}\right) \qquad (7\text{-}112)$$

where

$$k_{0c} = \frac{\sigma_0^2 + \omega_0^2}{\sigma_c} \qquad (a)$$

$$k_{12} = \frac{(\sigma_0 - \sigma_c)^2 + \omega_0^2}{\sigma_c} = k_{0c} + \sigma_c - 2\sigma_0 \qquad (b)$$

$$(7\text{-}113)$$

We must now choose the functions y_{11c} and y_{22c} such that the resulting set of functions is realizable. The details of the realization procedure will depend on the choice made at this point.

The simplest section we can think of is a symmetrical one. But requiring symmetry of each zero-producing section certainly appears unduly restrictive. A relatively simple network, one that includes the symmetrical case as well, is a network whose y parameters satisfy the condition

$$\frac{y_{11} + y_{12}}{y_{22} + y_{12}} = a \tag{7-114}$$

This expression was first introduced in Sec. 7-5. There we saw that an Ozaki-type realization can be obtained for y parameters satisfying this condition. Let us, then, seek zero-producing sections whose y parameters satisfy Eq. (7-114). At the outset we have no assurance of success. But as we develop the procedure, we shall find that all conditions will be satisfied with sections of this type.

Another condition we shall impose on the zero-producing sections is the condition of compactness. This is not really a stringent requirement. If there are any noncompact poles, the excess in the residues of y_{22c} over the amount necessary for compactness can be removed as a shunt branch across the output of the section. This branch can then be considered part of the remainder of the network after the zero-producing section is removed.

From the partial-fraction expansion of $-y_{12c}$ we see that the positive part involves only the pole at infinity and the constant term, while the negative part contains only the finite pole. We previously found that, from the basic condition given in the last equation, the two relationships given in Eqs. (7-68) follow. These involve the residues of the positive part and the negative part of the three y parameters. From the first of these conditions we deduced in Sec. 7-5 that compactness requires $k_{11p} = k_{22p} = k_{12p}$. Thus the residue at infinity and the constant term of y_{11c} and y_{22c} must be the same as the corresponding ones of $-y_{12c}$. Now let us set $k_{22n} = xk_{12n}$ at the finite pole. Compactness will require $k_{11n} = k_{12n}/x$. The second of the relationships in Eqs. (7-68) will then dictate that $x = 1/a$. Consequently we can now write the y parameters of the zero-producing section as

$$-y_{12c} = k\left(s + k_{0c} - \frac{k_{12}s}{s + \sigma_c}\right) \tag{a}$$

$$y_{11c} = k\left(s + k_{0c} + a\,\frac{k_{12}s}{s + \sigma_c}\right) \tag{b} \quad (7\text{-}115)$$

$$y_{22c} = k\left(s + k_{0c} + \frac{1}{a}\frac{k_{12}s}{s + \sigma_c}\right) \tag{c}$$

No matter what the structure of the zero-producing section, its pi equivalent will have the form shown in Fig. 7-31. This is obviously not realizable as an RC network, since y_b is required to have complex zeros. Neverthe-

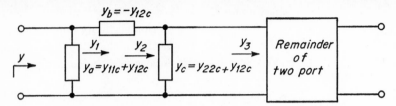

Fig. 7-31. Pi equivalent of zero-producing section.

less, we know how to find realizations of the section according to the methods discussed in Sec. 7-5. The branch admittances of the pi are

$$y_a = k(1 + a)k_{12} \frac{s}{s + \sigma_c} \qquad (a)$$

$$y_b = \frac{k[(s + \sigma_0)^2 + \omega_0^2]}{s + \sigma_c} \qquad (b) \quad (7\text{-}116)$$

$$y_c = k \frac{1 + a}{a} k_{12} \frac{s}{s + \sigma_c} = \frac{y_a}{a} \qquad (c)$$

Starting with $y(s)$, which is the short-circuit admittance of the entire network, we subtract an admittance y_a such that the remaining admittance has a zero at s_0. Thus

$$y_1(s_0) = y(s_0) - y_a(s_0) = y(s_0) - y_{11c}(s_0) = 0 \qquad (7\text{-}117)$$

The remainder function is $y_1 = y - y_a$. From the reciprocal of this function we now subtract $1/y_b = 1/-y_{12c}$, leaving an impedance z_2.

$$z_2 = \frac{1}{y - y_a} + \frac{1}{y_{12c}} = \frac{y - y_{11c}}{y_{12c}(y - y_a)} \qquad (a)$$
$$\qquad\qquad\qquad\qquad\qquad\qquad\qquad\qquad (7\text{-}118)$$
$$y_2 = \frac{y_{12c}(y - y_a)}{y - y_{11c}} \qquad (b)$$

Since the pair of complex zeros was completely removed in the y_b branch, y_2 is not zero at $s = s_0$. But both y_{12c} and $y - y_a$, which appear in the numerator of the last equation, have the factor $s - s_0$. Hence the denominator must have this factor twice, which means the derivative of the denominator evaluated at $s = s_0$ is also zero. Thus

$$y'(s_0) - y'_{11c}(s_0) = 0 \qquad (7\text{-}119)$$

where the primes indicate differentiation. These two conditions, Eqs. (7-117) and (7-119), must be satisfied simultaneously if the contemplated procedure is to be successfully used.

In their present form these conditions are not easy to interpret. Hence one of our objectives will be to express these equations in a form involving the parameters of the zero-producing section and the poles and residues of the original driving-point function. To this end, let us write

$$y(s_0) = g_0 + jb_0$$
$$y'(s_0) = g_0' + jb_0' \tag{7-120}$$

Then, using these and Eqs. (7-115) in the condition equations, after considerable manipulation, we shall get

$$g_0 = k(1 + a)\frac{\sigma_0^2 + \omega_0^2 - \sigma_0\sigma_c}{\sigma_c} = k(1 + a)(k_{0c} - \sigma_0) \qquad \text{(a)}$$

$$b_0 = k(1 + a)\omega_0 \qquad \text{(b)}$$

$$g_0' = k\frac{(\sigma_c - \sigma_0)^2 + \omega_0^2 + a[(\sigma_c - \sigma_0)^2 - \omega_0^2]}{(\sigma_c - \sigma_0)^2 + \omega_0^2} \qquad (7\text{-}121)$$

$$= k\left(1 + a - \frac{2a\omega_0^2}{\sigma_c k_{12}}\right) \qquad \text{(c)}$$

$$b_0' = \frac{-2ka\omega_0(\sigma_c - \sigma_0)}{(\sigma_c - \sigma_0)^2 + \omega_0^2} = -\frac{2ak\omega_0(\sigma_c - \sigma_0)}{\sigma_c k_{12}} \qquad \text{(d)}$$

In simplifying these expressions use has been made of Eqs. (7-113). Note that there are only three unknown quantities of the zero-producing section, that is, k, a, and σ_c, which can be varied in order to satisfy these four equations. Hence, for an arbitrarily given $y(s)$ and a given pair of transmission zeros, these equations will probably not be simultaneously satisfied. They will be satisfied only for special forms of $y(s)$. To find the condition on $y(s)$, let us eliminate the unknowns k, a, and σ_c from the right-hand sides. After much manipulation the result will be

$$\frac{g_0}{b_0} = \frac{1 + \dfrac{\omega_0}{\sigma_0}\dfrac{b_0 - \omega_0 g_0'}{\omega_0 b_0'}}{\dfrac{b_0 - \omega_0 g_0'}{\omega_0 b_0'} - \dfrac{\omega_0}{\sigma_0}} \qquad (7\text{-}122)$$

This is a fairly complicated expression, involving the real and the imaginary parts of the driving-point function $y(s)$, and their derivatives, evaluated at the transmission zero $s_0 = \sigma_0 + j\omega_0$. Furthermore, it is still not in a very useful form. It would be much more useful to have an expression involving the poles and the residues at the poles. Suppose we write the partial-fraction expansion of $y(s)$. (We actually expand y/s and then multiply by s.)

$$y(s) = k_\infty s + k_0 + \sum_{i=1}^{n}\frac{k_i s}{s + \sigma_i} \qquad (7\text{-}123)$$

From this we can form the derivative and then identify the quantities g_0, b_0, g_0', and b_0'. Finally, these are substituted into the previous equation.

You can readily appreciate that the algebra will become tremendously complicated. If you carry out the details, you will get the following result:

$$k_\infty \sum_{i=1}^{n} \frac{k_i \sigma_i}{|\sigma_i + s_0|^4} - k_0 \sum_{i=1}^{n} \frac{k_i \sigma_i^2}{\omega_0^2 |\sigma_i + s_0|^4}$$

$$+ \frac{1}{2} \sum_{i=1}^{n} \sum_{j=1}^{n} \frac{k_i k_j (\sigma_i - \sigma_j)^2 (\sigma_i \sigma_j - \omega_0^2)}{|\sigma_i + s_0|^4 |\sigma_j + s_0|^4} = 0 \qquad (7\text{-}124)$$

We have now found a condition involving all the poles of the original driving-point admittance $y(s)$, the residues of y/s at these poles, and the transmission zero which is to be realized by the section. We will refer to this equation as the *condition equation*. If this condition is not satisfied by $y(s)$, then the contemplated procedure will not work. At the moment this appears to be a severe handicap. However, note that the first term in this equation is always positive, the second term is always negative, while the third may be either positive or negative. Suppose that, for a given $y(s)$ with the partial-fraction expansion given in Eq. (7-123), the left-hand side of the equation is negative (and not zero, as it should be to satisfy the equation). Consider reducing the value of k_0. This will make the left-hand side of the equation less negative. It may be that for a small enough value of k_0 the left-hand side will reduce to zero. This means that before removing the zero-producing section we should reduce the constant term in $y(s)$ by removing a shunt-resistance branch. The remaining function will then satisfy the required condition. We shall call this a *preparation* branch since it prepares the function for the removal of a zero-producing section.

The question arises, "Is it always possible to find a preparation branch such that the remaining function will satisfy the required condition?" If this question is to be answered in the affirmative, we should be able to satisfy the condition equation by reducing one or more of the residues of $y(s)$. If the expansion of $y(s)$ contains both k_0 and k_∞, then it will clearly be possible to "prepare" the function by partial removal of one or more poles because the condition equation will contain both positive and negative terms. It remains to consider those cases in which k_0 or k_∞ or both are missing from $y(s)$.

Suppose that $y(s)$ has no pole at infinity ($k_\infty = 0$) and the third term in the equation is negative. Or possibly $k_0 = 0$, and the third term is positive. Then the procedure will be blocked. As an example, suppose that $s_0 = -\frac{1}{2} + j1$ and

$$y(s) = \frac{1}{100} \left(2s + \frac{2s}{s+1} + \frac{s}{s+2} \right) \qquad (7\text{-}125)$$

With these numerical values the condition equation becomes

$$10^{-4}\left[2\left(\frac{2}{\frac{25}{16}}+\frac{2}{\frac{169}{16}}\right)+\frac{1}{2}\left(\frac{4}{\frac{25}{16}\cdot\frac{169}{16}}\right)\right]>0 \qquad (7\text{-}126)$$

Since both terms in the equation are positive, it is impossible to fulfill the required condition by partially removing any of the poles of $y(s)$.

When we were first discussing the zero-shifting technique in Chap. 5 in connection with lossless networks, we found that there was a finite range on the $j\omega$ axis to which no zeros of admittance could be shifted. We are now at a similar impasse. We solved the former problem by inverting and proceeding on an impedance basis; so let us attempt to do similarly now.

In order to proceed on an impedance basis, it will be necessary to derive a condition equation which involves the poles and residues of the impedance $z(s) = 1/y(s)$. The entire previous development must be paralleled. Let us find the z parameters corresponding to the y parameters of Eqs. (7-115), using the z-y relationships given in Table 1-2. The result is

$$z_{12c} = k_z\left(1 + \frac{\sigma_c}{s} - \frac{k_{12}}{s + k_{0c}}\right) \qquad\qquad (a)$$

$$z_{11c} = k_z\left(1 + \frac{\sigma_c}{s} + \frac{1}{a}\frac{k_{12}}{s + k_{0c}}\right) \qquad (b) \quad (7\text{-}127)$$

$$z_{22c} = k_z\left(1 + \frac{\sigma_c}{s} + a\frac{k_{12}}{s + k_{0c}}\right) \qquad\quad (c)$$

where

$$k_z = \frac{a}{(a+1)^2 k k_{12}} \qquad\qquad (7\text{-}128)$$

It is apparent that s times these parameters is the same as the corresponding y's except that the roles of σ_c and k_{0c} have been interchanged and k_z replaces k.

Instead of dealing with the pi section, we now consider the tee equivalent shown in Fig. 7-32. Analogous to Eqs. (7-117) and (7-119), we find

$$z(s_0) - z_{11c}(s_0) = 0 \qquad\qquad (a)$$
$$z'(s_0) - z'_{11c}(s_0) = 0 \qquad\qquad (b) \qquad (7\text{-}129)$$

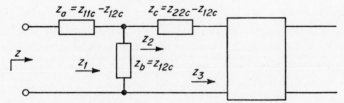

Fig. 7-32. Tee equivalent of zero-producing section.

Equating the real and imaginary parts of the left-hand sides of these to zero, we get four equations analogous to Eqs. (7-121). Again this implies a special form for $z(s)$. If we consider the partial-fraction expansion in Eq. (7-123) to be s times the expansion of $z(s)$ (instead of being s times the expansion of y/s), we will again get the same condition equation, Eq. (7-124). Now, however, the poles are those of $z(s)$. The algebraic details are left for you.

Let us return to the impasse we were facing. If the condition equation cannot be satisfied on an admittance basis because one or the other of the residues k_∞ and k_0 is missing, we invert and deal with $z(s)$. If $y(s)$ has no constant term, for example, this means that it has a zero at $s = 0$. Its reciprocal $z(s)$ will have a pole at $s = 0$ and hence a term k_0/s in its partial-fraction expansion. Consequently the quantity $sz(s)$ will have a constant term.

As an illustration, let us return to the function in Eq. (7-125) and take its reciprocal. We shall get

$$sz(s) = \frac{50(s + 1)(s + 2)}{(s + \frac{3}{2})(s + 3)} = \frac{50}{9}\left(4 + \frac{s}{s + \frac{3}{2}} + \frac{4s}{s + 3}\right) \quad (7\text{-}130)$$

Let us now form the condition equation, but keep k_0 as a parameter. We shall get[†]

$$-10.84k_0 + 4.62 = 0$$

or $$k_0 = 0.426$$

But the constant term in Eq. (7-130) is $200/9$. Hence we must subtract $\frac{200}{9} - 0.426 = 21.8$ from $sz(s)$ in order to have a function which satisfies the condition equation. This means that we remove a series capacitance $C_0 = 1/21.8$ as a preparation branch.

Thus, when the condition equation cannot be satisfied on an admittance basis, we invert and proceed on an impedance basis. One or the other of these will always work. On an impedance basis we remove a tee section as in Fig. 7-32, while on an admittance basis we remove a pi section as in Fig. 7-31. However, these two will be equivalent if we use Eq. (7-128) and interchange k_{0c} and σ_c. Actually, we do not need to construct the pi or the tee—all we need are the values of the parameters k, a, and σ_c. In the next section we shall discuss a method for obtaining realizable zero-producing sections after these quantities have been determined.

At this point let us review what we have done. We started with a given y_{12} and y (which is the given y_{22} or the admittance remaining after any existing negative real transmission zeros are realized). We showed that it is always possible to remove a "preparation" branch, either in parallel or in series, such that the remaining admittance or impedance satisfies the relatively complicated condition given in Eq. (7-124). This permits us to remove a "zero-producing" section whose y parameters are given in Eqs. (7-115).

There are still several jobs to be done before we are finished. (1) We must still show that the solution of Eqs. (7-121) for the quantities k, a, and σ_c leads to positive values. (2) We must find an RC realizable equivalent of the nonrealizable pi section. (3) We must show that the function remaining after the removal of the zero-producing section is positive real and RC.

The first and third of these tasks is left for you to do. Some guides to the first are given in Prob. 7-6, while the third is outlined in Prob. 7-7.

7-10. Zero-producing sections for complex transmission zeros

In this section we shall discuss the second task enumerated in the last section—that of determining a realizable equivalent of the zero-producing section. The y parameters are given in Eqs. (7-115). Since they satisfy the condition given in Eq. (7-114), we can use the Ozaki realization technique. Step 2 in the Ozaki procedure consists in removing any part of the positive part of $-y_{12}$ as a bridging admittance provided that the remaining function satisfies Fialkow's condition. (We have dropped the subscript c from the y parameters of the zero-producing section for simplicity.) What we remove from the positive part should include the entire constant term or the entire pole at infinity in order that the z parameters of the remainder have a noncompact pole at the origin or a noncompact constant term, thus permitting further decomposition. Four possibilities exist:

1. Remove entire pole at infinity.
2. Remove entire pole at infinity, plus a fraction of the constant term.
3. Remove entire constant term.
4. Remove entire constant term, plus a fraction of the pole at infinity.

We shall outline the procedure for the first two of these possibilities and leave the details of the other two to you.

If we remove the entire pole at infinity from the y parameters in Eqs. (7-115) and realize it as a bridging capacitance, the remaining functions will be

$$-y_{12}' = k\,\frac{(2\sigma_0 - \sigma_c)s + k_{0c}\sigma_c}{s + \sigma_c} \qquad \text{(a)}$$

$$y_{11}' = k\left(k_{0c} + a\,\frac{k_{12}s}{s + \sigma_c}\right) \qquad \text{(b)} \quad (7\text{-}131)$$

$$y_{22}' = k\left(k_{0c} + \frac{1}{a}\,\frac{k_{12}s}{s + \sigma_c}\right) \qquad \text{(c)}$$

The first of these equations has been simplified by the use of Eq. (7-113b). The remaining y_{12} will be minimum-phase only if $2\sigma_0 - \sigma_c \geq 0$. Hence the contemplated realization is possible only if this condition is satisfied. The next step is to compute the z parameters of the remainder. The result is

$$z_{12} = \frac{a(2\sigma_0 - \sigma_c)}{k_{0c}k_{12}k(a + 1)^2} + \frac{a\sigma_c}{k_{12}k(a + 1)^2 s} \qquad \text{(a)}$$

$$z_{11} = z_{12} + \frac{1}{kk_{0c}(a + 1)} \qquad \text{(b)} \quad (7\text{-}132)$$

$$z_{22} = z_{12} + \frac{a}{kk_{0c}(a + 1)} \qquad \text{(c)}$$

This set is immediately recognized as the z parameters of a simple tee network. The resulting complete structure is shown in Fig. 7-33.

Consider now the second possibility. Removing part of the constant

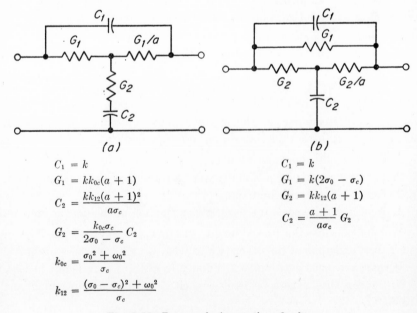

$$
\begin{aligned}
C_1 &= k \\
G_1 &= kk_{0c}(a + 1) \\
C_2 &= \frac{kk_{12}(a + 1)^2}{a\sigma_c} \\
G_2 &= \frac{k_{0c}\sigma_c}{2\sigma_0 - \sigma_c}\,C_2 \\
k_{0c} &= \frac{\sigma_0{}^2 + \omega_0{}^2}{\sigma_c} \\
k_{12} &= \frac{(\sigma_0 - \sigma_c)^2 + \omega_0{}^2}{\sigma_c}
\end{aligned}
$$

$$
\begin{aligned}
C_1 &= k \\
G_1 &= k(2\sigma_0 - \sigma_c) \\
G_2 &= kk_{12}(a + 1) \\
C_2 &= \frac{a + 1}{a\sigma_c}\,G_2
\end{aligned}
$$

Fig. 7-33. Zero-producing section; $2\sigma_0 \geq \sigma_c$.

term as well as the pole at infinity means that there will be an additional element in the bridging network. Hence there would be no purpose in doing this unless there were a possibility of reducing the number of elements required in the remaining tee. We can eliminate the resistance in the shunt branch of the tee if we can cause the z_{12} of the tee to have a zero at infinity. This will be possible if the y_{12} of the tee has a zero at infinity. That is, we subtract from $-y_{12}$ the function $k(s + x)$, leaving

$$y'_{12} = k \left(k_{0c} - x - \frac{k_{12}s}{s + \sigma_c} \right) = k \frac{s(k_{0c} - k_{12} - x) + \sigma_c(k_{0c} - x)}{s + \sigma_c} \quad (7\text{-}133)$$

For this function to have a zero at infinity, x must have the value $k_{0c} - k_{12} = 2\sigma_0 - \sigma_c$. Since kx is the value of a bridging conductance, it must be positive, which leads to the same condition as before, $2\sigma_0 - \sigma_c \geq 0$.

The remaining y parameters become

$$y'_{12} = \frac{kk_{12}\sigma_c}{s + \sigma_c} \qquad\qquad\qquad\qquad\qquad\qquad\qquad \text{(a)}$$

$$y'_{11} = k \left(k_{12} + a \frac{k_{12}s}{s + \sigma_c} \right) = \frac{kk_{12}}{s + \sigma_c} [s(a + 1) + \sigma_c] \quad \text{(b)} \quad (7\text{-}134)$$

$$y'_{22} = k \left(k_{12} + \frac{1}{a} \frac{k_{12}s}{s + \sigma_c} \right) = \frac{kk_{12}}{s + \sigma_c} \left(s \frac{a + 1}{a} + \sigma_c \right) \quad \text{(c)}$$

The corresponding z parameters will be

$$z'_{12} = \frac{a\sigma_c}{kk_{12}(a + 1)^2 s} \qquad\qquad\qquad\qquad\qquad \text{(a)}$$

$$z'_{11} = z'_{12} + \frac{1}{kk_{12}(a + 1)} \qquad\qquad\qquad\qquad \text{(b)} \quad (7\text{-}135)$$

$$z'_{22} = z'_{12} + \frac{a}{kk_{12}(a + 1)} \qquad\qquad\qquad\qquad \text{(c)}$$

As anticipated, these are the parameters of a tee network with single elements in the branches. The complete realization is shown in Fig. 7-33(b).

The remaining two possibilities can also be handled in this fashion. For these two cases we find that the condition which must be satisfied is $2\sigma_0\sigma_c \geq \sigma_0^2 + \omega_0^2$. Again we find two bridged-tee realizations. These are shown in Fig. 7-34.

Now suppose neither of the conditions $2\sigma_0 \geq \sigma_c$ and $2\sigma_0 \geq (\sigma_0^2 + \omega_0^2)/\sigma_c$ are satisfied. Then the Ozaki separation theorem can be employed, provided that $\sigma_0 \geq 0$, that is, provided that the transmission zero is in the left half plane or on the $j\omega$ axis. The present situation corresponds to case B of the Ozaki realization, to which Eqs. (7-32) and (7-33) apply. In the

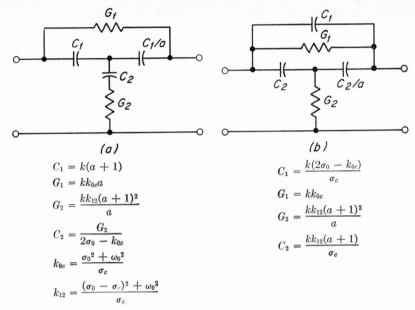

$$C_1 = k(a + 1)$$
$$G_1 = kk_{0c}a$$
$$G_2 = \frac{kk_{12}(a + 1)^2}{a}$$
$$C_2 = \frac{G_2}{2\sigma_0 - k_{0c}}$$
$$k_{0c} = \frac{\sigma_0{}^2 + \omega_0{}^2}{\sigma_c}$$
$$k_{12} = \frac{(\sigma_0 - \sigma_c)^2 + \omega_0{}^2}{\sigma_c}$$

$$C_1 = \frac{k(2\sigma_0 - k_{0c})}{\sigma_c}$$
$$G_1 = kk_{0c}$$
$$G_2 = \frac{kk_{12}(a + 1)^2}{a}$$
$$C_2 = \frac{kk_{12}(a + 1)}{\sigma_c}$$

Fig. 7-34. Zero-producing section; $2\sigma_0 \geq (\sigma_0^2 + \omega_0^2)/\sigma_c$.

notation of those equations we must determine which of the two quantities $K_0 = \sigma_0^2 + \omega_0^2$ and $K_1 = (\sigma_c - \sigma_0)^2 + \omega_0^2$ is smaller. In the present situation $\sigma_c > 2\sigma_0$ so that $\sigma_c - \sigma_0 > \sigma_0$. Hence K_0 is the smaller of the two constants. This means that in Eqs. (7-32) we should use the values $\sigma_m = 0$ and $K = \sigma_0^2 + \omega_0^2 = \sigma_c k_{0c}$. The two components into which y_{12} will be separated become

$$-y_{12a} = \frac{ks(s + 2\sigma_0)}{s + \sigma_c} = k\left(s - \frac{(\sigma_c - 2\sigma_0)s}{s + \sigma_c}\right) \quad \text{(a)}$$
$$\qquad\qquad\qquad\qquad\qquad\qquad\qquad\qquad\qquad (7\text{-}136)$$
$$-y_{12b} = \frac{k\sigma_c k_{0c}}{s + \sigma_c} = kk_{0c}\left(1 - \frac{s}{s + \sigma_c}\right) \quad \text{(b)}$$

Finally, apportioning the y_{11} and y_{22} functions between the two components in the only way possible, the y parameters of the two components become

$$-y_{12a} = k\left[s - \frac{(\sigma_c - 2\sigma_0)s}{s + \sigma_c}\right] = \frac{ks(s + 2\sigma_0)}{s + \sigma_c} \quad \text{(a)}$$

$$y_{11a} = k\left[s + a\frac{(\sigma_c - 2\sigma_0)s}{s + \sigma_c}\right] = \frac{ks[s + \sigma_c(a + 1) - 2a\sigma_0]}{s + \sigma_c} \quad \text{(b)} \quad (7\text{-}137)$$

$$y_{22a} = k\left[s + \frac{1}{a}\frac{(\sigma_c - 2\sigma_0)s}{s + \sigma_c}\right] = \frac{ks\left(s + \sigma_c\dfrac{a + 1}{a} - \dfrac{2\sigma_0}{a}\right)}{s + \sigma_c} \quad \text{(c)}$$

and

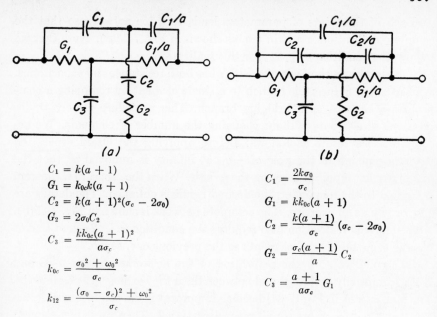

$$C_1 = k(a + 1)$$
$$G_1 = k_{0c}k(a + 1)$$
$$C_2 = k(a + 1)^2(\sigma_c - 2\sigma_0)$$
$$G_2 = 2\sigma_0 C_2$$
$$C_3 = \frac{kk_{0c}(a + 1)^2}{a\sigma_c}$$
$$k_{0c} = \frac{\sigma_0{}^2 + \omega_0{}^2}{\sigma_c}$$
$$k_{12} = \frac{(\sigma_0 - \sigma_c)^2 + \omega_0{}^2}{\sigma_c}$$

$$C_1 = \frac{2k\sigma_0}{\sigma_c}$$
$$G_1 = kk_{0c}(a + 1)$$
$$C_2 = \frac{k(a + 1)}{\sigma_c}(\sigma_c - 2\sigma_0)$$
$$G_2 = \frac{\sigma_c(a + 1)}{a}C_2$$
$$C_3 = \frac{a + 1}{a\sigma_c}G_1$$

Fig. 7-35. Zero-producing section; $2\sigma_0 \geq \sigma_c$.

$$-y_{12b} = kk_{0c}\left(1 - \frac{s}{s + \sigma_c}\right) = \frac{k\sigma_c k_{0c}}{s + \sigma_c} \qquad \text{(a)}$$

$$y_{11b} = kk_{0c}\left(1 + a\frac{s}{s + \sigma_c}\right) = kk_{0c}\frac{s(a + 1) + \sigma_c}{s + \sigma_c} \qquad \text{(b)} \quad \text{(7-138)}$$

$$y_{22b} = kk_{0c}\left(1 + \frac{1}{a}\frac{s}{s + \sigma_c}\right) = kk_{0c}\frac{s\dfrac{a + 1}{a} + \sigma_c}{s + \sigma_c} \qquad \text{(c)}$$

The corresponding z parameters are found to be

$$z_{12a} = \frac{a}{k(a + 1)^2(\sigma_c - 2\sigma_0)} + \frac{2\sigma_0 a}{k(a + 1)^2(\sigma_c - 2\sigma_0)s} \qquad \text{(a)}$$

$$z_{11a} = z_{12a} + \frac{1}{k(a + 1)s} \qquad \text{(b)} \quad \text{(7-139)}$$

$$z_{22a} = z_{12a} + \frac{a}{k(a + 1)s} \qquad \text{(c)}$$

and $$z_{12b} = \frac{a\sigma_c}{kk_{0c}(a + 1)^2 s} \qquad \text{(a)}$$

$$z_{11b} = z_{12b} + \frac{1}{kk_{0c}(a + 1)} \qquad \text{(b)} \quad \text{(7-140)}$$

$$z_{22b} = z_{12b} + \frac{a}{kk_{0c}(a + 1)} \qquad \text{(c)}$$

Each of these sets of parameters leads to a tee network so that the complete realization is a twin tee, as shown in Fig. 7-35(a). Note that we require the condition $\sigma_c \geq 2\sigma_0$ for this realization.

The shunt branch of one of the tee's has both resistance and capacitance. We can again reduce this branch to a single element by removing a compensating element as a bridging branch. This procedure merely trades positions of elements without changing the number of elements. We accomplish this result as follows: Before applying the Ozaki separation theorem, enough of the pole of $-y_{12}$ at infinity is removed so that the remainder has a pair of zeros on the $j\omega$ axis. When the separation theorem is applied to the remainder, the desired result is obtained. The details are left for you as an exercise. The complete network is shown in Fig. 7-35(b). Note that this realization also requires the condition $\sigma_c \geq 2\sigma_0$ and that it has the same number of elements as the previous one, seven.

The conditions for the realization of the networks of Figs. 7-33 and 7-35 are mutually exclusive, and between them they exhaust all possibilities. The realizations in Eq. (7-34) become important if the conditions $\sigma_c \geq 2\sigma_0$ and $2\sigma_0\sigma_c \geq \sigma_0^2 + \omega_0^2$ are simultaneously satisfied. Then these five-element networks can be used instead of the seven-element networks in Fig. 7-35.

7-11. Dasher synthesis—completed

Let us now pause and review our progress in obtaining a cascade realization of RC two-ports. We start with a transfer function having poles exclusively on the negative real axis and no zeros in the right half plane. This may be considered as either the open-circuit voltage transfer ratio $T_{12}(s)$ or the transfer impedance $Z_{12}(s)$ or transfer admittance $Y_{12}(s)$ with a resistance load. In any case, from the given function, we next derive two of the three open-circuit or short-circuit parameters, one transfer and one driving-point. If there are any transmission zeros on the negative real axis, these are realized by partially developing the driving-point function in a ladder network. We are then left with two functions, say, y_{22} and y_{12}, where y_{22} is an RC admittance and y_{12} has complex zeros only, none of which lie in the right half plane.

The next step is to remove a shunt admittance y_0 from y_{22} or a series impedance z_0 from the reciprocal $1/y_{22}$ such that the remaining admittance or impedance satisfies the rather complicated condition given in Eq. (7-124). One or the other of these will always be possible. A zero-producing section realizing a pair of conjugate transmission zeros is now removed. This takes one of the forms of Figs. 7-33, 7-34, or 7-35 depending on the location of the realized zeros. In order to do this, it is necessary to determine the values of the quantities k, a, and σ_c. Of course, these values may be determined by the simultaneous solution of Eqs. (7-120) or (7-121). However, they are more easily determined as follows:

Let y be the admittance remaining after the preparation section is removed. Thinking in terms of the pi equivalent of the zero-producing section shown in Fig. 7-31, we must now determine the first shunt branch $y_a(s)$. Looking at Eq. (7-116a), we see that this requires a knowledge of k, a, k_{12}, and σ_c. Actually, all we need are σ_c and the product $k(1 + a)$ because k_{12} can be computed from Eq. (7-113) once σ_c is established. The desired quantities can be calculated from the first two of Eqs. (7-121). The result is

$$k(1 + a) = \frac{b_0}{\omega_0} \qquad \text{(a)}$$

$$\sigma_c = \frac{\sigma_0^2 + \omega_0^2}{\sigma_0 + \omega_0 g_0/b_0} \qquad \text{(b)}$$

$$(7\text{-}141)$$

Thus y_a is completely determined. Knowing y_a, we now form $y_1 = y - y_a$. This should have a zero at the desired transmission zero so that its reciprocal should have a pole there. From the reciprocal we now subtract $z_b = 1/y_b$. At this stage all parameters in z_b are known except k, and this can now be determined by requiring that the remaining admittance, y_2, have no zero at the transmission zero. Then Eqs. (7-141) will give the value of a, and all the parameters of the zero-producing section will be known. The zero-producing section can now be realized. However, we still need to subtract the second shunt admittance of the pi, $y_c = y_a/a$, in order to have the remainder function available for the removal of the rest of the transmission zeros.

After one zero-producing section is removed, the remaining function is again "prepared" by the removal of a shunt branch or a series branch. Another zero-producing section can now be removed, and this procedure can be repeated until all the transmission zeros are realized.

We shall now illustrate the Dasher synthesis with a numerical example. Let us again synthesize the transfer admittance function for which we have already obtained a Fialkow-Gerst and a parallel-ladders realization. The two y parameters which were given in Eqs. (7-104) are repeated here.

$$y_{22} = \frac{(2s + 1)(s + 2)}{(s + 1)(s + 3)} = \frac{2}{3} + \frac{s/2}{s + 1} + \frac{5s/6}{s + 3} \qquad \text{(a)}$$

$$-y_{12} = K \frac{s^2 + 2s + 2}{(s + 1)(s + 3)} \qquad \text{(b)}$$

$$(7\text{-}142)$$

There are a pair of conjugate left-half-plane transmission zeros and no real zeros, and so we immediately proceed with the Dasher synthesis.

In the first step we investigate the possibility of subtracting a shunt admittance y_0 such that the remaining admittance, $y = y_{22} - y_0$, satisfies the condition equation, Eq. (7-124). The partial-fraction expansion of y must have the same poles as y_{22}, with residues at most equal to the corresponding residues of y_{22}. Let us try

$$y = k_0 + \frac{s/2}{s+1} + \frac{5s/6}{s+3} \qquad (7\text{-}143)$$

That is, we contemplate removing a shunt conductance $y_0 = \frac{2}{3} - k_0$. We have no assurance that this is possible, but if Eq. (7-124) can be satisfied with a value of k_0 less than $\frac{2}{3}$, the procedure will be possible. In the present case Eq. (7-124) is relatively easy to evaluate, and we obtain the result

$$-\frac{4k_0}{5} + \frac{2}{15} = 0 \quad \text{or} \quad k_0 = \frac{1}{6}$$

Thus removal of a shunt conductance $\frac{2}{3} - \frac{1}{6} = \frac{1}{2}$ will "prepare" the way for a realization. With the determined value of k_0 substituted into Eq. (7-143) we get

$$y = \frac{1}{6} + \frac{s/2}{s+1} + \frac{5s/6}{s+3} = \frac{3s^2 + 6s + 1}{2(s+1)(s+3)}$$

The next step is to find the value of this admittance at the transmission zero. In the present case $\sigma_0 = \omega_0 = 1$. Thus

$$y(s_0) = g_0 + jb_0 = \tfrac{1}{2} + j$$

With these values we find σ_c and $k(1 + a)$ from Eqs. (7-141) and k_{12} from Eqs. (7-113).

$$\sigma_c = \tfrac{4}{3}$$
$$k(1 + a) = 1 \qquad (7\text{-}144)$$
$$k_{12} = \tfrac{5}{6}$$

Substituting these values into Eqs. (7-116), we find y_a to be

$$y_a = \frac{5}{6} \frac{s}{s + \frac{4}{3}} \qquad (7\text{-}145)$$

The next step is to subtract y_a from y. The result of this operation is

$$y_1 = y - y_a = \frac{(2s+1)(s^2 + 2s + 2)}{3(s+1)(s+3)(s+\frac{4}{3})} \qquad (7\text{-}146)$$

This has the factor $s^2 + 2s + 2$, as it should. Now we invert and subtract the shunt arm of the pi, $z_b = -1/y_{12c}$. The result is

$$z_2 = z_1 - z_b = \frac{3(s+\frac{4}{3})[s^2 + (4 - 2/3k)s + (3 - 1/3k)]}{(2s+1)(s^2 + 2s + 2)} \qquad (7\text{-}147)$$

Since z_b must completely remove the complex poles, the quadratic factor in the numerator must equal $s^2 + 2s + 2$ in order to cancel with the denominator. This criterion fixes k to be $1/3$. Knowing k, we now find a from the product $k(1 + a)$ given in Eq. (7-144). This completes the evaluation of all the parameters of the zero-producing section. They are collected here.

$$\sigma_0 = 1 \qquad \sigma_c = \tfrac{4}{3}$$
$$\omega_0 = 1 \qquad k = \tfrac{1}{3}$$
$$a = 2$$

We see that the conditions $2\sigma_0 > \sigma_c$ and $2\sigma_0 > (\sigma_0^2 + \omega_0^2)/\sigma_c$ are both satisfied; so any one of the sections in Figs. 7-33 and 7-34 can be used. However, those in Fig. 7-33 are preferable since they have one reactive element fewer.

Finally we take the reciprocal of z_2 and subtract $y_c = y_a/a$. The result is

$$y_3 = y_2 - y_c = \frac{2s + 1}{3(s + \tfrac{4}{3})} - \frac{5}{12}\frac{s}{s + \tfrac{4}{3}} = \frac{1}{4} \qquad (7\text{-}148)$$

The complete realization is shown in Fig. 7-36. The values given are those of resistance and capacitance.

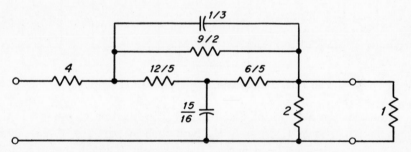

Fig. 7-36. Cascade realization of numerical example.

The value of the gain constant which is achieved by the realization can be obtained by finding the transfer admittance of the network at zero frequency. It is found to be $K = 1/4$.

On comparing the cascade realization with the parallel ladders and the tree realizations for this example, we find an improvement over both of these in the number of elements used but a substantial reduction in the gain constant. We should not, however, form general conclusions regarding these matters from the results of a single example.

This example completes the discussion of Dasher's cascade realization technique. The mechanics of the procedure are straightforward, although establishing the validity of the results involves considerable effort. When the given functions are more complicated than a ratio of quadratics, the removal of a preparation section may involve some trial and error and considerable computation.

A variation of the general procedure is possible when the given functions are no more complicated than a ratio of quadratics. This variation considerably simplifies the computational work. The procedure is outlined in Prob. 7-9.

7-12. Cascade synthesis—network partitioning

Up to the present time the starting point of our synthesis has been the transfer impedance $Z_{12}(s)$ or transfer admittance $Y_{12}(s)$ of a resistance-terminated RC network or the open-circuit voltage ratio $T_{12}(s)$. From these we have obtained z_{12} and z_{22} or y_{12} and y_{22}, respectively, which are the parameters of the RC network without the termination.

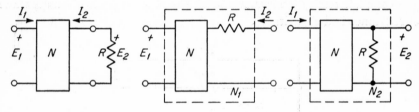

Fig. 7-37. Termination, separate or part of network.

Consider the network of Fig. 7-37(a). The function of interest is the transfer admittance $Y_{12}(s) = I_2/E_1$. Now look at part (b) of the figure. The resistance is considered part of the network. If the output terminals of network N_1 are short-circuited, the current I_2 will be the same as that of the first network. Thus the short-circuit transfer admittance of the second network is the same as the transfer admittance (not short circuit) of the first. If $Y_{12}(s)$ is specified for the terminated network (a), we can treat it as the short-circuit admittance of the network of (b), provided that we ensure the appearance of a series resistance in the output lead. Then, simply short-circuiting this network and taking the output across the resistance R, we arrive at the desired result.

In order to carry out a realization, we must choose a driving-point function, say, y_{22} to go with the given transfer function. This must be an RC admittance function having the same poles as y_{12}. In addition, it must be so chosen that the resistance R will be present in the realization. This will be guaranteed if we choose y_{22} to have no pole at infinity $[y_{22}(\infty) = k_0]$. The reciprocal of y_{22} will then have a nonzero value at infinity, and any fraction of this can be removed as a series resistance before proceeding with the rest of the realization. It is always possible to choose y_{22} with no pole at infinity because the given transfer function cannot have a pole at infinity.

A similar result is possible if the given function is the transfer impedance $Z_{12}(s)$ corresponding to the network in Fig. 7-37(a). If we now consider the termination as part of the network, as in Fig. 7-37(c), then the open-circuit transfer impedance of this network will equal the function $Z_{12}(s)$ for the previous network. Thus we may treat a given transfer impedance as the open-circuit transfer impedance of the network of Fig. 7-37(c) provided that in the realization we ensure the appearance of a shunt resistance across the output. A driving-point impedance, say z_{22}, must be chosen in such a way that this requirement is satisfied. One having no pole at $s = 0$ will serve, since its reciprocal will have a nonzero value at the origin. Any fraction of this can be removed as a shunt resistance before continuing the realization.

The procedure we have just outlined constitutes an alternative method of procedure for the synthesis of the transfer impedance or transfer admittance of a terminated two-port. It does not normally offer any outstanding advantage over our first method of obtaining z or y parameters from the given function. The major difficulty in the realization techniques that we have discussed is one of computation, especially when the functions involved are of high order. Any device that will reduce the computational labor would be very useful. The network-partitioning theorems (see Prob. 1-10) afford just such a device.

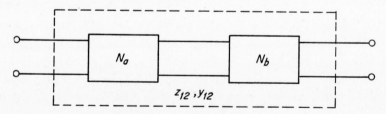

Fig. 7-38. Network partitioning.

Consider Fig. 7-38, which shows a network composed of the cascade connection of two subnetworks. The over-all z_{12} or y_{12} parameters may be expressed in terms of the parameters of the subnetworks as follows:

$$z_{12} = \frac{z_{12a} z_{12b}}{z_{11b} + z_{22a}} \qquad \text{(a)}$$

$$\qquad\qquad\qquad\qquad\qquad (7\text{-}149)$$

$$y_{12} = -\frac{y_{12a} y_{12b}}{y_{11b} + y_{22a}} \qquad \text{(b)}$$

(These expressions can be easily established by the use of Thévenin's theorem.) If only y_{12} or only z_{12} is specified, we can use these expressions to find the parameters of the two subnetworks, thus reducing the problem to two simpler problems. This is done in the following way:

Suppose that we are given $z_{12} = P/Q$, where P and Q are high-order polynomials. We can write the numerator as the product of two polynomials P_a and P_b by assigning some of the numerator factors to P_a and the rest to P_b. We now divide both numerator and denominator by a polynomial which we can also write as the product of two polynomials. Thus formally we have

$$z_{12} = \frac{P}{Q} = \frac{P_a P_b}{Q} = \frac{(P_a/Q_a)\,(P_b/Q_b)}{Q/Q_a Q_b} \qquad (7\text{-}150)$$

Comparing this with the expression for z_{12} in the previous equation, we can identify z_{12a} and z_{12b} immediately, but the rational function $Q/Q_a Q_b$ gives us only the sum $z_{11b} + z_{22a}$. The fact that this last must be an RC impedance function puts the only restriction on the polynomial $Q_a Q_b$. In order to find z_{11b} and z_{22a} individually, we expand $Q/Q_a Q_b$ in partial fractions. We then assign the terms in the expansion to z_{11b} or z_{22a} as dictated by the poles of z_{12a} and z_{12b}. If these two have any common poles, we must split the term corresponding to that pole between z_{11b} and z_{22a}.

Normally, however, the prescribed function is not z_{12} alone or y_{12} alone, but the transfer function of the terminated two-port. Nevertheless, we can still use the partitioning theorem by availing ourselves of the ideas presented in the first part of this section. Thus suppose that the given function is the transfer admittance Y_{12} of the terminated network of Fig. 7-37(a). We can consider this to be the y_{12} function of the network of Fig. 7-37(b) and use the procedure just outlined to find the y parameters of the two cascaded subnetworks which are to constitute the realization. Now we must form y_{11b} from the sum $y_{11b} + y_{22a}$ in such a way that a resistance at the output is guaranteed. This will be the case if y_{11b} has no pole at infinity.

As an illustration, consider the following transfer-admittance function of a resistance-terminated RC two-port:

$$-Y_{12}(s) = K\frac{(s^2 + s + 3)(s^2 + 2s + 2)}{(s + 2)(s + 4)(s^2 + \frac{25}{3}s + 6)} \qquad (7\text{-}151)$$

There are two pairs of complex transmission zeros. Considering this function to be the negative short-circuit transfer admittance of the modified network having a series resistance in the output lead, we can apply Eqs. (7-149). We need to divide numerator and denominator of the given function by a polynomial whose zeros alternate with the zeros of the denominator. This must be of the third or fourth degree. An acceptable polynomial would be $(s + 1)(s + 3)(s + 5)$. Thus we can write

$$-Y_{12}(s) = K\frac{\dfrac{(s^2 + s + 3)(s^2 + 2s + 2)}{(s + 1)(s + 3)(s + 5)}}{\dfrac{(s + 2)(s + 4)(s^2 + 25s/3 + 6)}{(s + 1)(s + 3)(s + 5)}} \qquad (7\text{-}152)$$

In order to assign the correct factors to the parameters of the a and b networks, note that we require y_{11b} to be regular at infinity. This means that y_{12b} must also be regular at infinity. Hence, by arbitrarily assigning poles, we can write

$$-y_{12a} = K_a\frac{s^2 + s + 3}{s + 5} \qquad (a)$$

$$\qquad\qquad\qquad\qquad\qquad\qquad\qquad\qquad\qquad (7\text{-}153)$$

$$-y_{12b} = K_b\frac{s^2 + 2s + 2}{(s + 1)(s + 3)} \qquad (b)$$

where $K_a K_b = K$. The next step is to make a partial-fraction expansion of the denominator of Eq. (7-152). When we do this, we obtain

$$y_{11b} + y_{22a} = s + \frac{48}{15} + \frac{\frac{1}{2}s}{s + 1} + \frac{\frac{5}{6}s}{s + 3} + \frac{\frac{4}{5}s}{s + 5} \qquad (7\text{-}154)$$

All the terms in this equation can now be uniquely assigned to y_{11b} or y_{22a} except for the constant term. Since both y_{12a} and y_{12b} have a constant term in their expansion, both y_{22a} and y_{11b} must also have a constant term. Hence the term $48/15$ in Eq. (7-154) must be shared by both. The exact amount assigned to each is arbitrary. Thus, if we assign $2/3$ to y_{11b}, we shall get

$$y_{22a} = s + \frac{38}{15} + \frac{\frac{4}{5}s}{s + 5} = \frac{s^2 + \frac{25}{3}s + \frac{38}{3}}{s + 5} \qquad (a)$$

$$\qquad\qquad\qquad\qquad\qquad\qquad\qquad\qquad\qquad (7\text{-}155)$$

$$y_{11b} = \frac{2}{3} + \frac{\frac{1}{2}s}{s + 1} + \frac{\frac{5}{6}s}{s + 3} = \frac{(2s + 1)(s + 2)}{(s + 1)(s + 3)} \qquad (b)$$

Each of the two subnetworks can now be realized by any one of the synthesis procedures we have discussed in this chapter, except that the parallel-ladders realization cannot be used for the N_b network since this realization will not give the desired series resistance in the output lead. If we compare the y parameters of the N_b network with those of the numerical example given in Eqs. (7-142), we shall find that they are identical, except that y_{22} in that example is here replaced by y_{11}. (As you undoubtedly suspect, this was by design.) Thus the realization of the N_b network will be the same as in Fig. 7-36, but with the termination absent and with the network inverted so that the one and two ends are interchanged. The desired series resistance in the output lead is in evidence. The remainder of the realization is left to you as an exercise.

PROBLEMS

7-1. It was shown (Prob. 2-7) that, if $P(s)$ is a polynomial with simple negative real zeros only, then its derivative $P'(s)$ is also such a polynomial whose zeros alternate with those of $P(s)$. Using this information, obtain a decomposition of the denominator polynomial $P(s)$ of an RC transfer admittance function into two polynomials whose ratio is a realizable y_{22} function.

7-2. Obtain a realization of the functions given in Eqs. (7-40) by decomposing the factor $s + 4$ and proceeding according to Ozaki's method. Compare the complexity of the network with the realizations in Fig. 7-9.

7-3. Obtain the realization shown in Fig. 7-10, starting from the short-circuit parameters given in Eqs. (7-43).

7-4. The following y parameters of an RC two-port are specified:

$$-y_{12} = \frac{(s^2 + 1)(s^2 + s + 1)}{(s + 1)(s + 2)(s + 3)}$$

$$y_{11} = \frac{6s^4 + 343s^3 + 1092s^2 + 773s + 6}{6(s + 1)(s + 2)(s + 3)}$$

$$y_{22} = \frac{36s^4 + 533s^3 + 1572s^2 + 1183s + 36}{36(s + 1)(s + 2)(s + 3)}$$

Obtain an unbalanced realization, using the Ozaki method.

7-5. Obtain an alternate realization for the functions given in Eqs. (7-99).

7-6. Using Eqs. (7-121), solve for the parameters k, a, and σ_c of the zero-producing section in the Dasher synthesis procedure. Show that these are positive, finite, and nonzero. To show that σ_c is positive, make use of the results of Prob. 3-22. To show that a is positive, use a bilinear transformation

$$W = \frac{1 - a}{1 + a}$$

which maps positive real values of a onto the real W axis between -1 and $+1$, the extremities corresponding to $a = 0$ and infinity. The problem is reduced to showing that $W \neq \pm 1$. Use the results of Prob. 2-12.

7-7. Starting with an RC admittance function $y(s)$, show that removal of a Dasher section realizing a pair of complex transmission zeros leaves a remainder which is a realizable RC admittance. Use the notation of Fig. 7-31 in the text, and let the parameters of the section be given by Eqs. (7-115). It will be useful to sketch $y(\sigma)$ as well as the remaining functions after each branch of the pi is removed. Note that $y_1 = y - y_a$ has only one pair of complex zeros, the rest being all real and lying between the original poles of y, which are also poles of y_1. Show that the residue of $z_1 = 1/y_1$ at its complex pole $s = s_0$ is equal to the residue of $z_b = -1/y_{12c}$ so that removal of z_b from z_1 leaves an RC remainder.

7-8. Consider the lattice shown in Fig. P 7-8. This is the same as the lattice treated in Prob. 5-2, with R_1 and R_2 replacing L_1 and L_2, respectively. (a) From the results of that problem write the y parameters of the RC lattice.

(b) Draw the bridged-tee and twin-tee equivalents of the RC lattice from the corresponding equivalents of the LC lattice.

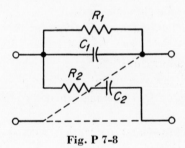

Fig. P 7-8

7-9. It is desired to obtain a Dasher realization when two functions y_{11} and $-y_{12}$ are given, where y_{11} is a ratio of two quadratics and y_{12} has a pair of complex zeros $-\sigma_0 \pm j\omega_0$. (a) Show that removal of a suitable constant from $1/y_{11}$ will leave a remainder y'_{11} which is a ratio of a quadratic to a linear factor.

(b) Next show that the constant term in the numerator of y'_{11}, which is equal to the product of its zeros, can be made equal to $\sigma_0^2 + \omega_0^2$ by partial removal of either the pole at infinity or the zero-frequency value.

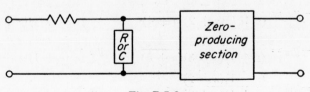

Fig. P 7-9

(c) Compare the remainder function with the general expression for y_{11c}, thus showing that it will qualify as the y_{11} function of a zero-producing section. The complete realization will take on the form shown in Fig. P 7-9. Note that there is no series resistance in the output lead.

7-10. Each of the following functions is the transfer admittance of an *RC* network with a resistance load:

1. $$-Y_{12}(s) = K\frac{s^2 + 1}{(s + \frac{1}{2})(s + 2)(s + 5)}$$

2. $$-Y_{12}(s) = K\frac{s^2 + 2s + 2}{(s + 1)(s + 3)(s + 5)(s + 7)}$$

3. $$-Y_{12}(s) = K\frac{(s^2 + s + 2)(s^2 + s + 3)}{(s + \frac{1}{2})(s + 2)(s + 4)(s + 6)}$$

(a) Obtain a symmetrical lattice realization for each function, with the maximum possible gain constant. Find an unbalanced equivalent of each lattice.

(b) Obtain an unbalanced symmetrical realization by the Ozaki procedure, using the same gain constant.

(c) Obtain a parallel-ladders realization for each function. Compute the gain constant achieved.

(d) Obtain a cascade realization by the Dasher procedure, and again compute the achieved gain constant.

(e) Use the network-partitioning theorem to obtain a cascade realization.

(f) Obtain a Fialkow-Gerst realization with the maximum possible gain constant.

(g) Tabulate the number of elements and gain constants for each of these realizations.

7-11. The following sets of nonminimum-phase y parameters are given. Obtain a symmetrical lattice and a Fialkow-Gerst realization. Also obtain a parallel-ladders realization where possible. Establish the value of the gain constant in each case.

(a) $\quad -y_{12} = K\dfrac{s^2 - 2s + 3}{(s + 2)(s + 4)(s + 5)} \qquad y_{22} = \dfrac{(s + 1)(s + 3)(s + \frac{9}{2})}{(s + 2)(s + 4)(s + 5)}$

(b) $\quad -y_{12} = \dfrac{1 - s^2}{(s + \frac{1}{2})(s + 2)(s + 4)} \qquad y_{22} = \dfrac{s(s + 1)(s + 3)}{(s + \frac{1}{2})(s + 2)(s + 4)}$

(c) $\quad -y_{12} = \dfrac{(s^2 - 2)\frac{3}{4}}{(s + 1)(s + 3)(s + 5)} \qquad y_{22} = \dfrac{(s + \frac{1}{3})(s + 2)(s + 4)}{(s + 1)(s + 3)(s + 5)}$

(d) $\quad -y_{12} = \dfrac{(s - 1)(s - 2)}{(s + 1)(s + 2)} \qquad y_{22} = 1$

7-12. When an RC transfer function $F(s)$ is prescribed, it is always possible to obtain a symmetrical realization by accepting a low enough gain constant. Within this framework it is possible to achieve the largest gain constant by suitably choosing the poles, as demonstrated in Sec. 7-4. Now, contemplate a realization for which the y parameters satisfy the condition.

$$\frac{y_{11} + y_{12}}{y_{22} + y_{12}} = a$$

in which a is a positive constant. For such a realization show that the conditions

$$|F(\sigma_i)| \leq 1 \qquad |F| > 0$$
$$|F(\sigma_i)| \leq a \qquad |F| < 0$$

must be satisfied. Here σ_i are the poles of the y parameters. Hence show that, for minimum-phase transfer functions, a larger gain constant can be achieved by the contemplated realization whenever the largest peak of $|F(\sigma)|$ between its poles falls at a negative value of $F(\sigma)$.

In the numerical example of Eq. (7-54) the maximum gain constant for a symmetrical realization was found to be $K = 6/10$. Obtain a realization in the form contemplated here, with a gain constant $K = 9/10$ and with the same number of elements.

7-13. Several synthesis techniques were developed in this chapter which apply equally well to the case of lossless coupling networks. Show how the Ozaki, the Fialkow-Gerst, and the Dasher synthesis procedures can be applied to LC networks.

7-14. Carry out the details of the Fialkow-Gerst realization shown in Fig. 7-23 starting with the transfer function given in Eq. (7-95).

7-15. Starting from the short-circuit parameters given in Eqs. (7-99), obtain the ladder network shown in Fig. 7-27(b).

7-16. In Sec. 7-4 when discussing the procedure for choosing poles of the z or y parameters for the purpose of maximizing the gain constant for a symmetrical realization, it was stated that Fialkow's condition will be automatically satisfied. Show this statement to be true.

7-17. Derive the Dasher condition given in Eq. (7-124) starting from Eqs. (7-122) and (7-123).

7-18. Repeat the previous problem starting from Eq. (7-129) and using Eq. (7-127,b) for z_{11c} and Eq. (7-123) for $sz(s)$.

7-19. Start from the y parameters given in Eqs. (7-115) and obtain the realizations shown in Fig. 7-34 using the Ozaki synthesis procedure.

7-20. Start from the y parameters given in Eqs. (7-115) and remove enough of the pole at infinity as a bridging branch to cause the transmission zeros of the remainder to fall on the $j\omega$ axis. Then apply the Ozaki separation theorem to arrive at the realization shown in Fig. 7-35(b).

7-21. Complete the cascade realization of the transfer admittance given in Eq. (7-151).

8

Realization of General Passive Two-Ports

The general properties of network functions describing the behavior of RLC two-ports were discussed in Chap. 4. We are now ready to complete the task of realizing a two-port when a transfer function is prescribed, provided only that the function satisfies the necessary conditions of realizability in a passive network. When the transfer function satisfies certain restricted conditions, special kinds of networks can be realized. For example, if all the poles of the transfer function lie on the negative real axis, then an RC two-port realizing the function can be obtained. The structure of the two-port will depend on the locations of the transmission zeros. If the given function satisfies none of the special conditions for realizability in a lossless or an RC two-port, then we must resort to a more general RLC realization. As a matter of fact, we may even choose to obtain an RLC realization of a given function even though it can be realized as a lossless network, for the purpose of achieving some other advantage. It will be useful to review the properties of two-port functions discussed in Chap. 4 before starting the present chapter.

8-1. Constant-resistance lattice

The concept of a constant-resistance network arises in image parameter theory. If the image impedance of a symmetrical two-port is real, the two-port is labeled "constant-resistance." Thus we can define a constant-resistance two-port as one whose driving-point impedance is equal to a constant R when the two-port is terminated in a resistance R.

The symmetrical lattice shown in Fig. 8-1 will be a constant-resistance two-port if the arm impedances are inverse with respect to R^2, that is, if $Z_a Z_b = R^2$.

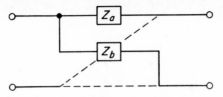

Fig. 8-1. Constant-resistance lattice: $Z_a Z_b = R^2$.

Under this condition, the transfer impedance of Fig. 8-1 will be

$$Z_{12} = \frac{R(R - Z_a)}{R + Z_a} \tag{8-1}$$

or, normalizing with respect to R,

$$Z_{12} = \frac{1 - Z_a}{1 + Z_a} \tag{8-2}$$

This result was established in Prob. 1-6. If you have not yet worked out that problem, now is the time to do so.

Because of the constant-resistance property, all the transfer functions —$Z_{12}(s)$, $Y_{12}(s)$, $T_{12}(s)$, and $H(s)$ (the insertion ratio)—differ from each other only by a multiplicative constant. As a matter of fact, when we normalize with respect to the termination, we shall have

$$Z_{12}(s) = -Y_{12}(s) = T_{12}(s) = H(s) \tag{8-3}$$

Hence we can talk about all these functions interchangeably. In the following discussion we shall use the voltage transfer function $T_{12}(s)$.

Let us now invert Eq. (8-2) to solve for Z_a in terms of T_{12} (which is the same as Z_{12}). We get

$$Z_a = \frac{1 - T_{12}}{1 + T_{12}} \tag{8-4}$$

The question that we have before us now is the following: If a transfer function satisfying necessary realizability criteria is prescribed, is it possible to realize the function as a constant-resistance lattice? If the answer is to be affirmative, Z_a in Eq. (8-4) must be a positive real function.

Suppose that we write $T_{12}(j\omega) = r_{12} + jx_{12}$. Then we can compute the real part of $Z_a(j\omega)$ from the last equation. The result is

$$\text{Re } [Z_a(j\omega)] = \frac{1 - |T_{12}(j\omega)|^2}{(1 + r_{12})^2 + x_{12}^2} \tag{8-5}$$

Thus the real part of Z_a on the $j\omega$ axis will certainly not be negative on condition that $|T_{12}(j\omega)| \leq 1$. This condition precludes the possibility of poles of T_{12} on the $j\omega$ axis. If we can show that Z_a is also regular in the right half plane, this will complete the proof that Z_a is pr. Z_a will have a pole in the right half plane if $1 + T_{12}$ has a zero there, which is possible only if $T_{12} = -1$ at some point in the right half plane. Recall that $T_{12}(s)$ is regular in the right-half s plane. Hence, if $|T_{12}|$ is no greater than unity on the $j\omega$ axis, it will certainly be less than unity in the entire right half plane, according to the maximum modulus theorem. Hence T_{12} can never equal -1 in the right half plane, which means that $1 + T_{12}$ can have no zeros in the right half plane.

It follows from this discussion that Z_a will be positive real under the condition that the magnitude of the given T_{12} be no greater than unity for $s = j\omega$. The contemplated realization of a given $T_{12}(s)$ in a constant-resistance lattice is possible, then, under the conditions:

1. $T_{12}(s)$ has no poles on the $j\omega$ axis.
2. $|T_{12}(j\omega)| \leq 1$.

Let us assume that the given function has no poles on the $j\omega$ axis so that the first condition is satisfied. The second condition can always be satisfied provided that we can tolerate a reduction of the gain constant. In this respect the present situation is similar to the realization of an RC or LC transfer function in a symmetrical lattice—it can always be done, but at a sacrifice of transmission gain.

Thus the realization of a transfer function with no poles on the $j\omega$ axis is reduced to the realization of a positive real function and its inverse. If the transfer function is of a high order, the arms of the lattice will be relatively complicated.

The same results can be obtained by proceeding on a dual basis. The lattice-arm admittance Y_a will be given in terms of T_{12} (which is equal to $-Y_{12}$) by Eq. (8-3). The same conditions on the realizability will be obtained.

This type of realization is not very appealing, for several reasons. We have already seen the disadvantages of a symmetrical realization in connection with RC two-ports: excessive number of elements and low gain constant. The symmetrical *lattice* brings in another undesirable feature, its balanced nature. In some cases it is possible to overcome this last objection by finding an unbalanced equivalent of the lattice, as we did for LC and RC lattices. But if such an unbalanced equivalent can be found, would it not be preferable to establish realization procedures for obtaining the network directly rather than through the realization of a lattice first? This line of thought will be pursued further in later sections of this chapter.

Another undesirable feature of the realization as a single lattice is the complexity of the lattice arms for high-order transfer functions. This disadvantage can be overcome in a relatively simple manner. Consider the cascade connection of constant-resistance two-ports shown in Fig. 8-2.

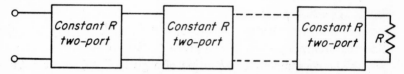

Fig. 8-2. Cascade of constant-resistance two-ports.

The terminating impedance of each two-port is the input impedance of the succeeding one. If the termination on the right is equal to the common constant image impedance of these two-ports, then each one will be terminated properly to yield a constant input impedance, with the result that the over-all network will be constant-resistance.

This consideration motivates us to contemplate the decomposition of a given T_{12} function in the form

$$T_{12} = T_{12a}T_{12b} \ldots T_{12n} \tag{8-6}$$

If each component T_{12} can be realized as a constant-resistance two-port, then the cascade connection of these two-ports will realize the given function. It remains, then, to determine whether a given T_{12} function satisfying necessary realizability conditions can be decomposed in the manner indicated.

Consider the following types of function, which are to constitute the component T_{12} functions.

$$T_{12a} = \frac{K_1}{s+a} \qquad\qquad K_1 \leq a \qquad\qquad \text{(a)}$$

$$T_{12b} = K_2\frac{s+c}{s+a} \qquad\qquad K_2 \leq \frac{a}{c} \text{ or } K_2 \leq 1 \quad \text{(b)}$$

$$T_{12c} = \frac{K_3}{s^2+as+b} \qquad\qquad K_3 \leq b \qquad\qquad \text{(c)} \quad \text{(8-7)}$$

$$T_{12d} = K_4\frac{s+c}{s^2+as+b} \qquad\qquad\qquad\qquad \text{(d)}$$

$$T_{12e} = K_5\frac{s^2+cs+d}{s^2+as+b} \qquad\qquad\qquad\qquad \text{(e)}$$

The a, b, and d coefficients must be positive , while c may be positive or negative, the latter corresponding to a nonminimum-phase function. The coefficient c may also be zero, corresponding to a pair of zeros on the $j\omega$ axis in the last function and to a zero at the origin in the second and fourth. From our previous discussion it is clear that each of these can be realized as a constant-resistance lattice, provided that the gain constants are made small enough. For the first three functions the required conditions on the K's are given. When there is a choice, the smallest one must be chosen. For the remaining two, these conditions are too complicated to be useful in literal form.

You can now easily show that any realizable transfer function can be decomposed into a product of functions having the form of one or more of the component functions in Eqs. (8-7). As a matter of fact, such a decomposition is not unique; the factors of the numerator can be paired off with those in the denominator in any order. Of course, the price that we must usually (but not always) pay for such a decomposition is a reduction in the over-all transmission gain. The truth of this statement becomes evident from the consideration that, even though the original function has a magnitude no greater than unity on the $j\omega$ axis, it is not guaranteed that each component also fulfills this condition without lowering the gain constant.

As an example, consider the function

$$T_{12}(s) = K \frac{s + 1}{(s + 2)(s + 3)} \tag{8-8}$$

We are not concerned here with the fact that this function is also realizable as an RC two-port. The series branch of a constant-resistance lattice realizing this function will be

$$Z_a = \frac{s^2 + (5 - K)s + (6 - K)}{s^2 + (5 + K)s + (6 + K)} \tag{8-9}$$

By applying the methods of Chap. 3 we find that the largest value of K which will make this function positive real is $K = 4.56$. For this value of K, Z_a will be a minimum function and will require a transformer in the Brune realization.

Now suppose that we write the original function as

$$T_{12}(s) = \frac{K_1}{s + 3}\left(K_2 \frac{s + 1}{s + 2}\right) \tag{8-10}$$

The realization is to be a cascade connection of two lattices. The series arms of the two lattices will be

$$Z_{a1} = \frac{s + (3 - K_1)}{s + (3 + K_1)} \tag{a}$$

$$\tag{8-11}$$

$$Z_{a2} = \frac{(1 - K_2)s + (2 - K_2)}{(1 + K_2)s + (2 + K_2)} \tag{b}$$

For these functions to be positive real, we must require that

$$K_1 \leq 3 \tag{a}$$

$$\tag{8-12}$$

$$K_2 \leq 1 \tag{b}$$

Even choosing the maximum permissible values leads to the product $K_1 K_2 = 3$ as compared with $K = 4.56$ for the single-lattice realization. The compensating feature of simpler lattices is evident from Fig. 8-3,

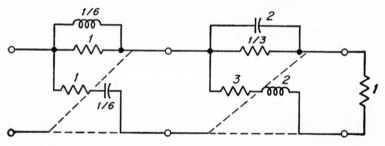

Fig. 8-3. Realization of example in cascaded constant-resistance lattices.

which shows the realization obtained for the maximum gain constants $K_1 = 3$ and $K_2 = 1$.

In the present simple example the realization can be simplified even further by converting each lattice to an unbalanced equivalent. We should expect that this is possible since the original function in Eq. (8-8) satisfies Fialkow's condition. The result is shown in Fig. 8-4.

It is instructive to compare the number of elements required in the different realizations. In the case of the single constant-resistance lattice

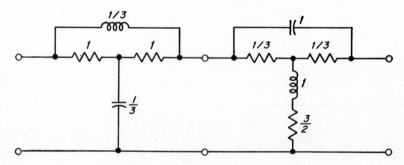

Fig. 8-4. Unbalanced equivalent of lattice realization.

the Bott-Duffin realization requires 8 elements in each of the lattice arms for a total of 32. The Brune realization requires a total of 20 elements (counting a transformer as 3). The cascaded-lattices realization in Fig. 8-3 uses only 16 elements, while the unbalanced equivalent brings the total down to 9. Even the unbalanced realization, being symmetrical, uses more elements than necessary for the realization of the original function. An RC ladder realization of the function requires only 5 elements. You can verify this by obtaining such a realization according to the methods of the last chapter.

In the preceding discussion there was no consideration of the locations of transmission zeros. The same procedure is followed whether the zeros are in the right half or the left half plane. When we discussed the properties of transfer functions in Chap. 4, we saw that a nonminimum-phase function can always be written as the product of a minimum-phase function and an all-pass function. Thus, given a nonminimum-phase transfer function $T_{12}(s)$, we can write

$$T_{12}(s) \;=\; T_{12m}(s) \cdot T_{12o}(s) \tag{8-13}$$

where T_{12m} is a minimum-phase function and T_{12o} is an all-pass function. In realizing this function by the procedure we have described in this section the resulting network will be the cascade connection of a minimum-phase two-port and an all-pass two-port.

Now the zeros of an all-pass network are the negatives of the poles, and they all lie in the right half plane. We established in Chap. 4 that an all-pass function can be written

$$T_{12o} \;=\; \frac{m - n}{m + n} \;=\; \frac{1 - n/m}{1 + n/m} \tag{8-14}$$

where m and n are the even and odd parts of the Hurwitz denominator. Let us consider realizing this function as a constant-resistance lattice. If we compare this expression with Eq. (8-2) (remembering that $Z_{12} = T_{12}$), we see that the series-branch impedance of the constant-resistance lattice which realizes this function is

$$Z_a \;=\; n/m \tag{8-15}$$

The all-pass lattice is thus lossless.

Any all-pass function can be written as the product of simple first-order and second-order all-pass functions by grouping the poles and zeros in an obvious way. These have, respectively, a single real zero and pole and a pair of complex zeros and poles. A first-order all-pass function can be written†

† The numerator factor is written $a - s$ instead of $s - a$ so that the angle of the function will be zero at zero frequency. See Chap. 4 for details.

$$T_{12} = \frac{a - s}{a + s} = \frac{1 - s/a}{1 + s/a} \qquad (8\text{-}16)$$

In view of the last two equations we see that $Z_a = s/a$. Thus the constant-resistance-lattice realization of this function takes the form shown in Fig. 8-5(a).

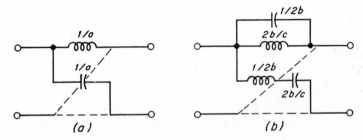

Fig. 8-5. First- and second-order all-pass lattices.

Now consider the following second-order all-pass function:

$$T_{12} = \frac{s^2 - 2bs + c}{s^2 + 2bs + c} = \frac{1 - 2bs/(s^2 + c)}{1 + 2bs/(s^2 + c)} \qquad (8\text{-}17)$$

The right-hand side of this expression also has the form of Eq. (8-2). The lattice arm impedance has the form $Z_a = 2bs/(s^2 + c)$. The lattice realization is shown in Fig. 8-5(b).

We have now demonstrated that an arbitrary transfer function, minimum-phase or nonminimum-phase, (with no poles on the $j\omega$ axis) can be realized as a cascade connection of constant-resistance two-ports. Those of the two-ports which realize the all-pass components of the given function will be lattices similar to one or the other of those of Fig. 8-5. The remainder will realize the minimum-phase component of the given function. In the following section we shall show that a minimum-phase transfer function can always be realized as a constant-resistance ladder. Thus the complete realization will take the form of a ladder network in cascade with first- and second-order all-pass lattices.

There is still the possibility that unbalanced equivalents of some or all of the all-pass lattices may be found. Of course, no unbalanced equivalent of a first-order lattice exists, since an unbalanced two-port cannot have a positive real transmission zero. In Chap. 5 we saw that bridged-tee and twin-tee equivalents of a lattice having the form of Fig. 8-5(b) can be obtained when the elements satisfy certain conditions (see Probs. 5-2 and 5-3). With the element values given in the figure these conditions become

$$\frac{1}{2b} \geq \frac{2b}{c} \qquad \text{(a)}$$

$$\frac{c}{2b^2} \geq 1 \qquad \text{(b)}$$

(8-18)

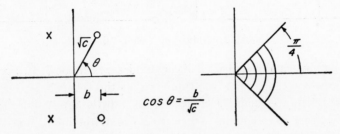

Fig. 8-6. Pole-zero locations of second-order all-pass function.

Using the geometry of the location of the zero of the transfer function shown in Fig. 8-6, we can write these two conditions as

$$\theta \geq \pi/3 \qquad \text{(a)}$$

$$\theta \geq \pi/4 \qquad \text{(b)}$$

(8-19)

Thus an unbalanced equivalent of the second-order all-pass lattice can be found if the zeros of the transfer function lie outside the pie-shaped wedge shown in the figure.

8-2. Constant-resistance ladder

In the last section we showed that any realizable transfer function, except one having poles on the $j\omega$ axis, can be realized as a cascade connection of constant-resistance lattices. This realization takes no account of the locations of transmission zeros, all zeros being treated in the same manner.

Let us now restrict ourselves to minimum-phase functions. In this class we shall include those which have zeros on the $j\omega$ axis as well as in the interior of the left half plane. In Chap. 4 we showed that the transfer function of a ladder network will be minimum-phase. It seems sensible to inquire whether the minimum-phase condition is sufficient, as well as necessary, for the realizability of a ladder network. In seeking the answer to this question, consider again the cascade connection of constant-resistance two-ports shown in Fig. 8-2. If each of the component two-ports is an L two-port as shown in Fig. 8-7, then the over-all network will be a ladder.

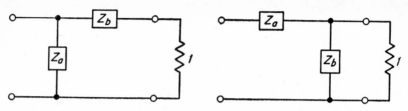

Fig. 8-7. Constant-resistance L two-ports.

Let us now establish the conditions under which the L two-port will be constant-resistance. That is, suppose that the two-port is terminated in a unit resistance; under what conditions will the input impedance be equal to unity? It is a simple matter to calculate the input impedance of Fig. 8-7(a) when the two-port is terminated in a unit resistance. The result is

$$Z = \frac{1 + Y_b}{Y_b + Y_a(1 + Y_b)} \tag{8-20}$$

We have used the branch admittances instead of the impedances for ease of interpretation. If the L is to be constant-resistance, the input impedance must be equal to unity. When this condition is used, we find

$$Y_a(1 + Y_b) = 1$$

or

$$Z_a = 1 + Y_b \tag{8-21}$$

Thus, for the L to be a constant-resistance two-port, the shunt admittance should be the inverse of unity plus the series-branch admittance. (Compare this with the condition $Z_a Z_b = 1$ for a constant-resistance lattice.)

Our next objective will be the determination of the transfer function of the constant-resistance L two-port when terminated in a unit resistance. This is easily accomplished, leading to the result

$$T_{12L} = \frac{Z_a}{Z_a + Z_b + 1} = \frac{Y_b}{Y_b + Y_a(1 + Y_b)} \tag{8-22}$$

The constant-resistance condition in Eq. (8-21) reduces this expression to

$$T_{12L} = \frac{Y_b}{1 + Y_b} = \frac{1}{1 + Z_b} \tag{8-23}$$

This is an extremely simple expression. We immediately notice that the transfer function of a constant-resistance L network is necessarily a positive real function. Furthermore, writing $Z_b(j\omega) = R_b + jX_b$ and computing the real part of $T_{12L}(j\omega)$, we find

$$\text{Re}\,[T_{12L}(j\omega)] = \frac{1 + R_b}{(1 + R_b)^2 + X_b^2} \tag{8-24}$$

Since R_b cannot be negative, we conclude that *the real part of T_{12L} can* *never vanish on the jω axis.* Hence, not only is T_{12L} a positive real function, it is necessarily a nonminimum-resistance pr function. Another fact is also apparent from Eq. (8-23): *the magnitude of T_{12L} is never greater than unity on the jω axis.*

We will now inquire whether this condition on T_{12}—nonminimum-resistance positive realness—is sufficient as well as necessary for the realizability of a constant-resistance L two-port. Of course we must immediately rule out positive real functions with a pole at infinity. You can easily establish that an arbitrary nonminimum-real-part pr function (with no pole at infinity) *cannot* be expressed in the form of the right side of Eq. (8-23). To do this, suppose a given nonminimum-real-part pr function *can* be so expressed. You will then find that its reciprocal, which is also a nonminimum-real-part pr function, cannot be. The reason is that the coefficients in the numerator of a pr function are not necessarily less than corresponding ones in the denominator, whereas they must be for the transfer function of an unbalanced realization. But this requirement on the numerator coefficients can always be achieved if we multiply the function by a small enough constant. Hence any nonminimum real-part pr function with no pole at infinity can be written in the desired form.

As an illustration of these ideas, consider again the transfer function of the numerical example in the last section.

$$T_{12}(s) = \frac{K(s+1)}{(s+2)(s+3)} \tag{8-25}$$

You can easily show that this is a nonminimum real-part pr function. Let us rewrite this in the form

$$T_{12}(s) = \frac{1}{1 + \dfrac{s^2 + (5-K)s + 6 - K}{K(s+1)}} \tag{8-26}$$

The second term in the denominator will be pr only if $K \leq 4$, as you can demonstrate. Choosing the maximum value $K = 4$ then yields

$$T_{12}(s) = \frac{1}{1 + \dfrac{s^2 + s + 2}{4(s+1)}} \tag{8-27}$$

We can now realize the given transfer function in a constant-resistance L. The branch-impedance functions will be

$$Z_b(s) = \frac{s^2 + s + 2}{4(s+1)} = \frac{s}{4} + \frac{\frac{1}{2}}{s+1} \tag{a}$$

$$Z_a(s) = 1 + Y_b(s) = 1 + \frac{1}{\dfrac{s}{4} + \dfrac{\frac{1}{2}}{s+1}} \tag{b}$$

$$\text{(8-28)}$$

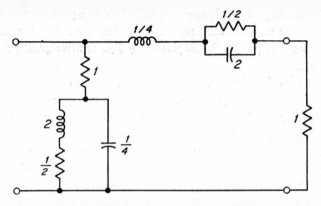

Fig. 8-8. Constant resistance L realization.

The realization is shown in Fig. 8-8. Note that only seven elements are used in the realization with a gain constant of $K = 4$, as compared with nine elements and $K = 3$ in the realization of Fig. 8-4.

Let us now return to the problem of realizing a given minimum-phase function. We have seen that, in the special case when the given function is a nonminimum-real-part pr function with no poles on the $j\omega$ axis, a simple L network will realize it. If this is not the case, let us again contemplate decomposing the given function in a product of functions as in Eq. (8-6). If each of these is a nonminimum-real-part pr function, each may be realized as an L network. The cascade connection of these will yield the desired realization. The question that must be answered, then, is whether or not an arbitrarily given minimum-phase transfer function can always be written as a product of nonminimum-real-part pr functions. The poles and zeros of the given function must be assigned to the components in such a way as to satisfy this condition. Of course a pair of conjugate poles or zeros should be kept together to ensure realness of coefficients.

To answer this question, note that any minimum-phase transfer function can be written as a product of functions having the form of one or more of the simple functions given in Eqs. (8-7), in which none of the coefficients are negative. The first and second of these will always be positive real, while the last two might be, depending on the sizes of the coefficients. The third one cannot be pr. However, consider multiplying numerator and denominator of such a function by the factor $s + e$. The result can be written

$$\frac{K}{s^2 + as + b} = \left(K_1 \frac{s + e}{s^2 + as + b} \right) \frac{K_2}{s + e} \qquad (8\text{-}29)$$

The second factor on the right is pr for any value of e, while the first one will also be pr for $e \leq a$.

This idea of multiplying by surplus factors can be used in the other two cases also. In the case of the linear-divided-by-quadratic function, the surplus factor $s + e$ with $e \leq a$ will lead to the product of two pr functions. The biquadratic function requires a quadratic surplus factor (if it is not already nonminimum-real-part pr). Use of such a factor will lead to

$$\frac{s^2 + cs + d}{s^2 + as + b} = \left(K_1 \frac{s^2 + es + f}{s^2 + as + b} \right) \left(K_2 \frac{s^2 + cs + d}{s^2 + es + f} \right) \qquad (8\text{-}30)$$

To determine the conditions on the coefficients e and f in order that each of these biquadratic functions be positive real (and nonminimum-real-part), we apply Eq. (3-62). The result is

$$e > \frac{(\sqrt{f} - \sqrt{b})^2}{a} \qquad \text{(a)}$$

$$\qquad\qquad (8\text{-}31)$$

$$e > \frac{(\sqrt{f} - \sqrt{d})^2}{c} \qquad \text{(b)}$$

For any value of f that we choose each of the two right-hand sides will be nonnegative. Hence choosing e greater than the larger of these will satisfy both inequalities. Thus there are an infinite number of pairs of e and f coefficients that we can use.

No mention was made in the previous discussion of possible poles of the transfer function on the $j\omega$ axis. If there are a pair of such poles, let us consider them as a separate factor and use a quadratic surplus factor. The result will be

$$\frac{1}{s^2 + \omega_0^2} = \left(K_1 \frac{s^2 + es + f}{s^2 + \omega_0^2} \right) \frac{K_2}{s^2 + es + f} \qquad (8\text{-}32)$$

The factor on the far right can be treated as in Eq. (8-29). Our main concern here is with the first factor. This function will be positive real if $f = \omega_0^2$, in which case it will have a constant real part for all $s = j\omega$. The value of e is unimportant in this consideration.

The discussion we have just completed proves that *any realizable minimum-phase transfer function, including one with poles on the $j\omega$ axis, can be written as a product of positive real functions of the nonminimum real-part variety.* Of course, surplus factors will not always be necessary, but their use will always guarantee the stated result.

According to our discussion of the constant-resistance L two-port, each of the pr functions into which a transfer function is factored, except those which have poles on the $j\omega$ axis, can be realized as a constant-resistance L. It follows that *any realizable minimum-phase transfer function having no poles on the $j\omega$ axis can be realized as a constant-resistance ladder network.*

As an example, consider the following minimum-phase transfer function:

$$T_{12}(s) = K \frac{s^2 + s + 2}{20s^3 + 41s^2 + 62s + 3} = K \frac{s^2 + s + 2}{(s^2 + 2s + 3)(20s + 1)} \qquad (8\text{-}33)$$

You can easily establish that this is not a positive real function. However, it can be written as a product of two functions as follows:

$$T_{12}(s) = \left(K_1 \frac{s^2 + s + 2}{s^2 + 2s + 3}\right) \frac{K_2}{20s + 1} = T_{12a} T_{12b}$$

Each of these is a nonminimum-real-part positive real function, and hence each may be realized as a constant-resistance L according to the method we have discussed. The details of the realization are left for you as an exercise. The final network is shown in Fig. 8-9 for the choice $K_1 = K_2 = 1$.

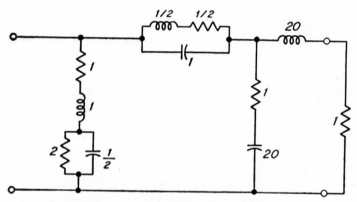

Fig. 8-9. Constant-resistance ladder realization.

This development of a constant-resistance ladder network realization can be carried out in a dual manner by starting with the L network shown in Fig. 8-7(b). The condition that the L be constant-resistance, given in Eq. (8-21), and the expression for the transfer function, given in Eq. (8-23), are still valid, but with impedances and admittances interchanged. If there is a source resistance, either of these two dual structures may be used, but with a current source use the first one and with a voltage source the second.

Now that we have established the fact that any realizable minimum-phase transfer function (with no poles on the $j\omega$ axis) can be realized as a ladder network, let us illustrate the realization of any arbitrary transfer function as a cascade connection of a constant-resistance ladder and one or more all-pass networks. Such a realization was mentioned briefly at the end of the last section. Of course, the all-pass networks will be needed only if the function is nonminimum-phase. Suppose

$$T_{12}(s) = K \frac{2s^2 - s + 2}{s^2 + 6s + 1} = \frac{2s^2 - s + 2}{2s^2 + s + 2} K \frac{2s^2 + s + 2}{s^2 + 6s + 1} \qquad (8\text{-}34)$$

This is to be realized as a resistance-terminated two-port. The first factor on the right-hand side is an all-pass function. According to Eq. (8-15), the series-arm impedance of its lattice realization will be

$$Z_a = \frac{s/2}{s^2 + 1} \qquad (8\text{-}35)$$

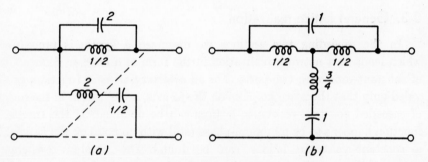

Fig. 8-10. All-pass lattice and bridged-tee equivalent.

This leads to the lattice shown in Fig. 8-10. The angle of the transmission zero is easily found to be 75.5° so that a bridged-tee equivalent of the lattice exists. This is also shown in the figure.

The remaining factor on the right-hand side of Eq. (8-34) is minimum-

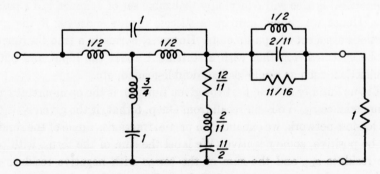

Fig. 8-11. Constant-resistance realization of nonminimum-phase function.

phase. We quickly determine that it is also positive real so that it can be realized in an L network. We find the series-branch impedance of the L to be

$$Z_b = \frac{(1 - 2K)s^2 + (6 - K)s + (1 - 2K)}{K(2s^2 + s + 2)} = \frac{11s}{2s^2 + s + 2} \qquad (8\text{-}36)$$

The right-hand side is obtained with the choice of $K = 1/2$, which is the maximum value of K permitted by Fialkow's condition. The shunt-branch impedance is then given by

$$Z_a = 1 + Y_b = \frac{12}{11} + \frac{2s}{11} + \frac{2}{11s} \qquad (8\text{-}37)$$

The complete realization of the given function is shown in Fig. 8-11.

8-3. General lattice realization

In the preceding two sections we discussed a synthesis procedure which leads to a network realization in the form of a cascade connection of constant-resistance two-ports. For an arbitrary transfer function, provided only that there are no poles on the $j\omega$ axis, a realization in the form of cascaded constant-resistance lattices can be obtained. If the transfer function happens to be minimum-phase (still with no poles on the $j\omega$ axis), a constant-resistance ladder can be found. The constant-resistance nature of these realizations requires the lattice arms, in the one case, and the branches of the L two-ports which make up the ladder, in the second case, to be related.

Forcing branch impedances to be related from the start seems unduly restrictive. Suppose that we relax the constant-resistance requirement but still seek a lattice realization. In Prob. 4-5 it was established that a symmetrical lattice will realize any realizable set of symmetrical z parameters. Hence we should anticipate success in our endeavor if the given functions are a set of z parameters. However, normally a transfer function will be specified, together with a statement about the input and output termination, such as single-loaded, double-loaded, etc.

Let us initially assume that the given function is the open-circuit transfer impedance z_{12}. You will recall from Chap. 5 that, if the given z_{12} is that of a lossless network, we expand it in partial fractions. Some of the residues will be positive, some negative. We label the sum of the terms with positive residues z_{12p} and the sum of the terms with negative residues z_{12n}. Both z_{12p} and z_{12n} are reactance functions. Then the branches of the lattice are given in Eqs. (5-6) as $Z_a = 2z_{12n}$ and $Z_b = 2z_{12p}$.

In the more general case the situation is not quite so simple. Suppose that we expand z_{12} in partial fractions. We shall get

$$z_{12} = k_0 + \frac{k_1}{s - s_1} + \frac{k_2}{s - s_2} + \frac{k_2^*}{s - s_2^*} \qquad (8\text{-}38)$$

It is assumed that z_{12} has only simple poles. The first term (not counting k_0) is typical of all real poles, while the second two are typical of complex poles. Since z_{12} is given in terms of the lattice impedances by

$$z_{12} = \tfrac{1}{2}(Z_b - Z_a) \qquad (8\text{-}39)$$

we should like to separate the terms on the right-hand side of Eq. (8-38) into the difference between two positive real functions. In order to do this, we need to know the conditions under which the terms in that equation can represent positive real functions (conjugate poles being grouped together, of course). The answer to this question was established in Prob. 3-12. Denoting the complex poles and residues by

$$\begin{aligned} s_i &= -\sigma_i + j\omega_i \\ k_i &= a_i + jb_i \end{aligned} \qquad (8\text{-}40)$$

the condition that a term in Eq. (8-38) representing a pair of conjugate poles be positive real was there found to be

$$\frac{\sigma_i}{\omega_i} \geq \frac{|b_i|}{a_i} \qquad (8\text{-}41)$$

Suppose that this condition is not fulfilled at a pair of the poles. The inequality shows that the real part of the residue should be increased in order to satisfy the condition. Thus let us add to the pair of terms involving the conjugate poles the function

$$Z_i = \frac{a_i'}{s - s_i} + \frac{a_i'}{s - s_i^*} = \frac{2a_i'(s + \sigma_i)}{s^2 + 2\sigma_i s + \sigma_i^2 + \omega_i^2} \qquad (8\text{-}42)$$

where a_i' is a positive number. It is chosen large enough so that the new residue at the pole s_i, which is now $a_i + a_i' + jb_i$, *does* satisfy the positive real condition given in Eq. (8-41).

We can now assign this pair of poles with augmented residue to Z_b. To retain the given z_{12} unchanged, we must subtract the function Z_i which was added. But this is already a positive real function, and so we can assign it to Z_a.

All the complex poles can be taken care of by this procedure. As for the real poles, some of the residues may be negative, some positive. Those with positive residue we assign to Z_b, while those with negative residue go to Z_a (with the sign changed). Thus the separation of the given z_{12} into the difference between two pr functions is complete.

The realization of the lattice arms can now proceed. Recall from Prob. 3-12 that both Z_a and Z_b can be realized in a Foster-like realization. Thus the present realization procedure involves very little computational labor beyond the expansion of z_{12} into partial fractions.

It should be clear that there is considerable flexibility in identifying Z_a and Z_b. The value of a_i' used to satisfy the condition in Eq. (8-41) can vary from a minimum value on up. For the real poles some additional flexibility is available. We need not assign all the poles with negative residue to Z_a. Suppose that we combine the term involving a real pole with a negative residue together with the constant term. The result will be

$$\frac{k_j}{s + \sigma_j} + k_0 = \frac{k_0 s + (k_0 \sigma_j + k_j)}{s + \sigma_j} \qquad (8\text{-}43)$$

This expression is evidently positive real under the condition

$$k_0 \geq \frac{|k_j|}{\sigma_j} \qquad (8\text{-}44)$$

By combining enough of the constant term with the real pole in this fashion, a positive real function is obtained which is then assigned to Z_b. If there is no constant term in the expansion of the original function, or if the constant term is not large enough to satisfy the last condition, we can resort to further "padding." † We can add a constant to z_{12}, and assign it to Z_b, large enough to give the desired result. The same constant is then assigned to Z_a, thus leaving z_{12} unchanged.

The same procedure can be applied if the given function is the short-circuit admittance y_{12}. The discussion proceeds in terms of the admittances Y_a and Y_b of the lattice arms.

It remains to consider the situation in which the prescribed function is one of the transfer functions of a resistance-terminated network. Suppose that the prescribed function is $Z_{12} = E_2/I_1$ and a resistance termination is specified. It would be possible to consider this function to be the open-circuit transfer impedance of a network provided that we could guarantee the appearance of a resistance across the output of the realized network. This resistance would then constitute the load.

At this stage recall the procedure for finding an unbalanced equivalent of a lattice. Glance back at Fig. 5-4. Any common admittance of the lattice arms can be removed in shunt across the input and output terminals. Thus, if both Y_a and Y_b have a constant term in their partial-fraction expansions, the desired terminating resistance is obtained.

† This is the term applied by Guillemin (63) to the process we have just described.

This circumstance can always be guaranteed. Note that each term in the expansion of Z_a and Z_b is positive real, with a real part that does not become zero anywhere on the finite $j\omega$ axis, except possibly at the origin. (Terms involving conjugate poles are of course grouped together.) Thus the real part of Z_a and Z_b will not be zero on the $j\omega$ axis except possibly at the origin and at infinity. It follows that the real parts of the reciprocals, Y_a and Y_b, can be zero only at zero or infinity. If they are not zero at these two frequencies, then Y_a and Y_b will each have a constant term in their partial-fraction expansions. If one or both real parts are zero at one of the extreme frequencies, we can use resistance padding on both Z_a and Z_b. Hence the real parts of the padded Y_a and Y_b will not be zero anywhere on the $j\omega$ axis. A real constant can be subtracted from each to give the desired termination, while leaving remainders that are still pr.

If the given function is the transfer admittance Y_{12} of a resistance-terminated network, we can consider this to be the short-circuit admittance y_{12} of a network, provided that we can guarantee the appearance of a resistance in series at the output terminal. This resistance will then constitute the load when we short-circuit the output.

Again consider the unbalanced equivalent of a lattice, this time according to the step illustrated in Fig. 5-3. The desired series resistance will be obtained if both Z_a and Z_b have a constant term in their partial-fraction expansion. By an argument similar to one used in the previous case we can guarantee this possibility by padding the Y_a and Y_b determined from the given Y_{12} function.

In summary, the realization in terms of a lattice is always possible for a prescribed transfer impedance or transfer admittance whether or not a finite resistance load is prescribed, *provided that the given function has no multiple poles*. Of course, under some conditions an unbalanced equivalent of the lattice can be found.

Let us illustrate this procedure by resynthesizing the transfer function given in Eq. (8-33). With a unit resistance load T_{12} is the same as $-Y_{12}$. According to our procedure, we take Y_{12} to be the same as the short-circuit transfer admittance of a network which we shall later modify. Thus

$$-y_{12} = \frac{s^2 + s + 2}{(s^2 + 2s + 3)(20s + 1)}$$

$$= \frac{\frac{781}{1161}}{20s + 1} + \frac{a + jb}{s + \sigma_1 - j\omega_1} + \frac{a - jb}{s + \sigma_1 + j\omega_1} \qquad (8\text{-}45)$$

where $\qquad \sigma_1 = 1 \qquad a = \dfrac{9.5}{1161}$

$$\omega_1 = \sqrt{2} \qquad b = \dfrac{10\sqrt{2}}{1161}$$

For the above numerical values the condition in Eq. (8-41) is not satisfied, and so we must resort to padding. In order to satisfy Eq. (8-41), the real part of the residue after padding must be no less than $b\omega_1/\sigma_1 = 20/1161$. If we satisfy the condition with the equality sign, the residue a' that we must supply will be

$$a' = \frac{20}{1161} - \frac{9.5}{1161} = \frac{10.5}{1161}$$

According to Eq. (8-42) the padding admittance will be

$$Y_1 = \frac{21}{1161} \frac{s+1}{s^2 + 2s + 3} \tag{8-46}$$

Adding and subtracting this admittance in Eq. (8-45) leads to

$$-y_{12} = \frac{\frac{781}{1161}}{20s+1} + \frac{40s/1161}{s^2 + 2s + 3} - \frac{21}{1161} \frac{s+1}{s^2 + 2s + 3} \tag{8-47}$$

The lattice-arm admittances now become

$$Y_a = \frac{1}{1161} \left(\frac{1562}{20s+1} + \frac{80s}{s^2 + 2s + 3} \right) \qquad \text{(a)}$$

$$Y_b = \frac{42}{1161} \frac{s+1}{s^2 + 2s + 3} \qquad \text{(b)} \tag{8-48}$$

We now invert these and obtain

$$Z_a = \frac{1161}{3162} \frac{20s^3 + 41s^2 + 62s + 3}{s^2 + 1.013s + 1.481}$$

$$= \frac{1161}{3162} \left(20s + 2.024 + \frac{18.71s^2 + 30.3s}{s^2 + 1.013s + 1.481} \right) \qquad \text{(a)}$$

$$Z_b = \frac{1161}{42} \frac{s^2 + 2s + 3}{s+1} = \frac{1161}{42} \left(s + 1 + \frac{2}{s+1} \right) \qquad \text{(b)} \tag{8-49}$$

Z_a and Z_b do have a common resistance (as well as a common inductance),

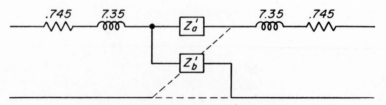

Fig. 8-12. Partial unbalancing of lattice.

so that the desired series resistance will be obtained in the unbalanced equivalent of the lattice. Removing the common resistance and inductance from Z_a and Z_b leads to the partial realization shown in Fig. 8-12. The branch impedances of the remaining lattice are

$$Z_a' = \frac{6.88s(s + 1.62)}{s^2 + 1.013s + 1.481} \tag{a}$$

$$(8\text{-}50)$$

$$Z_b' = 20.3s + 26.9 + \frac{55.3}{s + 1} \tag{b}$$

We can now either realize the primed lattice or convert it into an unbalanced equivalent. The details of finding an unbalanced equivalent of this lattice will be left to you. After the realization is complete, we short-

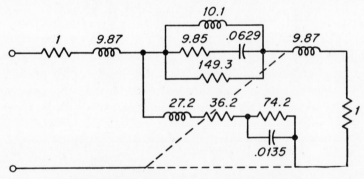

Fig. 8-13. Realization of numerical example.

circuit the output terminals and consider the resistance to be the load. To make this a unit resistance, we must raise the impedance level by $1/0.745$. The complete realization will take the form shown in Fig. 8-13.

8-4. Matrix-factorization methods

The lattice realization discussed in the last section does not take advantage of possible simplifications that should be possible when the given transfer function is minimum-phase. All transfer functions are treated in the same fashion. It seems reasonable to assume that the power of a lattice realization is wasted on minimum-phase transfer functions. More direct methods should lead to unbalanced realizations (specifically ladders) for such functions. One such realization, the constant-resistance ladder, was discussed in Sec. 8-2. However, the constant-resistance property introduces a restriction on the branches of the ladder that should be avoidable.

Suppose that we relax the constant-resistance condition but still seek a ladder realization for a given minimum-phase transfer function. In the preceding discussion we considered a ladder to consist of the cascade connection of L networks. However, the L itself is the cascade connection of the two simpler components shown in Fig. 8-14, and, therefore, so also is the ladder.

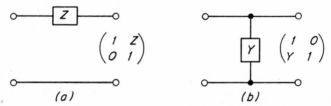

Fig. 8-14. Component branches of ladder network.

You will recall that the external behavior of a two-port made up of the cascade connection of other two-ports is most easily expressed in terms of the chain parameters $(ABCD)$ of the component two-ports. The chain matrices of the simple structures shown in Fig. 8-14 are given in the figure. Thus the chain matrix of the ladder network will be given by the product of alternate series- and shunt-branch chain matrices such as these. The

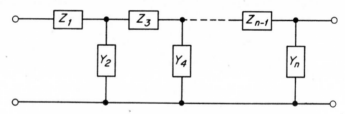

Fig. 8-15. Ladder two-port.

chain matrix of the ladder network shown in Fig. 8-15 in terms of the chain matrices of the branches is given by

$$\begin{bmatrix} A & B \\ C & D \end{bmatrix} = \begin{bmatrix} 1 & Z_1 \\ 0 & 1 \end{bmatrix} \begin{bmatrix} 1 & 0 \\ Y_2 & 1 \end{bmatrix} \cdots \begin{bmatrix} 1 & Z_{n-1} \\ 0 & 1 \end{bmatrix} \begin{bmatrix} 1 & 0 \\ Y_n & 1 \end{bmatrix} \tag{8-51}$$

Suppose that the external behavior of a network is prescribed in the form of its chain matrix. If we could factor this matrix into factors such as those on the right-hand side of the last equation, then we could identify the branches of the ladder which realizes the original chain matrix. We shall now discuss a general method for factoring a chain matrix which was originally introduced by Ho (65). At times the development of the method might appear "cluttered up" with masses of matrix algebra, but the method itself is straightforward.

First of all consider the following transformation, which diagonalizes the chain matrix:

$$
\begin{bmatrix} 1 & 0 \\ \dfrac{-C}{A} & 1 \end{bmatrix}
\begin{bmatrix} A & B \\ C & D \end{bmatrix}
\begin{bmatrix} 1 & \dfrac{-B}{A} \\ 0 & 1 \end{bmatrix}
=
\begin{bmatrix} A & 0 \\ 0 & \dfrac{1}{A} \end{bmatrix}
\tag{8-52}
$$

The diagonal matrix obtained on the right is equivalent to the chain matrix. We can solve this expression for the chain matrix in terms of its equivalent diagonal form as follows: Premultiply both sides of the equation by the inverse of the left-hand transformation matrix, and postmultiply by the inverse of the right-hand transformation matrix. The result will be

$$
\begin{bmatrix} A & B \\ C & D \end{bmatrix}
=
\begin{bmatrix} 1 & 0 \\ \dfrac{C}{A} & 1 \end{bmatrix}
\begin{bmatrix} A & 0 \\ 0 & \dfrac{1}{A} \end{bmatrix}
\begin{bmatrix} 1 & \dfrac{B}{A} \\ 0 & 1 \end{bmatrix}
\tag{8-53}
$$

This expression now represents the first step in the factoring process.

In a realization problem the starting point is not the entire chain matrix but a prescribed transfer function. Let us assume that the prescribed function is the voltage transfer ratio $T_{12}(s)$. We can relate this function to the A parameter of the chain matrix by assuming that the network is open-circuited. If there is actually to be a resistance termination, this can be included as part of the network in the fashion of Fig. 7-29. Thus, from the equation

$$
E_1 = A E_2 - B I_2 \tag{8-54}
$$

we find, with $I_2 = 0$, that

$$
T_{12}(s) = \frac{E_2}{E_1} = \frac{1}{A} \tag{8-55}
$$

Thus the voltage transfer ratio is the reciprocal of the A parameter.

Since a ladder network is necessarily minimum-phase, let us restrict ourselves to minimum-phase transfer functions. We have already seen that a minimum-phase transfer function with no poles on the $j\omega$ axis can always be written as a product of positive real functions. Since the reciprocal of a pr function is also pr, it follows that the A parameter can also be written as a product of pr functions. Thus

$$
A(s) = \frac{1}{T_{12}(s)} = \prod_{i=1}^{n} k_i f_i(s)
$$

$$
= [k_1 f_1(s)][k_2 f_2(s)] \ldots [k_n f_n(s)] \tag{8-56}
$$

where the k's are positive constants.

Now look at the diagonal matrix on the right-hand side of Eq. (8-53).

Both A and $1/A$, the elements on the diagonal, consist of the product of several factors. Such a diagonal matrix can always be written as the product of several diagonal matrices, the diagonal elements of each of which consist of one factor of the corresponding diagonal element in the original matrix. Thus

$$
\begin{bmatrix} A & 0 \\ 0 & \dfrac{1}{A} \end{bmatrix} = \begin{bmatrix} k_1 f_1 & 0 \\ 0 & \dfrac{1}{k_1 f_1} \end{bmatrix} \begin{bmatrix} k_2 f_2 & 0 \\ 0 & \dfrac{1}{k_2 f_2} \end{bmatrix} \cdots \begin{bmatrix} k_n f_n & 0 \\ 0 & \dfrac{1}{k_n f_n} \end{bmatrix} \tag{8-57}
$$

You can easily verify this result by performing the indicated multiplication of the matrices on the right. If this expression is substituted into Eq. (8-53), the result will be

$$
\begin{bmatrix} A & B \\ C & D \end{bmatrix} = \begin{bmatrix} 1 & 0 \\ \dfrac{C}{A} & 1 \end{bmatrix} (M_1)(M_2) \ldots (M_n) \begin{bmatrix} 1 & \dfrac{B}{A} \\ 0 & 1 \end{bmatrix} \tag{8-58}
$$

where the matrix (M_i) is defined as

$$
(M_i) = \begin{bmatrix} k_i f_i & 0 \\ 0 & \dfrac{1}{k_i f_i} \end{bmatrix} \tag{8-59}
$$

This is a valid factorization of the chain matrix. However, the component matrices do not resemble the component matrices of the ladder network as given in Eq. (8-51). We still need to apply some transformations or matrix identities to the component matrices in order to obtain the desired form. One such identity is the following:

$$
\begin{bmatrix} k_i f_i & 0 \\ 0 & \dfrac{1}{k_i f_i} \end{bmatrix} = \begin{bmatrix} 1 & 0 \\ \dfrac{1}{k_i f_i} - 1 & 1 \end{bmatrix} \begin{bmatrix} 1 & 1 \\ 0 & 1 \end{bmatrix} \begin{bmatrix} 1 & 0 \\ k_i f_i - 1 & 1 \end{bmatrix} \begin{bmatrix} 1 & \dfrac{-1}{k_i f_i} \\ 0 & 1 \end{bmatrix} \tag{8-60}
$$

You can verify this identity by performing the indicated multiplications on the right. Suppose that we use this identity to replace the first diagonal matrix (M_1) in Eq. (8-58). The result will be

$$
\begin{bmatrix} A & B \\ C & D \end{bmatrix} = \begin{bmatrix} 1 & 0 \\ \dfrac{C}{A} & 1 \end{bmatrix} \begin{bmatrix} 1 & 0 \\ \dfrac{1}{k_1 f_1} - 1 & 1 \end{bmatrix} \begin{bmatrix} 1 & 1 \\ 0 & 1 \end{bmatrix} \begin{bmatrix} 1 & 0 \\ k_1 f_1 - 1 & 0 \end{bmatrix} \begin{bmatrix} 1 & \dfrac{-1}{k_1 f_1} \\ 0 & 1 \end{bmatrix}
$$

$$
\cdot (M_2) \ldots (M_n) \begin{bmatrix} 1 & \dfrac{B}{A} \\ 0 & 1 \end{bmatrix} \tag{8-61}
$$

This can be simplified somewhat by multiplying together the first two matrices on the right-hand side as indicated by the brackets.

Now consider the following matrix identity:

$$\begin{bmatrix} 1 & x \\ 0 & 1 \end{bmatrix} \begin{bmatrix} d_1 & 0 \\ 0 & d_2 \end{bmatrix} = \begin{bmatrix} d_1 & 0 \\ 0 & d_2 \end{bmatrix} \begin{bmatrix} 1 & \dfrac{d_2}{d_1} x \\ 0 & 1 \end{bmatrix} . \qquad (8\text{-}62)$$

This expression indicates that premultiplying a diagonal matrix by a triangular matrix is equivalent to postmultiplying the same diagonal matrix by a suitably modified triangular matrix. The use of this identity will simplify Eq. (8-61) considerably.

Return now to Eq. (8-61). Immediately to the left of the matrix (M_2) there is a triangular matrix. If we use the identity given in the last equation, this triangular matrix can be moved to the right of all the diagonal matrices (M_i) with the proper modification. If we now perform the multiplication of the last matrix in Eq. (8-61) by this modified triangular matrix, Eq. (8-61) can be written

$$\begin{bmatrix} A & B \\ C & D \end{bmatrix}$$

$$= \begin{bmatrix} 1 & 0 \\ \dfrac{C}{A} - 1 + \dfrac{1}{k_1 f_1} & 1 \end{bmatrix} \begin{bmatrix} 1 & 1 \\ 0 & 1 \end{bmatrix} \begin{bmatrix} 1 & 0 \\ k_1 f_1 - 1 & 1 \end{bmatrix} (M_2) \dots (M_n) \begin{bmatrix} 1 & \dfrac{B}{A} - \dfrac{k_1 f_1}{A^2} \\ 0 & 1 \end{bmatrix}$$

$$(8\text{-}63)$$

To complete the factorization of the chain matrix, the same cycle of transformations is applied to each of the diagonal matrices (M_i) in succession. One diagonal matrix at a time is replaced by the product of four matrices, using the identity in Eq. (8-60). Of these four the one on the far left is premultiplied by the matrix immediately preceding it, while the one on the far right is moved through the remaining diagonal matrices on its right, using the identity in Eq. (8-62). This matrix is then combined with the last matrix in the chain. The result of these operations is the following:

$$\begin{bmatrix} A & B \\ C & D \end{bmatrix} = \begin{bmatrix} 1 & 0 \\ \dfrac{C}{A} - 1 + \dfrac{1}{k_1 f_1} & 1 \end{bmatrix} \begin{bmatrix} 1 & 1 \\ 0 & 1 \end{bmatrix} \begin{bmatrix} 1 & 0 \\ k_1 f_1 - 2 + \dfrac{1}{k_2 f_2} & 1 \end{bmatrix} \begin{bmatrix} 1 & 1 \\ 0 & 1 \end{bmatrix}$$

$$\begin{bmatrix} 1 & 0 \\ k_2 f_2 - 2 + \dfrac{1}{k_3 f_3} & 1 \end{bmatrix} \cdots \begin{bmatrix} 1 & 1 \\ 0 & 1 \end{bmatrix} \begin{bmatrix} 1 & 0 \\ k_n f_n - 1 & 1 \end{bmatrix} \begin{bmatrix} 1 & y \\ 0 & 1 \end{bmatrix} \qquad (8\text{-}64)$$

where y in the last matrix is a very complicated function involving the A and B parameters and all the pr functions f_i.

The chain matrix has now been factored in the form appropriate for a ladder realization. [Compare Eq. (8-51) with the last equation.] However, note that the first and last matrices represent a shunt input branch and a series output branch. But these branches have no effect on the transfer voltage ratio. Since the prescribed function *is* the voltage transfer ratio, we can disregard the first and last matrices in Eq. (8-64). The realization that is obtained is a ladder network all of whose series branches are unit resistances. The form of the network is shown in Fig. 8-16(a).

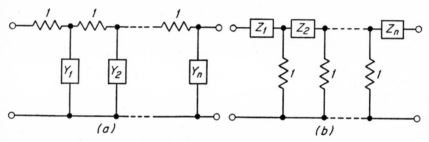

Fig. 8-16. Ladder networks obtained by matrix factorization.

It remains to determine whether the functions representing the shunt-branch admittances can always be made positive real. From Eq. (8-64) these functions are

$$F_i(s) = k_i f_i - 2 + \frac{1}{k_{i+1} f_{i+1}} \qquad i = 2, 3, \ldots, n-1$$
$$F_n(s) = k_n f_n - 1 \tag{8-65}$$

Recall that each of the positive real functions f_i is nonminimum-real-part. Starting from the right-hand end, we first choose k_n large enough to make $F_n(s)$ positive real. Then we choose k_{n-1} to make $F_{n-1}(s)$ pr, and so on. This will certainly always be possible. However, note that the product of all the k's is the reciprocal of the realized gain constant. Making the k's large will mean a small gain constant.

Let us now pause and reflect on what we have accomplished. Starting with a prescribed voltage transfer function, we write its reciprocal as a product of nonminimum-real-part pr functions $k_i f_i$ as in Eq. (8-56). We then form the functions given in Eq. (8-65) and choose the constants large enough to make each of these functions positive real. Each one is then realized as the admittance of a shunt branch of the ladder network shown in Fig. 8-16(a).

In developing the factorization of the chain matrix, the crucial step consisted in using the matrix identity of Eq. (8-60) for each of the diagonal matrices in Eq. (8-58). It seems reasonable to assume that use of other matrix identities at this point in the development will lead to alternative network realizations.

An identity which is quite similar to the one we have already used is the following:

$$
\begin{bmatrix} k_i f_i & 0 \\ 0 & \dfrac{1}{k_i f_i} \end{bmatrix} = \begin{bmatrix} 1 & 0 \\ \dfrac{-1}{k_i f_i} & 1 \end{bmatrix} \begin{bmatrix} 1 & k_i f_i - 1 \\ 0 & 1 \end{bmatrix} \begin{bmatrix} 1 & 0 \\ 1 & 1 \end{bmatrix} \begin{bmatrix} 1 & \dfrac{1}{k_i f_i} - 1 \\ 0 & 1 \end{bmatrix}
\tag{8-66}
$$

In substituting this identity for the diagonal matrices in Eq. (8-58), we start from the right-hand end, first replacing (M_n). The first matrix on the left in Eq. (8-66) is now moved through all the other (M_i) matrices on its left, using the identity

$$
\begin{bmatrix} d_1 & 0 \\ 0 & d_2 \end{bmatrix} \begin{bmatrix} 1 & 0 \\ x & 1 \end{bmatrix} = \begin{bmatrix} 1 & 0 \\ \dfrac{d_2}{d_1} x & 1 \end{bmatrix} \begin{bmatrix} d_1 & 0 \\ 0 & d_2 \end{bmatrix}
\tag{8-67}
$$

which is quite similar to the identity given in Eq. (8-62).

These two identities are used alternately, replacing each of the (M_i) in turn just as in the previous factorization. The final result is given by

$$
\begin{bmatrix} A & B \\ C & D \end{bmatrix} = \begin{bmatrix} 1 & 0 \\ y & 1 \end{bmatrix} \begin{bmatrix} 1 & k_1 f_1 - 1 \\ 0 & 1 \end{bmatrix} \begin{bmatrix} 1 & 0 \\ 1 & 1 \end{bmatrix} \begin{bmatrix} 1 & k_2 f_2 - 2 + \dfrac{1}{k_1 f_1} \\ 0 & 1 \end{bmatrix} \begin{bmatrix} 1 & 0 \\ 1 & 1 \end{bmatrix}
$$
$$
\cdots \begin{bmatrix} 1 & k_n f_n - 2 + \dfrac{1}{k_{n-1} f_{n-1}} \\ 0 & 1 \end{bmatrix} \begin{bmatrix} 1 & 0 \\ 1 & 1 \end{bmatrix} \begin{bmatrix} 1 & \dfrac{B}{A} - 1 + \dfrac{1}{k_n f_n} \\ 0 & 1 \end{bmatrix}
\tag{8-68}
$$

In the first matrix on the right-hand side y is a complicated function of all the pr functions $k_i f_i$ and of the A and C parameters. The details of this development will be left for you as an exercise. The matrix product on the right can be identified with the chain matrix of a ladder network each of whose shunt branches is a unit resistance. The structure is shown in Fig. 8-16(b). If only T_{12} is specified, the first and last matrices can be ignored since they correspond to a shunt input branch and a series output branch.

The expressions given in Eqs. (8-65) for the branch admittances of the previous ladder realization can be used for the branch impedances of the present realization, as a comparison of corresponding matrices in

Eqs. (8-64) and (8-68) will show. However, the order of the factors is inverted. Thus we should replace n by 1 and i by $i + 1$, and vice versa.

We shall discuss one other identity which leads to a ladder network. In contrast with the previous two, the series or shunt branches of this ladder are not restricted to be resistances. This realization was independently discovered by Pantell (96), using a somewhat different approach. Pantell's work actually preceded that of Ho. You can easily verify that the following expression is an identity:

$$
\begin{bmatrix} x_1 x_2 & 0 \\ 0 & \dfrac{1}{x_1 x_2} \end{bmatrix} = \begin{bmatrix} 1 & 0 \\ \dfrac{-1}{x_1} & 1 \end{bmatrix} \begin{bmatrix} 1 & x_1 - \dfrac{1}{x_2} \\ 0 & 1 \end{bmatrix} \begin{bmatrix} 1 & 0 \\ x_2 & 1 \end{bmatrix} \begin{bmatrix} 1 & \dfrac{1 - x_1 x_2}{x_1 x_2^2} \\ 0 & 1 \end{bmatrix} \tag{8-69}
$$

. Suppose that we use this identity to substitute for the diagonal matrices in Eq. (8-58) one by one. At each step we move the last matrix in this expression to the right through the remaining diagonal matrices, using Eq. (8-62) just as we did in the first case. Actually, we must first combine the (M_i) matrices in pairs in order that each diagonal term contain two positive real factors. This requires that there be an even number of positive real factors of the prescribed transfer function. However, this is no real restriction because, if the simplest decomposition of A into positive real factors results in an odd number, we can consider unity to be an additional factor, thus making the total number even. If the factor unity is considered to be the last one, we shall see that this corresponds to a terminating resistance. The result of this operation will be the factorization

$$
\begin{bmatrix} A & B \\ C & D \end{bmatrix} = \begin{bmatrix} 1 & 0 \\ \dfrac{C}{A} - \dfrac{1}{k_1 f_1} & 1 \end{bmatrix} \begin{bmatrix} 1 & k_1 f_1 - \dfrac{1}{k_2 f_2} \\ 0 & 1 \end{bmatrix} \begin{bmatrix} 1 & 0 \\ k_2 f_2 - \dfrac{1}{k_3 f_3} & 1 \end{bmatrix}
$$

$$
\cdots \begin{bmatrix} 1 & k_{n-1} f_{n-1} - \dfrac{1}{k_n f_n} \\ 0 & 1 \end{bmatrix} \begin{bmatrix} 1 & 0 \\ k_n f_n & 1 \end{bmatrix} \begin{bmatrix} 1 & y \\ 0 & 1 \end{bmatrix} \tag{8-70}
$$

where y is again a complicated function of the pr factors. The first and last matrices can again be ignored since they will have no influence on the realization of a given transfer voltage ratio. You may carry out the details of this factorization as an exercise.

This factorization also leads to a ladder network, but the series or shunt branches are not restricted to be resistances. The functions representing the series-branch impedances or the shunt-branch admittances are given by

$$F_i(s) = k_i f_i - \frac{1}{k_{i+1} f_{i+1}} \qquad i = 1, 2, \ldots, n-1$$

$$F_n(s) = k_n f_n \tag{8-71}$$

Since the functions $k_i f_i$ are nonminimum real-part pr functions, you can easily show that each of the functions $F_i(s)$ can be made positive real by choosing the constants large enough, again starting with k_n and working toward the front of the ladder. As a matter of fact, the nonminimum real-part restriction on the factors of A can be relaxed. We require only that, if the real part of $f_i(j\omega)$ has a zero on the $j\omega$ axis, then the real part of $f_{i+1}(j\omega)$ have a zero there also. Furthermore, a factor $f_i(s)$ *can* have zeros on the $j\omega$ axis. However, if $f_{i+1}(s)$ has a j-axis zero, then f_i must have a pole there for $F_i(s)$ to be pr. This is no real restriction; $f_{i+1}(s)$ can have a j-axis zero only if we introduce it as a surplus factor, in which case one of the other factors will necessarily have a pole at the same point. The stated restriction, then, is a restriction on the order of choosing the pr factors of A (or T_{12}) if a factor s or $s^2 + \omega_0^2$ is chosen as a surplus factor.

Note that the ladder realizations we have just discussed can be used when a resistance termination is prescribed at one or at both ends of the network. The two terminations may be the same, or they may be different.

To illustrate the method, let us resynthesize the transfer function given in Eqs. (8-45) and (8-33). In the notation of the present section

$$k_2 f_2 = k_2 \frac{s^2 + 2s + 3}{s^2 + s + 2} \tag{a}$$

$$k_1 f_1 = k_1(20s + 1) \tag{b}$$

$$(8\text{-}72)$$

Let us seek a ladder network having the form of Fig. 8-16(a). The shunt-branch admittances are given by Eqs. (8-65). In the present case $n = 2$. Hence for the terminating branch we find

$$Y_2(s) = k_2 \frac{s^2 + 2s + 3}{s^2 + s + 2} - 1 = k_2 - 1 + \frac{1}{\dfrac{s}{k_2} + \dfrac{2/k_2}{s+1}} \tag{8-73}$$

The right-hand side gives a continued-fraction expansion of the admittance. It is clear that $Y_2(s)$ will be pr if $k_2 \geq 1$; however, if k_2 is equal to unity, it will be a minimum-real-part function. In this case it would not be possible to have a resistance termination. The remaining shunt-branch admittance will be

$$Y_1(s) = k_1(20s + 1) - 2 + \frac{s^2 + s + 2}{k_2(s^2 + 2s + 3)}$$

$$= \frac{20k_1 k_2 s^3 + [(41k_1 - 2)k_2 + 1)]s^2 + (62k_1 k_2 - 4k_2 + 1)s + 3k_2(k_1 - 2) + 2}{k_2(s^2 + 2s + 3)}$$

This function will be positive real for $k_1 \geq 2$ and any value of k_2. For $k_1 = 2$ the continued-fraction expansion of $Y_1(s)$ becomes

$$Y_1(s) = 40s + \cfrac{1}{k_2 + \cfrac{1}{\cfrac{s}{k_2} + \cfrac{1}{\cfrac{k_2 s}{2} + \cfrac{k_2}{2}}}} \tag{8-74}$$

The complete realization of the function is shown in Fig. 8-17(a). This is to be compared with the constant-resistance ladder obtained for the same transfer function in Fig. 8-9. The number of elements in the two realizations are the same. In the present realization there is one inductance fewer and one resistance more than in the previous one.

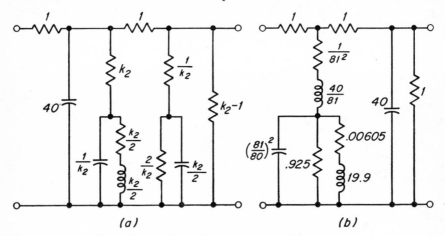

Fig. 8-17. Ladder realizations of numerical example.

An alternative realization can be obtained by choosing the functions in Eqs. (8-72) in the opposite order. For $k_1 = k_2 = 2$ this realization is shown in Fig. 8-17(b). Note that this realization has one capacitance fewer than the previous one.

This example demonstrates the general result that the matrix-factorization procedures discussed in this section are applicable whether or not a resistance termination is desired at either end of the network. Furthermore, different values of resistance may be called for at the two ends of the network and these can be easily accommodated.

8-5. Nonminimum-phase functions—parallel-ladders realization

We have up to this point discussed several methods of realizing a given transfer function. The lattice realizations, be they constant-resistance or otherwise, take no account of the locations of transmission zeros and treat all functions without discrimination (provided always that there are no poles on the $j\omega$ axis). Unbalanced equivalents of the lattice can be found for special types of transfer function.

An alternative realization for the most general transfer function consists in the cascade connection of a ladder network and an all-pass network; the realization of the latter is effected by means of a cascade of simple all-pass lattices. This procedure does take account of the locations of transmission zeros.

For minimum-phase transfer functions we have discussed several realizations all of which lead to a ladder network directly. In this section we shall discuss a realization procedure for nonminimum-phase functions which is based on the matrix-factorization procedure discussed in the last section. We shall be seeking an unbalanced realization. Hence transmission zeros on the positive real axis will be ruled out.

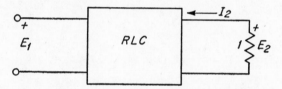

Fig. 8-18. Resistance-terminated RLC network.

Consider the RLC two-port with a unit resistance termination shown in Fig. 8-18. Since $E_2 = -I_2$, we can write

$$E_1 = AE_2 - BI_2 \qquad \text{(a)}$$

or $$\frac{E_1}{E_2} = A + B = \frac{1}{T_{12}(s)} \qquad \text{(b)}$$

$$(8\text{-}75)$$

Presumably $T_{12}(s)$ is prescribed, and we must choose A and B in order to satisfy this equation. One possible choice is

$$A = B = \frac{1}{2}\frac{1}{T_{12}} \qquad (8\text{-}76)$$

Having made this choice, we can now rewrite Eq. (8-75a) as

$$I_2 = \frac{AE_2}{B} - \frac{E_1}{B} = E_2 - 2T_{12}E_1 \qquad (8\text{-}77)$$

Since $A/B = y_{22}$ and $1/B = -y_{12}$, Eq. (8-76) implies that we have chosen $y_{22} = 1$ and $-y_{12} = 2T_{12}$. Since we are looking for an unbalanced realization, we shall require that the numerator coefficients of T_{12} be all positive. This may require the use of surplus factors but will always be possible provided that there are no positive real transmission zeros.

You will recall that a realization technique that is always applicable for a lossless or an RC two-port terminated in a resistance, when the prescribed function is $T_{12}(s)$ or $Y_{12}(s)$ and when there are no transmission zeros on the positive real axis, is the parallel-ladders realization. We shall endeavor to obtain such a realization in the present case as well. Suppose that we have m ladders in parallel. The over-all y_{22} and y_{12} functions will be equal to the sum of the component y_{22} and y_{12} functions, respectively. Thus

$$y_{22} = y_{22a} + y_{22b} + \ldots + y_{22m} = 1 \qquad \text{(a)}$$
$$y_{12} = y_{12a} + y_{12b} + \ldots + y_{12m} = -2T_{12} \qquad \text{(b)}$$
$$(8\text{-}78)$$

where the literal subscripts refer to the component two-ports. The first of these equations can be satisfied by choosing

$$y_{22a} = y_{22b} = \ldots = y_{22m} = \frac{1}{m} \qquad (8\text{-}79)$$

To satisfy the second equation, we shall write the numerator of $T_{12}(s)$ as the sum of several polynomials, each of which is Hurwitz. One way in which this can be done is to group three consecutive powers of s starting from the highest power. If some powers of s are missing, then fewer than three terms must be grouped. In any case, the polynomials into which the numerator is decomposed will consist of quadratics or linear factors times powers of s. Let us write

$$\frac{-y_{12}}{2} = T_{12} = K\frac{P}{Q} = K\frac{P_1}{Q} + K\frac{P_2}{Q} + \ldots + K\frac{P_m}{Q}$$
$$= T_{12a} + T_{12b} + \ldots + T_{12m} \qquad (8\text{-}80)$$

Thus, for the jth-component two-port, we can write

$$-y_{12j} = \frac{1}{B_j} = 2T_{12j} = \frac{2KP_j(s)}{Q(s)} \qquad (8\text{-}81)$$

Using the fact that $A_j/B_j = y_{22j}$ and also that $y_{22j} = 1/m$, we can write

$$A_j = \frac{B_j}{m} = \frac{Q(s)}{2mKP_j(s)} \qquad (8\text{-}82)$$

In this way we have succeeded in finding the A and B parameters of m two-ports which, when connected in parallel and terminated in a unit resistance, will realize a given T_{12} ($= -Y_{12}$) function. The transmission zeros of each of the two-ports lie in the left half plane or on the $j\omega$ axis, and hence each two-port can be realized as a ladder. It remains to realize these ladders from the A and B parameters determined from the last equation.

Glance back at the factorization of the chain matrix given in Eq. (8-68). When both the A and the B parameters are specified, the first matrix in the chain can be ignored but the last matrix, representing a series branch, cannot be since it involves the B parameter. The impedance of the output series branch is

$$Z_{nj} = \frac{B_j}{A_j} - 1 + \frac{1}{k_{nj}f_{nj}} = m - 1 + \frac{1}{k_{nj}f_{nj}} \tag{8-83}$$

Since m is the number of component ladders and certainly greater than 1, this function will be pr. Thus the realization of each ladder is assured. However, you will remember that we are able to realize the transfer function of each ladder only to within a constant multiplier. Denoting by primes the A parameters of the realized ladders, we shall have

$$A_j' = \frac{Q(s)}{K_j P_j(s)} \tag{8-84}$$

If the parallel connection of the ladders is to give the desired transfer function, these realized constants must each be of the correct value to make the last equation coincide with Eq. (8-82). Thus we must have $K_j = 2mK$. When we were dealing with a similar problem in the case of lossless two-ports, we solved the problem by modifying the admittance level of each network after it was realized. The same procedure can be applied in the present case as well, but now we have another alternative.

For each ladder network there is a maximum value of the gain constant that we can achieve. Higher values of the gain constant cannot be realized, but realizations can be obtained for lower values. To solve our present problem, then, we find the maximum obtainable gain constant for each of the ladders. Then we realize each of the ladders to have a gain constant equal to the smallest of these maxima. This, then, completes the problem.

As an illustration of this procedure, consider the following nonminimum-phase transfer function:

$$T_{12}(s) = \frac{K(2s^2 - s + 2)(s + 1)}{(s^2 + 6s + 1)(s + 1)} = \frac{K(2s^3 + s^2 + s + 2)}{(s^2 + 6s + 1)(s + 1)} \tag{8-85}$$

A realization of this function was obtained previously in Fig. 8-11. A surplus factor is needed to make all the coefficients in the numerator positive. The numerator can be decomposed into the sum of two polynomials ($m = 2$) in several ways. One breakdown leads to the following identifications:

$$2T_{12a} = \frac{1}{B_a} = \frac{2Ks(2s^2 + s + 1)}{(s^2 + 6s + 1)(s + 1)} = \frac{1}{2A_a} \quad \text{(a)}$$

$$2T_{12b} = \frac{1}{B_b} = \frac{4K}{(s^2 + 6s + 1)(s + 1)} = \frac{1}{2A_b} \quad \text{(b)}$$

(8-86)

The next step is to factor each of the A parameters into positive real factors. This is done as follows:

$$A_a = \left(K_a \frac{s^2 + 6s + 1}{2s^2 + s + 1} \right) \left(\frac{1}{4K_aK} \frac{s + 1}{s} \right) \quad \text{(a)}$$

$$A_b = \left(K_{b1} \frac{s^2 + 6s + 1}{s + a} \right) [K_{b2}(s + a)] \frac{s + 1}{8KK_{b1}K_{b2}} \quad \text{(b)}$$

(8-87)

Each of these functions will be realized as a ladder having the structure of Fig. 8-16(b). The branch impedances are calculated from Eqs. (8-65), with the appropriate changes in the order of numbering the factors. Note that A_b requires a surplus factor to permit writing it as a product of pr functions. The coefficient a in the surplus factor must be less than 6 if the first factor of A_b is to be pr, as you can easily verify.

Using Eqs. (8-65) to calculate the branch impedances, we find for the first ladder that K must be no greater than 1/16, while for the second ladder we need $K \le 1/32$. Hence we must choose K to be no greater than 1/32 to satisfy both of these requirements simultaneously. With $K = 1/32$, $K_a = 1$, $K_{b1} = a = 5$, and $K_{b2} = 2/a = \frac{2}{5}$, and using the factorization of Eq. (8-68), we obtain the realization shown in Fig. 8-19. The details

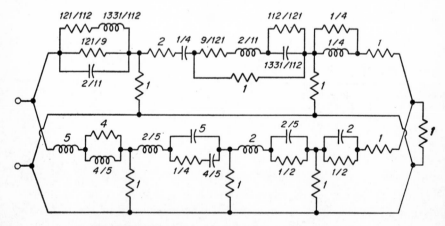

Fig. 8-19. Realization of nonminimum-phase network.

are left for you as an exercise. It is evident that the number of elements required for the realization of even a low-order nonminimum-phase transfer function is quite large by this procedure. Incidentally, the largest value of K which will satisfy Fialkow's condition is $K = 1/2$.

8-6. Alternative parallel-ladders realization

The parallel-ladders realization we have just discussed was based on relating a given nonminimum-phase transfer function to the A and B chain parameters. The realization was accomplished through factorization of the chain matrix. In this section we shall discuss a skillful realization technique, which was developed by Ho (66), which again leads to a parallel-ladders structure.

We proceed by recalling that a voltage transfer function can be written as $T_{12}(s) = -y_{12}/y_{22}$. In order to identify the two short-circuit parameters, we need to divide both numerator and denominator of a given transfer function by a Hurwitz polynomial of appropriate degree, in a now familiar fashion. Thus

$$T_{12}(s) = \frac{a_0 + a_1 s + \ldots + a_n s^n}{Q(s)} = \frac{P(s)}{Q(s)} = \frac{P(s)/Q_1(s)}{Q(s)/Q_1(s)} \qquad (8\text{-}88)$$

Of course, the function Q/Q_1 must be a positive real function. Further restrictions on the polynomial $Q_1(s)$ will become apparent as we discuss the realization procedure.

Suppose that we consider realizing the positive real function y_{22} by the Miyata procedure, temporarily without worrying about y_{12}. To refresh yourself on the details of this technique, refer back to Sec. 3-7. This procedure starts by writing the even part of an admittance function as a sum of terms by decomposing the numerator of the even part. Thus

$$U(-s^2) = \frac{y_{22}(s) + y_{22}(-s)}{2} = \sum_{k=0}^{n} \frac{A_k s^{2k}}{Q_1(s)Q_1(-s)} = \sum_{k=1}^{n} U_k(-s^2) \qquad (8\text{-}89)$$

where

$$U_k(-s^2) = \frac{A_k s^{2k}}{Q_1(s)Q_1(-s)} \qquad (8\text{-}90)$$

The even parts of the component admittances have zeros only at zero and infinity. The success of the method requires the A_k coefficients to satisfy the condition $(-1)^k A_k \geq 0$. When this condition is satisfied, the given admittance is realized as a number of lossless ladder networks connected in parallel at the input end and individually terminated in a resistance at the far end. The branches of each ladder consist of single inductances or capacitances. For example, in the case of only two ladders the structure is shown in Fig. 8-20(a). This has been redrawn in part (b) of the figure, placing the terminating resistance of each ladder in the output branch.

The outputs of the ladders are now connected in parallel. When the common output terminals thus created are short-circuited, this network becomes identical with the previous one.

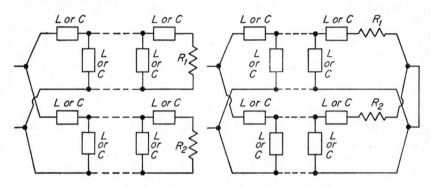

Fig. 8-20. Miyata realization of admittance function.

Now consider the transmission zeros of each ladder. Since the branches are composed of either inductance or capacitance, the transmission zeros will all lie at zero or infinity. (The transmission zero contributed by the output branch is not modified by the resistance.) In fact, the $-y_{12}$ function of the kth ladder will be $b_k s^k / Q_1(s)$ so that the over-all y_{12} function becomes

$$-y_{12} = \frac{b_0 + b_1 s + \ldots + b_n s^n}{Q_1(s)} \tag{8-91}$$

The numerator coefficients here will be different from the desired numerator coefficients shown in Eq. (8-88). This is corrected in the familiar manner of changing the admittance levels of the component ladders. The admittance level of the kth ladder is changed by the factor Ka_k/b_k. But when this is done, the y_{22} function of the kth ladder is also multiplied by Ka_k/b_k. We want this function to be y_{22k}, but we obtain $y_{22k}Ka_k/b_k$. The difference is an admittance

$$y_{rk} = \left(1 - \frac{Ka_k}{b_k}\right) y_{22k} \tag{8-92}$$

The desired y_{22k} will be obtained if we connect an admittance y_{rk}, which we shall call the *residual* admittance, across the output terminals of the kth ladder. If this admittance is to be realizable, we must require $Ka_k/b_k \leq 1$. This is a fundamental limitation on the gain constant that can be achieved by this procedure. The largest value of K will be obtained by computing the ratios a_k/b_k for all the ladders and choosing K to be the reciprocal of the largest of these. We now add all the *residual* admittances y_{rk} and get a single *residual* admittance

$$Y_r = \sum_{k=0}^{n} \left(1 - \frac{Ka_k}{b_k}\right) y_{22k} \tag{8-93}$$

The realization is completed by connecting this admittance across the output terminals.

To illustrate this realization technique, let us resynthesize the non-minimum-phase transfer function

$$T_{12} = K\frac{(2s^2 - s + 2)(s + 1)}{(s^2 + 6s + 1)(s + 1)} \tag{8-94}$$

for which two realizations have already been obtained in Figs. 8-11 and 8-19. If we divide numerator and denominator of the transfer function by the polynomial $Q_1(s) = s^3 + d_2s^2 + d_1s + d_0$, we can write

$$y_{22} = \frac{(s^2 + 6s + 1)(s + 1)}{s^3 + d_2s^2 + d_1s + d_0} = \frac{s^3 + 7s^2 + 7s + 1}{s^3 + d_2s^2 + d_1s + d_0} \quad \text{(a)}$$

$$-y_{12} = K\frac{2s^3 + s^2 + s + 2}{s^3 + d_2s^2 + d_1s + d_0} \quad \text{(b)} \tag{8-95}$$

The even part of y_{22} is found to be

$$U(-s^2) = \frac{-s^6 + (7d_2 - 7 - d_1)s^4 - (7d_1 - d_2 - 7d_0)s^2 + d_0}{Q_1(s)Q_1(-s)} \tag{8-96}$$

In order to satisfy the conditions on the numerator coefficients, we must have

$$7d_2 - 7 - d_1 \geq 0 \quad \text{(a)}$$

$$7d_1 - d_2 - 7d_0 \geq 0 \quad \text{(b)} \tag{8-97}$$

At this stage it is possible to choose the coefficients such that these conditions are satisfied and such that y_{22} is a pr function. However, let us leave them in literal form. The advantage in doing this will become apparent later.

The next step is to obtain a Miyata realization of y_{22}. Four ladders will be necessary in the present case. The component y_{22} functions are computed to be

$$y_{22a} = \frac{1}{d_1d_2 - d_0} \frac{d_2s^2 + d_2^2s + (d_1d_2 - d_0)}{s^3 + d_2s^2 + d_1s + d_0} \quad \text{(a)}$$

$$y_{22b} = \frac{7d_1 - d_2 - 7d_0}{d_1d_2 - d_0} \frac{s^2 + d_2s}{s^3 + d_2s^2 + d_1s + d_0} \quad \text{(b)}$$

$$y_{22c} = \frac{7d_2 - 7 - d_1}{d_1d_2 - d_0} \frac{d_1s^2 + d_0s}{s^3 + d_2s^2 + d_1s + d_0} \quad \text{(c)} \tag{8-98}$$

$$y_{22d} = \frac{1}{d_1d_2 - d_0} \frac{(d_1d_2 - d_0)s^3 + d_1^2s^2 + d_0d_1s}{s^3 + d_2s^2 + d_1s + d_0} \quad \text{(d)}$$

For these to be positive real, we have the additional restriction $d_1d_2 - d_0$
> 0. The ladder realizations of these functions are shown in Fig. 8-21.

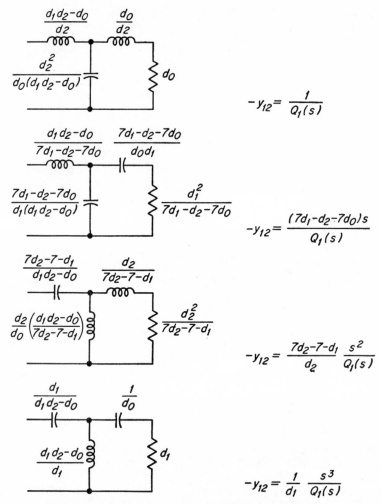

$$-y_{12} = \frac{1}{Q_1(s)}$$

$$-y_{12} = \frac{(7d_1 - d_2 - 7d_0)s}{Q_1(s)}$$

$$-y_{12} = \frac{7d_2 - 7 - d_1}{d_2}\frac{s^2}{Q_1(s)}$$

$$-y_{12} = \frac{1}{d_1}\frac{s^3}{Q_1(s)}$$

Fig. 8-21. Component ladders for numerical example.

The y_{12} function of each ladder is also shown in the figure, when we consider the ladders as two-ports. If the ladders are connected in parallel
without changing admittance level, the over-all y_{12} function will be

$$-y_{12} = \frac{\dfrac{1}{d_1}s^3 + \dfrac{7d_2 - 7 - d_1}{d_2}s^2 + (7d_1 - d_2 - 7d_0)s + 1}{s^3 + d_2s^2 + d_1s + d_0} \tag{8-99}$$

This expression is to be compared with the desired y_{12} function in Eqs. (8-95). If, by proper choice of the d coefficients, we can make some of the corresponding coefficients in the two numerators the same, the admittance level of the corresponding ladder will require no change. This, in turn, will lead to a simpler residual admittance. The advantage of retaining the coefficients in literal form until this point is now clear. Of course, for higher-order transfer functions, dealing with literal coefficients will become increasingly difficult.

The constant term in the numerator of the last equation does not depend on the d coefficients. We see that this term will become equal to the corresponding term in Eqs. (8-95) if we choose $K = 1/2$. With this choice of K the admittance level of the corresponding ladder will not require any change. Our objective now is to choose the d coefficients in such a way that, while satisfying the restrictions already imposed, as many as possible of the numerator coefficients in Eq. (8-99) are made equal to the corresponding ones in Eqs. (8-95), with $K = 1/2$. The various conditions that must be satisfied by the coefficients are

$$7d_2 - 7 - d_1 \geq 0$$

$$7d_1 - d_2 - 7d_0 \geq 0$$

$$d_1 d_2 - d_0 > 0$$

$$\frac{2K}{1/d_1} = d_1 \leq 1 \tag{8-100}$$

$$\frac{K}{(7d_2 - 7 - d_1)/d_2} = \frac{d_2}{2(7d_2 - 7 - d_1)} \leq 1$$

$$\frac{K}{7d_1 - d_2 - 7d_0} = \frac{1}{2(7d_1 - d_2 - 7d_0)} \leq 1$$

If any of the last three are satisfied with the equality sign, the admittance level of the corresponding ladder will require no change. We find that, with the choice $d_0 = 137/182$, $d_1 = 1$, and $d_2 = 16/13$, all three conditions will be satisfied with the equality sign. Hence no residual admittance will be necessary. Figure 8-22 shows the complete realization of the given transfer function with a gain constant $K = 1/2$.

The realization just obtained is appropriate if no load resistance is specified. If there is to be a finite load resistance, this realization will not be suitable. In order to provide a load resistance, we should have a non-minimum-real-part residual admittance so that removal of a shunt resistance from this will leave a pr remainder. However, you will note from Eq. (8-93) that the residual admittance Y_r is a sum of terms each of which has a zero at zero or infinity, or both, and hence, is minimum real-part. We conclude that the technique under discussion cannot be applied when a load resistance is specified.

However, a simple modification at the start will permit us to handle a finite resistance load as well. For a unit resistance load, $T_{12}(s) = -Y_{12}(s)$, the transfer admittance. Hence, after dividing numerator and denominator of the given function by $Q_1(s)$ as in Eq. (8-88), we make the identification

$$\frac{Q(s)}{Q_1(s)} = 1 + y_{22} \qquad \text{(a)}$$

or $$y_{22} = \frac{Q(s) - Q_1(s)}{Q_1(s)} \qquad \text{(b)}$$

(8-101)

The remainder of the procedure will apply in its entirety. There will now be some additional restrictions on the coefficients of Q_1; the last equation demands that the coefficients of Q_1 be less than the corresponding coefficients of Q. But this is not a severe restriction.

When we use this modification and leave the coefficients of $Q_1(s)$ in literal form, the computations become more tedious. If they become prohibitive, we may assign numerical values to some of the coefficients. But this leaves fewer parameters available for reducing the order of the residual admittance.

Let us now consider an alternative procedure which may be employed when a resistance termination is required. First we write

$$Y_{12}(s) = -\frac{P(s)}{Q(s)} = \frac{y_{12}}{1 + y_{22}} \qquad (8-102)$$

If we can decompose the denominator polynomial $Q(s)$ into the sum of two Hurwitz polynomials, whose ratio is a pr function, then dividing numerator and denominator by one of these two will lead to an identification of y_{12} and y_{22} according to the right-hand side of this equation. We have performed a similar operation on two occasions before. In the case of lossless two-ports the role of the two polynomials was filled by the even and odd parts of $Q(s)$. For RC two-ports we had a little more difficulty, but the job was simplified because the zeros of the desired two polynomials were real. There is no such simplification in the present case.

We shall now consider one method of decomposing a Hurwitz polynomial into the sum of two Hurwitz polynomials whose ratio is a pr function. This procedure was originally discovered by Weinberg (119). Suppose we write

$$Q(s) = Q_1(s) + K_1 Q_1'(s) \qquad (8-103)$$

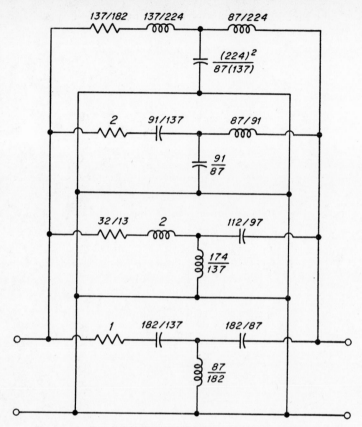

Fig. 8-22. Parallel-ladders realization of numerical example.

where K_1 is a positive constant and Q_1' is the derivative of the polynomial $Q_1(s)$ which we desire to be Hurwitz. When $K_1 = 0$, then $Q_1 = Q$. As K_1 increases from zero, the coefficients of Q_1 change in a continuous manner. For small values of K_1 the zeros of Q_1 will not differ greatly from those of Q_1. Consequently, since $Q(s)$ is Hurwitz, so also will $Q_1(s)$ be Hurwitz. There will be a limit beyond which K_1 cannot be increased if Q_1 is to remain Hurwitz.

To determine how the polynomial $Q_1(s)$ is obtained from a given $Q(s)$, let us write

$$Q(s) = s^n + \alpha_{n-1}s^{n-1} + \ldots + \alpha_1 s + \alpha_0 \qquad (8\text{-}104)$$

The coefficients in this polynomial are all known. The desired polynomial is now written with unknown coefficients and the derivative taken. Thus

$$Q_1(s) = s^n + \beta_{n-1}s^{n-1} + \ldots + \beta_1 s + \beta_0 \qquad \text{(a)}$$

$$K_1 Q_1'(s) = K_1[ns^{n-1} + (n-1)\beta_{n-1}s^{n-2} + \ldots + 2\beta_2 s + \beta_1] \qquad \text{(b)}$$

$$(8\text{-}105)$$

When we add the last two equations and compare coefficients with $Q(s)$, we get

$$\beta_{n-1} + nK_1 = \alpha_{n-1}$$

$$\beta_{n-2} + K_1(n - 1)\beta_{n-1} = \alpha_{n-2}$$

$$\beta_{n-3} + K_1(n - 2)\beta_{n-2} = \alpha_{n-3}$$

$$\cdots \cdots \cdots \cdots \cdots \cdots \cdots$$

$$\beta_1 + 2K_1\beta_2 = \alpha_1$$

$$\beta_0 + K_1\beta_1 = \alpha_0$$

(8-106)

In these n equations there are n unknown β coefficients and the unknown constant K_1. The equations can be solved consecutively for the β coefficients once a value of K_1 is chosen. After finding the β coefficients it is a simple matter to establish whether or not the polynomial $Q_1(s)$ is Hurwitz by expanding the ratio of its odd part to even part in a continued-fraction expansion. If we find $Q_1(s)$ is not Hurwitz, we can repeat the procedure with a smaller value of K_1. To this extent the procedure involves some trial-and-error.

Having decomposed the denominator polynomial, let us now turn to the realization. Equation (8-102) can now be written

$$Y_{12}(s) = \frac{-P(s)}{Q(s)} = \frac{-P}{Q_1 + K_1Q_1'} = \frac{-P/Q_1}{1 + K_1Q_1'/Q_1}$$

(8-107)

$$-y_{12} = \frac{P(s)}{Q_1(s)} \qquad \text{(a)}$$

$$y_{22} = \frac{K_1Q_1'(s)}{Q_1(s)} \qquad \text{(b)}$$

(8-108)

We must still determine whether or not Q_1'/Q_1 is positive real when $Q_1(s)$ is a Hurwitz polynomial. But this has already been established in Chap. 3 (see Prob. 3-11). Thus we have identified the y_{12} and y_{22} functions of the desired two-port which is to have a resistance load. The remainder of the procedure for obtaining a parallel-ladders realization which we have discussed can now be applied. However, now the only parameter that is available to provide flexibility is the constant K_1. Hence a high-order residual admittance will usually be obtained.

Note that the y_{22} obtained by this procedure has a zero at infinity. If the y parameters obtained in Eqs. (8-108) are to be a realizable set, y_{12} also must have a zero at infinity. This requires the original transfer function to have a zero at infinity. It follows that the contemplated decomposition technique cannot be applied to a function which has a non-zero value at infinity such as the one given in Eq. (8-85). For such functions we must decompose the denominator into two polynomials of the same degree.

8-7. Realization in a tree structure

In all the synthesis techniques we have discussed in this chapter, the gain constant that can be realized is determined after the synthesis is completed. In many cases this is considerably less than the maximum realizable value. We shall now discuss a procedure in which the gain constant is specified beforehand, its value being the maximum attainable, or close to it. An unbalanced realization is obtained for any realizable transfer function with no zeros on the positive real axis, i.e., both minimum-phase and nonminimum-phase. Transfer functions with positive real zeros are realized in a balanced structure. This technique is due to Fialkow and Gerst and is an extension of the RC realization procedure discussed in the last chapter.

A. *Unbalanced Realization*

Let us initially restrict ourselves to transfer functions which have no zeros on the positive real axis. (We still exclude poles on the $j\omega$ axis.†) If necessary, we can always use surplus factors to guarantee that none of the numerator coefficients of such a function are negative. An upper bound on the gain constant is established by the largest value which the normalized function attains at any point on the positive real axis, including zero and infinity. Using a value of K no greater than this upper bound, none of the numerator coefficients will be greater than the corresponding denominator coefficients.

Assuming that the given transfer function is written in this form, we have

$$T_{12}(s) = \frac{-y_{12}}{y_{22}} = \frac{P(s)}{Q(s)} = \frac{m_1 + n_1}{m_2 + n_2} \tag{8-109}$$

We shall initially assume an open-circuit output. The denominator polynomial $Q(s)$ is a Hurwitz polynomial. On the far right we have explicitly shown the even and odd parts of both numerator and denominator. Let us now formally make the following identification of the y parameters:

$$-y_{12} = \frac{P}{Q} = \frac{m_1 + n_1}{m_2 + n_2} \tag{a}$$
$$y_{22} = 1 \tag{b} \tag{8-110}$$

† Fialkow and Gerst have described a procedure which can be used to realize poles on the $j\omega$ axis as well. However, this case is of so little practical interest that we shall not discuss it here.

It may seem a little unnatural to require the short-circuit input admittance of the network to be constant, but it is certainly permissible.

Our objective is to seek a realization which consists of the parallel connection of two subnetworks. To this end, we must decompose y_{12} (and y_{22}) into the sum of two terms. One way in which this can be accomplished is the following:

$$-y_{12} = \frac{m_1}{m_2 + n_2} + \frac{n_1}{m_2 + n_2} \qquad \text{(a)}$$

$$-y_{12a} = \frac{m_1}{m_2 + n_2} \qquad \text{(b)} \quad \text{(8-111)}$$

$$-y_{12b} = \frac{n_1}{m_2 + n_2} \qquad \text{(c)}$$

Thus the two component y_{12} functions consist of the ratio of an odd or even polynomial to a Hurwitz polynomial. You will immediately recall that this is exactly the form of the transfer admittance of a resistance-terminated lossless two-port. Consider the LC network with a resistance load shown in Fig. 8-23(a). Let us denote its transfer admittance by Y_{12a}. If we break the output loop of this network, we will get the structure shown in the second half of the figure. The short-circuit transfer admittance of this network will certainly be the same as Y_{12a}.

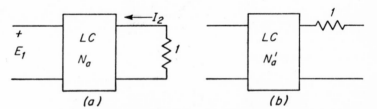

Fig. 8-23. Realization of component y_{12} function.

This observation reveals a synthesis procedure for each of the component y_{12} functions given in Eqs. (8-111). We simply treat each function as the transfer admittance of a resistance-terminated lossless two-port. After the two-port is realized, we perform the change shown in Fig. 8-23(b). The complete realization consists of the parallel connection of the resulting two-ports.

To implement this technique, let us write

$$-Y_{12a} = \frac{-y'_{12a}}{1 + y'_{22a}} = -y_{12a} = \frac{m_1/n_2}{1 + m_2/n_2} \qquad \text{(8-112)}$$

This leads to the identifications

$$-y'_{12a} = \frac{m_1}{n_2} \qquad \text{(a)}$$

$$\text{(8-113)}$$

$$y'_{22a} = \frac{m_2}{n_2} \qquad \text{(b)}$$

where the primed quantities refer to the parameters of the two-port in Fig. 8-23, exclusive of the resistance. The complete a network consists of the lossless two-port with the unity resistance in its output lead. Let us now compute the y_{22} function of the complete a network. We get

$$y_{22a} = \frac{1}{1 + 1/y'_{22a}} = \frac{m_2}{m_2 + n_2} \qquad \text{(8-114)}$$

The last step is obtained by substituting for y'_{22a} from Eqs. (8-113). Knowing both the y_{12} and the y_{22} parameters of the complete a network, we can form the voltage transfer ratio of this network as

$$T_{12a} = \frac{-y_{12a}}{y_{22a}} = \frac{m_1}{m_2} \qquad \text{(8-115)}$$

by substituting from Eqs. (8-112) and (8-114) for y_{12a} and y_{22a}, respectively.

This function is the ratio of two even polynomials in s, the denominator polynomial having only simple zeros on the $j\omega$ axis. Furthermore, none of the numerator coefficients is negative, and each is no greater than the corresponding denominator coefficient. These conditions are true because the two polynomials are the even parts of the numerator and denominator polynomials of the original transfer function, for which these conditions were true. Suppose that we now make the transformation $s^2 = p$ in this equation. The right-hand side will become an RC transfer function realizable in an unbalanced network according to the Fialkow-Gerst method described in Sec. 7-6. If we replace each R in this realization by an L having the same numerical value, this has the effect of carrying out the inverse transformation $p \rightarrow s^2$. A realization of the voltage transfer ratio T_{12a} in Eq. (8-115) is thus obtained.

Before we can celebrate our victory, however, one other consideration forces itself upon our attention. Suppose that y_{22a} in Eq. (8-114) (or y'_{22a} in the preceding equation) has a zero at infinity. This information is not contained in the voltage transfer ratio in Eq. (8-115). In order to guarantee the proper y_{22} function, let us take y_{22a} from Eq. (8-114) and write

$$\frac{1}{y_{22a}} = 1 + \frac{n_2}{m_2} = 1 + sk_{\infty a} + \frac{n'_2}{m_2} = 1 + sk_{\infty a} + \frac{1}{y''_{22a}} \qquad \text{(8-116)}$$

Thus, in addition to the unity resistance in the output lead, we shall have an inductance whose value is the residue at infinity of $1/y_{22a}$. The realization then takes the form shown in Fig. 8-24(a).

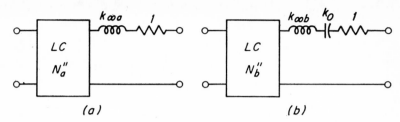

Fig. 8-24. Component two-ports in the complete realization.

The b network is treated in a completely similar manner. We contemplate realizing the y_{12b} function as a lossless two-port terminated in a unity resistance just as in Fig. 8-23. Similar to Eqs. (8-112) and (8-113), we write

$$-Y_{12b} = \frac{-y'_{12b}}{1 + y'_{22b}} = -y_{12b} = \frac{n_1/m_2}{1 + n_2/m_2} \qquad \text{(a)}$$

$$-y'_{12b} = \frac{n_1}{m_2} \qquad \text{(b)} \quad \text{(8-117)}$$

$$y'_{22b} = \frac{n_2}{m_2} \qquad \text{(c)}$$

If we now compute y_{22b}, we get

$$y_{22b} = \frac{1}{1 + 1/y'_{22b}} = \frac{n_2}{m_2 + n_2} \qquad \text{(8-118)}$$

This, together with $-y_{12b}$ from Eq. (8-117a), leads to the voltage transfer ratio

$$T_{12b} = \frac{-y_{12b}}{y_{22b}} = \frac{n_1}{n_2} \qquad \text{(8-119)}$$

This function has the same properties as T_{12a} (the factor s cancels from n_1 and n_2), and so the transformation $s^2 = p$ leads to an unbalanced RC realization. This is then changed to an LC network by replacing all R's by L's having the same numerical values, just as before.

This time we note that, since the factor s is canceled in the last equation, the network realizing T_{12b} does not carry the information that y_{22b} has a zero at $s = 0$. Of course, if y_{22b} has a zero at infinity, T_{12b} does not account for this either. So we write

$$\frac{1}{y_{22b}} = 1 + \frac{m_2}{n_2} = 1 + \frac{k_0}{s} + sk_{\infty b} + \frac{m'_2}{n_2/s} \qquad \text{(8-120)}$$

Thus, in addition to the unity resistance, we shall have a capacitance and an inductance in the series lead of the b network as shown in Fig. 8-24(b). Of course, one of the two inductances $k_{\infty a}$ or $k_{\infty b}$ will not be present.

It is interesting to add y_{22a} and y_{22b} in Eqs. (8-114) and (8-118). The result is

$$y_{22a} + y_{22b} = \frac{m_2 + n_2}{m_2 + n_2} = 1 \tag{8-121}$$

which is certainly heartening, inasmuch as this is the assumption we originally made.

This procedure can easily be extended to the case in which a resistance load is prescribed. Instead of Eq. (8-109), we shall then have

$$-Y_{12} = \frac{-y_{12}}{1 + y_{22}} = \frac{m_1 + n_1}{m_2 + n_2} \tag{8-122}$$

We can again choose $y_{22} = 1$, which then requires that

$$-y_{12} = 2\,\frac{m_1 + n_1}{m_2 + n_2} \tag{8-123}$$

The same procedure can now be employed. The only difference is that the maximum permissible value of the gain constant will now be only half what it was.

Let us illustrate this procedure by realizing the following nonminimum-phase transfer function:

$$T_{12} = K\,\frac{(2s^2 - s + 2)(s + 1)}{(s^2 + 6s + 1)(s + 1)} = K\,\frac{2s^3 + s^2 + s + 2}{s^3 + 7s^2 + 7s + 1} \tag{8-124}$$

This is the same function that we realized in Figs. 8-11, 8-19, and 8-22. The first job is to determine the maximum permissible value of K. The zero-frequency and infinite-frequency values of T_{12} permit $K = 1/2$. With $K = 1/2$ none of the numerator coefficients are negative, and each is no larger than the corresponding denominator coefficient. Hence there is no need to find the largest peak along the positive real axis. With $K = 1/2$ we get

$$T_{12a}(s) = \frac{s^2/2 + 1}{7s^2 + 1}$$

$$\frac{1}{y_{22a}} = 1 + \frac{s^3 + 7s}{7s^2 + 1} = 1 + \frac{s}{7} + \frac{48s}{7(7s^2 + 1)}$$

$$T_{12b}(s) = \frac{s^3 + s/2}{s^3 + 7s} = \frac{s^2 + \frac{1}{2}}{s^2 + 7}$$

$$\frac{1}{y_{22b}} = 1 + \frac{7s^2 + 1}{s(s^2 + 7)} = 1 + \frac{1}{7s} + \frac{48s}{7(s^2 + 7)}$$

Thus the a network has an inductance in the output, but the b network has not. When we make the transformation $s^2 = p$, both T_{12a} and T_{12b} become first-order transfer functions realizable in an L network. The complete realization of the original function as an unloaded two-port is shown in Fig. 8-25(a).

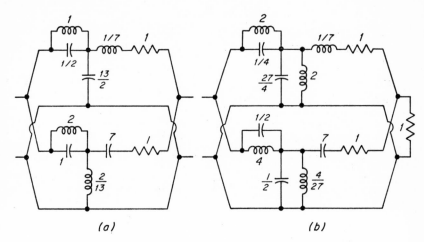

Fig. 8-25. Realization of numerical: (a) as unloaded network; (b) as resistance-loaded network.

If a unit resistance load is specified, the value of the gain constant that can be realized will be $K = 1/4$. With this value of K the only difference will be that T_{12a} and T_{12b} will be multiplied by $1/2$. The realization will take the form shown in Fig. 8-25(b).

B. Balanced Realization—Transmission Zeros on Positive Real Axis

To complete the discussion of a realization procedure which can be applied to any realizable transfer function, the only remaining consideration is the handling of transmission zeros on the positive real axis. We already have one possible realization in the form of cascaded constant-resistance networks. However, the gain constant is not known until after the realization has been obtained and is often quite small by this procedure.

In the present realization we fix the gain constant beforehand at a value permitted by the requirement that the size of the numerator coefficients of the transfer function be no greater than those of the corresponding denominator coefficients. Since there are positive real zeros, some of the numerator coefficients will be negative, so that we can write

$$T_{12}(s) = \frac{P(s)}{Q(s)} = \frac{P_1}{Q} - \frac{P_2}{Q} = T_{12a} - T_{12b} \qquad (8\text{-}125)$$

All the terms with positive coefficients are assigned to P_1, while those with negative coefficients are assigned to P_2. Each of the two transfer functions T_{12a} and T_{12b} is realizable as an unbalanced two-port by the method just described. The complete realization is then obtained by connecting these two networks in the manner shown in Fig. 8-26.

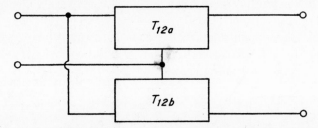

Fig. 8-26. Balanced two-port realization.

This procedure can be applied in the realization of nonminimum-phase functions, even if there are no zeros on the positive real axis, whenever some of the numerator coefficients of T_{12} are negative. By this procedure we avoid using surplus factors, with the accompanying increase in network complexity. However, we pay for this by having a balanced network realization instead of an unbalanced one.

PROBLEMS

8-1. The following functions are presented as the transfer voltage ratio of a resistance-terminated two-port. Obtain a ladder realization for each one as a constant-resistance ladder and also by the matrix-factorization methods of Sec. 8-4.

(a) $T_{12} = K \dfrac{s^2 + 2s + 3}{(s^2 + s + 2)(s + 1)}$

(b) $T_{12} = K \dfrac{(s^2 + 2)(s^2 + 3s + 3)}{(s^2 + 4s + 6)(s^2 + 3s + 4)}$

(c) $T_{12} = \dfrac{K}{(s + 1)(s^2 + s + 1)}$

(d) $T_{12} = K \left(\dfrac{s + 1}{s + 2}\right)^3$

(e) $T_{12} = \dfrac{K(s + 1)}{(s^2 + 3s + 4)(s^2 + 4s + 5)}$

(f) $T_{12} = K \left(\dfrac{s + 1}{s^2 + 2s + 2}\right)^2$

8-2. Obtain a ladder realization with resistive terminations at both ends for each of the transfer functions given in the previous problem. Let the ratio of input to output resistance be (a) $R_1/R_2 = 2$. (b) $R_1/R_2 = 10$.

8-3. Obtain a Fialkow-Gerst realization of the transfer functions in Prob. 8-1.

8-4. Discuss the possibility of realizing any minimum-phase transfer function as a cascade of pentode amplifier stages, as illustrated in Fig. P 8-4. The plate-circuit impedances constitute positive real functions into which the given transfer function can be factored. Obtain such a realization for the functions given in Prob. 8-1.

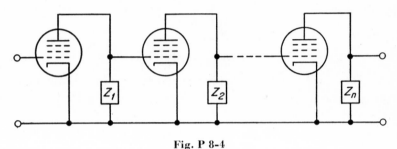

Fig. P 8-4

8-5. The following nonminimum-phase transfer functions are to be synthesized in a resistance terminated network:

$$(1) \quad T_{12}(s) = K \frac{s^2 - s + 2}{s^2 + 2s + 4}$$

$$(2) \quad T_{12}(s) = K \frac{s^2 - s + 1}{(s + 2)(s^2 + 2s + 2)}$$

$$(3) \quad T_{12}(s) = K \frac{s^2 - 3s + 4}{(s^2 + s + 1)^2}$$

(a) Obtain an unbalanced Fialkow-Gerst realization for the maximum realizable gain constant.

(b) To avoid using surplus factors with an attendant increase in number of elements, obtain a balanced realization in the form of **Fig. 8-26.**

(c) Obtain a realization as a constant-resistance ladder in cascade with simple all-pass lattices. Wherever possible, obtain an unbalanced equivalent of the lattices.

(d) Obtain a lattice realization (not constant-resistance), and convert to an unbalanced equivalent wherever possible.

(e) Obtain a parallel-ladders realization.

8-6. In the numerical example for which two alternative realizations are shown in Fig. 8-17, it is seen that, in addition to the resistance terminations at both ends, a shunt capacitance appears across either the input or the output. In many situations it would be desirable to have shunt capacitances across both the input and the output. Use a surplus factor $s + a$, with a suitable value of a, to obtain such a realization for the function under consideration.

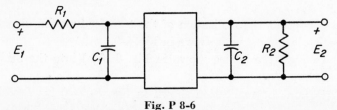

Fig. P 8-6

Show that a realization with capacitances across both input and output in the form of Fig. P 8-6 is always possible for a minimum-phase transfer function with no poles on the $j\omega$ axis, provided only that there be a transmission zero at infinity.

8-7. (a) Let $Z_{12} = (m_1 + n_1)/m + n$ be a minimum-phase transfer impedance. Discuss the possibility of realizing this function in the form of a balanced network as shown in Fig. P 8-7.

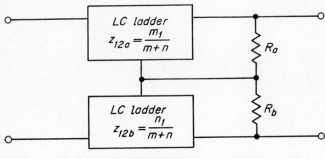

Fig. P 8-7

(b) Obtain a realization of the following transfer impedance in this form:

$$Z_{12} = K \frac{s^2 + s + 2}{20s^3 + 41s^2 + 62s + 3}$$

(c) Let the functions given in Prob. 8-1 be transfer impedance functions. Obtain realizations of these functions in the form of Fig. P 8-7.

8-8. Obtain a constant-resistance lattice realizing the transfer function given in Eq. (8-8) with the maximum realizable gain constant $K = 4.56$. Obtain both a Brune and a Bott-Duffin realization of the lattice arms.

8-9. Supply the details in the realization of the network shown in Fig. 8-3 starting with Eqs. (8-11). Convert the lattices to unbalanced equivalents yielding the network of Fig. 8-4.

8-10. Obtain an RC ladder with a unity resistance load realizing the transfer function given in Eq. (8-8). Compare the number of elements, ease of realization, and the achieved gain with the realization given in Fig. 8-4.

8-11. Carry out the realization of the transfer function given in Eq. (8-33) to obtain the network shown in Fig. 8-9.

8-12. Convert the lattice shown in Fig. 8-10(a) into the bridged-tee equivalent shown in Fig. 8-10(b).

8-13. Obtain the realization shown in Fig. 8-17(b) by choosing the factors given in Eqs. (8-72) in the reverse order with the choice $k_1 = k_2 = 2$.

8-14. Supply the details necessary to obtain the network shown in Fig. 8-19 from the functions given in Eqs. (8-87) with the values $K = 1/32$, $K_a = 1$, $K_{b1} = a = 5$ and $K_{b2} = 2/a = 2/5$.

9

The Approximation Problem

As pointed out in the Introduction, the two major divisions into which the field of network synthesis is divided are *approximation* and *realization*. The major emphasis in this book has been on the realization part of synthesis. That is, we assume that the network functions are already available as realizable rational functions, and our preoccupation is with obtaining an exact realization of these functions.

In any practical synthesis problem, performance criteria are specified in some manner, either graphically or analytically or as the response desired at a set of discrete points. The specified performance may be in terms of either magnitude or angle of a transfer function or the transient response desired for a given input function, or any combination of these. For a physical network there are interrelationships among all these, so that, when more than one of these functions is prescribed, we must ensure that they are consistent.

In a filter problem, for example, the design specifications usually involve a statement about the maximum permissible loss or maximum permissible reflection coefficient in a given frequency *passband*, the minimum allowable loss in another frequency band, the *stopband*, and a statement about the selectivity or the tolerable interval between the two bands. From these requirements a network function must be found which meets the specifications. At the same time it must be a realizable rational function for the class of network desired.

Another example is that of *loss equalizers* or *delay equalizers*. Certain fixed parts of a transmission system, such as a telephone cable, introduce distortions in the loss or delay. In order to compensate for these distortions, a corrective network is to be incorporated in the transmission system whose loss or delay characteristic is to be the inverse of the distortion introduced by the rest of the system.

The general problem, then, is the following: An arbitrary function of frequency is prescribed as a desirable magnitude or angle function. It is required to find a rational function of s whose j-axis magnitude or angle will approximate the prescribed function with a specified tolerance. At the same time the rational function must be a realizable one. The process of solving this problem can be labeled *function synthesis* or *function generation*.

There is great flexibility inherent in function synthesis. A given set of requirements may be met with many different rational functions, differing not only in their order but also in the locations and distributions of the poles and transmission zeros. Thus it may be possible to meet a given requirement by means of a function appropriate for a resistance-terminated lossless ladder, or more general unbalanced structure, or an RC network. It is therefore essential that a function synthesizer be well acquainted with realization procedures in order that he may generate functions which can be realized with some advantage, either computational or economic (in terms of number of elements) or pertaining to the network structure.

When the transient response to a given input function is specified, it is, of course, possible to reformulate this situation as a frequency-domain problem by the use of Laplace transforms. However, tolerances and permissible approximation errors which may be specified in the time domain are not easily translated, if at all, into tolerances in the frequency domain. Hence this procedure, which is theoretically possible, is not practically useful.

In this book we shall not treat the approximation problem in the time domain. In fact, there is some question whether the approximation problem should be treated at all. There is a considerable body of knowledge, both in the mathematical literature and in the literature of network theory, bearing on this subject. To treat the approximation problem in all its facets and with some generality requires the use of topics in mathematics which are normally considered "advanced," such as Jacobian elliptic functions. Even if we do not concede that these topics are advanced, we must admit that readers of this book probably do not have these mathematical topics as part of their background, at least to the same extent as, say, matrix algebra. Consequently, in order to treat the approximation problem effectively, it would be necessary to develop the required mathematical tools in considerable detail. Such an undertaking would constitute a considerable digression from the main theme of this book.

In this chapter we shall deal with certain simple cases of function generation, leaving the general treatment of the problem to a more comprehensive text. This does not imply that we shall just list a few isolated and unrelated techniques. On the contrary, even the simple problems that we treat will be handled in as general a manner as possible in the context of the preceding discussion.

9-1. Types of approximation

Before discussing techniques for approximating a given function by means of another, we must decide on what is meant by "approximation." How do we tell when we have a satisfactory approximation? What is our criterion? As a matter of fact we can state several different criteria for approximation, each of which may be suitable in different circumstances.

In presenting the following discussion, we shall use x as the independent variable instead of ω. This serves the purpose of indicating the generality of the discussion. Furthermore, the approximation is often carried out after a frequency transformation has been made, so that the variable is not always ω anyway.

Let $g(x)$ be a function of x prescribed in an interval (a,b) of the x axis, and let $f(x)$ be the approximating (realizable) function we are looking for. The function $g(x)$ may be the desired magnitude or angle function. It may be given as an analytic expression, but more usually it will be presented graphically. On the other hand $f(x)$ is a realizable network function. Let us assume that both $g(x)$ and $f(x)$ are well behaved in the interval (a,b). Then both of them can be expanded in Taylor's series about some point x_0. Let us suppose that both series converge in the interval (a,b). Write

$$g(x) = a_0 + a_1(x - x_0) + a_2(x - x_0)^2 + \ldots$$
$$f(x) = b_0 + b_1(x - x_0) + b_2(x - x_0)^2 + \ldots \tag{9-1}$$

The error in the approximation will be the difference between these two.
$$g(x) - f(x)$$
$$= (a_0 - b_0) + (a_1 - b_1)(x - x_0) + (a_2 - b_2)(x - x_0)^2 + \ldots \tag{9-2}$$

We shall say that $f(x)$ approximates $g(x)$ in the *Taylor sense* if the first k coefficients in the two series are equal term by term (counting a_0 and b_0 as the zeroth terms). In this case the error function will start out with the $(k + 1)$st power of x. Thus

$$g(x) - f(x) = (a_{k+1} - b_{k+1})(x - x_0)^{k+1} + \ldots \tag{9-3}$$

This equation is the Taylor's series of the error function about $x = x_0$, and so we see that the first k derivatives of the error function vanish at $x = x_0$. This is a property of the Taylor approximation. As a matter of fact, we can give the following definition: $f(x)$ *is a kth-order Taylor approximation to* $g(x)$ *at* $x = x_0$ *if the first* k *derivatives of* $g(x) - f(x)$ *vanish at* $x = x_0$.

In the Taylor-type approximation the error will vanish at $x = x_0$ and will become increasingly larger as $x - x_0$ increases. Thus the approximation favors values of x near x_0 at the expense of points near the ends of the interval. In fact, the approximation is made very good at one point, x_0, where not only do the two functions coincide but several of their derivatives do also.

Another error criterion is the *principle of least squares*. Instead of requiring very good approximation in the vicinity of a single point, we require that $f(x)$ be so chosen that the square of the error integrated over the interval be a minimum. More generally, we may wish certain parts of the interval to weigh more heavily than others. Hence we multiply the square of the error by a weighting function $w(x)$ before integrating. Thus the quantity that is to be minimized is

$$I = \int_a^b w(x) \, [g(x) - f(x)]^2 \, dx \qquad (9\text{-}4)$$

It should be quite apparent that the type of approximation obtained will depend on the weighting function $w(x)$. Normally $f(x)$ will oscillate about $g(x)$. For $w(x) = 1$ the peaks of the oscillations will increase toward the ends of the interval. The least-squares error criterion is difficult to apply and has not been used in simple approximation problems in the frequency domain. We shall not discuss it further in this chapter.

If the approximating function $f(x)$ oscillates about the desired function $g(x)$, the difference between the two will have a series of peaks and valleys. Some of these peaks may be large, and some may be small. The more complicated we make $f(x)$, that is, the more adjustable parameters $f(x)$ has, the better the approximation we should expect to get. Suppose that we restrict $f(x)$ to have n parameters [for instance, $f(x) = 1 + a_1 x + \ldots + a_n x^n$, a polynomial with n adjustable coefficients]. One way to define a "best" approximation is to adjust the parameters in such a way that the largest peak of the error is minimized. We shall call such an approximation a "Tchebyscheff approximation." More precisely, let $f(x, a_1, a_2, \ldots, a_n)$ be a function with n parameters. Then we shall say that $f(x)$ *approximates* $g(x)$ *in the Tchebyscheff sense if the parameters are deter-*

mined in such a way that the largest value of $|g(x) - f(x)|$ *in the interval* (a,b) *is a minimum.*†

Figure 9-1 shows an arbitrary function $g(x)$ and a function $f(x)$ having n parameters, which is an approximation to $g(x)$. The error curve is shown

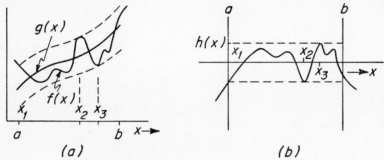

Fig. 9-1. Approximating function and error.

in part (b). We shall suppose that the parameters have been determined in order to minimize the largest peak in the error curve and that this largest peak is actually attained at r points. In the figure we have taken $r = 3$, one of the points being at one boundary of the interval. We have set $g - f = h(x,a_1,\ldots,a_n)$.

Let us now hold x constant and take the total differential of h.

$$dh = h_1\,da_1 + h_2\,da_2 + \ldots + h_n\,da_n \tag{9-5}$$

where we have set $h_k = \partial h/\partial a_k$. This gives us an expression for the change in h at any fixed value of x when the parameters a_k are changed. Let the r points at which the maximum value of $|h|$ is achieved be labeled x_1, x_2, $\ldots, x_r$. If we evaluate dh at these points, we shall get

$$dh(x_1) = h_1(x_1)\,da_1 + h_2(x_1)\,da_2 + \ldots + h_n(x_1)\,da_n$$
$$dh(x_2) = h_1(x_2)\,da_1 + h_2(x_2)\,da_2 + \ldots + h_n(x_2)\,da_n$$
$$\cdots\cdots\cdots\cdots\cdots\cdots\cdots\cdots\cdots\cdots\cdots\cdots\cdots\cdots \tag{9-6}$$
$$dh(x_r) = h_1(x_r)\,da_1 + h_2(x_r)\,da_2 + \ldots + h_n(x_r)\,da_n$$

If we arbitrarily choose values for the left-hand sides, this will be a set of r equations with n unknowns (the da's). The set *cannot* be solved if there are more equations than unknowns. It *can* be solved if $r \leq n$; in the case $r = n$ there will be a unique solution; with $r < n$, $n - r$ of the unknowns can be arbitrarily chosen and a solution for the rest obtained in terms of these.

† The following discussion of the Tchebyscheff approximation is adapted from Cauer (33).

Let us assume that at each of the points x_k at which the maximum of $|h|$ is attained the value of $dh(x_k)$ has the opposite sign to that of the value of $h(x_k)$. If the set of equations can be solved under these conditions, we shall have a contradiction. Solving the set of equations means that we can find values for da_k, the changes in the parameters, such that $dh(x_k)$ has the opposite sign from $h(x_k)$. If we make these changes in the parameters by adding da_k to a_k, we shall get a new set of parameters. With these new parameters what will happen to the largest peaks? Each positive peak will have a negative amount added to it, while each negative peak will have a positive amount added to it, and so the peaks will all become smaller in size. This is not possible, since we presumably had already chosen the parameters to give us the minimum possible peaks. The conclusion is that Eqs. (9-6) should not be solvable; that is, $r > n$. This means that in the interval (a,b) *there should be at least one more point at which $|h|$ reaches a value equal to its maximum peak than there are parameters in $f(x)$.*

The type of approximating functions we shall be looking for will be rational functions. Such a function having n parameters can be written

$$h(x) = \frac{1 + a_1 x + \ldots + a_m x^m}{1 + b_1 x + \ldots + b_{n-m} x^{n-m}} \qquad (9\text{-}7)$$

where we have normalized with respect to the value at $x = 0$. The maximum number of extremum points of such a function can be determined by finding the number of zeros of its derivative. Differentiating this function will lead to another rational function whose numerator is of the $(n - 1)$st degree, so that the maximum number of extremum points is $n - 1$. Even if the values of the function at all these extremum points are equal (and so all the peaks have attained the maximum value of $|h|$), the condition given in the previous paragraph will not be satisfied. If the values of $|h|$ at the two boundaries of the interval are also equal to the value of the peaks, there will be a total of exactly $n + 1$ points at which $|h|$ attains its maximum value and so the condition for a Tchebyscheff approximation will be satisfied. We can summarize the above discussion in the following theorem:

When a rational function $f(x)$ having n parameters approximates a real function $g(x)$ in a given interval in the Tchebyscheff sense [i.e., in such a way that the largest peak deviation of $f(x)$ from $g(x)$ is minimized], all the peak deviations of $f(x)$ from $g(x)$ will be equal in magnitude and will be equal to the magnitudes of the deviations at the edges of the interval.

This property leads to the nickname *equal ripple* for the Tchebyscheff approximation. The same holds true for a polynomial approximating function, since a polynomial is a special kind of rational function. We shall have more to say about this type of approximation in a later section.

9-2. Filter characteristic—maximally flat response

Having discussed the approximation criteria in which we shall be interested, we are now ready to consider methods of approximation. But before we proceed with this topic, let us review briefly the notation introduced in Chap. 4 regarding the magnitude and angle functions.

Let $F(s)$ denote an output/input transfer function. Then we can write

$$F(j\omega) = \epsilon^{\alpha(\omega^2)+j\phi(\omega)} \tag{9-8}$$

where $\alpha(\omega^2)$ is the logarithmic gain, an even function of ω, and ϕ is the angle. The analytic continuation of these functions can be written $\alpha(-s^2)$ and $\phi_1(s)$, respectively. If we take the square of $F(j\omega)$, the resulting function will have a magnitude which is the square of that of $F(j\omega)$ and an angle which is twice that of $F(j\omega)$. We can write

$$[F(j\omega)]^2 = [F(j\omega)F(-j\omega)]\frac{F(j\omega)}{F(-j\omega)} = G(\omega^2)A(j\omega) \tag{9-9}$$

where

$$G(\omega^2) = F(j\omega)F(-j\omega) = |F(j\omega)|^2 = \epsilon^{2\alpha(\omega^2)} \tag{9-10}$$

$$A(j\omega) = \frac{F(j\omega)}{F(-j\omega)} = \epsilon^{j2\phi(\omega)} \tag{9-11}$$

The function $G(\omega^2)$, or its analytic continuation $G(-s^2)$, is referred to as the *magnitude squared* function, while $A(j\omega)$, or its analytic continuation $A(s)$, we have labeled the *A function*.

We are now ready to discuss the approximation problem in some simple cases. For a low-pass filter the ideal transfer function has a uniform magnitude over a frequency range extending from zero to some cutoff value and an angle which varies linearly over this range. Thus the ideal transfer function can be written

$$F_i(j\omega) = \epsilon^{-j(\omega/\omega_0)} \qquad 0 \le \frac{|\omega|}{\omega_0} \le 1$$

$$\tag{9-12}$$

$$F_i(j\omega) = 0 \qquad \frac{|\omega|}{\omega_0} > 1$$

where the subscript i stands for ideal and ω_0 is the normalizing frequency. We shall write $\omega' = \omega/\omega_0$ and then drop the prime for simplicity. This is equivalent to letting $\omega_0 = 1$. The magnitude has also been normalized.

This ideal function is not realizable, and so we are confronted with the need for approximating it. The approximating function must be a rational function whose squared magnitude approximates unity in the passband and zero outside the band. Let us initially assume that the transmission zeros are all at infinity. Then we can write

$$G(\omega^2) = |F(j\omega)|^2 = \frac{1}{P(\omega^2)} = \frac{1}{1 + B_1\omega^2 + \ldots + B_n\omega^{2n}} \quad (9\text{-}13)$$

It remains for us to determine the index n and the B coefficients in such a way that the desired function is approximated. The leading coefficient is chosen to be unity in order to make the approximating function and the desired function coincide at $\omega = 0$. In the passband the error function will be

$$G_i(\omega^2) - G(\omega^2) = 1 - \frac{1}{P(\omega^2)} = \frac{P - 1}{P}$$

$$= \frac{B_1\omega^2 + B_2\omega^4 + \ldots + B_n\omega^{2n}}{1 + B_1\omega^2 + \ldots + B_n\omega^{2n}} \quad (9\text{-}14)$$

Letting $x = \omega^2$, this becomes

$$G_i(x) - G(x) = \frac{P(x) - 1}{P(x)} = \frac{B_1x + B_2x^2 + \ldots + B_nx^n}{1 + B_1x + \ldots + B_nx^n} \quad (9\text{-}15)$$

The method of procedure for determining the B coefficients will depend on the approximation criterion we apply. If we seek a Taylor-type approximation, we shall require a few of the leading derivatives of the error to vanish at $x = 0$. To be more precise, for a kth-order Taylor approximation we should require the first k derivatives of the error to be zero. The first three derivatives of Eq. (9-15) evaluated at $x = 0$ are

$$\frac{d}{dx}\left(\frac{P-1}{P}\right)\bigg|_0 = \frac{P'}{P^2}\bigg|_0 = B_1 \quad \text{(a)}$$

$$\frac{d^2}{dx^2}\left(\frac{P-1}{P}\right)\bigg|_0 = \frac{PP'' - 2(P')^2}{P^3}\bigg|_0 = 2(B_2 - B_1^2) \quad \text{(b)} \quad (9\text{-}16)$$

$$\frac{d^3}{dx^3}\left(\frac{P-1}{P}\right)\bigg|_0$$

$$= \frac{P^2P''' - 6PP'P'' - 6(P')^3}{P^4}\bigg|_0 = 6(B_3 - 2B_1B_2 - B_1^3) \quad \text{(c)}$$

The primes indicate differentiation with respect to x. If the first derivative is to vanish, we must have $B_1 = 0$. Similarly, the vanishing of the second and third derivatives requires $B_2 = 0$ and $B_3 = 0$. You can readily appreciate that a kth-order Taylor approximation will require the vanishing of B_k and all lower-order coefficients. Thus the function

$$G(\omega^2) = \frac{1}{1 + B_{k+1}\omega^{2(k+1)} + \ldots + B_n\omega^{2n}} \tag{9-17}$$

will give a kth-order Taylor approximation to unity in the interval $|\omega| < 1$. For a given value of n the highest-order Taylor approximation possible with a function of the form of Eq. (9-13) will be n. In this case the function will reduce to

$$G(\omega^2) = \frac{1}{1 + B_n\omega^{2n}} \tag{9-18}$$

A response function such as this, in which the maximum possible number of derivatives is zero at the origin, is called a *maximally flat* response.

At the nominal band edge ($\omega = 1$) this will become

$$G(1) = \frac{1}{1 + B_n} \tag{9-19}$$

The coefficient B_n will determine the level of the response at the band edge. Thus, for $B_n = 1$, the nominal band edge is the half-power point. In this case the maximally flat approximation becomes

$$G(\omega^2) = \frac{1}{1 + \omega^{2n}} \tag{9-20}$$

It remains to find the function $F(s)$, knowing the function $G(\omega^2)$. If we replace ω^2 by $-s^2$ in the last equation, we shall get

$$G(-s^2) = F(s)F(-s) = \frac{1}{1 + (-1)^n s^{2n}} \tag{9-21}$$

The poles of this function can be found by setting the denominator equal to zero. This will give $s^{2n} = \pm 1$, the plus and minus signs holding for n odd or even, respectively. For the two cases we obtain

$$s_k = \epsilon^{j\frac{2k-1}{n}\frac{\pi}{2}} \qquad n \text{ even}$$

no roots at ±90° (j ω axis)

$$\tag{9-22}$$

$$s_k = \epsilon^{j\frac{2k}{n}\frac{\pi}{2}} \qquad n \text{ odd}$$

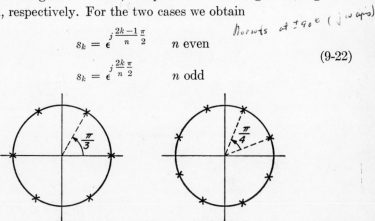

(a) n=3   (b) n=4

Fig. 9-2. Pole locations for maximally flat response.

These show that the poles lie on a unit circle with equal angular spacing. Figure 9-2 shows the pole positions for $n = 3$ and $n = 4$.

It is now a simple matter to form $F(s)$. All the poles of $F(s)$ should lie in the left half plane, while all those of $F(-s)$ should lie in the right half plane. Thus all the poles of Eq. (9-21) which lie in the left half plane belong to $F(s)$. The low-pass maximally flat transfer function can now be written

$$F(s) = \frac{1}{P_{Bn}} = \frac{1}{1 + b_1 s + b_2 s^2 + \ldots + s^n} \qquad (9\text{-}23)$$

where the polynomial P_{Bn} is called the nth-order *Butterworth* polynomial.

It should not be necessary to compute the required Butterworth polynomial each time the maximally flat approximation is to be used. These can be computed and tabulated once and for all. Tables 9-1 and 9-2 give the coefficients and the factors, respectively, of the Butterworth polynomials up to order 10 when the half-power angular frequency has been normalized to unity.

We have obtained a special kind of rational function giving a Taylor-type approximation of the ideal filter function—one that has all its transmission zeros at infinity. Let us now consider the case when $F(s)$ has finite zeros as well. However, we shall require at least a simple zero at infinity to satisfy the requirement outside the band. With this restriction we can write

$$G(\omega^2) = |F(j\omega)|^2 = \frac{P_1(\omega^2)}{P_2(\omega^2)} = \frac{1 + A_1\omega^2 + \ldots + A_m\omega^{2m}}{1 + B_1\omega^2 + \ldots + B_n\omega^{2n}} \qquad (9\text{-}24)$$

Again putting $\omega = x$ and considering the error function $G_i - G$ in the passband, we get

$$G_i - G = 1 - \frac{P_1(x)}{P_2(x)}$$

$$= \frac{(B_1 - A_1)x + \ldots + (B_m - A_m)x^m + B_{m+1}x^{m+1} + \ldots + B_n x^n}{1 + B_1 x + \ldots + B_n x^n}$$

$$(9\text{-}25)$$

The first three derivatives of this expression evaluated at $x = 0$ are

$$\frac{d}{dx}\left(1 - \frac{P_1}{P_2}\right)\bigg|_0 = \frac{P_1 P_2' - P_2 P_1'}{P_2^2}\bigg|_0$$

$$= B_1 - A_1 \qquad (a)$$

$$\frac{d^2}{dx^2}\left(1 - \frac{P_1}{P_2}\right)\bigg|_0 = \frac{P_2(P_1 P_2'' - P_2 P_1'') - 2P_2'(P_1 P_2' - P_2 P_1')}{P_2^3} \qquad (9\text{-}26)$$

$$= (B_2 - A_2) - 2B_1(B_1 - A_1) \qquad (b)$$

$$\frac{d^3}{dx^3}\left(1 - \frac{P_1}{P_2}\right)\bigg|_0 = 6(B_3 - A_3) - 4B_1(B_2 - A_2) + 2(A_1B_2 - A_2B_1)$$

$$+2B_1(3B_1 - 4B_2 - 2)(B_1 - A_1) \qquad \text{(c)}$$

The vanishing of the first derivative requires $A_1 = B_1$. Similarly, the vanishing of the second derivative requires $A_2 = B_2$ in addition to the previous requirement. The expressions for the higher derivatives become algebraically complicated, but you can appreciate that for a kth-order Taylor approximation corresponding coefficients of the numerator and denominator must be equal up to the kth power of x, provided that the numerator is at least of the kth power. If k is greater than m (the degree of the numerator), then the denominator coefficients from B_{m+1} to B_k must vanish. For example, suppose that the numerator of Eq. (9-24) is $1 + A_1\omega^2$, that is, that A_2 and higher coefficients are zero. Then, to make the second derivative in Eq. (9-26) vanish, besides $A_1 = B_1$ we must have $B_2 = 0$. Similarly, the vanishing of the third derivative will require these conditions plus the condition $B_3 = 0$.

So, for a given value of n, the highest-order Taylor approximation with a function of the form of Eq. (9-24) is

$$G(\omega^2) = \frac{1 + B_1\omega^2 + \ldots + B_m\omega^{2m}}{1 + B_1\omega^2 + \ldots + B_m\omega^{2m} + B_n\omega^{2n}} \qquad (9\text{-}27)$$

The B coefficients are still arbitrary and can be chosen to satisfy other requirements. One relationship among the B's is obtained by specifying the half-power frequency. The numerator coefficients are often chosen to give desired zeros of transmission. The problem of finding the pole locations now is the problem of factoring a polynomial of high degree. This is a tedious task for hand computation but becomes a simple one for a high-speed electronic computer.

Up to this point in the discussion of the maximally flat approximation, we have concentrated on the behavior of the approximating function in the passband. It is also of interest to determine the behavior in the stopband, in particular the asymptotic behavior for large values of ω. In this respect it is more convenient to talk about the logarithm of the magnitude function rather than the magnitude itself.

Glance back at Eq. (9-10). We shall refer to α as the *logarithmic gain* or simply the *gain*. The negative of α is referred to as the *loss*. It is measured in nepers. However, it is common practice to use the unit *decibel* (db), which is $20 \log \epsilon = 8.686$ times the number of nepers. We shall be deliberately inconsistent in our notation to the extent that we shall use the symbol α to represent $\ln |F(j\omega)|$ as well as $20 \log |F(j\omega)|$ in order to

Table 9-1. Coefficients of Butterworth Polynomials

Order n	b_1	b_2	b_3	b_4	b_5	b_6	b_7	b_8	b_9
2	1.4142								
3	2.0000	2.0000							
4	2.6131	3.4142	2.6131						
5	3.2361	5.2361	5.2361	3.2361					
6	3.8637	7.4641	9.1416	7.4641	3.8637				
7	4.4940	10.0978	14.5920	14.5920	10.0978	4.4940			
8	5.1528	13.1371	21.8462	25.6884	21.8462	13.1371	5.1258		
9	5.7588	16.5817	31.1634	41.9864	41.9864	31.1634	16.5817	5.7588	
10	6.3925	20.4317	42.8021	64.8824	74.2334	64.8824	42.8021	20.4317	6.3925

Note: b_0 and b_n are always unity.

Table 9-2. Factors of Butterworth Polynomials

Order n	Butterworth polynomial P_{Bn}
1	$s + 1$
2	$s^2 + 1.4142s + 1$
3	$(s + 1)(s^2 + s + 1)$
4	$(s^2 + 0.7654s + 1)(s^2 + 1.8478s + 1)$
5	$(s + 1)(s^2 + 0.6180s + 1)(s^2 + 1.6180s + 1)$
6	$(s^2 + 0.5176s + 1)(s^2 + 1.4142s + 1)(s^2 + 1.9319s + 1)$
7	$(s + 1)(s^2 + 0.4450s + 1)(s^2 + 1.2470s + 1)(s^2 + 1.8019s + 1)$
8	$(s^2 + 0.3902s + 1)(s^2 + 1.1111s + 1)(s^2 + 1.1663s + 1)(s^2 + 1.9616s + 1)$
9	$(s + 1)(s^2 + 0.3473s + 1)(s^2 + s + 1)(s^2 + 1.5321s + 1)(s^2 + 1.8794s + 1)$
10	$(s^2 + 0.3129s + 1)(s^2 + 0.9080s + 1)(s^2 + 1.4142s + 1)(s^2 + 1.7820s + 1)(s^2 + 1.9754s + 1)$

avoid defining a new symbol that differs from α merely by a multiplicative constant.

It is also common practice to change the frequency variable as well. Let us write

$$\omega = 10^v$$
$$\text{or} \qquad v = \log \omega \qquad (9\text{-}28)$$

The variable v is measured in *decades*. Thus the frequency interval between one frequency ω_1 and a second frequency $\omega_2 = 10\omega_1$ is a decade. Another unit, called an *octave*, is also in common use. This is defined by writing $\omega = 2^\mu$ or $\mu = \log 2 \log \omega \doteq 0.3 \log \omega$. Hence $\mu \doteq 0.3v$.

Now return to the maximally flat function in Eq. (9-20). The band edge is at $\omega = 1$. For large values of ω

$$G = \epsilon^{2\alpha} \longrightarrow \frac{1}{\omega^{2n}}$$

$$\text{or} \qquad -\alpha = 20n \log \omega \qquad (9\text{-}29)$$

If we now substitute for $\log \omega$ from the previous equation, we shall get

$$-\alpha = 20nv \qquad (9\text{-}30)$$

This is the equation of a straight line with a slope of $20n$ db per decade. In terms of octaves, since an octave is approximately three-tenths of a decade, the slope is approximately $6n$ db per octave.

When we combine this information with the fact that the maximally flat response is asymptotic to unity magnitude (or zero loss) in the pass-band, we get the diagram shown in Fig. 9-3. The band edge, $\omega = 1$, corre-

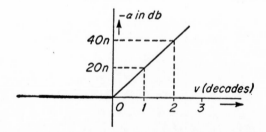

Fig. 9-3. Asymptotic behavior of Butterworth response.

sponds to the point $v = 0$ according to Eqs. (9-28). The farther we go from the band edge in either direction, the closer is the maximally flat approximation to its asymptotic values. The greatest error occurs at $v = 0$ ($\omega = 1$). At this point $G = 1/2$ so that $-\alpha = 10 \log 2 \doteq 3$ db. This is seen to be independent of the order n of the approximation.

Let us now illustrate the use of the maximally flat approximation by generating a suitable transfer function satisfying a given set of specifications. It is desired to design a low-pass filter with a useful band extending to $\omega_0 = 10,000$ radians per sec to operate between a current source and a resistive load of 500 ohms. In this band the magnitude of the transfer impedance is not to deviate from its nominal value by more than 10 per cent. At and beyond $\omega = 3\omega_0$, $|Z_{12}|$ should remain below 5 per cent of its nominal passband value.

Note that the half-power (or 3-db) frequency is not specified. The specified value of the load resistance has no bearing on the approximation; it will affect the element values after a realization has been obtained.

Let us normalize the frequency variable with respect to ω_0. In the present case we must use Eq. (9-18) since B_n is not unity. At $\omega = 1$ we shall have

$$|F(j\omega)| = \sqrt{G(\omega^2)} = \frac{1}{\sqrt{1 + B_n}} = 1 - 0.1$$

Hence we find

$$B_n = 0.245$$

A glance at Eq. (9-18) will show that the half-power frequency, which we shall label ω_h, is obtained by setting $B_n\omega_h^{2n} = 1$. Hence, before we can find ω_h, we must determine the index n. This is found from the stopband requirement. Thus

$$|F(j3)| = \frac{1}{\sqrt{1 + B_n 3^{2n}}} \leq 0.05$$

It follows that

$$n \geq \frac{\log 399/B_n}{2 \log 3} = 3.36$$

so that we must choose $n = 4$, the next highest integer.

With this value of n we can now find the half-power frequency from the expression $B_n\omega_h^{2n} = 1$. The result is

$$\omega_h = 1.192$$

based on the normalization $\omega_0 = 1$. If we want to use the tables of Butterworth polynomials which are based on the normalization $\omega_h = 1$, we must now change our normalization. Actually, as far as the approximation problem is concerned, we do not do anything. After a network is realized, we compute the "unnormalized" element values, using $1.192\omega_0$ as the normalizing frequency rather than ω_0. Using Table 9-1, we get for the desired transfer impedance

$$Z_{12}(s) = \frac{1}{1 + 2.6131s + 3.4142s^2 + 2.6131s^3 + s^4} \tag{9-31}$$

This function can be realized as a resistance-terminated lossless ladder network with series inductances and shunt capacitances.

9-3. Maximally flat delay

In the preceding section we directed attention to the approximation of the *magnitude* of the ideal function given in Eqs. (9-12). Let us now consider the problem of approximating the *angle* of the function. The ideal angle function is a linear function of ω. Instead of dealing with the angle function, it is often convenient to consider the *delay D* (also called *group delay*). This is defined as the negative derivative of the angle. Thus

$$D(j\omega) = -\frac{d\phi(\omega)}{d\omega} \qquad (9\text{-}32)$$

where $\phi(\omega)$ is the angle of $F(j\omega)$. The analytic continuation of this function can be written

$$D(s) = -\frac{d\phi_1(s)}{ds} \qquad (9\text{-}33)$$

Since $\phi_1(s)$ reduces to $j\phi(\omega)$ when $s = j\omega$, this equation reduces to the previous one when $s = j\omega$.

The ideal delay is obtained by differentiating the ideal angle function, which is just $\phi = -\omega/\omega_0$. Thus the ideal delay is just a constant, $t_0 = 1/\omega_0$. Since we normalize by taking $\omega_0 = 1$, the ideal delay is just unity.

Let us again seek a rational approximating function $F(s)$ all of whose zeros lie at infinity. Thus the function we are seeking is

$$F(s) = \frac{1}{1 + a_1 s + a_2 s^2 + \ldots + a_n s^n} = \frac{1}{P(s)} \qquad (9\text{-}34)$$

where $P(s)$ is a Hurwitz polynomial. To obtain the delay function corresponding to this transfer function, let us first write the function $\phi_1(s)$ in terms of $F(s)$ by taking the logarithm of the A function defined in Eq. (9-11). The result is

$$\phi_1(s) = \frac{1}{2} \ln \frac{F(s)}{F(-s)} \qquad (9\text{-}35)$$

When this is substituted into Eq. (9-33) and when Eq. (9-34) is used for $F(s)$, we get

$$D(s) = -\frac{1}{2}\frac{d}{ds}\ln\frac{P(-s)}{P(s)} = \frac{1}{2}\left[\frac{P'(s)}{P(s)} - \frac{P'(-s)}{P(-s)}\right]$$

$$= \frac{a_1 + (3a_3 - a_1 a_2)s^2 + (a_2 a_3 - 3a_1 a_4 + 5a_5)s^4 + \ldots}{1 + (2a_2 - a_1^2)s^2 + (2a_4 - 2a_1 a_3 + a_2^2)s^4 + (2a_6 - 2a_1 a_5 + 2a_2 a_4 - a_3^2)s^6 + \ldots} \qquad (9\text{-}36)$$

Since ϕ_1 is an odd function of s, the delay will be an even function. Hence we can treat it in the same manner that we treated the squared magnitude function.

The ideal $\phi_1(s)$ function corresponding to the ideal transfer function in Eqs. (9-12) is $\phi_1 = -s$. Hence the ideal delay function is $D_i = 1$. Our problem, then, is to choose the coefficients of $F(s)$ in such a way that the right-hand side of Eq. (9-36) approximates unity in the desired manner.

Let us consider a Taylor-type approximation for the delay. According to what we established in the previous section, a maximally flat approximation requires corresponding coefficients in the numerator and denominator of the right-hand side of Eq. (9-36) to be equal up to the highest power of the numerator. With this condition a set of simultaneous equations involving the a coefficients will be obtained. These equations will be nonlinear and difficult to solve when $F(s)$ is of high order.

Let us illustrate the procedure for a relatively simple case. Suppose that

$$F(s) = \frac{1}{1 + a_1 s + a_2 s^2 + a_3 s^3} \tag{9-37}$$

Then
$$P(s) = 1 + a_1 s + a_2 s^2 + a_3 s^3$$
$$P(-s) = 1 - a_1 s + a_2 s^2 - a_3 s^3$$
$$P'(s) = a_1 + 2a_2 s + 3a_3 s^2$$
$$P'(-s) = -a_1 + 2a_2 s - 3a_3 s^2$$

$$D(s) = \frac{a_1 + (3a_3 - a_1 a_2)s^2 + a_2 a_3 s^4}{1 + (2a_2 - a_1^2)s^2 + (a_2^2 - 2a_1 a_3)s^4 - a_3^2 s^6} \tag{9-38}$$

For a maximally flat delay we equate all the numerator coefficients to the corresponding denominator coefficients and get

$$a_1 = 1$$
$$3a_3 - a_1 a_2 = 2a_2 - a_1^2$$
$$a_2 a_3 = a_2^2 - 2a_1 a_3$$

The solution of this set of equations leads to

$$a_1 = 1 \qquad a_2 = \tfrac{2}{5} \qquad a_3 = \tfrac{1}{15}$$

so that
$$F(s) = \frac{1}{1 + s + \tfrac{2}{5}s^2 + \tfrac{1}{15}s^3} \tag{9-39}$$

Figure 9-4 shows the comparative pole locations of this function and the third-order maximally flat magnitude function. The delay scale has been reduced by a factor 2.32 in order to make the two real poles coincide.

The procedure for obtaining a maximally flat delay that has just been

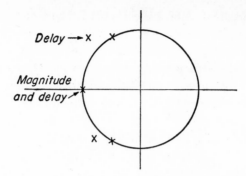

Fig. 9-4. Pole locations for third-order maximally flat magnitude and delay.

outlined is straightforward. However, solution of the simultaneous non-linear equations for the a coefficients becomes extremely difficult for high-order transfer functions.

Let us now consider an alternative approach to the problem of approximating a flat delay. The following discussion is based on some work of Leo Storch (112).

The ideal transfer function that we wish to approximate can be written

$$F_i(s) = \epsilon^{-s} = \frac{1}{\epsilon^s} = \frac{1}{\cosh s + \sinh s} \tag{9-40}$$

What we would like to do is to approximate the denominator of the right-hand side by means of a polynomial. Of course, this polynomial must be Hurwitz. Let us write

$$F(s) = \frac{b_0}{b_0 + b_1 s + \ldots + b_n s^n} = \frac{b_0}{m(s) + n(s)} = \frac{b_0}{P(s)} \tag{9-41}$$

We have written the denominator in the familiar form of the sum of its even and odd parts. The constant in the numerator is included in order for the function to have a unit magnitude at the origin. We want to determine the b coefficients in such a way that Eq. (9-41) approximates Eq. (9-40).

One method of procedure that is natural to think of is to expand ϵ^s in Eq. (9-40) in a Maclaurin series and retain only the first n terms. This will provide an approximation—what kind of approximation we do not know, but an approximation. We have no assurance beforehand that the nth degree polynomial we get by this method will even be Hurwitz. As a matter of fact, it turns out that, for $n > 4$, the polynomial is *not* Hurwitz (68). Hence, we cannot use this procedure for high-order functions, no matter how good the approximation.

A glance back at Eq. (9-40) shows that the denominator is already written as the sum of an even and an odd function. Suppose that we take the ratio of the even part (cosh s) to the odd part (sinh s). The desired approximation of this function is m/n, which is a reactance function, in view of the fact that $m + n$ must be a Hurwitz polynomial. Both cosh s and sinh s can be expanded in a Taylor's series about the origin. Then

$$\frac{\cosh s}{\sinh s} = \frac{1 + \frac{s^2}{2} + \frac{s^4}{4!} + \frac{s^6}{6!} + \cdots}{s + \frac{s^3}{3!} + \frac{s^5}{5!} + \cdots} \tag{9-42}$$

Let us now expand the right-hand side of this equation in an infinite continued fraction. The result is easily found to be

$$\frac{\cosh s}{\sinh s} = \frac{1}{s} + \cfrac{1}{\cfrac{3}{s} + \cfrac{1}{\cfrac{5}{s} + \cfrac{1}{\cfrac{7}{s} + \cfrac{1}{\cfrac{9}{s} + \cdot}}}} \tag{9-43}$$

Up to this point, no approximation has been made. Suppose that this infinite expansion is cut off at the nth term. The result will be an approximation to cosh s/sinh s in the vicinity of $s = 0$. Again, we do not know the type of approximation. The truncated continued-fraction expansion is

$$\frac{m(s)}{n(s)} = \frac{1}{s} + \cfrac{1}{\cfrac{3}{s} + \cfrac{1}{\cfrac{5}{s} + \cdot \cdot \cdot + \cfrac{1}{\cfrac{2n-1}{s}}}} \tag{9-44}$$

Note that all the coefficients are positive. Hence this looks like the Cauer expansion of a reactance function. If we recombine the expansion, we shall get a reactance function which is the ratio of an even to an odd polynomial. (The left-hand side of the last equation was written in anticipation of this fact.) The sum of m and n will be the desired Hurwitz polynomial.

It is clear that the coefficients of m and n will depend on the number of terms that are retained in the continued-fraction expansion. Let us consider the case when $n = 3$; in this case the continued-fraction expansion will be

$$\frac{m}{n} = \frac{1}{s} + \cfrac{1}{\cfrac{3}{s} + \cfrac{1}{\cfrac{5}{s}}} = \frac{15 + 6s^2}{15s + s^3} \qquad (9\text{-}45)$$

The corresponding transfer function will be

$$F(s) = \frac{15}{15 + 15s + 6s^2 + s^3} = \frac{1}{1 + s + \frac{2}{5}s^2 + \frac{1}{15}s^3} \qquad (9\text{-}46)$$

An extremely interesting observation can be made by comparing this expression with Eq. (9-39), which is the transfer function for a maximally flat delay approximation—the two are identical! Thus the procedure we have just followed gives a maximally flat approximation to the delay, at least in the case $n = 3$. The question naturally arises, Is this also true for other orders of approximation? To provide the answer to this question will require a slight digression.

We have already noted that the coefficients in the polynomial $P(s)$, which we get by recombining the continued fraction in Eq. (9-44), will depend on the order n. For any desired order we can get the numerical values of the coefficients. However, it would be useful to have a general expression for the coefficients. Let us make the substitution $p = 1/s$ in Eq. (9-44); the left-hand side will now be a function of p—call it $m_D(p)/n_D(p)$. Upon recombining the continued fraction and adding the numerator and denominator, we shall get a polynomial which we shall label $P_D(p)$. For a few low orders these will be

$$P_D(p) = 1 + 3p + 3p^2 \qquad\qquad\qquad\quad n = 2$$
$$P_D(p) = 1 + 2 \cdot 3p + 3 \cdot 5p^2 + 3 \cdot 5p^3 \qquad\qquad n = 3 \qquad (9\text{-}47)$$
$$P_D(p) = 1 + 2 \cdot 5p + 3 \cdot 3 \cdot 5p^2 + 3 \cdot 5 \cdot 7p^3 + 3 \cdot 5 \cdot 7p^4 \qquad n = 4$$

where

$$P_D(p) = m_D(p) + n_D(p) = b_0' + b_1'p + b_2'p^2 + \ldots + b_n'p^n \qquad (9\text{-}48)$$

From these expressions we can work out the following general formula for the b' coefficients:

$$b_k' = \frac{(n + k)!}{2^k(n - k)!k!} \qquad k = 0, 1, \ldots, n \qquad (9\text{-}49)$$

Hence we can write the nth order polynomial as

$$P_{Dn}(p) = \sum_{k=0}^{n} \frac{(n + k)!}{(n - k)!k!}\left(\frac{p}{2}\right)^k \qquad (9\text{-}50)$$

It turns out that these polynomials arise in other applications as well and have been called *Bessel* polynomials.† (We should therefore label them P_B. However, we have already used the subscript B for the Butterworth polynomials. The subscript D was chosen to imply *Delay*.) To convert back to the variable s, note that

$$P_n(s) = s^n P_{Dn}(p) = s^n P_{Dn}\left(\frac{1}{s}\right) \tag{9-51}$$

so that

$$P_n(s) = \sum_{k=0}^{n} \frac{(n+k)!}{2^k(n-k)!k!} s^{n-k} \tag{9-52}$$

For convenience, we can replace the index $n - k$ by k to get the following final form:

$$P_n(s) = \sum_{k=0}^{n} \frac{(2n-k)!}{2^{n-k}k!(n-k)!} s^k \tag{9-53}$$

The desired approximating function can now be written

$$F(s) = \frac{b_0}{P_n(s)} = \frac{b_0}{s^n P_{Dn}(1/s)} = \frac{b_0}{b_0 + b_1 s + \ldots + b_n s^n} \tag{9-54}$$

where

$$b_k = \frac{(2n-k)!}{2^{n-k}k!(n-k)!} \tag{9-55}$$

These coefficients are the same as those in Eq. (9-49) except that the subscripts are inverted. That is, $b_k = b'_{n-k}$.

Let us now investigate the magnitude and angle of the transfer function $F(s)$ for $s = j\omega$. A tremendous simplification in this job is made by observing some relationships between the Bessel polynomials and Bessel functions of half-integral order. One of these relationships is

$$P_{Dn}\left(\frac{1}{j\omega}\right) = \sqrt{\frac{\pi\omega}{2}} \frac{\epsilon^{j\omega}}{j^n} \left[(-1)^n J_{-(n+\frac{1}{2})}(\omega) - j J_{n+\frac{1}{2}}(\omega)\right] \tag{9-56}‡$$

Using this in Eq. (9-54) with $s = j\omega$, we get

$$F(j\omega) = \frac{b_0}{\omega^n \sqrt{\pi\omega/2}\left[(-1)^n J_{-(n+\frac{1}{2})}(\omega) - j J_{n+\frac{1}{2}}(\omega)\right]} \epsilon^{-j\omega} \tag{9-57}$$

This equation puts the transfer function in an extremely useful form. It

---

† These polynomials satisfy the differential equation

$$p^2 \frac{d^2 y}{dp^2} + (2p + 2)\frac{dy}{dp} = n(n+1)y$$

See H. L. Krall and O. Fink, "A New Class of Orthogonal Polynomials: the Bessel Polynomials," *Trans. Am. Math. Soc.*, **65**, Jan. 1949.

‡ See Krall and Fink, *op. cit.*

is the product of two functions, one of which is the ideal function $\epsilon^{-j\omega}$, while the other can be considered to be the error. Thus

$$F(j\omega) = F_e(j\omega)F_i(j\omega) = \sqrt{G_e(\omega^2)}\ \epsilon^{j\phi_e(\omega)}\epsilon^{-j\omega} \tag{9-58}$$

where

$$G_e(\omega^2) = \frac{b_0^2}{(\pi/2)\omega^{2n+1}[J_{n+\frac{1}{2}}^2(\omega) + J_{-(n+\frac{1}{2})}^2(\omega)]} \tag{9-59}$$

$$\tan\phi_e = (-1)^n \frac{J_{n+\frac{1}{2}}(\omega)}{J_{-(n+\frac{1}{2})}(\omega)} \tag{9-60}$$

and where the subscript e stands for error. The last two equations give the error in the squared magnitude and the angle function. The usefulness of these equations derives from the fact that, for a given order of approximation n, the errors can be computed by using tabulated values of half-integral-order Bessel functions.

We have yet to find what kind of approximation to the ideal transfer function is obtained by this procedure. Since the angle of the right-hand side of Eq. (9-58) is

$$\phi(\omega) = -\omega + \phi_e(\omega) \tag{9-61}$$

with ϕ_e given in Eq. (9-60), we can compute the delay, defined in Eq. (9-32), to be

$$D(j\omega) = -\frac{d\phi}{d\omega} = 1 - \frac{d}{d\omega}\left[\tan^{-1}(-1)^n \frac{J_{n+\frac{1}{2}}(\omega)}{J_{-(n+\frac{1}{2})}(\omega)}\right]$$

$$= 1 - \frac{(-1)^n[J_{-(n+\frac{1}{2})}J'_{n+\frac{1}{2}} - J_{n+\frac{1}{2}}J'_{-(n+\frac{1}{2})}]}{J_{n+\frac{1}{2}}^2(\omega) + J_{-(n+\frac{1}{2})}^2(\omega)} \tag{9-62}$$

The numerator of the second term has been evaluated† to give $2/\pi\omega$. Hence the delay becomes

$$D(j\omega) = 1 - \frac{1}{(\pi\omega/2)[J_{n+\frac{1}{2}}^2(\omega) + J_{-(n+\frac{1}{2})}^2(\omega)]} \tag{9-63}$$

This is in the form of the desired delay minus an error term, which we can label $D_e(j\omega)$. A more readily interpretable expression for the delay error can be obtained by substituting the series definition of the Bessel function,‡ thus obtaining the following power series for the delay error,

$$D_e(j\omega) = K\left[\omega^{2n} - \frac{\omega^{2n+2}}{2n-1} + \frac{2(n-1)\omega^{2n+4}}{(2n-1)^2(2n-3)}\cdots\right] \tag{9-64}$$

---

† G. N. Watson, *A Treatise on the Theory of Bessel Functions*, p. 42, Cambridge, 1948.

The desired expression is $J_v(x)J'_{-v}(x) - J'_v(x)J_{-v}(x) = -\dfrac{2\sin v\pi}{\pi x}$.

‡ $J_{n+\frac{1}{2}}(\omega) = \dfrac{(\omega/2)^{n+\frac{1}{2}}}{(n+\frac{1}{2})\,\Gamma\,(n+\frac{1}{2})}\left[1 - \dfrac{(\omega/2)^2}{n+\frac{3}{2}} + \dfrac{(\omega/2)^4}{2(n+\frac{3}{2})(n+\frac{5}{2})} + \cdots\right]$, where

$\Gamma(x)$ is the gamma function.

where
$$K = \frac{2^{2n}(2n+1)^2\Gamma\left[-(n+\tfrac{1}{2})\right]}{\pi} = \frac{1}{b_0^2} \qquad (9\text{-}65)$$

The right-hand side is obtained by expanding the gamma function and using b_0 as given in Eq. (9-55).

Since the Maclaurin series of the delay error starts with the nth power of ω^2, the first $n-1$ derivatives with respect to ω^2 are zero. Hence, by definition, the transfer function $F(s)$ given in Eq. (9-54) provides an $(n-1)$st-order Taylor-type (maximally flat) approximation to the delay! This result was certainly not anticipated when the continued fraction was truncated, but it is nevertheless welcome.

Another very interesting fact becomes apparent upon comparison of the delay error $D_e(j\omega)$ in Eq. (9-63) and the squared magnitude in Eq. (9-59). Thus

$$G_e(\omega^2) = \frac{b_0^2}{\omega^{2n}} D_e(j\omega) \qquad (9\text{-}66)$$

Using the power series for $D_e(j\omega)$, we can now find the series representing the squared magnitude. It is

$$G_e(\omega^2) = 1 - \frac{\omega^2}{2n-1} + \frac{2(n-1)\omega^4}{(2n-1)^2(2n-3)} \cdots \qquad (9\text{-}67)$$

Several observations can now be made. Since the delay is a monotonic function of frequency, so also is the squared magnitude. However, all the powers of ω^2 are present in the series expansion of $G_e(\omega^2)$ so that it is not maximally flat. On the other hand, the coefficients (which are the zero-frequency derivatives) decrease with increasing n. This means that $G_e(\omega^2)$ approaches a maximally flat shape for large values of n.

Let us now review the preceding discussion. We used some mathematics (Bessel functions) that is not normally met in network theory. Many of the steps in the development had to be left for you to carry out. However, the results obtained are easily interpreted and applied.

The squared magnitude, the phase, and the delay of the transfer function given in Eq. (9-54) are expressed, respectively, in Eqs. (9-59), (9-60), and (9-63) in terms of the order of approximation n. Remember that the variable ω here refers to the actual angular frequency multiplied by the flat delay $t_0 = 1/\omega_0$ with respect to which we have normalized.

In a given problem the order n is chosen to satisfy three requirements: (1) the flat delay t_0, (2) the frequency to which this delay is to be maintained within a specified tolerance (the delay bandwidth), and (3) the frequency to which the magnitude is to be maintained within a specified tolerance (the magnitude bandwidth). The last will usually (but not necessarily) be specified as the 3-db bandwidth. After n is chosen, the coefficients of $F(s)$ are calculated from Eq. (9-55) and the approximation is complete. Because all the transmission zeros are at infinity, the realization is easily obtained according to the methods of Chaps. 5 and 6.

Let us now illustrate the approximation procedure with a numerical problem. It is desired to synthesize a low-pass network for which the flat delay is $t_0 = 25$ microseconds. It is required that the delay error be no greater than 2 per cent up to a frequency of $\omega = 10^5$. In this range the loss should be no greater than 3 db.

All that is required is to find the order n. However, the smallest value of n that would satisfy the delay-error requirement may not be large enough to satisfy the loss requirement, or vice versa. Hence, it may be necessary to use a larger value of n than necessary for satisfying one of the requirements in order to satisfy the second one.

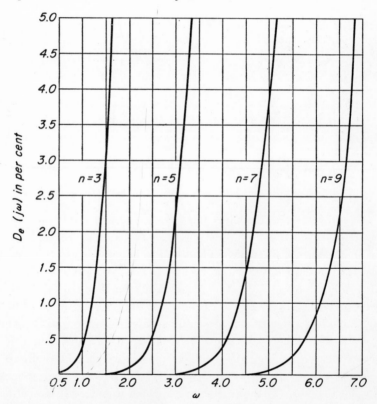

Fig. 9-5. Curves of delay error as a function of frequency.

In Figs. 9-5 and 9-6 we have drawn universal curves representing the delay error in per cent and the loss in decibels vs. the normalized frequency with the order n as a parameter. The curves were calculated from Eqs. (9-63) and (9-66). In the present problem the normalizing frequency is $\omega_0 = 1/t_0 = 4 \times 10^4$. Hence the normalized value of the band edge is $\omega = 2.5$. If we enter the delay chart at a normalized frequency of 2.5, we see that $n = 3$ will cause a delay error of more than 2 per cent but $n = 5$ will be more than adequate. However, Fig. 9-6 shows that a value of $n = 5$ will keep the loss below 3 db only up to a normalized frequency of $n = 2.4$. If the requirements are to be absolutely satisfied, we must choose the next higher value for n, namely, $n = 6$. If we can tolerate slightly poorer performance in the loss requirement, $n = 5$ will suffice. In any case, n will be determined.

We have tabulated the coefficients and the factors of the Bessel polynomials in Tables 9-3 and 9-4. In the present problem, with $n = 6$, with the help of Table 9-3 we find the desired transfer function to be

$$F(s) = \frac{10{,}395}{10{,}395 + 10{,}395s + 4725s^2 + 1260s^3 + 210s^4 + 21s^5 + s^6}$$

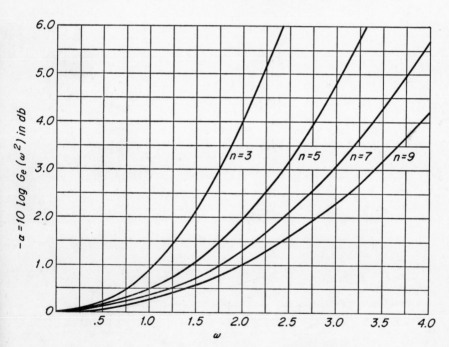

Fig. 9-6. Curves of loss as a function of normalized frequency.

Table 9-3. Coefficients of $P_n(s) = s^n P_{Dn}(1/s) = b_0 + b_1 s + \ldots + s^n$

Order n	b_0	b_1	b_2	b_3	b_4	b_5	b_6	b_7	b_8	b_9
1	1									
2	3	3								
3	15	15	6							
4	105	105	45	10						
5	945	945	420	105	15					
6	10,395	10,395	4,725	1,260	210	21				
7	135,135	135,135	62,370	17,325	3,150	378	28			
8	2,027,025	2,027,025	945,945	270,270	51,975	6,930	630	36		
9	34,459,425	34,459,425	16,216,200	4,729,725	945,945	135,135	13,860	990	45	
10	654,729,075	654,729,075	310,134,825	91,891,800	18,918,900	2,837,835	315,315	25,740	1,485	55

Table 9-4. Factors of $P_n(s) = s^n P_{Dn}(1/s)$

$$P_n(s) = s^n P_{Dn}(1/s)$$

Order n	
1	$s + 1$
2	$s^2 + 3s + 3$
3	$(s + 2.3222)(s^2 + 3.6778s + 6.4595)$
4	$(s^2 + 5.7924s + 9.1401)(s^2 + 4.2076s + 11.4877)$
5	$(s + 3.6467)(s^2 + 6.7039s + 14.2725)(s^2 + 4.6493s + 18.1563)$
6	$(s^2 + 8.4967s + 18.8011)(s^2 + 7.4714s + 20.8528)(s^2 + 5.0319s + 26.5140)$
7	$(s + 4.9718)(s^2 + 9.5166s + 125.6663)(s^2 + 8.1403s + 28.9365)(s^2 + 5.3714s + 26.5968)$
8	$(s^2 + 11.1758s + 31.9773)(s^2 + 5.6780s + 48.4320)(s^2 + 8.7366s + 38.5692)$
	$(s^2 + 10.4097s + 33.9347)$
9	$(s + 6.2970)(s^2 + 12.2587s + 77.2216)(s^2 + 11.2088s + 34.4296)(s^2 + 9.2769s + 49.7885)$
	$(s^2 + 5.9585s + 62.0414)$
10	$(s^2 + 13.8441s + 48.6675)(s^2 + 6.2178s + 77.4427)(s^2 + 13.2306s + 50.5824)$
	$(s^2 + 11.9351s + 54.8392)(s^2 + 9.7724s + 62.6255)$

9-4. Filter characteristic—Tchebyscheff response

We have now discussed procedures for obtaining a maximally flat approximation to a flat-top filter function and to a constant-delay function. These approximations are monotonic functions of frequency. The approximation is very good near the center of the band ($\omega = 0$) but gets progressively worse as frequency increases, the poorest approximation occurring at the band edge.

Let us now look for an approximation that oscillates about the desired function with the hope that the error can thereby be distributed more evenly over the band. In Section 9-1 we have already discussed a rippling kind of approximation. There we defined a *Tchebyscheff approximation* as one that minimizes the largest peak of the error. We also showed that this type of approximation is likewise an *equal-ripple* approximation.

We shall again seek an approximation to a low-pass flat-top magnitude squared function and again assume that all the transmission zeros are at infinity. Thus the output/input magnitude squared function is a constant divided by an even polynomial similar to Eq. (9-13). The reciprocal of this function will be simply a polynomial. Since it is so much easier to deal with a polynomial rather than its reciprocal, we shall deal with the input/output function in the following development.

We have the general problem, then, of determining the coefficients of an mth-degree polynomial, which, in the interval $(-1,1)$, approximates

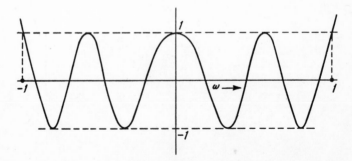

Fig. 9-7. Equal-ripple error.

a constant in the Tchebyscheff sense. (We have normalized the ω axis such that the band edges are ± 1.) The error function itself will be an mth-degree polynomial which we shall call $h(\omega)$. A sketch of the error is shown in Fig. 9-7, where the peak value of $|h|$ has been normalized to unity.

In Sec. 9-1 we established that the error of an mth-order Tchebyscheff approximation must attain its peak value exactly $m + 1$ times in the approximating interval: at $m - 1$ interior points and at the two edges. At the interior peak points the derivative of h must be zero, and all the zeros of the derivative must be simple. Now let us form the polynomial $1 - h^2$; this will be zero at all the $m + 1$ peak points of h since h is ± 1 at these points. Furthermore, it will have double zeros at the interior peak points. This can be seen by noting that the derivative of $1 - h^2$ is $-2hh'$, which is also zero at these points. At the end points $\omega = \pm 1$, $1 - h^2$ has simple zeros. Thus $1 - h^2$ has the factors $(h')^2$ and $(1 - \omega)(1 + \omega)$ and no other factors. Hence we can write

$$1 - h^2 = K^2(1 - \omega^2)\left(\frac{dh}{d\omega}\right)^2$$

$$\frac{dh}{\sqrt{1 - h^2}} = \pm\frac{1}{K}\frac{d\omega}{\sqrt{1 - \omega^2}} \tag{9-68}$$

where K is a constant. The solution for h is obtained by integrating this equation. The result is

$$\cos^{-1} h = \pm\frac{1}{K}\cos^{-1}\omega \tag{9-69}$$

We know that, when ω runs from -1 to $+1$, h oscillates between ± 1 exactly m times. This determines the constant K to be $1/m$ so that we get

$$h = \cos(m\cos^{-1}\omega) \qquad |\omega| \leq 1 \tag{9-70}$$

We can alternatively write

$$h = \cos my$$

$$\omega = \cos y \tag{9-71}$$

That the right-hand side of the equation for h is a polynomial in ω is easily demonstrated by expressing $\cos my$ as a polynomial in $\cos y$ and using $\omega = \cos y$. These polynomials are designated $T_m(\omega)$ and are called "Tchebyscheff polynomials"; m is the order of the polynomial. Thus

$$T_m(\omega) = \cos(m\cos^{-1}\omega) \qquad -1 \leq \omega \leq 1 \tag{9-72}$$

or $\qquad T_m(\omega) = \cos my, \qquad \omega = \cos y \tag{9-73}$

Some of the lower-order Tchebyscheff polynomials are shown in Table 9-5. Some of these are sketched in Fig. 9-8. A glance at the figures or a consideration of the polynomials in the table will show the following properties:

$$T_{2k}(0) = (-1)^k \qquad T_{2k+1}(0) = 0$$

$$T_{2k}(\pm 1) = 1 \qquad T_{2k+1}(\pm 1) = \pm 1 \text{ (respectively)} \tag{9-74}$$

The defining equation for the Tchebyscheff polynomial given in

Eq. (9-72) is valid only in the range $|\omega| \leq 1$. However, the polynomials listed in Table 9-5 are defined for all values of ω. Actually, we can general-

Table 9-5

Order n	Tchebyscheff polynomial, $T_n(\omega) = \cos(n \cos^{-1} \omega)$
0	1
1	ω
2	$2\omega^2 - 1$
3	$4\omega^3 - 3\omega$
4	$8\omega^4 - 8\omega^2 + 1$
5	$16\omega^5 - 20\omega^3 + 5\omega$
6	$32\omega^6 - 48\omega^4 + 18\omega^2 - 1$
7	$64\omega^7 - 112\omega^5 + 56\omega^3 - 7\omega$
8	$128\omega^8 - 256\omega^6 + 160\omega^4 - 32\omega^2 + 1$
9	$256\omega^9 - 576\omega^7 + 432\omega^5 - 120\omega^3 + 9\omega$
10	$512\omega^{10} - 1280\omega^8 + 1120\omega^6 - 400\omega^4 + 50\omega^2 - 1$

ize the definition to include complex values as well. Let $w = x + jy$, and consider the functions

$$\frac{s}{j} = \cosh w \qquad \text{(a)}$$
$$T_m\left(\frac{s}{j}\right) = \cosh mw \qquad \text{(b)} \qquad (9\text{-}75)$$

Upon expanding the hyperbolic cosines, these become

$$\omega - j\sigma = \cosh x \cos y - j \sinh x \sin y \qquad \text{(a)}$$
$$T_m\left(\frac{s}{j}\right) = \cosh mx \cos my - j \sinh mx \sin my \qquad \text{(b)} \qquad (9\text{-}76)$$

When $x = 0$, the first of these equations requires $\sigma = 0$. Hence these equations reduce to Eq. (9-73). Thus Eqs. (9-75) may be considered the general definition of the Tchebyscheff polynomials.

Let us return now to a consideration of the approximation. We have shown that, if the error between the squared magnitude of the realizable input/output function (that is, $1/G$) and the ideal (which is unity in the passband) is a Tchebyscheff polynomial, then an equal-ripple approximation will be achieved. The magnitudes of the peak error above and below unity will be equal. Several observations can be made: If we now consider the magnitude rather than its square, we shall no longer have an equal-ripple approximation. Likewise, if we take the reciprocal, $G(\omega^2)$, we no

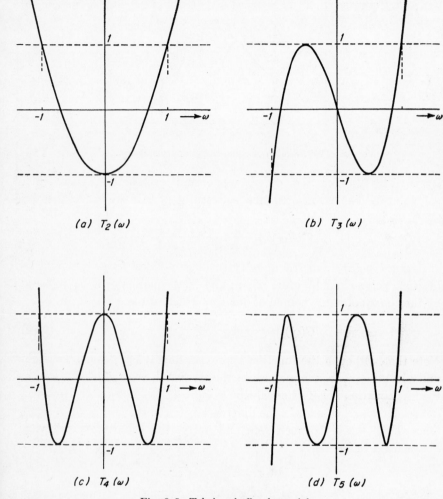

Fig. 9-8. Tchebyscheff polynomials.

longer have an equal ripple. However, the difference is extremely small, assuming the error is not large in the first place. Let us consider the quantitative aspects of these observations.

Consider Fig. 9-9, which shows a sketch of $1/G(\omega^2)$. The peak-to-peak deviation is labeled ϵ^2. Since the functions involved are all even, we must have only even-ordered polynomials.

For the error, we can write

$$\frac{1}{G(\omega^2)} - 1 = \frac{\epsilon^2}{2}T_{2n}(\omega) \tag{9-77}$$

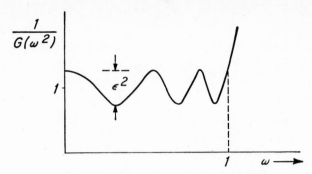

Fig. 9-9. Sketch of equal-ripple approximation.

By writing $2n$ for the order, we ensure even-order Tchebyscheff polynomials. The error oscillates between $\pm\epsilon^2/2$. If we solve this for $G(\omega^2)$, we get

$$G(\omega^2) = \frac{1}{1 + (\epsilon^2/2)T_{2n}(\omega)} \tag{9-78}$$

Using the trigonometric identity $\cos 2ny = 2\cos^2 ny - 1$, the Tchebyscheff polynomial of order $2n$ in the last equation can be replaced by the square of a polynomial of order n. The result is

$$G(\omega^2) = \frac{1}{1 - (\epsilon^2/2) + \epsilon^2 T_n^2(\omega)} \tag{9-79}$$

Note that, although the function approximating $1/G(\omega^2)$ oscillates about unity in an equal-ripple manner in the passband, the right-hand side of the last equation is *not* an equal-ripple approximation of unity. However, for small enough values of ϵ the difference between the two is quite small. Since $T_n^2(\omega)$ varies between zero and unity, the value of G will vary between the limits

$$\frac{1}{1 - \epsilon^2/2} \quad \text{and} \quad \frac{1}{1 + \epsilon^2/2}$$

The difference between these two quantities, which is the peak-to-peak ripple, is

$$\frac{1}{1 - \epsilon^2/2} - \frac{1}{1 + \epsilon^2/2} = \frac{\epsilon^2}{1 - (\epsilon^2/2)^2} \tag{9-80}$$

The value about which the approximation ripples can now be found by adding half this amount to the trough in the ripple. The result is

$$\frac{1}{1 + \epsilon^2/2} + \frac{1}{2}\frac{\epsilon^2}{(1 - \epsilon^2/2)^2} = \frac{1}{1 - (\epsilon^2/2)^2} \tag{9-81}$$

Thus the approximation of $G(\omega^2)$ ripples about a value slightly greater than unity.

It has become standard in the literature to modify the approximating function given in Eq. (9-79) by neglecting $\epsilon^2/2$ in comparison with unity in the denominator. With this modification the approximating function is taken to be

$$G(\omega^2) = \frac{1}{1 + \epsilon^2 T_n^2(\omega)} \qquad (9\text{-}82)$$

With this change the approximating function ripples about the value

$$\frac{1 + \epsilon^2/2}{1 + \epsilon^2}$$

with a peak-to-peak ripple of $\epsilon^2/(1 + \epsilon^2)$. Figure 9-10 shows a sketch of the approximation for $n = 4$ and $n = 5$. In view of Eqs. (9-74) the odd-

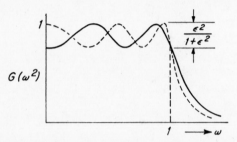

Fig. 9-10. Odd- and even-order Tchebyscheff approximations.

order approximations start from the peak of the ripple, while the even ones start from the trough. This is illustrated in the figure. At the band edge ($\omega = 1$) they all go through the minimum value.

The next order of business is to find the pole locations of $G(-s^2)$, which is the analytic continuation of the function in Eq. (9-82). This is done by setting $1 + \epsilon^2 T_n^2(s/j)$ equal to zero, or $\epsilon T_n(s/j) = \pm j$. By the use of Eqs. (9-76) this condition yields

$$T_n\!\left(\frac{s}{j}\right) = \cosh nx \cos ny - j \sinh nx \sin ny = \pm \frac{j}{\epsilon} \qquad (9\text{-}83)$$

Equating the real and imaginary parts on both sides of the equation yields

$$\cosh nx \cos ny = 0$$
$$\sinh nx \sin ny = \mp 1/\epsilon \qquad (9\text{-}84)$$

The first of these equations can be satisfied only if $\cos ny$ vanishes, which is possible if ny is an odd multiple of $\pi/2$. With this value of y it is possible to solve the second equation for x. The simultaneous solution of the two equations results in

$$y_k = \frac{2k-1}{n}\frac{\pi}{2} \qquad \text{(a)}$$

$$x_k = \pm\frac{1}{n}\sinh^{-1}\frac{1}{\epsilon} \qquad \text{(b)}$$

(9-85)

We have here used the fact that the hyperbolic sine is an odd function.

These expressions locate the poles in the w plane. To find the corresponding locations in the s plane, we use the relationship between the s and w planes whose expanded form is given in Eqs. (9-76). The result is

$$\sigma_k = \pm \sinh\left(\frac{1}{n}\sinh^{-1}\frac{1}{\epsilon}\right)\sin\frac{2k-1}{n}\frac{\pi}{2} \qquad \text{(a)}$$

$$\omega_k = \cosh\left(\frac{1}{n}\sinh^{-1}\frac{1}{\epsilon}\right)\cos\frac{2k-1}{n}\frac{\pi}{2} \qquad \text{(b)}$$

(9-86)

These expressions look extremely complicated. However, given the parameters n and ϵ and a table of hyperbolic functions, they can be readily calculated. A very interesting property of the pole locations can be derived from these equations. Let us divide each of them by the hyperbolic function appearing on the right; square both sides, and add. The result will be

$$\frac{\sigma_k^2}{\sinh^2\left(\frac{1}{n}\sinh^{-1}\frac{1}{\epsilon}\right)} + \frac{\omega_k^2}{\cosh^2\left(\frac{1}{n}\sinh^{-1}\frac{1}{\epsilon}\right)} = 1 \qquad (9\text{-}87)$$

This is the equation of an ellipse whose axes are the σ and ω axes of the s plane. Since the hyperbolic cosine is always larger than the hyperbolic sine, the major axis of the ellipse lies along the $j\omega$ axis. Thus the poles of $G(-s^2)$ are distributed on an ellipse in the s plane.

For fixed values of n and ϵ the hyperbolic functions appearing in Eqs. (9-86) will be constants. If we now compare these expressions with the real and imaginary parts of the maximally flat pole locations given in Eqs. (9-22), we observe an interesting fact. We find that the real part σ_k has the same value it would have if the poles were distributed uniformly on a circle, as in the maximally flat response, except that the radius of the circle is not unity but equal to the minor axis of the ellipse. Similarly, ω_k has the same value it would have if the poles were distributed on a circle whose radius is equal to the major axis of the ellipse.

These observations lead to a simple method for finding the pole locations of the Tchebyscheff approximation. For given n and ϵ we draw two concentric circles with radii equal to the two axes of the ellipse, as given by the hyperbolic functions in Eqs. (9-86). We locate $2n$ points equally spaced on each circle at the angles y_k given in Eqs. (9-85). The poles that we are to locate on the ellipse are to have the same real part as the points on the small circle, while they are to have the same imaginary part as the corresponding points on the large circle. Hence the poles are located at the intersections of vertical lines drawn from each of the equally spaced points on the small circle with horizontal lines drawn from the corresponding points on the large circle. This is illustrated for the case $n = 4$ in Fig. 9-11.

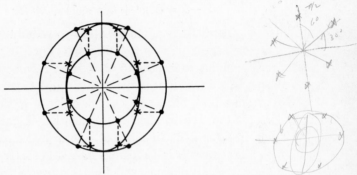

Fig. 9-11. Construction for locating poles of equal-ripple approximation.

Once the poles of $G(-s^2)$ are found, it is again a simple matter to find those of $F(s)$; they are simply all the left-half-plane poles of $G(-s^2)$. In the present case we cannot tabulate the denominator polynomial of $F(s)$ against the order n as we did in the cases of maximally flat magnitude and delay because of the additional parameter ϵ. It is possible to tabulate these polynomials for several representative values of ϵ. However, our purpose here is to concentrate on developing the methods rather than to provide design tables.

Note that the coefficient of the highest-power term in the denominator of Eq. (9-82) is not unity but $2^{2(n-1)}\epsilon^2$. However, if we multiply together the factors representing the poles of $F(s)$, the coefficient of the highest power of s will be unity. Hence we must multiply the product of the pole factors by $2^{n-1}\epsilon$ in order to obtain the correct $F(s)$.

It is of interest to compare the asymptotic behavior of the equal-ripple approximation with that of the maximally flat. For large values of ω the highest-power term of $T_n(\omega)$ will be the most important. A glance at Table 9-5 will show that the highest-power term of $T_n(\omega)$ is $2^{n-1}\omega^n$. From Eq. (9-82) we find that, when $\epsilon^2 T_n^2(\omega)$ is much greater than unity, which occurs for large values of ω, then

$$G(\omega^2) \doteq \frac{1}{\epsilon^2 T_n^2(\omega)} \qquad (9\text{-}88)$$

The loss in decibels will then be

$$-\alpha = 10 \log \frac{1}{G} \doteq 20 \log \epsilon T_n(\omega) \doteq 20 \log 2^{n-1}\epsilon\omega^n$$

$$= 20n \log \omega + 20(n - 1) \log 2 + 20 \log \epsilon \qquad (9\text{-}89)$$

Finally, remembering that $\log \omega$ is equal to v in decades and that $\log 2 \doteq 0.3$, we get

$$-\alpha = 20nv + 6(n - 1) + 20 \log \epsilon \qquad (9\text{-}90)$$

Values of ϵ normally required to satisfy passband tolerances range from a high of unity, corresponding to 3 db ripple, down to a low of about one-tenth, corresponding to less than 1/2 db ripple. Thus the last term in this expression will always be negative with a value that ranges from zero to -20. It follows that, for a high enough order of n, the asymptotic stop-band loss for the Tchebyscheff approximation is greater than the corresponding loss for a maximally flat approximation of the same order, even with a much closer in-band tolerance. Alternatively, it is clear that, for the same in-band tolerance and stopband loss, a Tchebyscheff approximation of lower order than a maximally flat approximation can be used.

Let us now illustrate the Tchebyscheff approximation by reworking the numerical example for which a maximally flat approximation was obtained in Sec. 9-2. The statement of the problem is repeated here for easy reference. It is desired to design a low-pass filter with a useful band extending to $\omega_0 = 10,000$ radians per sec to operate between a current source and a resistive load of 500 ohms. In this band the magnitude of the transfer impedance is not to deviate from its nominal value by more than 10 per cent. At and beyond $\omega = 3\omega_0$, $|Z_{12}|$ should remain below 5 per cent of its nominal passband value.

We again normalize frequency with respect to ω_0. The passband requirement is translated to mean that the magnitude of $Z_{12}(j\omega)$ should be no smaller than 0.9 in the passband. Hence the tolerable peak-to-peak ripple in the magnitude squared function is $1 - 0.9^2$, or 19 per cent. We can now determine ϵ from the relation

$$\frac{\epsilon^2}{1 + \epsilon^2} = 0.19$$

which gives $\epsilon^2 = 0.235$ and $\epsilon = 0.485$.

To find the order n, we use the stopband requirement in Eq. (9-82).

$$\frac{1}{1 + \epsilon^2 T_n^2(3)} \leq (0.05)^2$$

or
$$T_n(3) \geq 41.2$$

By consulting the Tchebyscheff polynomials in Table 9-5 we find that $T_2(3) = 17$, while $T_3(3) = 99$. Hence the lowest order of T_n we can use is $n = 3$. Using Eqs. (9-86) for the pole positions, we find the poles of $Z_{12}(s)$ to lie at -0.51 and $-0.255 \pm j0.972$. Hence, finally, for $Z_{12}(s)$ we get

$$Z_{12}(s) = \frac{0.515}{s^3 + 1.02s^2 + 1.27s + 0.515} \tag{9-91}$$

9-5. Transformations of the frequency variable

In the preceding sections of this chapter we concentrated exclusively on approximating the magnitude and angle of a transfer function in a low-frequency band. We are also interested in problems involving intervals on the $j\omega$ axis not centered about $\omega = 0$. It would not be necessary to solve the approximation problem separately for such problems if we could find a frequency transformation which would map the desired passband onto the low-pass interval. The problem could then be solved in the low-pass interval. Applying the inverse transformation would then lead to the solution in the desired interval.

It is not difficult to find such transformations. Let $\bar{s} = \bar{\sigma} + j\bar{\omega}$ be a normalized low-pass variable. That is, the frequency band of interest in this plane is centered about the origin and extends from $\bar{\omega} = -1$ to $\bar{\omega} = +1$. Let $s = \sigma + j\omega$ be a general unnormalized complex-frequency variable. Now consider the transformation

$$\bar{s} = \frac{\omega_0}{s} \tag{9-92}$$

This transforms the interval extending from $-j\omega_0$ through infinity to $+j\omega_0$ in the s plane to the low-pass interval on the j axis in the $\bar{s}$ plane. It is a low-pass to high-pass transformation. In particular, with $\omega_0 = 1$ the cutoff points in the two cases are the same.

Now suppose that a magnitude function is prescribed over a high-pass interval. With the use of Eq. (9-92) this is transformed into a function over the low-pass interval. Suppose that the low-pass problem is then solved and a realization obtained. This network gives the desired performance, but not in the correct band. We can achieve the desired result if we change the elements in the network in such a way that the impedance of each resulting element (or elements) at a point in the high-pass interval is the same as the impedance of the corresponding element at the corresponding frequency in the low-pass interval. Thus let L_0 and C_0 designate, respectively, an inductance and a capacitance in the low-pass realization. With the transformation $\bar{s} = \omega_0/s$ we require

$$L_0\bar{s} = L_0\frac{\omega_0}{s} = \frac{1}{C_h s} \qquad \text{(a)}$$

$$\frac{1}{C_0\bar{s}} = \frac{s}{C_0\omega_0} = L_h s \qquad \text{(b)}$$

(9-93)

where the subscript h refers to high-pass quantities. Hence we find

$$C_h = \frac{1}{L_0\omega_0} \qquad \text{(a)}$$

$$L_h = \frac{1}{C_0\omega_0} \qquad \text{(b)}$$

(9-94)

We conclude that, if in the normalized low-pass realization we replace each inductance by a capacitance and each capacitance by an inductance with the values given in Eqs. (9-94), we shall obtain a network which realizes the desired high-pass function.

Bandpass problems can be handled in a similar manner. Consider the transformation

$$\bar{s} = \frac{\omega_0}{w}\left(\frac{s}{\omega_0} + \frac{\omega_0}{s}\right) \qquad (9\text{-}95)$$

where
$$\longrightarrow \quad \omega_0^2 = \omega_{c1}\omega_{c2} \qquad \text{(a)}$$

$$w = \omega_{c2} - \omega_{c1} \qquad \text{(b)}$$

(9-96)

This transformation is illustrated in Fig. 9-12. The two edges of the band

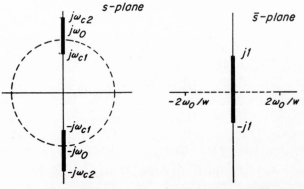

Fig. 9-12. The transformation $\bar{s} = \dfrac{\omega_0}{\omega}\left(\dfrac{s}{\omega_0} + \dfrac{\omega_0}{s}\right)$.

(corresponding to the cutoff frequencies in the case of filters) are labeled ω_{c1} and ω_{c2}. The geometric mean of the cutoff frequencies is designated ω_0, while w is the bandwidth.

Note that $\bar{s}$ remains unchanged if we replace s in Eq. (9-95) by ω_0^2/s. It follows that $\bar{s}$ is a double-valued function of s. In particular, a point in the low-pass interval in the $\bar{s}$ plane corresponds to two points in the s plane, one in the positive passband and one in the negative passband.

Now suppose that a bandpass function $G(\omega^2)$ is prescribed over the passband of the s plane. With the transformation of Eq. (9-95) this becomes $\bar{G}(\bar{\omega}^2) = G(\omega^2)$. If this is to be a single-valued function, we must require that the value of $G(\omega^2)$ at a point ω_1 in the passband be equal to its value at the point $-\omega_0^2/\omega_1$ because both these points correspond to a single point on the low-pass interval. That is, the prescribed magnitude function should satisfy the condition $G(\omega^2) = G(-\omega_0^4/\omega^2)$. We refer to this as *geometrical symmetry*. The same condition also applies if the prescribed function is the angle [or the A function defined in Eq. (9-11)].

For the case of a filter function, which requires a uniform magnitude in the passband, the geometrical-symmetry condition is fulfilled. Hence Eq. (9-95) can be used to convert the problem to a low-pass one. After a low-pass realization is obtained, the required bandpass network is realized by modifying each element in the low-pass realization in such a way that the impedance of this element as a function of $\bar{s}$ is the same as the impedance of the modification as a function of the bandpass variable s. Let us designate bandpass quantities with a subscript b. Then we can write

$$L_0\bar{s} = \frac{L_0}{w}s + \frac{L_0\omega_0^2}{ws} = L_{b1}s + \frac{1}{C_{b1}s} \qquad \text{(a)}$$

$$\frac{1}{C_0\bar{s}} = \frac{1}{\dfrac{s}{C_0w} + \dfrac{\omega_0^2}{C_0ws}} = \frac{1}{C_{b2}s + \dfrac{1}{L_{b2}s}} \qquad \text{(b)}$$

(9-97)

It is clear that each inductance in the low-pass realization should be replaced by a series-resonant circuit with the element values

$$L_{b1} = \frac{L_0}{w} \qquad \text{(a)}$$

$$C_{b1} = \frac{w}{L_0\omega_0^2} \qquad \text{(b)}$$

(9-98)

Similarly, each capacitance should be replaced by a parallel-resonant circuit with element values

$$L_{b2} = \frac{C_0w}{\omega_0^2} \qquad \text{(a)}$$

$$C_{b2} = \frac{1}{C_0w} \qquad \text{(b)}$$

(9-99)

This idea of transforming the frequency variable can be used for other more complicated problems as well. In the case of multiple pass-band filters we require certain points on the $j\omega$ axis, the band centers, to map onto the origin of the low-pass plane. Other points, corresponding to the cutoffs, should map onto $\omega = 1$, while still other points, which we can think of as constituting the centers of the stopbands, should map onto the point at infinity. If we glance back at the two transformations we have already considered, Eqs. (9-92) and (9-95), we notice that these are reactance functions. A little thought will show that reactance functions, as a class, are well suited to the contemplated mappings, since proper choice of the zeros and poles will perform the transformation of desired frequencies onto the origin and infinity. Further development of this idea will be left to you.

9-6. Predistortion

The topic under consideration in this section might seem out of place in a chapter on approximations since it is closely related to realization. However, as we shall see, the main problem is one of function synthesis. From this point of view it belongs in the present chapter.

The networks which we realize for a prescribed driving-point or transfer function by any one of the methods we have discussed in this book will contain ideal inductance and capacitance elements. However, when the networks are actually constructed with the physical counterparts of these ideal elements, parasitic elements invariably appear. These elements have the effect of shifting the locations of the poles and zeros of the function for which the network was synthesized. In this way the efforts expended in obtaining a suitable approximating function to satisfy specified performance criteria may be vitiated.

The greatest amount of difficulty is caused by the incidental dissipation associated with the reactive elements. This incidental dissipation can be accounted for in an approximate manner by combining a resistance in series with each inductance and in parallel with each capacitance. Let us assume that the time constants of the series RL combinations and the parallel RC combinations are all equal. The impedance of these combinations can be written

$$Z_L = Ls + R_L = L(s + d) = Lp \qquad \text{(a)}$$
$$Z_C = \frac{1}{sC + 1/R_C} = \frac{1}{C(s + d)} = \frac{1}{Cp} \qquad \text{(b)}$$

(9-100)

where
$$d = \frac{R_L}{L} = \frac{1}{CR_c} \qquad \text{(a)}$$

$$p = s + d \qquad \text{(b)} \qquad \text{(9-101)}$$

With the change of variable $p = s + d$, the impedance of a series R and L is the same function of the variable p that the impedance of a pure inductance is of the variable s. A similar statement applies to the capacitance. The transformation $p = s + d$ moves the vertical axis of the s plane parallel to itself d units to the right.

Suppose that we start with a prescribed transfer function and synthesize a network realizing this function. When the network is actually constructed, the actual response function will differ from the prescribed one because of the incidental dissipation. If we assume that the time constants of all the lossy inductors and capacitors are the same, then the actual transfer function realized by the network will be the desired one, but with $p = s + d$ substituted for s. Thus all zeros and poles will be shifted to the left by a constant amount d.

The faint trace of an idea begins to appear here. Since the actual network distorts the desired function by shifting all zeros and poles a constant amount to the left, why do we not compensate for this by deliberately shifting all of them to the right? In other words, let us *predistort* the desired function by replacing s by $p - d$. The resulting transfer function will not be the one we want, because all the poles and zeros will be moved an amount d to the right. If we now synthesize a network realizing this undesirable function, the incidental dissipation will restore the function to its original desired form.

To illustrate this idea, consider Fig. 9-13. The transfer impedance functions of the two networks are

$$Z_{12}(s) = \frac{1}{s^2 + \frac{1}{2}s + 1} \qquad \text{(a)}$$

$$Z_{12}(s) = \frac{1}{(s + R_L/2)(s + 2/R_C) + \frac{1}{2}(s + 2/R_C) + 1} \qquad \text{(b)} \qquad \text{(9-102)}$$

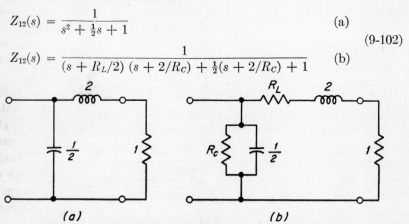

Fig. 9-13. Modification of a network by incidental dissipation.

respectively. If we assume that $R_L/2 = 2/R_C = d$, the last expression will become

$$Z_{12}(s) = Z'_{12}(p) = \frac{1}{p^2 + \frac{1}{2}p + 1} \qquad (9\text{-}103)$$

This is seen to be the same function of p that Eq. (9-102a) is of s.

Now suppose that we set $s = p - d$ in Eq. (9-102a). The predistorted transfer impedance will become

$$Z_{12}(p - d) = Z'_{12}(p) = \frac{1}{(p - d)^2 + \frac{1}{2}(p - d) + 1}$$

$$= \frac{1}{p^2 + \frac{1}{2}(1 - 4d)p + (1 - d/2 + d^2)} \qquad (9\text{-}104)$$

The realization of this function is shown in Fig. 9-14(a). With the incidental dissipation explicitly shown this takes on the form of

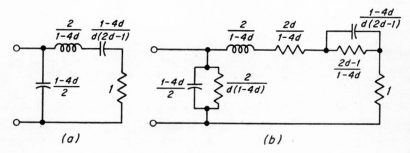

Fig. 9-14. Example of predistortion.

Fig. 9-14(b). The resistances are calculated from $R_L = Ld$ and $R_C = 1/Cd$. This network has the transfer impedance of Eq. (9-102a), as you can readily verify in this simple case.

We note from this example that the predistortion not only introduces resistive elements but may increase the number of reactive elements as well. Another observation follows by considering Eq. (9-104). If the value of d is made greater than $1/4$, the predistorted function will have poles in the right half plane. Hence there is a limit to the amount of predistortion that is possible. In terms of the pole locations of the original transfer function the permissible value of d is limited by the closeness of the poles to the $j\omega$ axis. The largest value of d that can be used is the magnitude of the real part of the pole of Z_{12} which is closest to the $j\omega$ axis. In this example Eq. (9-102a) shows this value to be $1/4$. For practical purposes, values of d close to this maximum limit are not suitable, as a consideration of the element values in Fig. 9-14 will show.

Another practical problem needs to be considered. In developing the idea of predistortion it was assumed that all R/L values for inductors and all $1/RC$ values for capacitors are the same. This assumption is not really valid, especially in regard to the capacitors. Practical capacitors are available with very little dissipation. In an actual problem a preliminary realization shows the range of inductance values that will be needed. A value of d is chosen equal to R/L for the inductor with the lowest Q (assuming that this falls in the permissible range). In the physical realization all other inductors will require additional series resistance, while all capacitors will require additional parallel resistance. Thus the price that must be paid for the luxury of predistortion is the requirement of additional elements with its attendant power loss. Even if no additional elements are used, the predistortion technique with some average value of d will permit considerable improvement in the distortion caused by incidental dissipation.

In the illustrative example that we considered, all the transmission zeros were at infinity. More generally, the transfer function appropriate for the synthesis of a resistance-terminated lossless two-port may have finite zeros represented by an odd or even polynomial in the numerator. The denominator is of course a Hurwitz polynomial. The transformation $s = p - d$ will leave the denominator polynomial Hurwitz (assuming that d is chosen small enough), but now the numerator will no longer be even or odd. (For example, s^2 becomes $p^2 - 2dp + d^2$.) Thus the predistorted function cannot be realized as a resistance-terminated lossless two-port but must be realized as a more general RLC network according to the methods of the last chapter.

This added complexity could be avoided if it were possible to retain the numerator as an even or odd polynomial. Let us consider the possibility of using the transformation $s = p - d$ in the denominator only, leaving the numerator the way it is. (We actually put $s = p$ in the numerator.) When the network is realized, the incidental dissipation will replace p by $s + d$ throughout the entire function. Thus the desired denominator will be obtained, but the numerator will have s replaced by $s + d$. It is of interest to determine the error that we shall get in such a case.

The transfer function of a resistance-terminated lossless two-port will be of the form

$$F(s) = \frac{N_{12}(s)}{m(s) + n(s)} \qquad (9\text{-}105)$$

where N_{12} is an even polynomial. (It may also be odd, but the same results will apply to this case.) Let us predistort only the denominator. After the network is realized and the dissipation is added, the error in the transfer function will be

$$\frac{N_{12}(s)}{m(s) + n(s)} - \frac{N_{12}(s + d)}{m(s) + n(s)} = F(s)\left[1 - \frac{N_{12}(s + d)}{N_{12}(s)}\right] \qquad (9\text{-}106)$$

To determine the error, we shall need an estimate of the quantity inside the brackets, for $s = j\omega$. Let us give the following definitions:

$$\ln\left[N_{12}(d + j\omega)\right] = u(d,\omega) + j\theta(d,\omega) \qquad \text{(a)}$$
$$\ln\left[N_{12}(j\omega)\right] = u_0(\omega) + j\theta_0(\omega) \qquad \text{(b)}$$
$$\qquad (9\text{-}107)$$

It is clear that, when $d = 0$, $u(d,\omega)|_{d=0} = u_0(\omega)$ and $\theta(d,\omega)|_{d=0} = \theta_0(\omega)$. The functions $u(d,\omega)$ and $\theta(d,\omega)$ are the real and imaginary parts of the analytic function $\ln\left[N_{12}(d + j\omega)\right]$. Hence they satisfy the Cauchy-Riemann equations

$$\frac{\partial u}{\partial d} = \frac{\partial \theta}{\partial \omega} \qquad \text{(a)}$$
$$\frac{\partial \theta}{\partial d} = -\frac{\partial u}{\partial \omega} \qquad \text{(b)}$$
$$\qquad (9\text{-}108)$$

Let us now consider the ratio of $N_{12}(d + j\omega)$ and $N_{12}(j\omega)$, which will determine the error. In view of the definitions in Eqs. (9-107) we can write

$$\frac{N_{12}(d + j\omega)}{N_{12}(j\omega)} = \frac{\epsilon^{u(d,\omega)+j\theta(d,\omega)}}{\epsilon^{u_0(\omega)+j\theta_0(\omega)}} = \epsilon^{(u - u_0)+j(\theta - \theta_0)} \qquad (9\text{-}109)$$

To determine the extent to which u differs from u_0 and θ from θ_0 for small values of d, let us expand u and θ in power series in d. The results will be

$$u(d,\omega) = u_0(\omega) + d\frac{\partial u_0}{\partial d} + \frac{d^2}{2}\frac{\partial^2 u_0}{\partial d^2} + \cdots \qquad \text{(a)}$$
$$\theta(d,\omega) = \theta_0(\omega) + d\frac{\partial \theta_0}{\partial d} + \frac{d^2}{2}\frac{\partial^2 \theta_0}{\partial d^2} + \cdots \qquad \text{(b)}$$
$$\qquad (9\text{-}110)$$

If we retain only the first two terms of these series and use the Cauchy-Riemann conditions in Eqs. (9-108), the ratio in Eq. (9-109) becomes

$$\frac{N_{12}(d + j\omega)}{N_{12}(j\omega)} \doteq \epsilon^{d\left(\frac{\partial \theta_0}{\partial \omega} - j\frac{\partial u_0}{\partial \omega}\right)} \qquad (9\text{-}111)$$

This equation indicates that, to a first-order approximation, which is good for small values of d, the magnitude of the ratio on the left-hand side depends on the derivative of the angle of $N_{12}(j\omega)$. But $N_{12}(j\omega)$ is an even polynomial in ω. If it has no j-axis zeros, its angle will be zero for all ω and so the derivative will also be zero. Suppose that N_{12} has zeros on the

$j\omega$ axis. The angle of N_{12} changes discontinuously by π at such zeros so that the derivative will become infinite. The actual error, of course, will not be infinite but quite large at such points.

Although we have not obtained a quantitative determination of the error, we have demonstrated that the error resulting from the contemplated procedure (predistorting the denominator only) will be small for all values of ω except near the j-axis transmission zeros. Since such zeros do not fall in the passband, we see that the results of predistorting the denominator only will be quite acceptable, at least in the passband.

PROBLEMS

9-1. A low-pass filter is to be designed to be inserted between a current source and a resistive load. The half-power frequency is to be $\omega_h = 10,000$ radians per sec. There is to be no transmission at the second harmonic of this frequency, while at very high frequencies the loss should increase at the rate of at least 20 db per decade.

(a) Determine a maximally flat $Z_{12}(s)$ for this network.

(b) Predistort the resulting function by a value of d equal to one-half the distance of the pole of Z_{12} which is closest to the $j\omega$ axis.

(c) Obtain a ladder realization of the predistorted function.

9-2. Determine an expression in terms of Bessel polynomials for the transfer function of an all-pass network that is to have a maximally flat delay. Show that such a function can be realized as a constant-resistance lattice.

9-3. It is desired to obtain a maximally flat delay network which provides taps corresponding to different amounts of delay. These taps are fed to networks with constant input impedances of different amounts. Discuss the possibility of using a cascade of constant-resistance all-pass lattices of the type mentioned in Prob. 9-2 to achieve this result. The taps are brought out at the connection between lattices, as shown in Fig. P 9-3.

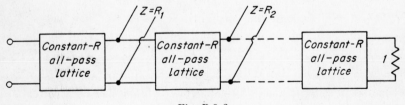

Fig. P 9-3

9-4. Based on the results of the previous problem, design a delay network having a delay of 400 μsec with taps at every 100 μsec. The delay error is to be no more than 5 per cent up to a frequency of $\omega = 10^5$. The load resistance is 100 ohms. The input resistances of the networks to which the taps are fed are as follows:

100-μsec tap, 100 ohms
200-μsec tap, open circuit
300-μsec tap, 200 ohms

9-5. Design a delay network to be realized as a ladder having a delay of 1 millisecond. The delay error should be no greater than 3 per cent up to a frequency of $\omega = 10^4$. In this band the loss should be no greater than 3 db. The network is to be fed with a voltage source and is to be terminated in a 500-ohm resistance. The realization is to use lossy coils but lossless capacitors.

9-6. (a) Find the transfer function of a low-pass filter with the following specifications: The passband loss should stay within 1 db of its nominal value up to a frequency of $\omega_0 = 5000$ radians per sec. At and beyond the fourth harmonic of this frequency the loss should be no less than 50 db. The network is to have a resistive load of 500 ohms and is to be driven by a voltage source. Obtain both a maximally flat function and an equal-ripple function.

(b) Predistort the functions obtained in part (a), using a value of d equal to half the magnitude of the real part of the pole closest to the $j\omega$ axis.

(c) Obtain a realization for the predistorted functions.

9-7. A bandpass filter is to have cutoff frequencies $\omega_{c1} = 10^5$ and $\omega_{c2} = 4 \times 10^5$ radians per sec. A 2-db loss can be tolerated in the passband, but at and beyond 10^6 radians per sec the loss should be not less than 50 db below its nominal passband value. The terminating resistance is 100 ohms, and the network is driven with a current source.

(a) Obtain an equal-ripple approximating function.

(b) Predistort this function by a suitable amount.

(c) Obtain a realization of the predistorted function.

9-8. Design a high-low constant-resistance filter pair with a 1-db equal-ripple passband approximation. The stopband loss of the low-pass filter at and beyond three times the cutoff frequency should be no less than 40 db. What is the restriction on n, the order of approximation, if both the filters are to be realized as ladders with no mutual inductance?

9-9. Suppose the magnitude squared of a transfer impedance function is given graphically. With $|Z_{12}|^2 = \epsilon^{2\alpha}$ we can assume that the loss $-\alpha$ is plotted with logarithmic frequency (in decades) as abscissa. Discuss a procedure for approximating this curve with a series of straight lines whose slopes are integral multiples (positive or negative) of 20 db per decade. The intersections of these lines are the *break* points. Each line is to be regarded as the asymptotic behavior of a maximally flat function so that an approximation to the given magnitude squared function becomes

$$|Z_{12}(j\omega)|^2 = \frac{[1 + (\omega/\omega_1)^{2n_1}]\,[1 + (\omega/\omega_2)^{2n_2}]\cdots}{[1 + (\omega/\omega_3)^{2n_3}]\,[1 + (\omega/\omega_3)^{2n_4}]\cdots}$$

where the n_i's correspond to the slopes of the lines and the ω_i's correspond to the break points.

9-10. The curve shown in Fig. P 9-10 is a prescribed loss function. Find a rational function $F(s)$ such that $-20 \log F(j\omega)$ approximates the given curve in the manner described in the last problem.

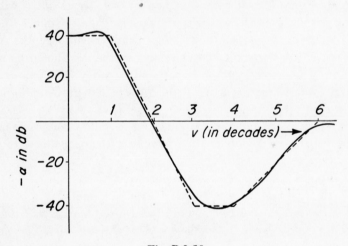

Fig. P 9-10

9-11. Obtain a realization of the approximating functions given in Eqs. (9-31) and (9-91), giving actual "unnormalized" values of the elements.

Bibliography

1. W. Bacon and D. P. Salmon, Resistance-Capacitance Networks with Over-unity Gain, *Wireless Engr.*, **30**, 20-23, 1953.
2. N. Balabanian and C. R. Cahn, A Note on Tee-Pi Transformations, *Proc. IRE*, **43**, p. 1530, October, 1955.
3. N. Balabanian and W. R. LePage, What Is a Minimum Phase Network?, *Trans. AIEE*, **75**, pp. 785-787, January, 1956.
4. T. R. Bashkow, A Contribution to Network Synthesis by Potential Analogy, *Stanford Univ. Electronics Research Lab. Tech. Rep.* 25, 1950.
5. R. F. Baum, A Contribution to the Approximation Problem, *Proc. IRE*, **36**, 863, 1948.
6. M. Bayard, Solution of the Problem of Synthesis of Kirchhoff Networks by the Determination of Purely Reactive Networks, *Cables & Trans. (Paris)*, **4**, 281-296, 1950.
7. M. Bayard, Synthesis of n-terminal Pair Networks, *Proc. Symposium Mod. Network Synthesis*, pp. 66-83, 1952.
8. V. Belevitch, Extension of Norton's Method of Impedance Transformation to Band-pass Filters, *Elec. Commun.*, **24**, 59-65, 1947.
9. V. Belevitch, Synthesis of $2n$-terminal Networks, *Wireless Eng.*, **28**, 128-129, 1951.
10. V. Belevitch, Synthesis of Passive Electrical Networks with n Pairs of Terminals and Prescribed Scattering Matrix (Matrice de Repartition), *Ann. Telecommun.*, **6**, 302-312, 1951.
11. V. Belevitch, Tchebyshev Filters and Amplifier Networks, *Wireless Eng.*, **29**, 106-110, 1952.
12. V. Belevitch, Topics in the Design of Insertion Loss Filters, *Trans. IRE*, CT-2, pp. 337-346, December, 1955.
13. C. Belove, A Note on the Synthesis of Resistor Capacitor Networks, *Proc. IRE*, **38**, 1453, 1950.
14. H. W. Bode and R. L. Dietzold, Ideal Wave Filters, *Bell System Tech. J.*, **14**, 215, 1935.
15. H. W. Bode, A General Theory of Electric Wave Filters, *J. Math. and Phys.*, **13**, 275, 1934.

16. H. W. Bode, *Network Analysis and Feedback Amplifier Design*, Van Nostrand, Princeton, N. J., 1945.

17. A. R. Boothroyd, Design of Electric Wave Filters with the Aid of the Electolytic Tank, *Proc. IEE*, (4) **98**, 65-93, 1951.

18. R. Bott and R. J. Duffin, Impedance Synthesis without Use of Transformers, *J. Appl. Phys.*, **20**, 816, 1949.

19. J. L. Bower and P. Ordung, The Synthesis of *RC* Networks. *Proc. IRE*, **38**, 263, 1950.

20. A. D. Bresler, On the Approximation Problem in Network Synthesis, *Proc. IRE*, **40**, 1724-1728, 1952.

21. O. Brune, Synthesis of a Finite 2-terminal Network Whose Driving Point Impedance Is a Prescribed Function of Frequency, *J. Math. and Phys.*, **10**, 191, 1930.

22. O. Brune, Note on Bartlett's Bisection Theorem for 4-terminal Electrical Networks, *Phil. Mag.*, (7) **14**, 806-811, 1932.

23. S. Butterworth, On the Theory of Filter Amplifiers, *Wireless Engr.*, **1**, 536, 1930.

24. C. A. Campbell and R. M. Foster, Maximum Output Networks for Telephone Substation and Repeater Circuits, *Trans. AIEE*, **39**, 231-280, 1920 (Campbell, *Collected Papers*, pp. 169-189. Amer. Tel. & Tel. Co., New York, 1937).

25. G. A. Campbell, Physical Theory of the Electric Wave-filter, *Bell System Tech. J.*, **1**, (2), 1-32, 1922 (*Collected Papers*, pp. 190-223. Amer. Tel. & Tel. Co., New York, 1937).

26. J. H. Carlin and R. LaRosa, Broad Band Reflectionless Matching with Minimum Insertion Loss, *Proc. Symposium Mod. Network Synthesis*, vol. 2, 1952.

27. J. H. Carlin and R. LaRosa, On the Synthesis of Reactance 4-poles, *J. Appl. Phys.*, **24**, 1336-1337, 1953.

28. J. H. Carlin and R. LaRosa, Limitations on Amplitude Equalizers, *IRE Convention Record*, pt. 2, 1954.

29. J. H. Carlin, The Scattering Matrix in Network Theory, *Trans. IRE*, CT3, pp. 88-97, June, 1956.

30. W. Cauer, Die Verwirklichung von Wechselstrom-Widerstanden Vorgescriebener Frequenzabhängigkeit, *Arch. Elektrotech.*, **17**, 355, 1926.

31. W. Cauer, Vierpole, *ENT*, **6**, (7), 1929.

32. W. Cauer, Ein Reaktanztheorem, *Sitzber. preuss. Akad. Wiss.*, *Physik-math. Kl.*, **30**, pp. 673-681, 1931.

33. W. Cauer, *Theorie der Linearen Wechselstromschaltungen*, Leipzig, Akademische Verlagsgesellschaft M.G.H., 1954.

34. M. V. Cerrillo and E. A. Guillemin, Rational Fraction Expansions for Network Functions, *Proc. Symposium Mod. Network Synthesis*, 1952, pp. 84-127.

35. S. Darlington, Synthesis of Reactance 4-poles. *J. Math. and Phys.*, **18**, 257-353, 1939.

36. S. Darlington, The Potential Analogue Method of Network Synthesis, *Bell System Tech. J.*, 315-365, 1951.

37. S. Darlington, Network Synthesis Using Tchebycheff Polynomial Series, *Bell System Tech. J.*, **31**, 613-665, 1952.

38. S. Darlington, A Survey of Network Realization Techniques, *Trans. IRE*, CT-2, pp. 291-297, December, 1955.

39. B. J. Dasher, Synthesis of *RC* Transfer Functions as Unbalanced Two Terminal Pair Networks, *MIT Research Lab. Electronics Tech. Rept.* 215, 1952 (also, *Trans. IRE*, CT-1, pp. 20-34, 1952).

40. H. Epstein, Synthesis of Passive *RC* Networks with Gains Greater than Unity, *Proc. IRE*, **39**, 833-835, 1951.

41. R. M. Fano, A Note on the Solution of Certain Approximation Problems in Network Synthesis, *MIT, Research Lab. Electronics Tech. Rept.* 62, 1948 (also, *J. Franklin Inst.*, **249**, pp. 189-205, 1950).

42. R. M. Fano, Theoretical Limitations on the Broadband Matching of an Arbitrary Impedance, *J. Franklin Inst.*, **249**, pp. 139-154, 1950.

43. V. Fetzer, Modern Filter Theory with Special Attention to Cauer's Work, *Arch. Elek. Übertragung*, **5**, 499-508, 1951.

44. A. Fialkow and I. Gerst, The Transfer Function of an *RC* Ladder Network, *J. Math. and Phys.*, **30**, 49-72, 1951.

45. A. Fialkow and I. Gerst, The Transfer Function of General Two-terminal Pair *RC* Networks, *Quart. Appl. Math.*, **10**, 113-127, 1952.

46. A. D. Fialkow, Two-terminal-pair Networks Containing Two Kinds of Elements Only, *Proc. Symposium Mod. Network Synthesis*, 1952, pp. 50-65.

47. A. Fialkow and I. Gerst, The Transfer Function of Networks without Mutual Reactance, *Quart. Appl. Math.*, **12**, pp. 117-131, 1954.

48. J. T. Fleck and P. F. Ordung, The Realization of a Transfer Ratio by Means of an *RC* Ladder Network, *Proc. IRE*, **39**, 1069, 1951.

49. R. M. Foster, A Reactance Theorem, *Bell System Tech. J.*, **3**, 259-267, 1924.

50. T. Fujisawa, Realizability Theorem for Mid-series or Mid-shunt

Low Pass Ladders without Mutual Induction, *Trans. IRE*, CT-2, pp. 320-325, December, 1955.

51. C. Gewertz, Synthesis of a Finite, Four-terminal Network from Its Prescribed Driving Point Functions and Transfer Function, *J. Math. and Phys.*, **12**, 1-257, 1932-1933.

52. E. Green, *Amplitude Frequency Characteristics of Ladder Networks*, Marconi's Wireless Telegraph Co., Technical Department, London, England, 1954.

53. V. H. Grinich, Approximating Band Pass Attenuation and Phase Functions. *IRE Convention Record*, pt. 2, 1954.

54. E. A. Guillemin, A Recent Contribution to the Design of Electric Filter Networks, *J. Math. and Phys.*, **11**, 150-211, 1932.

55. E. A. Guillemin, *Communication Networks*, vol. II, The Classical Theory of Long Lines, Filters, and Related Networks, Wiley, New York, Chapman & Hall, London, 7-587, 1935.

56. E. A. Guillemin, Synthesis of *RC* Networks, *J. Math. and Phys.*, **28**, pp. 22-42, 1949.

57. E. A. Guillemin, *The Mathematics of Circuit Analysis*, Wiley, New York, 1949.

58. E. A. Guillemin, A Note on the Ladder Development of *RC* Networks, *Proc. IRE*, **40**, 482, 1952.

59. E. A. Guillemin, *Advances in Electronics*, vol. III, A Summary of Modern Methods of Network Synthesis, Academic Press, Inc., 1951.

60. E. A. Guillemin, *Introductory Circuit Theory*. Wiley, New York, Chapman & Hall, London, 1953.

61. E. A. Guillemin, New Methods of Driving Point and Transfer Impedance Synthesis, *Proc. Symposium Mod. Network Synthesis*, 1955, vol. 5.

62. E. A. Guillemin, A New Approach to the Problem of Cascade Synthesis, *Trans. IRE*, CT-2, December, 1955.

63. E. A. Guillemin, *Synthesis of Passive Networks*, Wiley, New York, 1957.

64. E. C. Ho and D. L. Trautman, Synthesis of Resistively Terminated *RLC* Ladder Networks, *IRE Convention Record*, pt. 2, 1954.

65. E. C. Ho, A General Matrix Factorization Method for Network Synthesis, *Trans. IRE*, CT-2, pp. 146-153, June, 1955.

66. E. C. Ho, *RLC* Transfer Function Synthesis, *Trans. IRE*, CT-3, pp. 188-190, September, 1956.

67. W. H. Huggins, The Potential Analogue in Network Synthesis and Analysis, *Air Force Cambridge Research Lab. Rept.* E5066, 1951.

68. K. E. Iverson, The Zeros of Partial Sums of ϵ^z, *MTAC*, **7**, July, 1953.
69. R. Kahal, Synthesis of the Transfer Function of 2-terminal Pair Networks, *Trans. AIEE*, (1) **71**, 129-134, 1952.
70. W. H. Kim, A New Method of Driving Point Function Synthesis, *Univ. Ill. Elec. Eng. Research Lab. Tech. Rept.*, April, 1956.
71. J. F. Klinkhamer, Empirical Determination of Wave Filter Transfer Functions with Specified Properties, *Phillips Research Repts.* **3**, 66, 378, 1948.
72. E. S. Kuh, A Study of the Network Synthesis Approximation Problem for Arbitrary Loss Function, *Stanford Univ. Electronics Research Lab. Tech. Rept.* 44, 1952.
73. E. S. Kuh, Special Synthesis Techniques for Driving Point Impedance Functions, *Trans. IRE*, CT-2, pp. 302-308, December, 1955.
74. V. D. Landon, Cascade Amplifiers with Maximal Flatness, *RCA Rev.*, 1941.
75. Y. W. Lee, Synthesis of Electric Networks by Means of the Fourier Transforms of Laguerre's Functions, *J. Math. and Phys.*, **11**, 83-113, 1932.
76. R. LeRoy, Synthesis of $2n$-terminal Passive Networks, *Cables & Trans. (Paris)*, **4**, 234-247, 1950.
77. R. LeRoy, Sur la synthèse des quadripoles passives les plus généraux, *Cables & Trans. (Paris)*, **3**, 141-158, 1949.
78. P. M. Lewis, II, The Concept of the One in Voltage Transfer Synthesis, *Trans. IRE*, CT-2, pp. 316-319, December, 1955.
79. J. G. Linvill, The Selection of Network Functions to Approximate Prescribed Frequency Characteristics, MIT Research Lab. Electronics, *Tech. Rept.* 145, 1950 (also, *Proc. IRE*, **40**, pp. 711-721, June, 1952).
80. H. M. Lucal, Synthesis of Three Terminal RC Networks, *Trans. IRE*, CT-2, pp. 308-316, December, 1955.
81. M. Marden, *The Geometry of the Zeros of a Polynomial in a Complex Variable*, Am. Math. Soc., New York, 1949.
82. G. L. Matthaei, A General Method for Synthesis of Filter Transfer Functions as Applied to LC and RC Filter Examples, *Stanford Univ. Electronics Research Lab. Tech. Rept.* 39 (also, *Proc. IRE*, **41**, 377-382, 1953).
83. G. L. Matthaei, Some Techniques for Network Synthesis, *Proc. IRE*, **42**, pp. 1126-1137, July, 1954.
84. G. L. Matthaei, Synthesis of Tchebyscheff Impedance Matching Networks, Filters and Interstages, *Trans. IRE*, CT-3, pp. 163-172, September, 1956.

85. B. McMillan, Introduction to Formal Realizability Theory, *Bell System Tech. J.*, **31**, 217, 541, 1952.

86. S. P. Mead, Phase Distortion and Phase Distortion Correction, *Bell System Tech. J.*, **7**, 195-224, 1928.

87. F. Miyata, A New System of Two-terminal Synthesis, *Trans. IRE*, CT-2, 297-302, December, 1955.

88. W. Nijenhuis, Impedance Synthesis Distributing Available Loss in the Reactance Elements, *Phillips Research Repts.*, **5**, 288-302, 1950.

89. E. L. Norton, Constant Resistance Networks with Applications to Filter Groups, *Bell System Tech. J.*, **16**, 178, 1937.

90. Y. Oono, Synthesis of a Finite $2n$-terminal Network by a Group of Networks Each of Which Contains Only One Ohmic Resistance, *J. Math. and Phys.*, **29**, 13-26, 1950.

91. H. J. Orchard, The Synthesis of RC Networks to Have Prescribed Transfer Functions, *Proc. IRE*, **39**, 428-432, 1951.

92. P. F. Ordung, Axelby, Krauss, and Yetter, Synthesis of paralleled 3-terminal RC Networks to Provide Complex Zeros in the Transfer Function, *Trans. AIEE*, **70**, 342, 1951.

93. P. F. Ordung, F. Hopkins, H. L. Krauss, and E. L. Sparrow, Synthesis of Cascaded 3-terminal RC Networks with Minimum Phase Transfer Functions, *Proc. IRE*, **40**, 1717, 1952.

94. H. Ozaki, Synthesis of RC 3-terminal Networks without Ideal Transformer, *Osaka Univ. Tech. Rept.*, **3**, (60), pp. 57-77, 1953.

95. H. Ozaki and T. Fujisawa, Approximation Problems in RC Network Synthesis, *Osaka Univ. Tech. Rept.*, **3**, 243-248, 1953.

96. R. H. Pantell, Minimum Phase Transfer Function Synthesis, *Trans. IRE*, CT-2, pp. 133-137, June, 1955.

97. R. H. Pantell, New Methods of Driving Point and Transfer Function Synthesis, *Stanford Univ. Electronics Research Lab. Tech. Rept. 76*, July, 1954.

98. R. M. Redheffer, Design of a Circuit to Approximate a Prescribed Amplitude and Phase, *MIT Research Lab. Electronics Tech. Rept. 54*, 1949 (also, *J. Math. and Phys.*, **28**, pp. 146-147, 1949).

99. F. M. Reza, Conversion of a Brune Cycle with Ideal Transformer into a Cycle without Transformer, *Trans. IRE*, CT-1, pp. 71-75, March, 1954.

100. F. M. Reza, A Supplement to the Brune Synthesis, *Trans. AIEE*, **74**, pp. 85-90, 1955.

100(a). F. M. Reza, A Generalization of Foster's and Cauer's Theorems, *IRE Convention Record*, Part 2, 1955.

101. F. M. Reza, Simple and Double Alternation in Network Synthesis, *IRE Convention Record*, pt. 2, p. 72, 1956.

102. P. I. Richards, General Impedance-function Theory, *Quart. Appl. Math.*, **6**, 21-29, 1948.

102(a). P. I. Richards, A Special Class of Functions with Positive Real Part in a Half Plane, *Duke Math. J.*, **14**, 1947.

103. W. Saraga, Minimum Inductor or Capacitor Filters, *Wireless Engr.*, **30**, 163-175, 1953.

104. R. E. Scott, Network Synthesis by the Use of Potential Analogs, *Proc. IRE*, **40**, 970-973, 1952.

105. R. E. Scott and R. L. Blanchard, An Iterative Method for Network Synthesis, *Trans. IRE*, CT-2, pp. 19-29, 1953.

106. R. E. Scott, Potential Analogue Methods of Solving the Approximation Problem of Network Synthesis, *Proc. NEC*, **9**, pp. 543-553, 1954.

107. S. Seely, W. R. LePage, and N. Balabanian, The Role of Analytic Continuation in Network Analysis, *Proc. NEC*, **9**, pp. 684-689, 1954.

108. S. Seshu, Topological Consideration in the Design of Driving Point Functions, *Trans. IRE*, CT-2, pp. 356-367, December, 1955.

109. S. Seshu and N. Balabanian, Transformations of Positive Real Functions, *Trans. IRE*, CT-4, December, 1957.

110. L. Storch, The Multisection *RC* Filter Network Problem, *Proc. IRE*, **39**, 1456-1458, 1951.

111. L. Storch, A Theorem on the Impedance-transforming Properties of Reactive Networks, *J. Appl. Phys.*, **24**, 833-838, 1953.

112. L. Storch, Synthesis of Constant Time Delay Ladder Networks Using Bessel Polynomials, *Proc. IRE*, **42**, pp. 1666-1676, November, 1954.

113. A. Talbot, A New Method of Synthesis of Reactance Networks, *IRE Mono.* 77, October, 1953.

114. B. D. H. Tellegen, Network Synthesis, Especially the Synthesis of Resistanceless Four-terminal Networks, *Phillips Research Repts.*, **1**, 169-184, 1946.

115. W. E. Thompson, Networks with Maximally Flat Delay, *Wireless Eng.*, **29**, 256–263, 1952.

116. W. E. Thompson, Delay Networks Having Maximally Flat Frequency Characteristics, *Proc. IEE*, (3) **96**, 487-490, 1949.

117. D. L. Trautman, The Application of Conformal Mapping to the Synthesis of Bandpass Networks, *Proc. Symposium Mod. Network Theory*, 1952, pp. 179-192.

118. H. S. Wall, Analytic Theory of Continued Fractions, Van Nostrand, Princeton, N. J., 1948.

119. L. Weinberg, New Synthesis Procedures for Realizing Transfer Functions of *RLC* and *RC* Networks, *MIT Research Lab. Electronics Tech. Rept.* 201, 1951 (also, *J. Appl. Phys.*, **24**, 207-216, 776-779, 1953; *Proc. IRE*, **41**, pp. 1139-1144, 1953; *Trans. IRE*, CT-2, pp. 55–70, 1953).

120. L. Weinberg, Network Design by Use of Modern Synthesis Techniques and Tables, *Proc. NEC*, **12**, 794-817, 1956.

121. J. H. Westcott, Driving Point Impedance Synthesis Using Maximally Lossy Elements, *Proc. Symposium Mod. Network Synthesis*, 1955, vol. V.

122. N. Wiener and Y. W. Lee, U. S. patent No. 2024900, 1935.

123. O. J. Zobel, Theory and Design of Uniform and Composite Electric Wavefilters, *Bell System Tech. J.*, **2**, (1), 1-46, 1923.

124. O. J. Zobel, Extensions to the Theory and Design of Electric Wavefilters, *Bell System Tech. J.*, **10**, 284-341, 1931.

125. J. E. Storer, *Passive Network Synthesis*, McGraw-Hill, New York, 1957.

Index

431